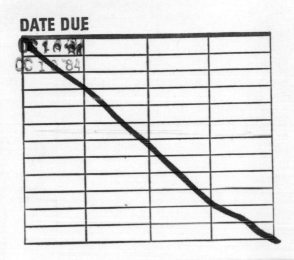

Antarctica

Edited by Trevor Hatherton

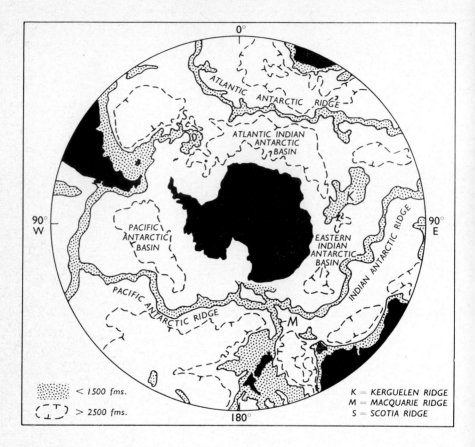

A NEW ZEALAND ANTARCTIC SOCIETY SURVEY

Antarctica

CONTRIBUTING AUTHORS

J. W. Beagley, C. R. Bentley, J. W. Brodie,
R. H. Clark, A. L. Cullington, R. K. Dell, M. Gadsden,
A. J. Gow, J. L. Gressitt, J. Hanessian,
J. A. Heap, G. A. M. King, P. G. Law, G. A. Llano,
J. H. Miller, M. J. Rubin, B. Stonehouse,
C. Swithinbank, G. Warren, W. S. Weyant
and J. H. Zumberge

FREDERICK A. PRAEGER · *Publishers* · NEW YORK · WASHINGTON

BOOKS THAT MATTER
Published in the United States of America in 1965
by Frederick A. Praeger, Inc., Publishers
111 Fourth Avenue, New York 3, N.Y.
Second printing 1966

Printed in Great Britain

Contents

THE SOUTH POLAR ATMOSPHERE

Illustrations

Preface

In 1952, A. H. and A. W. Reed of Wellington in conjunction with the New Zealand Antarctic Society published *The Antarctic Today*, a mid-century survey by the Society. This volume became widely accepted as the standard treatise on Antarctica and was subsequently translated into Russian[1] and Spanish.[2] The new wave of scientific and exploratory activity in the Antarctic, which started with the International Geophysical Year (1957–8) and which is supported by the most advanced logistic techniques, has outdated many of the chapters in *The Antarctic Today*. To meet the need for a new comprehensive survey of Antarctica the Society has prepared the present volume. The authors are all men currently active in Antarctic research. Three of them contributed to *The Antarctic Today* and a measure of the rapid increase in our knowledge of the Antarctic (particularly in the physical sciences) can be obtained by comparing the chapters on the ionosphere by J. W. Beagley in *The Antarctic Today* (1 figure) with the equivalent chapter by J. W. Beagley and G. A. M. King (16 figures) in this volume. The New Zealand Lands and Survey Department has produced a new edition of its *Map of the Antarctic Regions* for the book and the Society is grateful to Denys Rainey for his work on this map.

The Antarctic Today was also a polemical weapon. In his foreword, Dr R. A. Falla, then President of the Society, criticized the 'negative policy which has marked the administration of the Ross Dependency since it became a New Zealand responsibility in 1923', and numerous plates illustrated the Antarctic bases which were the outward and visible symbols of other nations' interest in the southern continent. Happily, *Antarctica* needs no such lance, for in the past eleven years the Antarctic situation has been transformed. New Zealand has one Antarctic station (Scott Base) and shares another with the United States (Hallett Station). It has an Antarctic supply ship, HMNZS *Endeavour*. Every summer field-parties roam among the great ranges that stretch from the Liv Glacier in the south to Cape Adare in the north, and oceanographers and geophysicists are systematically examining the Southern Ocean south of New Zealand. Universities and mountain clubs send their own expeditions and the Victoria University of Wellington currently has its *eighth* expedition in the McMurdo Sound area. In the past six years over 250 papers and books about Antarctica have been published by New Zealand authors. The recent Antarctic history of several other nations has followed a similar course.

[1] *Sovremennaya Antarktika*, Izdatel'stvo Inoctrannoy Literatury (Moscow, 1957).
[2] *La Antartida de hoy*, Editorial Kapelusz (Buenos Aires, 1962).

Truly, the concern of a decade ago might well yield to complacency today. But an even more important development has taken place. On 1 December 1959 in Washington DC, twelve nations including New Zealand signed The Antarctic Treaty, which is reproduced in Appendix 1 of this book.

Altogether this has been the most significant decade in the fitful history of Antarctica. In its events the Society and its members are pleased to have had their parts.

J. HOLMES MILLER
President
New Zealand Antarctic Society

Wellington, NZ
1963

PART ONE

The Nations in Antarctica

. . . Recognizing that it is in the interest of all mankind that Antarctica shall continue to be used exclusively for peaceful purposes and shall not become the scene or object of international discord; . . .

From the preamble to The Antarctic Treaty, 1959.

CHAPTER ONE

National Interests in Antarctica[1]

JOHN HANESSIAN JR, *American Universities Field Staff*

Introduction

In recent years Antarctic political relations have been changing rapidly. From a purely national approach, which has in the past characterized political interests in Antarctica, the various countries concerned have begun to appreciate the advantages of a cooperative or even international solution to the complex situation that has developed in the frigid southern continent.

For centuries the *terra Australis nondum cognita* has literally served as a magnet to explorers from many nations. Their motivation has been largely personal, or occasionally economic (sealing and whaling activities since the early part of the nineteenth century). Although many of these explorers invariably claimed newly found territory for their states or rulers, it was really the love of exploration, the finding of new places, that drew them on.

But gradually, with the quickening development of technology, expeditions to Antarctica began to be more complex. With Borchgrevink's successful wintering in 1899 at Cape Adare (see p. 32), a new era was inaugurated. The British expeditions of Scott and Shackleton, during the first two decades of this century, utilized a number of exploratory innovations, and the use of aircraft, beginning in 1928, has revolutionized Antarctic field activities.

With the employment of aircraft, the development of specialized foods, fuels and mechanized over-snow vehicles, Antarctic exploration began to take on a new dimension. Vast new areas could be overflown, mapped and explored. But at the same time costs sky-rocketed, and it was soon evident that privately

[1] For an excellent up-to-date, country-by-country annotated bibliography on this subject see Hayton, R., *National Interests in Antarctica*, Washington, 1959. For a convenient source of texts of Antarctic claims see United States Naval War College, 'Declarations Concerning Antarctic Territories', *International Law Documents* 1948–1949, Washington, 1950 (217–45), and Dater, H., *Summary of National Claims with Selected Documents*, Washington, United States Antarctic Project Officer, 1957. For a useful collection of recent official national statements on Antarctic policy see United States Department of State, *The Conference on Antarctica, Conference Documents, the Antarctic Treaty and Related Papers*, Washington, Department of State Publication No. 7060, 1960 (1–39, 43–55). For an annotated list of Antarctic expeditions see Roberts, B., 'Chronological List of Antarctic Expeditions', *The Polar Record*, **9**: 97–134 and 191–239, 1958.

sponsored efforts would need to give way to government-financed national expeditions. Gradually the individual exploration of the so-called 'heroic age' was replaced by centrally coordinated group efforts. Scientific objectives began to receive more attention, and expeditionary personnel began to be drawn from scientific sources as well as from groups simply interested in adventure.

Meanwhile, the world's scientists have more and more looked at Antarctica as an ideal scientific laboratory in which to examine the geophysical secrets of planet Earth. This movement culminated in 1957–8 with the International Geophysical Year (IGY) which engendered a magnificent cooperative effort, during which political considerations were put aside and scientists from twelve

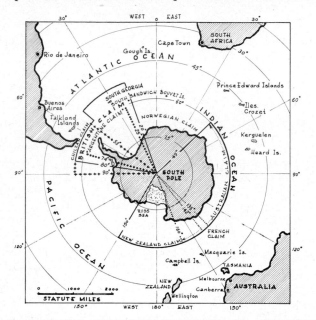

FIG. I NATIONAL TERRITORIAL CLAIMS TO ANTARCTICA

nations established Antarctic stations without regard to political claims and carried out an internationally coordinated scientific research programme.

As governments have become more enmeshed in Antarctic expeditionary machinery, political motives have assumed greater significance. Beginning with the assertion of the British claim in 1908 to the 'Falkland Islands Dependencies', some eight nations (Argentina, Australia, Chile, France, Great Britain, New Zealand, Norway and the Union of South Africa) have carved out territorial claims on Antarctica and the Subantarctic islands. As can be seen in Figure I, all of these claims, except that of Norway, are 'pie-shaped' and terminate at the South Geographic Pole. South Africa's claim is limited to several Subantarctic islands.

Although there has been some mutual recognition of these claims (among the British Commonwealth nations, France and Norway), it has been quite disappointing to these countries that their Antarctic territorial announcements have gone practically unrecognized by the rest of the world. In addition, the territorial claims of Argentina, Chile and Great Britain overlap, a factor which has caused considerable diplomatic heat, and on one occasion, gunfire.

A number of other nations, although not formally making claims, have demonstrated their interest in Antarctica by sending expeditions or carrying out whaling operations. These include such diverse countries as Belgium, Japan, Germany, Sweden and Poland. Of these Belgium and Japan participated in the IGY Antarctic programme and, though they have had to evacuate their Antarctic stations for financial reasons, continue to maintain a strong interest in and membership of the Antarctic Treaty consultative group and the Scientific Committee on Antarctic Research (SCAR).

Perhaps the most interesting aspect of the question of national interests in Antarctica, however, is the common attitude of the United States and the USSR. Neither nation has ever laid claim to Antarctic territory, nor has either recognized the claims of any other nation. Both have on numerous occasions 'reserved' their 'rights', both have supported strongly the attempts to internationalize the continent, and both are currently carrying out major permanent Antarctic scientific programmes.

Strategic and Economic Stimulus for National Antarctic Activity

The strategic significance of Antarctica has been the subject of considerable thought by many of the claimant nations. A glance at the map readily demonstrates the important geopolitical position of this huge continent. Argentina, Chile, New Zealand and Australia, all have had valid concern regarding the necessity of protecting their southern flank.

These four nations for years have been sensitive to the possible presence of hostile ships in southern waters, particularly following German activity in the Antarctic seas during World War II. Much has been written concerning the potential significance of the Drake Passage should the Panama Canal be destroyed during some future conflict, but it has not always been readily apparent that to these four states (and to a lesser extent South Africa) the Antarctic is not a distant frigid ice mass, but a nearby continent on which hostile military activity could easily threaten national security. Australia for example has for some years been uneasy regarding Soviet Antarctic intentions.

In Argentina, Chile and Australia particularly, national feelings concerning Antarctica are strong, and it has been only with considerable reluctance that these nations have consented to part with even a small portion of their 'sovereignty' over their Antarctic territorial claims for the Antarctic Treaty, which was fully ratified by mid-1961 (see Appendix 1).

In recent years there has been considerable discussion of trans-Antarctic civil air routes. The commercial success achieved, first by SAS and then by other international air carriers, in flying across the Arctic, has raised the question of the feasibility of establishing similar air lanes across the Antarctic. The importance

of controlling possible bases and air lanes has received a certain degree of
public discussion in New Zealand and Australia, particularly after Pan American
Airlines, in October 1957, demonstrated its ability to fly a commercial aircraft
from Christchurch, New Zealand, to the Antarctic and land on an ice strip
adjacent to the United States Naval Air Facility at McMurdo Sound. Flyers
of many nations have shown that polar navigational problems can be solved,
and the current network of Antarctic stations provides a reliable and necessary
communications network as well as meteorological data on a continental scale.

Nevertheless, little progress has taken place, largely because of the limited
passenger interest at the present time. Southern Hemisphere populations are
small and the cities are located in such relatively low latitudes that regular trans-
Antarctic civil airline routes are not likely to develop in the near future. For
example, Santiago, Buenos Aires, Melbourne, Sydney and Cape Town are
located between 34° and 38° South Latitude. Even Wellington, the closest major
city to Antarctica, stands almost 5000 km north of the South Pole. In contrast
many major Northern Hemisphere cities lie substantially north of 50° North
Latitude. However, as the tempo of Antarctic activity and the technical com-
petency of commercial jet aircraft increase, the establishment of such routes
must be considered a distinct possibility, and it will certainly continue to interest
the Southern Hemisphere nations.

Although the economic possibilities of the Antarctic have always seemed
highly speculative, and the forbidding nature of the Antarctic Continent has
largely prevented geological exploration, the various interested nations continue
to hope (or even to expect), that Antarctica will one day reveal great mineral
wealth. Inaccurate accounts of a uranium find a few years ago quickly became
the source of widespread discussion, and on occasion substantial exposed coal
and copper deposits have been found.

Yet, to date, no signs of economic worth have been sufficient to stimulate
commercial mining enterprises on the continent. Whatever mineral wealth Antarctica may hold (see p. 314 for a discussion of economic geology), it is certain
to remain locked up under the almost impenetrable ice sheet. Exploitation of
the available ice-free areas is long likely to be less profitable than in more easily
worked fields elsewhere.

Apart from the ice, the problems of climate, isolation, the hazards of transport
and the enormous costs that would be entailed hardly afford favourable circumstances for exploitation. Yet it must be recognized that the discovery of metallic
gold or some other rare or strategically important mineral may well alter the
entire situation.

Subantarctic whaling, however, has presented a somewhat different picture.
Norway and to some extent Japan and the Soviet Union have exploited the rich
Antarctic whaling grounds for many years. The development of pelagic whaling
by catcher ships using 'mother' factory ships as their base, has greatly facilitated
the carrying out of whaling operations and has reduced measurably the reliance
of whalers on shore bases in adjacent countries. The International Whaling

Convention of 1946 and subsequent International Whaling Conferences have not only provided stringent regulations for the whaling industry, but have served as an effective international forum.

International Law and Antarctic Claims

The acquisition of territorial sovereignty over the polar regions has long presented a complex problem to nations and international lawyers alike. In general, claims to Antarctic territory have been characterized by three doctrines, (i) discovery, (ii) the application of the so-called 'sector theory', and (iii) effective occupation. Argentina and Chile have also used geographical proximity, geological affinity and succession to presumed Spanish title as forming the bases of claims.

Of these principles only one, that of continuous and effective occupation, is a generally recognized concept of international law. The others are alleged by their proponents as bases of state policy, or as rules which they would like to have included within the body of the law of nations. However, all three of these conceptions have been used in varying combinations by the claimant states in justification of their Antarctic territorial ambitions.

During the late fifteenth and sixteenth centuries, in the early days of European exploration, especially in Africa and the Western Hemisphere, most states maintained that discovery of previously unknown territory by their nationals was a sufficient basis for the acquisition of an absolute title to the territory. But as early as the beginning of the seventeenth century, Hugo Grotius rejected the assertion that mere discovery in the sense of physical discovery or simple visual apprehension provided a valid basis for title. This attitude generally became accepted during the following two centuries. To it was added the rule that simple disembarkation upon a portion of newly discovered territory, or even extended penetration and exploration within such an area, was not regarded as sufficient itself to establish such right to title.

In recent years these convictions have been reaffirmed on several occasions. In the Palmas Island Arbitration of 1928 (Netherlands–United States), Dr Max Huber, Arbitrator, held that if there had been no further consolidation of title after discovery, the requirements of international law had not been met. He maintained that since 1750 international law had undergone profound modifications and now required that occupation must be effective, not only for the act of acquisition, but also for the maintenance of the right. Judge Huber held, therefore, that the continuous display of territorial sovereignty by the Dutch was of more importance than the title received by the United States (through cession from Spain), which derived from prior Spanish discovery.

In another arbitration, over Clipperton Island (Mexico–France) in 1931, the Arbitrator, King Victor Emmanuel III of Italy, held that the proof of an historic right of Mexico was not supported by any manifestation of her sovereignty over the island, and mere conviction that this was territory belonging to Mexico, although general and long-standing, could not be retained.

Related to the doctrine of discovery is 'inchoate title', according to which, although a discovery does not give title, it does give rise to an exclusive right to occupy the area. Although this theory has been advanced by a number of writers it has also been rigorously criticized. Judge Huber, in the Palmas Island case, stated that an inchoate title of discovery must be completed within a reasonable period by the effective occupation of the region claimed to be discovered.

Thus, through the centuries, the rule has gradually crystallized that discovery alone is not sufficient to give a good title to a new unoccupied land and that in order to perfect the right given by discovery it must be followed by continuous and effective occupation. Such occupation is to be effected through taking possession and establishing an administration over territory in the name of and for the acquiring state. These two requirements – possession and administration – are considered essential facts constituting effective occupation. Possession means uninterrupted and permanent settlement on the territory accompanied by some formal act which announces that the territory has been taken possession of and that the possessor intends to keep it under his sovereignty. The mere hoisting of a flag or other symbolic act without settlement is considered only as 'fictitious occupation'. After taking possession of a territory the occupying state must also establish, within a reasonable time, some kind of responsible administration which shows that the territory is really governed.

The application of these rules of international law to territorial problems in uninhabited polar regions, or *terra nullius*, has been complicated by several problems, including: (i) the circumstance that the objective may be an area of which the surface above the level of the sea is ice rather than land, (ii) the assertion of initial claims is made at a time when the requirements of international law in relation to the acquisition of the original rights of sovereignty are fairly well understood, and yet which in the course of their evolution there has been slight occasion to apply or to adapt to polar areas, (iii) the inability of a claimant state, because of rigorous climatic conditions, to attain the kind and degree of control over a polar territory as is considered essential by international law for the perfecting of a right of sovereignty, and (iv) the issue of whether ice shelves can be regarded as territory.

The question of ice shelves presents a puzzling territorial problem in the Antarctic. Often many metres thick and thousands of square kilometres in extent, these floating ice masses are firmly anchored to land, usually in such a manner that without seismic techniques it is difficult to ascertain just where the land ends and the ice shelf begins. Except for the edge of the shelf, from which tabular icebergs occasionally break off, these ice masses are remarkably stable and in many ways the surface is indistinguishable from that of the ice-covered continental interior.

On these shelves a number of permanent scientific stations have been constructed and considerable activity takes place on them annually. Many writers, including Smedal, Waultrin and Balch, have maintained that ice shelves resemble land more than sea, should be regarded as land and can be the object of territorial sovereignty. In this connection it is interesting to note that the 1959 Antarctic Treaty includes ice shelves as well as the continent within its coverage.

With respect to the international legal requirements for the consolidation of title and the acquisition of territorial sovereignty in Antarctica, the problem is whether the peculiar geographic and climatic characteristics of this region require a modification of the usual tests of effective occupation.

There is general (but by no means unanimous) agreement that the usual rule of permanent settlement should be modified for application in Antarctica, which is not only uninhabited but virtually uninhabitable. The question is how much manifestation of state activity is required? Some support can be found for claims to large interior areas on the basis of small coastal settlements in the history of Africa, Australia and North and South America. But, in general, this 'hinterland' theory does not meet with general approval today.

However, new and arbitrary techniques have been devised for the solution of polar territorial problems, the most interesting being the so-called 'sector principle'. Proposed by a Canadian in 1907, the method provides that when the territory of a state within the Arctic Circle, such as that of Canada, is contiguous to areas of ice or land that extend toward the North Pole, and which are not possessed by another state, the right of sovereignty over the entire intervening space may be in fact asserted. It indicates that the state concerned, such as Canada, may claim all the area between a base line connecting the longitudinal meridians marking the eastern and western limits of its frontiers and extending as far north as the final intersection of those meridians at the North Pole.

This method, which is without standing in international law, is indifferent to the nature of the area concerned, whether it is land, ice or water. It is unconcerned with the matter of discovery or exploration and even less with effective occupation. It simply purports to justify the reservation of particular areas deemed to possess a convenient geographical relationship with the claimant state.

Whatever the merit of this method in the Arctic, which is a mass of floating ice bridging the continents that close in on it, it has little relationship to reality in the Antarctic, which is itself a continent that is detached from any other. Coveted areas of the latter, unlike those in the Arctic, are relatively remote and separated from the nearest land mass by broad expanses of water.

The application of the sector theory in the Antarctic, therefore, lacks the foundation upon which it rests in the north, and has no recognizable legal basis. Nevertheless, as a convenient, if arbitrary, method of procedure, sector claims to extensive Antarctic areas have been made, beginning with the 1908 British Letters Patent to the 'Falkland Islands Dependencies'.

In the case of uninhabited territory, such as the Antarctic, some writers feel that an occupation would be rendered sufficiently effective by the establishment of a system of administration (however rudimentary) which, having regard to the conditions under which the area appropriated was being used or was likely to be used, was reasonably sufficient to maintain control.

It has also been suggested that 'the necessary degree of intensity of administrative control is relative only to the requirements of the area. It would not be necessary for a state to make its authority felt at all times and in all places. It should be necessary only for the state to maintain a general supervision over the whole area which it claims.' (Goldie, 1958.) Relevent precedents are to be found in Denmark's control of Greenland and Canada's administration of her Arctic archipelago. In both of these examples not only is there general legislation and the establishment of scientific and administrative posts, but there is an administration sufficiently active to carry out supervision of the subject areas.

In the Eastern Greenland Case (Norway–Denmark) in 1933, the Permanent Court of International Justice concluded that Danish sovereignty had been exercised to 'a sufficient extent' and therefore extended over the entire island and was not limited to colonized portions. This conclusion was based partly on 'the Arctic and inaccessible character of the uncolonized parts of the country'.

Although there has not been recent adjudication on polar territorial problems it is generally held that, if the claimant countries were to submit their claims to the International Court of Justice for review, the court would certainly use the Eastern Greenland Case as precedent, and perhaps strike out even more strongly on the necessity of modifying existing international legal requirements regarding the acquisition of territorial sovereignty in the Antarctic. It is also certain that mere discovery or even subsequent symbolic taking of possession would be considered insufficient to provide valid title. Probably the court would examine the history of continuous occupation by the claimant nation, and the record of that state with respect to its ability to maintain a measure of administrative control over the claimed territory. Based on this reasoning it seems probable that the court might well accept some territorial claims including the coast and a reasonable (that which is easily controlled) amount of hinterland such as a few hundred miles, but would disallow any claims to the vast interior of Antarctica.

Meanwhile, in support of their tenuous claims, the claimant nations have executed considerable activity in Antarctica such as intermittent ceremonial acts of administration, the designation of postmasters, coroners and magistrates, and the issuance of postage stamps indicating the boundaries of their claims. Claimant states have operated radio and weather stations, issued administrative decrees, and some have incorporated their claimed lands into the homeland provinces.

Nevertheless, with the successful ratification of the 1959 Antarctic Treaty (see Appendix 1) there exists some degree of optimism that the Antarctic nations, in spite of strong national feelings and security considerations, will eventually agree that the most feasible solution to Antarctic political and territorial problems lies in the establishment of some sort of an international regime.

The Claimant Nations

Argentina[1]

Argentine Antarctic activity began in 1903 when the Argentine ship *Uruguay* penetrated Antarctic waters and ultimately rescued the Nordenskjöld party of the Swedish South Polar Expedition at Snow Hill Island, where the Swedish party had wintered after their ship *Antarctic* had been crushed in the ice. The following year, at the invitation of Dr W. S. Bruce, leader of the Scottish National Antarctic Expedition, Argentina relieved the Scottish meteorological station on Laurie Island in the South Orkneys. This station has been continuously maintained by Argentina since that date.

Until 1939 Argentine concern toward the Antarctic was more or less limited to the annual relief of the Laurie Island station. In July 1939 a permanent inter-departmental National Antarctic Commission was established as a direct result of Norway's delineation of its claim made earlier that year, and its subsequent invitation to all interested parties to attend an International Exhibition of Polar Exploration to be convened in Bergen in 1940.

As a consequence of the work of this Commission, expeditions were sent in 1942 and 1943 to the Graham Land[2] area and to the South Shetlands. With the election of Juan Peron in February 1946, and the establishment of the government on a firm constitutional basis, the Antarctic became one of the major facets of Argentine political, military and diplomatic activity. She inaugurated a major Antarctic expeditionary programme establishing a number of small stations on Graham Land. With some changes these stations have since been maintained. In the same year, 1946, the Antarctic Commission was reactivated, and an intensive publicity campaign was launched to make Argentina 'Antarctic-conscious'. Since that date Argentina has pursued a relatively vigorous policy of exploration and the establishment of bases to support its contention of effective occupancy.

In 1951 the Instituto Antartico Argentino was created and placed under the Ministry of the Army. Its function has been to centralize Antarctic matters within the Argentine Government. Since 1955, it has been under the dedicated leadership of Rear-Admiral Rodolfo Panzarini, and has played an integral role in the prosecution of Argentina's Antarctic activities.

A measure of Argentine interest in the Antarctic may be gauged by noting that she is the only nation other than the United States using a modern ice-breaker in the Antarctic. Purchased from Germany in 1954, the capabilities of the *General San Martin* were soon utilized to establish, in January 1955, a

[1] For a comprehensive review of Argentine Antarctic activity and the related interlocking claims of Argentina, Chile and the United Kingdom, see Hayton, R. (1956).

[2] Until the March 1964 agreement between the USA, Great Britain, New Zealand and Australia naming this area the 'Antarctic Peninsula', it was called 'Graham Land' by the Commonwealth nations and 'Palmer Peninsula' by the USA. Chile uses 'Tierra O'Higgins' and Argentina calls it 'Tierra San Martin'.

major station, 'General Belgrano' on the Filchner Ice Shelf. In January 1959, following an agreement with the United States, Argentina occupied Ellsworth Station and continued its annual operation with partial scientific support supplied by the United States until December 1962, when the Station was evacuated.

Justification for the Argentinian claim is primarily based on (i) the succession of original Spanish 'rights', (ii) geographical proximity, (iii) geological affinity based on the presumed geological continuation of the Andes through the island chains into the nearby Antarctic region, and (iv) effective occupation including the maintenance of the Laurie Island station since 1904.

For many years Argentina did not issue a formal claims statement, while consistently taking the position that 'Antártida Argentina' has been an integral part of her metropolitan territory since the very foundation of the republic. Nevertheless, as early as 1904, by Executive Decree, Argentina took possession of the South Orkneys, and in 1946, delimited the western limit of the claim.

On 28 February 1957 the Argentine Government 're-established' what is now called 'The National Territory ot Tierra del Fuego, the Antarctic and the Islands of the South Atlantic'. Administrative arrangements were extended for the new national territory to include the Falkland Islands, and for the capital to be at Ushuaia.

The claim itself comprises a sector between 25° and 74° West Longitudes, bordered on the north by the 60th parallel South Latitude. From 53° to 70° West Longitude 'Antártida Argentina' overlaps the Chilean claim, and the Argentinian claim is entirely within the sector claimed by Britain. With respect to the conflicting Chilean claim, Argentina has maintained a cooperative attitude, but, by mutual consent, has postponed the determination of the precise area to which each of the two Latin American countries might be entitled.

The international rivalry in Graham Land, with Argentina, Chile and the United Kingdom all having conflicting claims, has strongly affected the growth of Argentine Antarctic activity. Although Argentina (and Chile) refused the opportunity to defend legally her claim before the International Court of Justice on Britain's application in 1955, her writers and lawyers have, since 1946, issued a flood of literature attempting to justify Argentina's Antarctic 'rights'.

The Antarctic question for many years has constituted an important element in Argentine domestic politics, an aspect which has been directly responsible for the ultra-nationalistic attitude of the country towards her Antarctic 'territory'. The relative nearness of Antarctica to Argentina (less than 1000 km separates, Tierra del Fuego from Graham Land across the Drake Passage) has made the control of the sea lanes and air routes a matter of particular concern.

But, more importantly, the 'colonial issue' or any alleged intervention of European countries in the Western Hemisphere (i.e. British activities in Graham Land) has always served the Argentine Government as a useful rallying point in domestic politics. Any official assertion of Argentina's Antarctic position invariably wins broad popular support.

On the international scene, Argentine governments have jealously guarded their Antarctic 'rights' and have violently opposed any moves which might give away their 'sovereignty' over 'Antártida Argentina'. Internationalization moves have always been strongly opposed, as was evident during the 1948 United States proposals, the 1959 Antarctic Treaty Conference, and in the subsequent international meetings devoted to Antarctic problems. Argentina only reluctantly ratified the Antarctic Treaty, and for the foreseeable future it is to be expected that Argentina will continue to be the least enthusiastic Antarctic nation towards the growth of such international controls.

Australia

Although Australians were active in British expeditions to the Antarctic even before the foundation of the Commonwealth in 1908, and several Australian expeditions were mounted between 1911 and 1931, Australia made no formal claim to Antarctica until 1933.

The territories explored by British and Australian expeditions were discussed by the British Imperial Conference of 1926, but it was not until 7 February 1933 that a British Order-in-Council formally claimed the following territory and placed it under Australian authority: the area south of 60° South Latitude and lying between 160° and 45° East Longitudes. The thin sector from 136° to 142° East Longitudes, which has been claimed by France, was specifically excluded in the claim statement.

This Australian claim (the largest in geographic extent on the Antarctic Continent—about 6½ million square kilometres) is supported chiefly by the discoveries and exploration of Biscoe, Kemp, Balleny and Ross, all Britishers, during the first half of the nineteenth century, and by Australian expeditions, particularly the Australasian Antarctic Expedition of 1911–14 under Sir Douglas Mawson. The British-Australian-New Zealand Antarctic Research Expedition (BANZARE) of 1929–31, also under Mawson, contributed much to cementing the Australian claim.

In 1947 a post-war revival of interest led to the establishment of an Antarctic Division within the Department of External Affairs, the expansion of the Cabinet's special Antarctic Expedition Planning Committee and the organization of a succession of expeditions, known collectively as the 'Australian National Antarctic Research Expeditions' (ANARE).

The function of ANARE was 'to maintain Australian and British interests in Antarctica and to find a suitable site for a permanent base and to carry out scientific work'. Plans were made to explore thousands of square miles of Antarctic territory by ship, aeroplane, snow vehicle and dog.

During the 1947–8 austral summer the first ANARE (also the first Antarctic expedition to be wholly financed by the Australian Government) established stations at Heard Island (maintained until 1954) and at Macquarie Island (since developed into a permanent station). Because of the lack of an adequate ship, plans to locate a base on the Antarctic Continent had to be postponed.

Finally, during the 1954–5 season, a permanent base was established on the

MacRobertson Coast of Antarctica. Named Mawson Station, this base has since served as the field headquarters of the extensive Australian Antarctic activities under the leadership of Phillip Law. A strong scientific and exploratory programme was carried out during the IGY, during which an additional base, Davis Station, was established in the Vestfold Hills area in early 1957. In recent years an extensive mapping programme has been under way, and in January 1959 Australia also occupied, by agreement with the United States, Wilkes Station, which she currently maintains with some scientific support from the United States.

In 1954, in conjunction with the establishment of Mawson Station, the Australian Antarctic Territory Bill was passed. This law provides for the application of Australian Capital Territory laws within the Australian-claimed Antarctic sector.

Australia's active Antarctic policy is based on considerations of security, prestige, science and possible economic gain. It has strong bipartisan support in Parliament and in the press. Popular interest in Antarctica is widespread – the publicizing of recent Australian Antarctic activity has created an impression of the existence of a tangible and potentially valuable Australian interest in the region, an attitude which has not been denied by the Government. The strong interest of Australia's leaders, such as Prime Minister Robert Menzies and especially former Minister of External Affairs, Richard Casey, also had its effect on the public.

Because Antarctica could be used by a hostile power as a base threatening Australian security, she has opposed the entrance of other nations, particularly the Soviet Union (and to a lesser extent, Japan) into her polar 'back door'. She has consistently refused to consider renouncing her Antarctic claims, partly because of strong nationalistic feeling, but partly because of the fear that the continent (although nearly 3000 km distant) might be used as a base for attack by a hostile force.

As a consequence Australian officials have hoped that the United States might join New Zealand and Australia (perhaps in a multiple condominium) to circumvent Soviet activity in the Antarctic and as an alternative to internationalization, which would involve Soviet (and perhaps even United Nations) participation.

But when in 1958 it became clear that the United States did not intend to press a claim, and that the USSR planned to remain in the Antarctic (all her IGY bases in Antarctica were constructed in the sector claimed by Australia), Australia reluctantly began to support the idea of continuing the international cooperative arrangements which had evolved during the IGY. At the Antarctic Treaty Conference, although she agreed readily to general international coordination, the Australian delegation argued strongly (and successfully) for the avoidance of an international secretariat. Today, she is still uneasy about the continuing Soviet presence in 'her' sector, but does maintain cordial relations within the framework provided by SCAR and the Antarctic Treaty.

Chile

Despite the existence of considerable official and public Chilean interest in the Antarctic, her efforts in the area have been severely limited by lack of sufficient funds and resources. Although there has long been awareness of the importance of the Antarctic to Chilean security, it was not until 1940 that Chilean President, Aguirre Cerda, following a report on Chilean Antarctic claims prepared on request of the government by Professor Julio Escudero in 1939, claimed for Chile a broad sector from 53° to 90° West Longitudes – all of the Graham Land area and to the exact western limit of the Security Zone later established by the Inter-American Treaty of Reciprocal Assistance (Rio Treaty) of 1947. The sector, which overlaps that of her neighbour, Argentina, as well as Britain's claim, was named the 'Territorio Chileno Antártico'.

Except for some whaling and fishing concessions granted during 1902–16 and the assistance given to Shackleton in 1916, Chile did not actually commence serious Antarctic activity until 1947, when she established a permanent base at Greenwich Island in the South Shetlands off the Antarctic coast. Three other permanent year-round stations have since been established, partially to offset the greatly expanded British activity in Graham Land, and partly as the Chilean contribution to the IGY programme.

The able Chilean Navy has carried most of the burden of Chile's Antarctic endeavours under the leadership of the Naval Ministry's Antarctic Section, which in October 1948 was transferred to the General Staff of the Armed Forces. A Chilean Antarctic Commission was established in 1942 and later reorganized under the Foreign Ministry. Finally, in 1955 and 1956, the 'Statute of the Chilean Antarctic Territory' was issued, which removed jurisdiction over the claimed area from the Foreign Ministry and placed the territory under the Governor of the Magallanes Province.

Chilean interest in Antarctica has been manifested in many ways, including the 1948 visit of the Chilean President, Gonzalez Videla to inaugurate the new O'Higgins Station (the first visit by a head of state to Antarctica), and the first genuine tourist flight over Antarctica in December 1956 by the Chilean National Airlines.

Chile has always taken a strong nationalistic attitude towards its Antarctic claim. She has resisted all attempts at internationalization, but has welcomed opportunities for scientific cooperation. A curious aspect of the Chilean position has been its lack of comment regarding the fact that her claim overlaps that of Argentina. She joined Argentina in refusing to discuss the matter at the Hague Court, but, strangely, has also refused to agree to any form of international government. To some extent her interest in the Antarctic is derived from strategic considerations due to her close geographic proximity to the continent. The value of meteorological observations has also often been stressed. Although Chile ratified the Antarctic Treaty, and does participate in the various Antarctic international meetings, she has no present intention of giving up her claim.

France

French expeditions have been active in the Antarctic region since 1738–9, when Bouvet de Lozier discovered Bouvetøya, and 1772 when Yves Kerguelen discovered and took possession for France of the archipelago which bears his name. The same year Captain Dufresne and his mate Crozet discovered a group of islands now known as the Îles Crozet. A half-century later Captain Dumont d'Urville's 1837–40 expedition (sponsored by the French Government) landed on some small windswept islands just off a newly discovered Antarctic coast, which he promptly named 'Terre Adélie', after his wife. Early in the twentieth century several French expeditions to the Graham Land area were conducted by Charcot, but it was not until 1949 that France was able to begin a permanent concentrated programme of Antarctic exploration and scientific reasearch – under the leadership of Paul-Emile Victor.

Although Kerguelen was formally annexed in 1893, broad French Antarctic claims were not announced until 1924. In a Presidential Decree that year, which was occasioned by the United Kingdom's assignment of the 'Ross Dependency' to New Zealand in 1923, Terre Adélie was claimed for France along with the Subantarctic islands of St Paul, New Amsterdam, Kerguelen and Crozet. Terre Adélie was defined as a narrow quadrilateral between 136° and 142° East Longitudes and between 66° and 67° South Latitudes. A later Presidential Decree in 1938 enlarged the territory to include all the area south of 60° South Latitude and between 136° and 142° East Longitudes, terminating at the South Pole.

Also in 1924, acting on a report submitted by the Minister of Colonies, which urged a permanent administrative organization for Terre Adélie and the Subantarctic islands claimed by France, the French Government approved the attachment of these territories to the Governor-General of Madagascar as an administrative dependency of that colony. There, Antarctic administrative matters languished for decades until finally in 1955 the French-claimed Antarctic and Subantarctic areas were renamed 'Terres Australes et Antarctiques Françaises' (TAAF) and were removed from this unlikely administrative arrangement and placed under the control of an 'Administrateur Superior' in the Colonial Ministry in Paris. Xavier Richert was given the post and held it until 1958 when Pierre Rolland took over the TAAF leadership.

The post-war revival of French polar interest was led by Paul-Emile Victor, who had worked in Greenland with Charcot during the 1930s. In 1946 and 1947 he took the initiative in an attempt to convince the French Government that France should mount a series of scientific expeditions to Terre Adélie and to Greenland.

In February 1947 the French Council of Ministers gave their approval to Victor's proposals for the organization of two simultaneous expeditions. His newly created private organization, 'Expéditions Polaires Françaises' (EPF) was given the responsibility and the funds to go ahead.

After an unsuccessful attempt during the 1948–9 season to penetrate the Antarctic pack ice off the Adélie Coast, the EPF group in January 1950 successfully established a station at Pointe Géologie on a small island adjacent to the Adélie Coast. This station was operated for three seasons, and then evacuated until late 1955, when it was again occupied by EPF to commence French Antarctic scientific activities for the IGY. Since that date, the station, now named Dumont d'Urville, has been continuously occupied. In December 1956 an additional station, 'Charcot' was established some 300 km inland on the icecap, near the South Magnetic Pole, and manned for two years. EPF, although still retaining its private character, has been institutionalized by the French Government and named as the official agent to carry out French Antarctic research.

Meanwhile, in January 1951, a meteorological station was established on Kerguelen. Now administered by TAAF, the station, which is permanent and houses a large staff, is also used as a supply depot by French and Australian expeditions. The station was established in an effort to demonstrate French interest in her Subantarctic islands. In 1949, when funds were approved for the expedition, there was a flurry of interest over the possible use of Kerguelen as a refuelling station for future commercial flights between South Africa and Australia. However, this possibility has never been realized, and French public and press interest in the Antarctic region has again relapsed despite Victor's well publicized expeditions.

The French Government has strongly opposed any move toward the relinquishment of her national sovereignty in the Antarctic region. In 1948 and again in 1958 the lukewarm French response to United States proposals for internationalization was explicit. French sensitivity on this subject has, of course, been heightened in recent years by the loss of practically all of French possessions in Africa and Asia. She is even less inclined to give up additional sovereignty – even over a territory as distant and desolate as the TAAF.

France has, however, favoured international regulation of scientific activity, and has participated vigorously in the IGY and in the continuing internationally coordinated SCAR programme. She has also cooperated closely with Australia and Britain in the Antarctic. In 1934 and 1938 the three nations mutually recognized each other's claims in the Antarctic and Subantarctic regions, observers have been exchanged, and, as noted above, Australia uses Kerguelen as a supply base for its Antarctic programme.

New Zealand

Even though New Zealand has often been used as a port of call for Antarctic expeditions of many nations, curiously, New Zealanders themselves until very recently took very little notice of the Antarctic Continent which, except for Australia, 2000 km distant, is their closest neighbour. Her current Antarctic territorial claim is based not on her own activities, but rather on extensive British discovery and exploration in the area (James Clark Ross, Scott and Shackleton) dating back over a century. Until 1956 there were no New Zealand expeditions

B

and very few New Zealanders had been included in British and Australian Antarctic expeditions.

The official connection of New Zealand to the Antarctic began in 1923, when a British Order-in-Council staked out an Antarctic claim 'comprising all islands and territories' lying between 160° East Longitude and 150° West Longitude and south of 60° South Latitude. This new territory, which includes the huge Ross Ice Shelf, was proclaimed a British 'settlement', named the 'Ross Dependency', and placed under the administrative authority of the Governor-General of New Zealand.

Through the years these functions have proved to be almost nominal. Technically, the 'Dependency' is still only administered by New Zealand on behalf

FIG. 2

JAMES CLARK ROSS

From a water colour by an unknown artist in the possession of the Royal Geographical Society

of the United Kingdom, but, for all practical purposes, it is a New Zealand claim. A New Zealander, Captain H. Ruegg (the Marine Department's Nautical Adviser) does, however, hold the post 'Administrator of the Ross Dependency'. Appointed by the New Zealand Governor-General, he is empowered to appoint for the 'Ross Dependency' such officers as 'Magistrate', 'Coroner', and 'Postmaster'.

New Zealand has also claimed sovereignty over the following group of small Subantarctic islands, all lying between 49° and 52° South Latitudes and 166° and 179° East Longitudes: Antipodes Islands, Auckland Islands, Bounty Islands, Campbell Island, and Snares Islands.

Two New Zealanders participated in the Australian-directed British–Australian–New Zealand Antarctic Research Expedition (BANZARE) of 1929–31, and the resulting interest was responsible for the creation of the New Zealand

Antarctic Society in 1933. For several decades this private organization carried the burden in New Zealand for promoting interest in the Antarctic. During this period the New Zealand Government exhibited complete disregard for the 'Ross Dependency', and little attempt was made at even the nominal administration of the New Zealand-claimed Antarctic territory.

Immediately following World War II New Zealand watched several other nations mount expeditions to the Antarctic. Public interest began to grow again, especially after the US Navy expeditions of 1946 and 1947 visited New Zealand en route to the ice.

In 1949 the re-activated New Zealand Antarctic Society began the publication of the *Antarctic News Bulletin*,[1] and in 1952 the Society published *The Antarctic Today*, a volume which is still considered as one of the most informative compendiums of Antarctic information. The government of Prime Minister S. G. Holland, however, was still unconvinced of the value of an Antarctic expedition.

It was not until late 1953 that strong Antarctic interest was generated in New Zealand. Even at this time it was not New Zealand initiative, but rather the news of the British plans for the Trans-Antarctic Expedition (TAE) which caught the imagination of the New Zealand public. Coincident with these preparations was the planning for the IGY, and the combination of these two elements caused public and press interest to mount rapidly.

In May 1955 the New Zealand Government finally yielded and reversed its policy. It declared that New Zealand had an inescapable geographic interest in Antarctica, and announced its approval of New Zealand's participation in the proposed TAE.[2] A 'Ross Sea Committee' was created to organize New Zealand's contribution and to coordinate with the main British organization. A few months later, Sir Edmund Hillary was selected as leader of the New Zealand TAE group. At about the same time, in August 1955, the New Zealand Government approved New Zealand's IGY programme, which included the establishment of a base in the Antarctic.

During the 1956–7 season, with the logistic assistance of the United States, the New Zealand 'Scott Base' was constructed at Pram Point on Ross Island, just a few miles from the United States Naval Air Facility on McMurdo Sound. The station was jointly occupied by Hillary's TAE team and the IGY contingent under the leadership of Trevor Hatherton, who acted as New Zealand's Chief Scientist for the Antarctic during the IGY.

The 1957–8 season saw the successful conclusion of the TAE, with Hillary actually reaching the South Pole in December 1957, leading the first overland party to accomplish the feat since the ill-fated journey of Captain Robert

[1] In March 1956 the name was changed to *Antarctic*. The journal has since proven to be a most useful source of New Zealand expeditionary information. News of other nations' activities is also regularly included.

[2] The New Zealand Government, however, did not provide all the funds. Some additional £100,000 was subsequently collected by an energetic public subscription campaign.

Scott a half-century earlier. Following the termination of the TAE, the station continued the prosecution of the New Zealand scientific programme.

During the IGY a second Antarctic base, 'Hallett Station', was established in 1956 and operated jointly with the United States. In February 1958, looking ahead to the termination of the IGY, the New Zealand Prime Minister Walter Nash announced that his Government had approved the post-IGY continuation of the New Zealand Antarctic programme. The Department of Scientific and Industrial Research (DSIR), which had had the responsibility of executing the Antarctic IGY programme, was given the authority to continue, and a 'Ross Dependency Research Committee' (RDRC) was created.

As the 1958–9 season closed, the New Zealand Government, seeing that most of the IGY nations had resolved to remain indefinitely in Antarctica, itself decided that New Zealand should establish a permanent programme. On 4 May 1959, the DSIR set up an Antarctic Division with G. W. Markham as Superintendent. This organization, with the scientific assistance of the RDRC, has since managed the New Zealand Antarctic programme smoothly and efficiently with annual scientific teams being sent to Scott and Hallett Stations.

Although most New Zealanders have long felt that Antarctica is not strategically or economically important, the government's large-scale scientific, geological and survey activities in recent years testify to the growing significance of the Antarctic Continent to New Zealand. The necessity of 'securing the southern frontier' has often been asserted, and, as in Australia (although to a much lesser extent) vague arguments concerning security have been made to explain New Zealand's sensitivity to Japanese and Soviet whalers in the adjacent Subantarctic waters.

The strategic importance of controlling possible bases and air lanes on the Southern Hemispheric great circle routes across Antarctica has also received considerable journalistic attention, although it is generally conceded that the significance of such routes lies in the future. It has further been argued that Antarctic bases could prevent raiders from moving through southern waters to prey on shipping as they did during World War II. When the US Defense Department, in 1958, was examining the feasibility of constructing a major year-round asphalt airstrip at Cape Bernacchi, a low, rocky promontory on the west side of McMurdo Sound and well within the boundaries of the Ross Dependency, the New Zealand Government expressed considerable concern lest such an airfield be used for military purposes.

Although for many years making little pretence of administrative activity in the 'Ross Dependency' New Zealand has always maintained close cooperation with the other members of the British Commonwealth, and has always expressed pride in the achievements of British Antarctic expeditions. Like Australia, New Zealand has championed the United Kingdom's Antarctic claims, and, as has been noted, participated enthusiastically in the British-organized TAE.

Relations with the United States have been particularly close, beginning with the favourable public relations engendered by the several expeditions led by

Admiral Richard E. Byrd. The New Zealand–United States cooperative arrangements for the occupation and management of Hallett Station is another typical example of this close relationship.

Strong public and governmental support for the internationalization of Antarctica has also characterized New Zealand policy. Walter Nash, for many years New Zealand's Prime Minister, has been an especially strong proponent for this solution to Antarctica's difficult political problems. In January 1956 he made the first of his several proposals suggesting the abandonment of national claims to Antarctic territory and the creation of Antarctica as a 'world territory' under the control and jurisdiction of the United Nations. New Zealand was an enthusiastic supporter of the United States during the 1958–9 talks which led to the Antarctic Treaty, and it is believed that New Zealand will be among the leaders in pushing for an eventual international administration for Antarctica.

Norway

Since 1892 Norwegians have been prominent in Antarctic whaling, and a Norwegian, Roald Amundsen, was the first to reach the South Pole in December 1911.[1] Other Norwegian Antarctic activity, during which her ships have traversed almost every portion of the Antarctic and Subantarctic seas, especially the exploration and extensive mapping programme of Riiser-Larsen and Lars Christensen in the 1930s, brought Norway considerable respect among Antarctic-oriented nations. The successful management of the Norwegian–British–Swedish Antarctic Expedition of 1949–52 (led by Captain John Giaever of the Norsk Polarinstitutt) and the establishment, in late 1956, of 'Norway Station' in Dronning Maud Land in conjunction with the IGY, have continued the strong tradition of Norwegian Antarctic activity.

In January 1939, concerned over the comprehensive German expedition, then conducting extensive exploration and mapping in the portion of Antarctica previously explored only by Norwegians, the Norwegian Government issued an Order-in-Council proclaiming Norwegian sovereignty over 'that part of the mainland coast' between 20° West Longitude and 45° East Longitude.

The claimed area lay exactly between the British and Australian claims. Norway did not specifically invoke the 'sector' policy used by other Antarctic claimants, and it must be assumed that her claim does not extend to the South Pole as do all the others.[2]

The statement was based on a Norwegian Foreign Ministry Memorandum

[1] Amundsen claimed for Norway a circular area comprising the plateau around the South Pole (the apex of all Antarctic claims except that of Norway) and named it 'King Haakon VII Plateau'. Norway has never taken action on this potential claim, although on several occasions, in 1929 and 1939, the Norwegian Government reminded the United States that she still maintained a priority of interest in this area as a result of Amundsen's expedition and exploration.

[2] Norway has been careful to avoid even the appearance of recognizing the 'sector principle' in order not to prejudice certain of her rights or interests in the Arctic, where the application of this principle would be a disadvantage.

issued the same day, which outlined Antarctic territorial claims and the history of Norwegian Antarctic activity.

Previously, in order to provide shore bases for her whalers operating in these areas, Norway, in 1928 and 1930, had proclaimed her sovereignty over Bouvetøya and in 1931 over Peter I Øy. Bouvetøya was first visited by a Norwegian in November 1927 and again during the next three years, during which several huts were built. In 1928 Nils Larsen landed on Peter I Øy and took possession on behalf of Norway.

Mainly because of the long history of Norwegian activity in Antarctic exploration and whaling, the Norwegian public has always been interested in the development and political future of Antarctica. Since World War II, her interest has reflected nationalistic concern for Norwegian prestige, and pride in her Antarctic accomplishments. The Norwegian–British–Swedish expedition attracted considerable public and press interest, which was maintained through the IGY and the recent Antarctic Treaty discussions.

In addition, during the past several decades, Norwegian scientific interest in both polar regions has grown steadily – a direct influence of the operations of the Norsk Polarinstitutt in Oslo. With such active leaders as H. U. Sverdrup, Anders Orvin and, since 1960, Tore Gjelsvik, this organization has provided the stimulus and the personnel for many of Norway's recent polar ventures.

Apart from national prestige and scientific interest, Norway's interest in the Antarctic and Subantarctic regions is heavily based on whaling, for many years a tangible and profitable asset in this area. Exploratory activities of Norwegian whaling interests are among the fundamental bases supporting Norwegian assertion of Antarctic territorial claims. At times, Norwegian annual production of whale oil in the Antarctic has amounted to 150,000 tons, with over 6000 Norwegian men engaged in the operations. International whaling agreements in recent years have curtailed the industry's expansion, which had threatened the extinction of the whales, but the high level of Norwegian investment in whaling has been sustained by the increased rate of capitalization.

Norway's position toward the claims of other nations in the Antarctic has traditionally been characterized by conciliation and accommodation, especially with the United Kingdom, with whom she shares a common Antarctic territorial claim border. The United Kingdom, New Zealand and Australia have all recognized the Norwegian claim, although Australia's Antarctic claim has never been recognized by Norway, which gave up a vast potential claim in that area in the early 1930s in deference to the importance of cooperation with the United Kingdom.

Although Norway has given little indication that she would be willing to give up her Antarctic claims for the sake of internationalization, her attitude during the 1958–9 Washington discussions has indicated that she would not be averse to backing an international regime provided that the other Antarctic nations moved in that direction.

After three years occupation Norway was forced to evacuate Norway Station in January 1960, owing to lack of funds, but she was able to arrange for the loan of the station to South Africa. Meanwhile, through the substantial work of the Norsk Polarinstitutt and of Norwegian scientists in SCAR, Norway continues to play an important policy role in Antarctic developments.

FIG. 3 THE FIRST RECORDED VISIT TO ANTARCTICA

The *Resolution* among the ice islands – engraving from *Voyages Round the World Performed by Captain Cook*, London, 1820

(*Photo. Alexander Turnbull Library*)

United Kingdom

British explorers were among the first to journey to Antarctic waters. Beginning with Captain James Cook's circumnavigation of Antarctica in 1772–5 (see Fig. 23) and his discovery of the South Sandwich Islands in 1775, a large number of British expeditions, with such illustrious leaders as Ross, Weddell, Biscoe, Shackleton and Scott, have conducted extensive exploration in many parts of the Antarctic region.

Between 1790 and 1830 many sealing voyages were made to Antarctic waters. It was in this period that Edward Bransfield surveyed the South Shetlands in 1819–20, and may have been the first to sight the Antarctic Continent.

More intimately associated with the discovery, exploration and development of the region than any other country, British activity in Antarctica has, since 1925, gradually changed its nature and increased in tempo. The Wilkins–Hearst expeditions of 1928–30 (with the first use of aircraft in Antarctica), the BANZAR Expedition of 1929–31, the *Discovery* oceanographic and mapping expeditions in the 1930s and the British Graham Land Expedition of 1934–7, under the leadership of John Rymill, did much to bring in government support to an already enthusiastic British public.

During World War II, partially to counter Argentine and Chilean claims to Graham Land and partly to begin 'effective occupation' as required by international law, the British Government created, in 1943, the 'Falkland Islands Dependencies Survey' (FIDS), and instituted 'Operation Tabarin', during which a number of small stations were established on Graham Land. A joint venture of the British Admiralty and the Colonial Office (under which FIDS

FIG. 4 BEAUFORT ISLAND AND MOUNT EREBUS

Discovered 28 January 1841. Lithograph from *A Voyage of Discovery and Research in the Southern and Antarctic Regions during the years 1839–43* by Captain Sir James Clark Ross

(*Photo. Alexander Turnbull Library*)

was placed), this event marked the changeover from ship-borne activities to land-based operations.

The new bases were intended to carry out a detailed economic survey, establish weather stations, and complete the work of mapping Graham Land that had been initiated by the Rymill Expedition. Under the new programme a large number of bases have been established through the years, many of them permanently manned by four or five technicians who are employed by FIDS.

During the 1947–8 season FIDS exploratory operations were intensified. The largely military composition of the group emphasized FIDS' political character. Until the IGY, when several of the bases were enlarged to accommodate stronger scientific programmes, the size, equipment, composition and training of the United Kingdom parties precluded large-scale scientific investigations.

The headquarters of FIDS, which in January 1962 was renamed the 'British Antarctic Survey', is at Port Stanley in the Falkland Islands under the direction of the Governor. In recent years the FIDS London office has been under the leadership of Sir Vivian Fuchs who, during 1957–8, made a successful crossing of the Antarctic Continent.

Although the United Kingdom participated in the Norwegian–British–Swedish expedition in 1949–52, it was not until the 1955–6 season that Britain established a permanent Antarctic continental station. Named 'Halley Bay', and located not far from the TAE 'Shackleton Base', the station was constructed under the direction of the Royal Society and served during the IGY as an

FIG. 5
JAMES WEDDELL
(*Photo. Alexander Turnbull Library*)

important British contribution to the international chain of Antarctic IGY stations. After the termination of the IGY programme the management of the base was turned over to FIDS (Shackleton Base was evacuated after the departure of the TAE team).

Occupying a unique place in the British polar tradition is the Scott Polar Research Institute in Cambridge. With money remaining from the memorial fund of Scott's last expedition, the Institute was established in 1926 under the leadership of Frank Debenham with the assistance of Sir Raymond Priestley. Although not technically a government agency, the Institute enjoys financial support not only from the British Government, but from several of the Commonweath countries as well. It does not directly sponsor expeditions, but contains a wealth of information (including the most comprehensive polar library in the

world) and a small but select staff expert in everything from polar ice studies to
Soviet polar problems. The current Director, Gordon Robin, also serves as
Secretary of the international body SCAR. Its publication *The Polar Record* not
only contains valuable information on expeditions, their techniques and results,
but also provides details of political and diplomatic events concerning the
Antarctic.

For the British, Antarctica has been a focus of public attention ever since
Scott's tragic death in 1911 in his effort to be the first to reach the South Pole.
The British are proud of their record in Antarctica, not only for reasons of
political prestige, but also because they regard British exploits in this region
as a foremost example of British heroism and love of adventure.

This widespread public pride and interest, coupled with a natural political
sensitivity arising from the many recent enforced retrenchments and losses
of power, help to explain why the protection of British interests in Antarctica
has been so important, and why the government and press have sought to enlist
support for a vigorous Antarctic policy. The strong government financial assistance to the TAE reflects an example of British regard for the prestige engendered by polar exploration.

Although nationalism is an important element in shaping British feeling toward the Antarctic, economic, scientific and strategic interests also influence
British policy. Whaling, although of diminished importance, remains the major
economic incentive. Since 1932 whale oil has become a significant part of British
food supply, being used in margarine, lard and soap. The desire to control the
rich whaling grounds in the British-claimed Antarctic sector in the past has
been one of the major reasons for British assertion of sovereignty.

However, since 1930, revenues from whaling licenses have fallen sharply, and
with the Norwegian introduction of pelagic whaling, the importance of controlling
shore bases (from which fees and taxes were collected) has measurably declined.

Aside from economic and scientific interests, the strategic position of Graham
Land and the Drake Passage separating it from the tip of South America has
been the primary reason for British Antarctic territorial concern. To the British,
the current paramount importance of air power in modern warfare has not
eliminated the potential importance of the Drake Passage should the Panama
Canal be destroyed in time of war.

The United Kingdom has also been interested in the possibility of developing
strategic air routes across the Antarctic Continent or Subantarctic islands as a
wartime alternative to the northern Indian Ocean route. In 1938, when the
United Kingdom, Australia and New Zealand made an agreement with France
on aerial navigation in the Antarctic, the British invited Commonwealth consideration of an airline between Cape Town and Sydney via Terre Adélie. Since
World War II interest in a strategic route has often been revived. The occupation in 1947 of certain Subantarctic islands by South Africa and Australia was
widely ascribed to this motive, although the islands have serious disadvantages
as air bases.

The first British claim to Antarctic territory (the earliest to be made by any nation) was asserted in 1908 with the creation of the 'Falkland Islands Dependencies' (FID) under the control of the Governor of the Falkland Islands. The claim, although based on British discoveries and exploration, was haphazardly defined with an ambiguity of language by which the United Kingdom appeared to be claiming portions of Argentina and Chile south of 50° South Latitude.

The Letters Patent of 1917 more carefully delimited the claim to include all islands and territories between 20° and 50° West Longitudes and south of 50° South Latitude and between 50° and 80° West Longitudes and south of 58° South Latitude.[1] The 'Dependencies' consisted of two groups, the first including the South Orkney and South Sandwich Islands and South Georgia (the group's administrative centre), and the second comprising the South Shetland Islands and Graham Land and its offshore islands. By this definition of the claim a precedent was established for the pie-shaped sector approach, which has since been followed by every Antarctic claimant nation except Norway. In addition to the 'Dependencies' the United Kingdom also has claimed the Subantarctic Gough Island as a British dependency of St Helena since 1938.

As noted earlier, a 1923 Order-in-Council formally asserted a territorial claim over all the area comprising the 'Ross Dependency', stating that it was a 'British settlement', and placed it under the administration of the Governor-General of New Zealand. Similarly, in 1933, another Order-in-Council laid claim to a vast area (now called 'Australian Antarctic Territory'), and placed it under Australian authority. These two claims combined with the British-claimed 'FID' cover over two-thirds of the continental area of Antarctica. In March 1962 the British-claimed area was separated from the Falkland Islands and transformed into a new colony. It was renamed the 'British Antarctic Territory', and the Governor of the Falkland Islands was named High Commissioner of the new colony.

The United Kingdom international political relations with respect to the Antarctic have long been dominated by Britain's dispute with Argentina and Chile, both of which also claim Graham Land and the offshore islands. The history of these conflicts reveals the often bitter atmosphere which this rivalry has generated, mainly since 1947–8. The United Kingdom has accused Argentina and Chile of 'territorial violations', 'provocative demonstrations of force', and 'flagrant disregard of international law'. Argentine and Chilean replies have been equally strong. British efforts to resolve the dispute with the two South American nations reflect a legalistic approach to the problem. However, in spite of repeated Argentine and Chilean rejections of the United Kingdom's offer to accept adjudication by the International Court of Justice, the British Government (partly to maintain international public opinion) has continued to pursue this approach, including a unilateral application to the court in May 1955.

The British Government is sensitive to possible repercussions of the Argentine and Chilean frontal assault on United Kingdom prestige elsewhere in the

[1] For reproductions of both the 1908 and 1917 documents see *The Polar Record*, **5**: 241–3, 1948.

Southern Hemisphere. She has also been concerned about the possible adverse effects of this conflict on her considerable commercial interests in Latin America.

Referring the problem to the United Nations is another alternative, but this possible solution has won little support in the United Kingdom. The Foreign Office, while anxious to avoid a prolonged dispute, has feared the complications which United Nations consideration might bring – especially the involvement of unwanted parties and the possible adverse effects to Anglo-American and inter-American relations. But strong sentiment favouring some sort of international control for Antarctica has been expressed in the Labour Party, in press circles, and by British polar scientists who decry the assertion of national sovereignty in a region where only scientific activities seem justifiable.

In response to this pressure the British Government supported the United States 1948 proposal for the establishment of a multiple condominium (limited to the interested nations), and has since favoured this approach rather than the internationalization of the continent. During 1957–8 Prime Minister Macmillan and the Foreign Office examined the matter in detail with Australia and New Zealand, and worked closely with the United States in the preparation of the 1959 Antarctic Treaty. Since then the United Kingdom has been a participating member of SCAR and the Antarctic Treaty consultative group. But it is unlikely that she will be a leader in the establishment of a strong international regime for Antarctica.

Union of South Africa

In January 1960, when she took over occupation of 'Norway Station' in Dronning Maud Land, South Africa joined the ranks of those nations operating year-round stations on the Antarctic mainland. In the past her official interest has been limited to the two Subantarctic islands comprising the Prince Edward Islands: Marion Island and Prince Edward Island (both situated at approximately 47° South Latitude and 38° East Longitude, halfway between South Africa and Antarctica), sovereignty over which had been declared in 1948, following their occupation during December 1947–January 1948.[1]

Initiative for this and subsequent Antarctic action has been provided by the South African Weather Bureau, which established a weather station on Marion Island. The Bureau has continued to resupply it annually. The need for additional meteorological observations has consistently provided South Africa with the stimulus to continue and expand her modest Antarctic programme. The Union contributed £20,000 to the Trans-Antarctic Expedition, and in 1956 occupied the meteorological station on Gough Island, constructed the year before by a British team. During the 1961–2 season South Africa constructed a new station some 20 km distant from 'Norway' Station. This new base, 'SANAE' (South African National Antarctic Expedition), is now in permanent occupation.

Matters of policy concerning her general programme and research are directed by the inter-departmental South African National Council for Antarctic Re-

[1] For text see *The Polar Record*, **5**: 243–4, 1948.

search (SANCAR), headed by M. P. Van Rooy, Director of the South African Weather Bureau, and a long-time proponent of South African Antarctic activity. The administration of the South African stations is invested in the Department of Transport, which also provides logistic support.

The Non-Claimant Nations

USSR

After more than a century of Russian lack of interest in the Antarctic, the Soviet Government since 1939 has expressed considerable concern regarding the political future of Antarctica. When the Norwegian Government placed Dronning

FIG 6
THADDEUS VON BELLINGS-
HAUSEN
(*Photo. Alexander Turnbull Library*)

Maud Land under her sovereignty in that year the USSR, on 27 January 1939, protested in a Note to Norway observing that it would 'reserve its opinion as to the national status of territories discovered by Russian citizens'.[1] This reference, which has been frequently cited by Moscow as proof of its 'long-standing' interest in the Antarctic, was to the 1819–21 voyage of Captain Thaddeus von Bellingshausen to Antarctic waters.

Sent by Czar Alexander I, Bellingshausen successfully circumnavigated the Antarctic Continent, discovered Peter I Øy and Alexander Island, and conceivably may have been the first to sight the Antarctic mainland. Since 1949 a stream of Soviet literature has been issued in an attempt to prove that Bellingshausen was the first to discover Antarctica, and to build up Soviet Antarctic rights on the strength of this one expedition in spite of modern international law which negates discovery as the sole basis for the acquisition of territorial sovereignty.

[1] For text see *Izvestia*, Moscow, 28 January 1939.

Although the essence of the Soviet position is that priority in the matter of discovery of Antarctica by Bellingshausen belongs to Russia, and by state succession to the USSR, this same doctrine of discovery would seem to be ruled out by the Soviet decree of 15 April 1926, which placed under Soviet territorial jurisdiction a large portion of the Arctic regardless of who had discovered it, as well as islands and territory 'which are to be discovered in the future'. In any event the emphasis of the Soviet campaign has remained on the Soviet Union's having a stake in the region rather than on a specific territorial claim.

When the United States, in August 1948, approached the claimant States about the possibilities of setting up an international regime for Antarctica, reaction in the Soviet Union (which had not been invited to participate) soon formalized. At a general meeting of the Geographical Society of the USSR (Vsesoyuznoye Geograficheskoye Obshchestvo), held on 10 February 1949 in Leningrad, Academician L. S. Berg, the President of the Society, gave a report outlining Russian discoveries in the Antarctic and current interests in the area (Berg, 1949).

Several important resolutions were made by the Society, including the assertion of Russian priority in the discovery of Antarctica, and a statement that the Soviet Government had 'irrefutable rights' to participate in such a multilateral conference as that envisaged by the United States. The Leningrad meeting was immediately followed by a series of other meetings and events dealing with the Antarctic. The discovery of several new documents dealing with the 1819–21 voyage was also announced.

The following year the Soviet Government, on 10 June 1950, issued a formal Memorandum to seven of the claimant states[1] which reiterated the points made by the 1949 Geographical Society resolutions, and explicitly stated her position:

> The Government of the Soviet Union cannot agree that such a question as that of the regime for the Antarctic should be decided without their participation. . . . The Soviet Government . . . are prepared to examine any proposals of the interested governments both regarding the procedure for the discussion of this question and the nature of the regime for the Antarctic.

This statement has since 1950 provided the backbone of Soviet Antarctic policy. Soviet jurists and writers such as B. V. Kostritsyn, V. Durdenevksy, and S. Molodtsov in the past decade have actively pressed this point of view: that the USSR must participate in any solution of the Antarctic political problem. However, there have been certain disagreements as to just what is the best solution. (See Toma, 1956, for a careful review of the Soviet juridical opinion regarding the acquisition of territorial sovereignty in Antarctica.) Although most Soviet writers seem to feel that national sector claims are impractical in the Antarctic and that an international regime would be the best solution, others have spoken for the creation of a multi-national condominium.

[1] Chile was excluded since at that time diplomatic relations did not exist between the two countries.

Another reason for the post-war intensification of Soviet interest in the Antarctic has been its participation in Antarctic whaling activities. Since 1946 annual Soviet whaling expeditions – called the *Slava* fleet – have operated in Antarctic waters. Although the catch has not been large, the expeditions have also been useful in demonstrating Soviet Antarctic interest. At the same time certain oceanographic observations have been made.

The USSR participated in the International Whaling Conference held in Washington in November–December 1946, and signed the International Whaling Convention on 2 December 1946. Soviet delegates have attended periodic meetings of the International Whaling Conference, and the Soviet Union played host for the Conference held in 1955 in Moscow.

A few years later, with the commencement of the discussions for the IGY, an excellent opportunity was provided for the Soviet Union finally to participate actively on the Antarctic Continent without incurring political difficulties with the claimant nations. Her scientists were genuinely interested in the opportunity afforded, and with the vast experience gained in the Arctic by the Chief Administration of the Northern Sea Route (Glavsevmorput') and the Arctic Research Institute (in 1958 changed to the Arctic and Antarctic Research Institute – Arkticheskiy Antarkticheskiy Nauchno-Issledovatel'skiy Institut) in Leningrad, the Soviet Union enthusiastically prepared to establish scientific research stations in the Antarctic for the first time.

Her representatives were cooperative during the international IGY Antarctic meetings, and her programme was prepared to coordinate with those of the other participating countries. During the 1955–6 season the first Soviet Antarctic expedition (under the leadership of M. M. Somov, an experienced Arctic scientist) established its primary base, Mirnyy, along the Queen Mary Coast, and in later seasons established additional stations, including several in the interior of the continent.

During the IGY a number of inland expeditions (using modern oversnow equipment) were made including, in December 1958, a 4000 km trip to the so-called 'Pole of Relative Inaccessibility', where a temporary camp was established, and in December 1959 a journey to the United States Amundsen–Scott Station at the South Pole, 2700 km from Mirnyy.

Soviet aircraft were active during these expeditions over a large portion of the Antarctic plateau. At Mirnyy and the other stations scientific observations were carried out in accordance with the IGY programme. Each year, both before and after the annual servicing of Mirnyy Station, the Soviet expeditionary diesel-electric ship *Ob* completed comprehensive oceanographic voyages in Antarctic waters, including a circumnavigation of the continent in 1959–1960.

Since the commencement of the current series of Soviet Antarctic expeditions in 1955, considerable attention has also been paid to mapping. In 1959 the Ministry of the Merchant Fleet published a series of land maps based on aerial photography and ground control obtained by the Soviet expeditionary personnel. These maps cover the area between 72° and 120° East Longitudes.

Following the termination of the IGY several of the Soviet Antarctic stations were closed (Pionerskaya, Komsomolskaya, Sovetskaya and Oazis). A new station, Lazarev, was constructed on the Prinsesse Astrid Kyst in 1959 and operated for two years, and Novalazarevskaya was constructed about 30 km west of Lazarev in 1961.

The Soviet Antarctic expeditions have been under the scientific direction of the USSR Academy of Sciences (Akademiya Nauk SSSR) while executive responsibility and logistics are the concern of the Chief Administration of the Northern Sea Route (Glavsevmorput'). The primary scientific organ of Glavsevmorput' is the Arctic and Antarctic Research Institute in Leningrad, which has

FIG. 7 THE FIRST FOOTHOLD
Borchgrevink's hut, Ridley Beach, Cape Adare
(*Photo. Alexander Turnbull Library*)

been, since late 1960, under the leadership of A. F. Treshnikov, an experienced polar scientist and leader of the second Soviet Antarctic expedition of 1956–8.

The coordinating body was at first the Academy of Sciences Council for Antarctic Investigations (Soviet po Antarkticheskim Issledovaniyam) created in 1955 under the chairmanship of Academician D. I. Shcherbakov. The Academy replaced this body in September 1958 by the Inter-Departmental Antarctic Commission (Mezhduvedomstvennaya Antarkticheskaya Komissiya) with Shcherbakov as Chairman.

As has been noted, all the Soviet IGY bases were erected on territory claimed by Australia. During the IGY Australia had grave apprehensions concerning the Soviet presence as Mirnyy is located within 3500 km of Australia and could conceivably be used to command the sea routes around Cape Horn and the Cape of Good Hope. Yet, as the USSR soon demonstrated, no submarine bases were built, the Soviet bases were open to any nation to visit (several expeditions have visited Mirnyy), and the Soviet stations carried out a comprehensive scientific programme. In actual fact, the IGY served as a most effective lever in obtaining Soviet Government support for the polar programmes sought by the USSR Academy of Sciences and the Leningrad Institute.

During this period Australian–Soviet relationships were more strained than usual because of the 1954 Petrov defection and the cessation of normal diplomatic relations. Nevertheless, acting under the international good will generated by the IGY, Australian Minister of External Affairs, R. G. Casey, invited the USSR (and any other nation) to set up Antarctic scientific research stations on 'Australian Antarctic Territory' in connection with IGY activities. No assurance was sought that the bases would be vacated at the conclusion of the IGY, and this particular problem troubled Australia during 1957, when it became clear that the USSR had decided to remain in the Antarctic indefinitely.

During this period the USSR was a leading supporter of the United States move to prolong the IGY Antarctic arrangements for an additional year (to December 1959). It was precisely this Soviet attitude that caused a less than enthusiastic reception of this idea in the United Kingdom and Australia in 1957.

Soviet post-IGY Antarctic plans were outlined at the February 1958 meeting of SCAR at The Hague by Somov, the Soviet delegate. He also proposed at this meeting that a number of additional stations be established in Antarctica. He indicated that the USSR was prepared to continue, as during the IGY, international scientific coordination in Antarctica through membership in SCAR.

In June 1958 the Soviet Government enthusiastically welcomed the United States proposal to call an international conference to deal with the Antarctic political situation. It noted 'with satisfaction' the successful operation of the IGY and stated that the Soviet Government was 'prepared to render all possible help in the development of international scientific cooperation in the Antarctic in the future'. After noting that an important aim of the projected international agreement should be the 'prevention of any international misunderstandings that could hinder successful scientific investigations in this area', the Soviet Note restated the position the Soviet Government had taken on earlier occasions regarding the question of territorial claims in Antarctica:

> The Soviet Government considers it necessary to state again that it has not recognized and cannot recognize as lawful any separate settlement of the question regarding state jurisdiction over the Antarctic . . . the Soviet Government reserves all rights based on the discoveries and explorations by Russian navigators and scientists, including the right to present appropriate territorial claims on the Antarctic.

During the 1958–9 negotiations preceding the Antarctic Treaty Conference (15 October–1 December 1959), the Soviet Embassy in Washington worked closely with the other Antarctic national representatives in preparing draft treaty language. These discussions were measurably helped in August 1958, when word was received from Geneva that an East–West agreement had been reached on a moratorium of nuclear weapon tests.

At the opening of the Conference Vasili Kuznetsov, First Deputy Minister of Foreign Affairs, could hardly have been more cooperative. He stated that the Soviet Government considered 'that there should be established in Antarctica an international regime that would contribute to the strengthening of peace', and emphasized the Soviet desire for the non-militarization of Antarctica, including a ban on 'the testing of any types of weapons', and on the construction of military bases.

At the conference and during the past several years the Soviet Union, whose Antarctic aims seem to coincide so closely with those of the United States, has cooperated fully in her Treaty obligations and with those nations seeking to hasten the development of an international regime for Antarctica. It is assumed that this policy will be maintained as long as the Soviet Government continues to feel that an international Antarctic administration will remain in her best interest.

USA

Numerous private and official United States expeditions have been active in the Antarctic for a period of over 150 years. Motivated by economic and scientific interests these expeditions have been responsible for the discovery and exploration of vast areas of Antarctica as well as many Antarctic and Subantarctic islands.

An important series of expeditions conducted by United States commercial sealers to Antarctic waters took place in the years from 1819–31. During this period, the *Hero*, with Nathanial B. Palmer as captain, in November 1820 and in January 1821 sailed along the coast of the peninsula which until 1964 carried his name on all United States maps.[1]

The first official United States Government expedition to the Antarctic was the United States Exploring Expedition of 1838–42 under the command of Lieutenant (later Rear-Admiral) Charles Wilkes of the United States Navy. Authorized by Congress in 1836, the expedition, with Wilkes in the *Vincennes*, succeeded in January and February 1840 in sailing along the edge of the pack ice fringing the coast of Antarctica from 160° to 100° East Longitudes, a distance of 1500 nautical miles.

As a result of sighting land at many points during the cruise, Wilkes concluded he had demonstrated the existence of an Antarctic Continent. However, from the beginning, Wilkes' conception (as displayed on his charts) was challenged by many authorities, including Sir James Clark Ross, who based their counterclaims on voyages through the same waters when no land was seen. Nevertheless, after more than a century of discredit, almost all of Wilkes' landfalls have been

[1] Whether Palmer's was the first confirmed sighting of the Antarctic Continent or whether he was preceded by the British Lieutenant Edward Bransfield, in January 1820, is still in dispute among historians.

confirmed by recent Australian and American mapping programmes – although
it has been shown that considerable longitudinal errors had been made by Wilkes.

Almost a century passed before the United States sent another important
expedition to the Antarctic. American interest in the area declined in the latter
part of the nineteenth century, partly because the sealing resources there had been
exploited almost to the point of extinction, and also in part because of the great
interest in the opening up of the western United States.

But since 1928, American activities in Antarctica have again been extensive,
and with the adaptation of modern equipment, have revolutionized the techniques of Antarctic exploration. That year, Rear-Admiral Richard E. Byrd's

FIG. 8
CHARLES WILKES
(*Photo. Alexander Turnbull Library*)

first expedition (privately sponsored) established a base camp, Little America,
at the Bay of Whales on the edge of the Ross Ice Shelf, and during the 1928–9
and 1929–30 seasons, explored the surrounding territory, made the first flight
over the South Pole (on 29 November 1929), and claimed Marie Byrd Land for
for the United States.

At the same time the Australian Sir Hubert Wilkins led the first Wilkins–
Hearst expedition to Antarctica. With an American pilot he inaugurated the use
of aircraft in Antarctica on 26 November 1928 and explored the east coast of
Graham Land and adjacent areas. A second Wilkins–Hearst expedition (sponsored by the United Kingdom Foreign Office as well as by private organizations)
was also carried out during 1929–30.

Admiral Byrd's considerable organizational skill was successful in raising public funds for a second Antarctic expedition conducted during 1933–5. Great emphasis was placed on geological and other scientific activities, while extensive geographical exploration was again carried out using Little America II as a base.

The value of aircraft as a tool of Antarctic exploration was further emphasized during the 1930s by another American, Lincoln Ellsworth. After two unsuccessful attempts (1933 and 1934) Ellsworth and H. Hollick-Kenyon, from 21 November–5 December 1935, made the first trans-Antarctic flight, travelling from Dundee Island to the Bay of Whales. On his fourth expedition, in 1938–9, Ellsworth flew over the American Highland and claimed for the United States the area south of 70° S to a distance of 150 miles east and 150 miles west of his line of flight, which was 79° East Longitude.

While Byrd and Ellsworth made great contributions to the technique of Antarctic exploration, the growing complexity of their activities forecast the end of small private expeditions. When Byrd travelled to the Antarctic a third time with the United States Antarctic Service Expedition of 1939–41, he went under United States Government sponsorship. Two bases were established, one at the site of the two previous Little Americas and the other at Marguerite Bay off the west side of Graham Land. It was the original intention that both of these stations should be permanently occupied, but the project was terminated in 1941 by the deteriorating international situation.

With the conclusion of World War II American attention was again turned toward the Antarctic. The Navy Department, with Byrd's assistance, established in 1946 the United States Antarctic Development Project, a principal aim of which was to explore and study the continent using new equipment and techniques developed during the war.

Late in 1946 Task Force 68 (13 ships and 4000 men) was created under the operational command of Rear-Admiral R. H. Cruzen and (with Rear-Admiral Byrd along in the confusing role of 'Officer in Charge') left the United States in what has been called 'Operation Highjump'.

The largest expedition ever to be sent to the Antarctic, 'Highjump' witnessed many innovations such as the employment of icebreakers, helicopters and the launching of six twin-engine planes from an aircraft carrier. A base was established at Little America III, and an extensive exploration programme was carried out by air, sea and tractor. Although a vast amount of aerial photography was accomplished with new trimetragon aerial cameras, ground control was very poor and provided a serious defect in the use of the film for accurate mapping.

The following year a second Antarctic Development Project, popularly known as 'Operation Windmill' was despatched as Task Force 39 in an attempt to correct this deficiency. Under Commander G. L. Ketchum's direction this expedition established a number of geodetic control points and carried out some 200 flights for aerial mapping.

The same year, in late 1947, the final American private expedition, led by Commander Finn Ronne, and known as the 'Ronne Antarctic Research Expedition of 1947–1948' or RARE, reoccupied the Marguerite Bay base of the 1939–41

United States Antarctic Service Expedition. Sledging and aerial exploration were carried out along Graham Land and the adjacent continental area during the expedition, which is also famous for the first entry of women into Antarctic exploration. Mrs Ronne and the wife of the chief pilot both wintered with the expedition team.

'Operation Windmill' marked the end of activity under the Navy's Antarctic Development Project, which was suspended in 1948 for lack of funds. The work accomplished, however, indicated the need for a far more comprehensive plan. During early 1948 the Department of State requested the United States National Academy of Sciences to review on a broad scale the feasibility of future United States scientific programmes in the Antarctic.

Several conferences were held, attended by a group of eminent scientists, and a formal report was published in May 1949.[1] The document pointed out the necessity for a coordinated international scientific programme with the free exchange of information among the various national groups involved. In many fields, it specified, significant results could best be obtained from synoptic observations continued over a period of years. For the United States, the Academy group recognized that the Department of Defense had the equipment and experience to provide the logistic support needed for such an Antarctic scientific programme. This report was later to furnish many of the scientific objectives for the United States IGY Antarctic programme.

Within two years the idea of an international polar scientific programme had germinated (originally proposed as the 'Third International Polar Year' but later broadened to the 'International Geophysical Year') among American scientists. In 1952 the International Council of Scientific Unions (ICSU), to which the proposal had been referred, established a special body, the Comité Spécial de l'Année Géophysique Internationale (CSAGI), to invite international participation in the IGY. From the beginning the ICSU stressed the importance of a strong international Antarctic programme and an 'adjoint' committee for the Antarctic was soon organized, and held several meetings from 1955 onward.

Also in 1952 the United States Academy of Sciences (the American affiliate of ICSU) established a United States National Committee for the IGY to prepare a programme for the United States. In January 1954 this Committee submitted to the National Science Foundation (a Government agency) a proposed programme of United States activities for the IGY and requested that the Foundation take responsibility for obtaining the necessary government funds. With respect to the Antarctic, the programme envisaged the establishment of three stations, one at Little America, one at the South Pole, and a third in the heart of Marie Byrd Land. It was the first time that any nation had contemplated establishing year-round stations in the interior of the continent. During 1954 the programme was approved and in 1954-5 a complex administrative pattern developed.

The Academy of Sciences Committee retained full responsibility for the

[1] United States National Academy of Sciences, *Antarctic Research, Elements of a Coordinated Program*, Washington, 1949.

preparation and management of the scientific programme, while the National Science Foundation had the fiscal responsibility for the proper expenditure of the funds. The Academy set up an Antarctic Committee under the chairmanship of Dr Laurence M. Gould (who had been second-in-command of Byrd's first expedition), who was later appointed Director of the United States IGY Antarctic programme.

During the same period, the Department of Defense was designated the agency to supply the logistic support for the Academy-planned programme and Captain (later Rear-Admiral) George Dufek was placed in command of Naval Task Force 43, which was created for this purpose on 1 February 1955. The code name 'Operation Deep Freeze' was given to the entire logistic support operation. The same year the Department of Defense named Admiral Byrd its senior policy officer on Antarctic matters and created a new but loosely defined position for him within the Department as 'Officer-in-Charge, United States Antarctic Projects'. This post was given to Admiral Dufek upon Byrd's death in 1957, in 1959 to Admiral Tyree, and to Admiral Reedy in 1962.

Partly because of Soviet intentions to establish Antarctic stations, the United States, in 1955, decided to construct two additional stations, one on the Knox Coast and the other on the Filchner Ice Shelf near its juncture with the Graham Land. Another small station was also planned, in conjunction with New Zealand, for the Cape Adare area, partly as an emergency and meteorological support base for the contemplated New Zealand–McMurdo Sound flights. All three stations were approved by CSAGI, which had the international responsibility for the allocation of new IGY station sites in Antarctica.

Meanwhile, during the 1954–5 austral summer season, the icebreaker *Atka* was despatched by the Defense Department to conduct a reconnaissance mission along the Antarctic coast to select suitable station sites for the American programme. The following season, 1955–6, the massive sealift began with 'Operation Deep Freeze I'. A new Little America Station was built at Kainan Bay and a Naval Air Facility was constructed on Ross Island in McMurdo Sound to be used as a logistics staging centre for the forthcoming South Pole effort. For the first time in history aircraft were flown into and landed on the Antarctic Continent from an outside land mass (New Zealand).

Five additional IGY stations (Hallett, Byrd, Amundsen–Scott South Pole, Ellsworth and Wilkes) were constructed the next season, 1956–7, during 'Deep Freeze II', in an even larger expeditionary programme. Again, aircraft were flown in and used extensively for aerial reconnaissance prior to the construction of the two inland stations. In November–December 1956 a heavy tractor train successfully traversed the 1000 km from Little America Station to the planned site of Byrd Station, which was quickly constructed.

On 31 October 1956 the first aircraft landing was made at the South Pole and during the following three months men and supplies were air-lifted to the site and the station erected. Meanwhile the construction of Hallett (the intended site at Cape Adare proved to be unsuitable), Ellsworth and Wilkes Stations was completed by ship operations. Except for the McMurdo Air Facility, each American station inaugurated a strong scientific programme in early 1957 which has since continued, except at Little America, which was evacuated at the termination of the IGY in January 1959, and Ellsworth, which was finally evacuated by Argentina in December 1962.

One CSAGI decision that was to have far-reaching implications regarding the lessening of possible political friction during the IGY Antarctic programme was the creation of the international Antarctic Weather Central at Little America. Although primarily under American supervision, personnel from several of the other participating countries, including the USSR, Australia, Argentina and France, served tours of duty at the Central. This led to an arrangement where an American meteorologist was stationed at Mirnyy. The continuing display of open cooperation in this exchange of scientists, especially between the USSR and the United States, has done much to create a feeling of goodwill among the Antarctic nations.

In January 1958 the United States announced her intention of continuing the American Antarctic scientific programme once the IGY was completed. By agreement with the Department of State in January 1959 Australia occupied Wilkes Station and Argentina took over Ellsworth. The United States volunteered to provide some scientists and equipment for these two stations, but was relieved of logistic support responsibility.

Control of the continuing United States Antarctic scientific programme was shifted in January 1959 from the Academy of Sciences to the National Science Foundation which has since managed what is now called the 'United States Antarctic Research Programme' (USARP) from its Office of Antarctic Programmes, with T. O. Jones as Director and A. P. Crary as Chief Scientist. The post-IGY Academy of Sciences 'Committee on Polar Research', with L. A. Gould as Chairman, maintains United States relations with SCAR and functions as the senior United States scientific organization planning long-range Antarctic research. Finally, in April 1959, after four hectic Antarctic expeditions, Admiral Dufek was relieved by Rear-Admiral David Tyree, who was placed in charge of the naval support force which continues to provide the logistic support necessary to maintain the United States group of stations in the Antarctic.[1]

There has been some effort in recent years to establish a 'Richard E. Byrd Antarctic Commission'. Its proponents, who foresee an independent administrative agency similar in structure to the Atomic Energy Commission, have on several occasions introduced legislation in both houses of Congress. However, little congressional action has taken place following a Hearing on 13–14 June 1960 before the Subcommittee on Territorial and Insular Affairs of the House of Representatives.

During the past few years several innovations have characterized the United States Antarctic research programme. Using a tunnelling technique, a new (and completely underground) Byrd Station was completed during the 1961–2 season.

[1] In November 1962, Admiral Tyree was succeeded by Rear-Admiral James Reedy.

(See Figs. 18–21.) By 1964 the South Pole Station is also expected to be rebuilt in the same manner. In July 1962 Antarctica's first nuclear power plant, built at a cost of $5 million, began delivering power at the McMurdo Station. With a net output of 1500 effective kilowatts and 650,000 BTU's per hour of steam (part of which will be used in the future to distil salt water for the station water supply), the plant is expected to have a life of twenty years with a fuel replacement every two years. Because of a clause in the Antarctic Treaty the nuclear waste will be transported to the United States for disposal.

FIG. 9 ANTARCTICA ENTERS THE 'NUCLEAR AGE'
A view of McMurdo Station's PM-3A nuclear power plant on Observation Hill. The *Discovery* expedition hut can be seen on Hut Point in right centre. The mountains of Victoria Land, with Blue Glacier at the left are in the distance across McMurdo Sound

(*US Navy photograph*)

By arrangement between the National Science Foundation and the Military Sea Transportation Service, the United States has in operation her first ship prepared exclusively for polar research. The USNS *Eltanin* was converted in 1961 to a floating research laboratory with facilities for thirty scientists, and is being used on a regular basis to conduct scientific research in Antarctic waters.

Strangely, with all of the considerable American activity in many parts of Antarctica the United States Government, while always reserving its rights, has never asserted a territorial claim. This failure and her corollary refusal to recognize the Antarctic claims of other countries rests on the traditional view, outlined by Secretary of State Charles Evans Hughes in 1924[1] that:

> The discovery of lands unknown to civilization, even when coupled with a formal taking of possession, does not support a valid claim to sovereignty unless the discovery is followed by an actual settlement of the discovered country.

He added in a separate statement the same year that meeting the actual settlement test of effective occupation in Antarctica 'would be an impossibility'.

This position was reasserted by Secretary of State Cordell Hull in 1934 and again in 1939 when the governments which communicated claims of sovereignty in the Antarctic to the United States were again informed that the United States reserved all rights which she might have in the area.

Nevertheless, in the 1930's the Department of State, not unaware of the importance of maintaining its position in the area, encouraged American citizens such as Ellsworth (in 1938) and Byrd (in 1939) to assert Antarctic claims. However, the government put forward no claims as a result of the activities of these expeditions. Curiously, the Department's attitude seems to have been unaffected by the 1933 decision of the Permanent Court of International Justice in the Eastern Greenland dispute between Norway and Denmark. The court's decision in this case has long been considered as authoritatively modifying the traditional international legal requirement of effective occupation for the acquisition of territorial sovereignty when applied to such territory as the Antarctic.

Beginning in 1939, the Department of State began to change its traditional attitude. Prior to this time United States policy had been one primarily of refusal to recognize the claims asserted by other governments and to emphasize the absence of acts of occupation or use of the territory which was considered necessary for the perfecting of a valid claim.

Although the Department at this time was not entirely prepared to abandon the rigid Hughes doctrine or to recognize other claims, it was concerned over the possibility that Great Britain and other countries would follow up their discoveries and proclamations of sovereignty by 'constructive occupation' and thereby strengthen their claims. The question of permanent occupation was given serious consideration in regard to the United States Antarctic Service Expedition, which departed in 1939, and might have been carried out if World War II had not interfered. In fact, a primary purpose of the latter expedition was to establish and strengthen the basis of United States Antarctic claims.

In 1946 pressure for American assertion of Antarctic claims was revived and given immediacy by 'Operation High jump'. The operational orders of this expedition, the first post-war United States Antarctic effort, listed as one of its objectives the extension and consolidation of 'United States sovereignty over the largest practicable area of the Antarctic Continent'. Following this order a

---

[1] Secretary Hughes to A. W. Prescott, 13 May 1924; quoted in Hackworth, 1940, pp. 399, 452.

number of objects was dropped on the Antarctic Continent containing claims statements.

The same year the Department of State began a revaluation of its position regarding the continent. It was realized that the United States, looking for a stable, permanent settlement of Antarctic political problems, could select one of several possible courses of action: (i) the assertion of a United States claim over the unclaimed area between 90° and 150° West Longitudes (it was recognized that more extensive claims would conflict directly with those of other states) and the subsequent partition of the continent and adjacent islands among the various claimants, with mutual recognition of claims and judicial settlement of conflicting claims, (ii) some form of multi-national condominium by the claimant states (including the United States) with group jurisdiction over the continent, or (iii) a form of broader international government, possibly under a United Nations trusteeship arrangement.

After many policy studies the position was gradually evolved that partition would present a difficult and unsatisfactory solution, and that a condominium or an international regime would be the most viable and would provide an arrangement under which the greatest benefit would be derived from scientific investigations – the only Antarctic activity that was considered to have real validity (the Department of Defense has consistently taken the position that the Antarctic area presents little strategic value to the United States).

Inter-departmental negotiations were conducted during 1947–8 and were later extended to include Great Britain, which was (and continues to be) opposed to any international solution giving control to the United Nations. Nevertheless, on 28 August 1948 the Department of State announced that it had approached the governments of Argentina, Australia, Chile, France, New Zealand, Norway and the United Kingdom with a view to opening discussions on a solution for the territorial problem of Antarctica. The Department suggested some form of internationalization as appropriate. An extended exchange of views took place during the next four years, but, except for New Zealand and the United Kingdom, no other nation was prepared to accept the United States proposals at that time. (For a discussion of these negotiations see Hanessian, 1960.)

The concept of the reservation of Antarctica for peaceful use and for cooperative scientific research (both principles had been accepted by all the claimant nations, who had balked at giving up national claims in favour of the American-proposed international regime) continued to be an integral part of United States Antarctic policy. Its realization was encouraged by the close cooperation among the twelve nations who participated in Antarctic research during the IGY. United States Antarctic programmes for the IGY were thoroughly supported by the Department of State in that they furthered this general policy.

Avoiding continual pressure from the Congress (through the years a number of Congressional Resolutions have been passed urging the Administration to claim portions of Antarctica), from private patriotic organizations and from within the Administration itself to press for American claims, the Department of State in 1957–8 again took the initiative and prepared a proposal for international action which, after careful preliminary discussions with the interested nations (including the USSR this time), was announced by President Eisenhower on 3 May 1958.

This time the Department's negotiations were successful with the Antarctic Treaty being signed on 1 December 1959 and fully ratified by all twelve Antarctic nations by mid-1961. Although the Treaty did not create an international regime, nor solve the long-standing problem of claims (which were shelved for the thirty-year duration of the Treaty), it represents a substantial advance toward an eventual international government for the area. Under the circumstances it must be assumed that the United States, although still retaining its Antarctic 'rights', will continue to press for stronger international controls.

Belgium

The *Belgica* expedition of 1897–9, under the leadership of Lieutenant Adrian de Gerlache, earned a permanent place for Belgium among the Antarctic nations – it was the first expedition ever to winter in the Antarctic. Sixty years later, de Gerlache's son, Gaston, led another Belgian party to Antarctica and successfully established in December 1957 an IGY station in Breidvtha on Prinsesse Ragnhild Kyst (within the Norwegian claim).

Fighting considerable public apathy de Gerlache campaigned among government officials in 1956 for the establishment of a Belgian Antarctic station. Only after an appeal to national pride did the Council of Ministers approve an eighteen-month expedition in late 1956, for which financial support was obtained from both public and private sources. In successive years two additional expeditions were approved and successfully carried out under the leadership of Commandant F. E. Bastin (1958–60) and Major G. Derom (1959–61).

Following the evacuation of the station, 'Roi Baudouin', at the end of the 1960–61 season, Belgium continued to keep active in Antarctic matters – primarily through the Centre National Récherches Polaires de Belgique (CNRPB) in Brussels and in her membership in SCAR and the Antarctic Treaty consultative group. During 1962 de Gerlache was able to form a joint Belgian–Dutch 'Comité Antarctique Benelux'. Under its direction a new expedition was formed, and Roi Baudouin Station was successfully re-occupied during the 1963–4 season.

Although she has never made a territorial claim, Belgium has always kept her interest and retained her pride in the *Belgica* expedition. On the basis of this voyage the Belgian Government on several occasions indicated that it expected to be included in any international discussions regarding the Antarctic, and did participate in the 1958–9 Antarctic Treaty conference. She has taken no stand on the issue of internationalization but, as she has no claim, it is probable that she would agree to an international regime.

Japan

Japanese interest in Antarctica dates back to 1910 when the growing Japanese national consciousness found expression in a desire to send the first expedition to reach the South Pole. That year an expedition (relying on private support after the government had refused financial assistance) left Japan for the Antarctic under the command of Lieutenant Choku Shirase.

Arriving in the Antarctic in late 1911 after an unsuccessful attempt the year before, Shirase and his men, in the tiny *Kainan Maru*, sailed along the Ross Ice Shelf, and made contact with the Norwegian expedition of Amundsen, who was at that time on his successful overland journey to the South Pole. Rather than also try for the Pole, the Japanese group conducted some sledge journeys over the Ross Ice Shelf and also landed at Kainan Bay and Okuma Bay.

Although Japan has never attempted to assert a claim on the basis of the discoveries of this expedition, the Japanese press and exploration groups enthusiastically agitated for official action – especially during the 1930s. By 1940, in referring to the Chilean decree establishing an Antarctic claim, the Japanese Government was sufficiently interested to send a diplomatic note to Chile stating that it regarded itself 'as one of the countries holding interests and rights' in Antarctica.

The same year the Japanese Antarctic Exploration Society and the *Asahi Shimbun* (a leading national newspaper with a large circulation) unsuccessfully attempted to persuade the Japanese Foreign Office to send an expedition to Antarctica to substantiate her rights and also to commemorate the twenty-sixth centennial of the founding of the Empire.

In the years following World War II, Japanese foreign policy went through a period of striking change. As one writer (Taijudo, 1959) has said:

> Japan has abandoned the aggressive expansionism of the past and has made a new start as a peace-loving cultured nation, desiring to occupy an honoured place in the international society. . . .

This new policy was evident when, in the 1951 Peace Treaty with the Allied Powers, Japan formally renounced 'all claim to any right or title or interest in connection with any part of the Antarctic area . . .'

Such a strong statement would seem to have precluded any further Japanese interest in the southern continent. Yet, during 1954–5, when the international discussions on the forthcoming IGY were taking place, a remarkable surge of national popular interest developed in Japan regarding the possibility of establishing a Japanese Antarctic scientific research station.

Not only were such respected organizations as the Science Council of Japan and the University of Tokyo involved, but a number of influential newspapers such as the *Asahi Shimbun* and the Kyodo News Service carried on a nationwide campaign to rally popular and government support. The successful effort resulted in the creation of a strong expedition under the general leadership of Takesi Nagata and the expeditionary command of E. E. Nishibori. During the 1956–7 season a base (Syowa Station) was established on Ongul Island in Lützow-Holmbukta in Kronprins Olav Land (within the Norwegian claim), and although the Japanese ships encountered annual difficulties in breaking through the pack ice, the station was maintained (except for 1958 when the ship could not reach the base site) until the end of 1961.

The Japanese Antarctic operations from 1956 onwards were carried out by the 'Japanese Antarctic Research Expedition' (JARE), which was organized under the 'Japanese Antarctic Office' within the Ministry of Education. The management of the scientific programme has been the responsibility of the Japanese National Antarctic Committee appointed by the Science Council of Japan. In June 1962 the Antarctic Office was 'disorganized' and the continuing work of the exchange of polar information is being carried out by the Polar Section in the National Science Museum in Tokyo. During 1963–4 construction began on an ice breaker, which will enable Japan to re-enter, on a regular basis, active participation in Antarctic research during the 1965–66 season.

Through the years, except for these two widely separated expeditionary efforts, Japan's primary interest in the Antarctic has been in whaling. Her Antarctic whaling fleet, although not as large as that of Norway's, has been one of the most active in the region since 1934. Her dependence on animal fats and oils to supplement her national food requirements, has been an important economic factor in these whaling operations.

Active Japanese political interest in the Antarctic has been practically non-existent, and is not likely to be aroused until Japanese whaling interests are threatened. Japan's remoteness from the Antarctic has resulted in little, if any, concern for the strategic importance of the area. She has in general favoured international cooperation in Antarctica as it would continue to afford Japan free access to the area. She supported the United States in the 1958–9 Washington discussions and, as she has little to lose, Japan would support the organization of an international regime for Antarctica.

Sweden

In common with the other Scandinavian countries, Sweden has long held an interest in polar exploration. Because of Sweden's geographic location, however, public interest in the polar regions has traditionally centred on the Arctic. The one truly Swedish Antarctic expedition, the voyage of the *Antarctic* in 1901–3, was led by Otto Nordenskjöld. This private expedition, which wintered for two years on Snow Hill Island near Hope Bay, might form the basis for a Swedish claim to a slice of Antarctic territory if a revival of public and official interest resulted in a willingness to contest strong British claims to the same sector.

Again, in 1949–52, Sweden played an important role in the Norwegian–British–Swedish Antarctic expedition which was initiated by Professor Hans Ahlman of Stockholm University. But Sweden has never shown an interest in the political or territorial problems of Antarctica, and in recent years has given no indication that she is interested in participating in the current internationally coordinated scientific research programme – although in 1956 she supported India's suggestion of internationalizing the Antarctic under the United Nations jurisdiction.

Poland

Polish explorers and scientists have a long tradition of polar work and moun-
taineering, especially in Spitzbergen, where they carried out a major research
operation from 1957–9. During the Antarctic summer of 1958–9 a Polish contingent under the leadership of Wojciech Krzeminski accompanied the Soviet
Antarctic expedition and for several weeks occupied the Soviet 'Oazis Station',
which was officially turned over to the Poles on 23 January 1959. It was renamed 'Antoni Dobrowolski Station', and plans were prepared for a full-scale
Polish wintering operation to begin during the following 1959–60 season. Apparently for fiscal reasons the Poles were not able to carry out their plans at that
time.

Meanwhile the Polish Government on 2 April 1959 unsuccessfully petitioned
the Antarctic Treaty conferees in Washington for Polish participation in the
discussions. A similar attempt was made to secure membership in SCAR. It is
understood that both organizations will be open to Poland once she completes
a year-round programme of research in Antarctica.

Germany

German Antarctic exploration began in 1873–4 with a journey by Captain Eduard
Dallman, and continued during the 1880s and 1890s. From 1901 to 1903 Professor Erich von Drygalski, partially with government support, conducted extensive scientific observations in Antarctica, and William Filchner in 1911–12
carried out exploration in the Weddell Sea area and discovered the ice shelf
which bears his name.

In 1938–9, just before the onset of World War II, the German Government
sent a major expedition to the Antarctic under the command of Captain Alfred
Ritscher with the vessel, *Schwabenland*, and two flying boats. The expedition
was conceived by Hermann Goering as a means of relieving fat shortage in
Germany, a problem which also led to the organization of a whaling fleet under
the Nazi regime. The expedition was also designed to engage in scientific research,
especially on biological conditions, and to map a portion of the continent by
means of aerial photography in order to support a claim to a land base for
Antarctic whaling.

Early in 1939 Ritscher's group carried out extensive exploration and conducted
aerial mapping operations over an area of over 350,000 km over Kronprinsesse
Märtha Kyst and Prinsesse Astrid Kyst. The area covered extended from 17°
East Longitude to 5° West Longitude and still bears the name 'Neu-Schwaben-
land' on many maps.

It was fully expected that a German claim would be made on the basis of this
work which is still considered to be among the most significant accomplished in
Antarctica. Numerous flags and proclamations were dropped by the expedition,
and various German newspapers reported in 1939 that the German Government was about to make a claim – but none was ever publicly stated.

During World War II Germany again entered Antarctic waters – this time for a different purpose. Using the Subantarctic waters as a secret refuge (and Kerguelen Island as a base) two German ships (Raider '33', *Pinguin*, and Raider '45', *Komet*) destroyed a total of 193,000 tons of Allied shipping, including the Australian light cruiser, *Sydney*. In January 1941 a part of the Norwegian Antarctic whaling fleet was also captured by the German raiders. These actions caused a certain amount of alarm among Southern Hemisphere nations, and have pinpointed the strategic value of Antarctic waters during wartime.

Despite strong post-World War II private and institutional revival of German interest in Antarctica, the government of the German Federal Republic has consistently refused to support suggested Antarctic activities. During 1955–8 a private group of Germans, led by a physician, Karl Herrligkoffer of Munich, attempted to induce the Federal Republic to establish a South Polar station in Dronning Maud Land in 1958 as a part of its contribution to the IGY. The German National IGY Committee with the concurrence of the German Government, however, decided against West German Antarctic activity.

The possibility that West German interest in the Antarctic may be reactivated and claims asserted is very remote. After World War II a suggestion was made that a German renunciation of whatever Antarctic claims it might have should be incorporated in a German Peace Treaty, but this was not done in the Convention on Relations between the Three Powers and the Federal Republic of Germany in October 1954.

German polar interest, however, is kept alive by the Archiv für Polarforschung in Kiel which was founded in 1926 in order to provide an information centre for German polar explorers. The organization publishes the journal *Polarforschung*, which along with such other journals as *Petermanns Geographische Mitteilungen* and *Geographisches Jahrbuch* keeps the polar image active in Germany.

Other Nations

A number of other countries, although never actually dispatching Antarctic expeditions, have expressed considerable interest in Antarctica. Italy has made contributions to polar literature, and an Italian observer joined the New Zealand IGY team at Scott Base in 1958. In 1959 Professor S. Zavatti, a prolific writer on Antarctic affairs and prime mover of the Istituto Geografico Polare (which publishes *Il Polo*), led a small reconnaissance voyage to Bouvetøya in an unsuccessful effort to discover a site suitable for a scientific station.

Although a Spanish expedition about which little is known is often credited with having sighted and circumnavigated South Georgia in 1756, Spanish interest in the Antarctic was entirely academic until 1955. In that year a Spanish group, 'Pro Antartide', approached the Spanish Government in an effort to mount a substantial Antarctic expedition as part of the IGY. Failing to receive government support, the proposed project was later abandoned.

Several South American states have also begun to take an interest. In recent years Brazil, Peru and Uruguay have appointed committees to investigate possible claims and activities in the Antarctic. An extension of the sector principle would appear to be the approach of these countries.

Although the scope of this chapter has been limited, an attempt has been made to assess the varied national interests in the Antarctic region. These activities have ranged in strength from the massive expeditions of the United States and the USSR to the relatively limited efforts of such countries as Belgium and Japan. Nevertheless, it has been the intention to examine these various Antarctic programmes, both from the point of view of recent expeditionary activity and as a reflection of the broader interests of the various nations. It would appear evident that in many of these nations interest in Antarctica is deep and of an extensive nature, especially when the element of national security is involved. However, since most Antarctic nations are also pragmatic, there is a certain degree of hope that experience under the Antarctic Treaty will eventually lead to a strong faith in the international approach and the consequent expiration of national sector claims.

Bibliography

AAGAARD, B. 1934: Norwegians in the Antarctic, *American-Scandinavian Review*, New York, 33–45.

ACHESON, D. 1947: Clarification of U.S. Position on Antarctic Claims, *Dept. of State Bulletin* 16(3).

ACUÑA de MONES RUIZ, P. 1948: *Conciencia Antártica Argentina*, Sante Fe.

ADMINISTRATION OF NORWEGIAN TERRITORIES IN THE ANTARCTIC, 1958: *The Polar Record*, Cambridge: 9(59), 159–60.

THE ANTARCTIC AND INTER-AMERICAN RELATIONS. 1947: *American Perspective* 1: 97–105.

ARAMAYO, A. 1949: *Historia de la Antártida*, Buenos Aires.

ARCHDALE, H. E. 1958: Claims to the Antarctic, *Yearbook of World Affairs*: 142–163.

ARGENTINA, COMISION NACIONAL del ANTÁRTICO, 1949: *Antártida Argentina*, Buenos Aires.

ARGENTINA, COMISION NACIONAL del ANTÁRTICO, 1947: *Soberanía Argentina en la Antártida*, Buenos Aires.

ARMSTRONG, T. 1950: Recent Soviet Interest in Bellingshausen's Antarctic Voyage of 1819–21, *The Polar Record*, Cambridge, 5(39): 475–78.

ASBROECK, J. VAN, 1946–47: L'Actualité des Questions Antarctiques et la Belgique, *Bulletin de la Société Royale de Géographie d'Anvers*, 61(1): 42–58.

AUBERT DE LA RÜE, E. 1953: *Les Terres Australes*, Paris.

AUSTRALIA 1954, DEPT. OF EXTERNAL AFFAIRS, ANTARCTIC DIVISION. *Australia and the Antarctic*, Canberra.

BALCH, T. W. 1910: The Arctic and Antarctic Regions and the Law of Nations, *American Journal of International Law* **4**: 265–75.

BAYLIS, E. P. and CUMPSTON, J. S. 1939: *Handbook and Index to Accompany a Map of Antarctica*, Department of External Affairs, Canberra.

BECKER, L. 1958: Statement of L. Becker, The Legal Advisor, Department of State, in U.S. Senate, Special Committee on Space and Astronautics, *National Aeronautics and Space Act. Hearings*, 85th Cong., 2nd Sess., (part 2): 13–15 May, 321, 322, 335–37.

BERG, L. 1949: Russkiye Otkrytiya v Antarktike i Sovremennyy Interes k ney, *Izvestiya Vsesoyuznogo Geographicheskogo Obshchestva*, Leningrad, **81**: 137–48.

BERRAZ MONTYN, C. 1951: *Nuestra Soberanía en la Antártida*, Sante Fe.

BERTRAM, G. C. L. 1957: Antarctic Prospect, *International Affairs*, **33**(2): 143–53.

BERTRAM, G. C. L. 1957: *Antarctica Today and Tomorrow*, Cambridge University Press.

BROWN, R. N. R. 1947: Political Claims in the Antarctic, *World Affairs* **1**: 393–401.

THE BRITISH TITLE TO SOVEREIGNTY IN THE FALKLAND ISLANDS DEPENDENCIES, 1956: *The Polar Record*, Cambridge, **8**(53): 125–51.

BUTCHER, H. 1949: Antarctica – Challenge to National Sovereignty, *World Affairs*, **5**(1): 1–12.

CALVOCORESSI, P., and HARDEN, S. 1952: The Antarctic, *Survey of International Affairs, 1947–1948*, Oxford University Press, 492–99.

CAMPBELL, S. 1949, Australasian Aims in the Antarctic, *The Polar Record*, **5**(37–38): 317–23.

CANEPA, L. 1948: *Historia Antártica, Nuestros Derechos*, Buenos Aires.

CARR, B. M. 1956: Claims to Sovereignty–Antarctica, *Southern California Law Review* **28**: 386–400.

CHARTERIS, A. 1929, Australasian Claims in Antarctica, *Journal of Comparative Legislation and International Law*, London, **2**(4): 226–32.

CHILE, MINISTERIO de RELACIONES EXTERIORES, 1948: *Soberania de Chile en la Antártica*, Santiago.

CUNNINGHAM, J. 1958: A Politico–Geographical Appreciation of New Zealand Foreign Policy, *New Zealand Geographer* **14**: 147–60.

CHRISTENSEN, L. 1935: *Such is the Antarctic*, London.

CHRISTIE, E. W. H. 1951: *The Antarctic Problem: An Historical and Political Study*, Allen & Unwin, London.

CLIFFORD, M. 1955: The Falkland Islands and their Dependencies, *Geographical Journal*, **121**(4): 405–16.

COSTA, J. F. de 1958: *Souveraineté sur l'Antarctique*, Librairie Générale de Droit et Jurisprudence, Paris, (Expéditions Polaires Françaises Publication No. 201.)

DANIEL, J. 1949: Conflict of Sovereignties in the Antarctic, *Yearbook of World Affairs* **3**: 241–72.

c

DATER, H. M. 1957: *Summary of National Claims with Selected Documents*, Office of U.S. Antarctic Projects, Washington.

DOLLOT, R. 1949: Le Droit International des Espaces Polaires, *Recueil des Cours*, *Académie de Droit International* 75 (part 2): 118–200.

DURDENEVSKY, V. N. 1950: Problema Pravovogo Rezhima Pripoliarnykh Oblastei Antarktika i Arktika, *Vestnik Moskovskogo Universiteta* 7: 111–14.

EVENSEN, J. 1957: Norway and the Antarctic, *American–Scandinavian Review*, 12–21.

EXPÉDITIONS POLAIRES FRANÇAISES, 1956: *Terre Adélie, Groenland, 1947–1955, Rapport d'Activités*, Paris.

FISKE, C. O., and FISKE, MRS. C. O. 1959: Territorial Claims in the Antarctic, *United States Naval Institute Proceedings* 85: 82–91.

FLEMING, W. L. S. 1947: Contemporary International Interest in the Antarctic, *International Affairs* 23: 546–57.

FRANCE, 1949: La Documentation Française, Notes et Études Documentaires (Paris), *L'Antarctide et les Problèmes Sóulevés par son Occupation* (1098): 1–10. Série Internationale 201.

FRANCE, 1950: La Documentation Française, Notes et Études Documentaires (Paris), *Les Terres Australes et l'Antarctide Françaises*, Série Internationale 1326.

FUCHS, V. and HILLARY, E. 1958: *The Crossing of Antarctica, the Common-wealth Trans-Antarctic Expedition 1955–1958*, London.

GEORGI, J. 1937: Deutschland in der Polarfarschung, *Natur und Volk*, Frank-fort a/M, 67: 419–29.

GERLACHE de GOMERY, A. 1960: *Retour dans l'Antarctique*, Tournai.

GERLACHE de GOMERY, A. 1962: Belgium in the Antarctic, *Geographical Magazine*, 35(1): 18–31.

GIAEVER, J. 1954: *The White Desert*, London.

GOLDIE, L. F. E. 1958: International Relations in Antarctica, *Australian Quarterly* 30: 7–29.

GOULD, L. M. 1948: Strategy and Politics in the Polar Areas, *Annals of the American Academy of Political and Social Science* 255: 105–14.

GOULD, L. M. 1958: *Antarctica in World Affairs*, Foreign Policy Association, Headline Series No. 128, New York.

GOULD, L. M. 1958: *The Polar Regions in their Relation to Human Affairs*, American Geographical Society, New York.

HACKWORTH, G. H. 1940: Polar and Subpolar Regions, *Digest of International Law* 1: 449–76, GPO, Washington. (Department of State Publication 1506.)

HAMRE, I. 1933: The Japanese South Polar Expedition, 1911–12, *Geographical Journal*, London, 82(5): 412–23.

HANESSIAN, J. 1958: Antarctica: Current National Interests and Legal Reali-ties, *Proceedings of the American Society of International Law 1958*: 145–74.

HANESSIAN, J. 1960: The Antarctic Treaty 1959, *International and Comparative Law Quarterly*, 9: 436–74.

HATHERTON, T. 1961: New Zealand IGY Antarctic Expeditions, Scott Base and Hallett Station, *New Zealand Department of Scientific and Industrial Research Bulletin* 140, Wellington.

HAYTON, R. D. 1956: The 'American' Antarctic, *American Journal of International Law* **50:** 583–610.

HAYTON, R. D. 1958: Polar Problems and International Law, *American Journal of International Law* **52:** 746–65.

HAYTON, R. D. 1959: *National Interests in Antarctica*, GPO, Washington. (Annotated bibliography.)

HAYTON, R. D. 1960: The Antarctic Settlement of 1959, *American Journal of International Law*, **54(2):** 348–71.

HAYTON, R. D. 1960: The Nations and Antarctica, *Österreichische Zeitschrift für Offentliches Recht* **10:** 368–412.

HERON, D. W. 1954: Antarctic Claims, *Foreign Affairs* **32:** 661–67.

HEYERDAHL, T. 1954: *Great Norwegian Expeditions*, Oslo.

HILLARY, E. 1961: *No Latitude for Error*, London.

HUNEEUS, G. A. 1948: *Antártida*, Santiago.

JAPAN 1958: Antarctic Society, *The Antarctic*, Tokyo.

JOERG, W. L. G. 1930: Political Sovereignty in the Arctic and Antarctic: Recent Developments, *Brief History of Polar Exploration Since the Introduction of Flying*, American Geographical Society Special Publication No. 11, New York: 61–79.

KING, J. 1952: South Africa in the Sub-Antarctic, *The Antarctic Today*, Wellington: 304–12.

KIRWAN, L. 1959: *The White Road*, London.

KOSACK, H. 1955: *Die Antarktis: eine Landerkunde*, Heidelberg.

KOSTRITSYN, B. V. 1951: K. Voprosu o Rezhime Antarktiki, *Sovetskoye Gosudarstvo i Pravo* **3:** 38–43.

KULSKI, W. W. 1951: Soviet Comments on International Law, *American Journal of International Law* **45:** 766–9.

LAW, P. G. and BÉCHERVAISE, J. 1957: *ANARE, Australia's Antarctic Outposts*, Melbourne.

LISSITZYN, O. J. 1959: The American Position on Outer Space and Antarctica, *American Journal of International Law* **53:** 126–31.

MACHOWSKI, J. 1953: *Antarktyka*, Wiedza Powszechna, Warzawa.

MCKITTERICK, T. E. M. 1939: The Validity of Territorial and Other Claims in Polar Regions, *Journal of Comparative Legislation and International Law* **21:** 89–97.

MCNICKLE, R. K. 1949: Antarctic Claims, *Editorial Research Reports* **2:** 781–94.

MALAURIE, J. 1956: L'Activité Géographique Française dans les Régions Polaires (1940–1955), *La Géographie Francaise au Milieu de XXᵉ Siecle*, Paris, 261–280.

MARAZZI, J. 1950: *La Soberanía Argentina en la Antártida*, Buenos Aires.

MARSH, J. 1948: *No Pathway here*, Capetown.

MARTENS, M. 1955: Soviet Expansion in the Antarctic, *Bulletin of the Institution for the Study of the History and Culture of the U.S.S.R.*, Munich, **2**(9): 19–25.

MITTERLING, P. 1959: *America in the Antarctic to 1840*, Urbana.

MOLODTSOV, S. V. 1954: *Sovremennoye Mezhdunarodno-Pravovoye Polozheniye Antarktiki*, Gosudarstvennoye Izdatel'stvo Yuridicheskoy Literatury, Moscow.

NAGATA, T. 1960: *National Report of Japanese Antarctic Research Expeditions 1958–1960*, Tokyo.

NORWAY, 1947: Royal Ministry of Foreign Affairs, *Norwegian Claims in the Antarctic*, Oslo.

PARFOND, P. 1950: La Terre Adélie et le Droit International, *La Revue Maritime* **50**: 741–52.

PINOCHET de la BARRA, O. 1955: *La Antártica Chilena, Estudio de Nuestros Derechos*, Santiago.

PINOCHET de la BARRA, O. 1955: *Chilean Sovereignty in Antarctica*, Santiago.

POLAND, 1959: Washington Embassy, *Poland Requests Participation in Antarctic Conferences*, 4 April 1959, Washington.

PRICE, A. G. 1963: *The Winning of Australian Antarctica, Mawson's BANZARE Voyages 1929–31*, Angus & Robertson, London.

PUIG, J. 1960: *La Antártida Argentina ante al Derecho*, Buenos Aires.

PUIG, J. C. 1949: La Adquisicion de Soberania Sobre Territorios Polares, *Revista de Derecho International* **1**: 201–72.

QUARTERMAIN, L. 1952: Gateway to the South, *The Antarctic Today*, Wellington, 245–65.

RICHERT, X. 1957: Terres Australes et Antarctiques Françaises, *T.A.A.F.*, Paris, **1**: 3–13.

RITSCHER, A. 1942: *Deutsche Antarktische Expedition 1938–39 mit dem Flugzeugstützpunkt der Deutschen Lufthause A.G., M.S. 'Schwabenland'*, Leipzig.

ROBERTS, B. 1958: Chronological List of Antarctic Expeditions, *The Polar Record* **9**: 97–134 and 199–239.

RODRIGUEZ, J. 1941: *La République Argentina y las Adquisiciones Territoriales en el Continente Antártico*, Buenos Aires.

LA ROSA, P. 1948: *Los Territorios Australes de la Republica Argentina*, Buenos Aires.

ROUCEK, J. S. 1951: The Geopolitics of Antarctica and the Falkland Islands, *World Affairs Interpreter* **22**: 44–56.

LE SCHACK, L. A. 1964: The French Polar Effort and the Expéditions Polaires Françaises, *Arctic*, Montreal, **17**(1): 3–15.

SCHOLES, W. 1953: *Seventh Continent: Saga of Australasian Exploration in Antarctica, 1895–1950*, London.

SIMPSON, F. 1952: Subantarctic Outposts, *The Antarctic Today*, Wellington, 327–44.

SIMPSON, F. 1954: New Zealand Antarctic, *New Zealand Geographer*, **10**(1): 1–24.

SULLIVAN, W. 1957: Antarctica in a Two-Power World, *Foreign Affairs* **36**: 154–66.

SULLIVAN, W. 1957: *Quest for a Continent*, McGraw-Hill, New York.

SWAN, R. 1961: *Australia in the Antarctic*, Melbourne.

TAIJUDO, L. 1959: Japan and the Problems of Sovereignty over the Polar Regions, *Japanese Annual of International Law* **3**: 12–17.

TAUBENFELD, H. J. 1961: A Treaty for Antarctica, *International Conciliation*, Nr. **531**: 245–322.

TAYLOR, G. 1955: Australian Antarctica, *Journal and Proceedings Royal Australian Historical Society*, 41.

TEAGUE, R. 1947: Behind Rhodes' Back, *Libertas*, Johannesburg, **7**: 22–7.

TERRITORIAL CLAIMS IN THE ANTARCTIC, *Documents on International Affairs* 1947–8: 803–16.

TOMA, P. A. 1956: Soviet Attitude Towards the Acquisition of Territorial Sovereignty in the Antarctic, *American Journal of International Law* **50**: 611–26.

UNITED KINGDOM, 1960: Central Office of Information, *The Antarctic*, London.

UNITED STATES, 1958: Congress, House of Representatives, Committee on Interstate and Foreign Commerce, *International Geophysical Year, The Arctic, Antarctica, Report. . . .*, Washington, House Report No. 1348: 71–130.

UNITED STATES, 1949: National Academy of Sciences, *Antarctic Research, Elements of a Coordinated Program*, Washington.

UNITED STATES, NAVAL WAR COLLEGE, 1950: Declarations Concerning Antarctic Territories, *International Law Documents*, 1948–9, GPO, Washington, 217–45.

UNITED STATES DEPARTMENT OF STATE, 1960: *The Conference on Antarctica, Conference Documents, The Antarctic Treaty, and Related Papers*, Dept. of State Pub. No. 7060, Washington.

WALDOCK, C. 1948: Disputed Sovereignty in the Falkland Islands Dependencies, *British Yearbook of International Law* **25**: 310–53.

WILSON, G. G. 1939: Jurisdiction and Polar Areas, *International Law Situations with Solutions and Notes*, 1937: US Naval War College, GPO, Washington, 60–131.

WILSON, R. E. 1964: National Interests and Claims in the Antarctic, *Arctic*, Montreal, **17**(1): 15–33.

WOLK, S. 1958: The Basis of Soviet Claims in the Antarctic, *Bulletin of the Institute for the Study of the USSR*, Munich, 43–8.

CHAPTER TWO

Techniques of Living, Transport and Communication

PHILLIP LAW, *Antarctic Division, Department of External Affairs, Melbourne*

Introduction

During the IGY the Antarctic Continent was subjected to the greatest assault by explorers and scientists that any major portion of the Earth has ever experienced. As a result of this work and that which has been done since, most of the geographical secrets of the region have been revealed. The scientific work has now been expanded and great quantities of data about this austere region are being obtained.

But this is still the first, or exploratory, phase of the opening up of Antarctica. One day pioneers will follow these expedition men, setting up villages, towns and industries, and the second phase of developing a great continent will have begun.

The Antarctic men of today are devising and testing the techniques of living and working which later pioneers will use in their battle with the most severe climatic conditions in the world. The research and development of the logistics of operating in Antarctica are fundamental to all work which may later go on there and this chapter summarizes briefly the technical level of proficiency which at present has been attained.

Antarctica is a large continent with an area (including ice shelves) of about 14 million square kilometres. Conditions of climate and terrain vary considerably over this area and logistics requirements must be modified accordingly. The thirty-four permanent stations at present being maintained in the Antarctic illustrate the wide diversity of techniques adopted by various nations to cope with the problems peculiar to their particular localities. Around the coast, climate is softened by the ameliorating influence of the sea; wide variations in latitude result in big differences in conditions between stations in Graham Land and those far south such as Byrd, Vostok and Amundsen–Scott; while altitude plays an important part in differentiating between McMurdo and Scott at sea level and Byrd and Vostok on the high plateau. Even around the coast of Antarctica at approximately the same latitude, local weather is kinder at Davis and Wilkes than at Mawson, Mirnyy and Dumont d'Urville.

Sea Transport

The first technical problem which any expedition must face is that of transporting men, stores and equipment to the site of their proposed operations. If dependent upon sea transport, an expedition can relieve a coastal station only once each year, during the short period in summer between the beginning of December and the end of February, when ice conditions permit a ship to break through the pack ice girdle to reach the coast of the continent. The use of large transport aircraft, however, considerably extends this period and gives greater flexibility to all establishment and relief operations. The maintenance of stations in the interior of the continent may be effected by either aircraft or surface vehicles and sledges, but in each case the season of operations extends only from about October to March, for the extremely low temperatures experienced in winter on the high plateau prevent routine transport operations by any method for the rest of the year.

Support operations by ships have followed two distinct patterns. The United States expeditions have used powerful, specialized icebreakers (*Glacier*, *Staten Island*) to carve out channels in the pack ice through which ships of more conventional design, carrying cargo and passengers, can pass. The other nations have preferred multipurpose ships (*Ob*, *Magga Dan*), combining reasonable icebreaking ability with good passenger accommodation and cargo capacity. Landings are made on rock, on fast or bay ice, or on ice shelves. In some cases ships simply tie up alongside the ice and unload directly onto sledges (Fig. 10); in others, unloading is carried out by DUKWs, barges or boats plying between rock coast and the ships. An unusual alternative was forced upon the Japanese when Syowa Base was isolated from *Soya Maru* by sixty miles of impenetrable fast ice; unloading was done by large helicopters running a ferry service between the ship and the station.

A large percentage of the cargo required for any Antarctic station consists of fuel. In many cases this is supplied in large drums and the effort required to unload quantities of these heavy objects is considerable. As stations have become consolidated, it has proved possible at a number of them to install bulk fuel tanks and to pump fuel ashore through pipe lines from the ship's bunkers. At McMurdo in 1956 the Americans moored two YOG fuel tankers, each containing more than 200,000 gallons of high octane fuel, against the shore of Ross Island and used them as bulk fuel tanks for the next five years. However, in March 1961 they broke their moorings during a storm and drifted out to sea, where heavy seas and autumn temperatures prevented their recovery.

A number of difficulties face ships engaged in supply work. Suitable harbours or anchorages are few and there are no piers or jetties. Ships must be prepared to put out to sea unless very firmly moored when threatened by violent weather. At Mawson in 1955, *Kista Dan* dragged her anchors when struck by a sudden squall and was driven onto the rocks at the side of the harbour. Since then, mooring points have been installed in the rock around the harbour to hold a ship firmly in any weather.

Unloading onto sea ice is risky, for there have been numerous cases in which cargo has been lost when fast ice has broken up and floated out to sea. Unloading onto high ice cliffs brought tragedy at Mirnyy in 1957 when two Russians were killed by a large block of ice which broke from the cliff and fell onto the deck of the *Ob*. The *Arneb* was severely holed by pack ice in 1957 when establishing Hallett Station. A number of ships (*Shackleton*, *Soya*, *Polarhav*, etc.) have been beset by pack ice and rescued with difficulty by more powerful ice ships.

The French at Dumont d'Urville are at present building an overhead cableway

FIG. 10 'THALA DAN' UNLOADING AT MAWSON
(*ANARE photograph*)

(téléférique) from the boat landing up to the station on the crest of the Île des Pétrels which will enable cargo to be lifted straight from the boats or barges and hauled to the storage sites.

Air Transport

The use of large aircraft for supplying Antarctic stations was pioneered by the United States during their various 'Deep Freeze' operations. Starting in December 1955, with Skymaster and Neptune aeroplanes, carrying men and cargo from Christchurch to McMurdo, they extended the use of aircraft to establish inland stations (Amundsen–Scott, Byrd) by cargo dropped by parachute from DC-3, DC-4 and Globemaster aircraft. Now the use of Globemasters and

Hercules on the route Christchurch–McMurdo and Hercules (on skis) for landings at Byrd and the Pole (Amundsen–Scott) has demonstrated the remarkable
efficiency of air operations for support programmes. The Russians since 1957
have been using IL-2 and IL-12 aircraft from Mirnyy to support surface operations in establishing and supplying their inland stations. It was not until
December 1961, however, that the Russians, using IL-18 and AN-10 aircraft,
first transported cargo from Russia to Antarctica by air.

The provision of adequate airfield facilities in Antarctica raises considerable
difficulties. So far no earth- or rock-based airstrip is in regular use on the
continent for transport aircraft, although the Americans have experimented with

FIG. 11 C-130 ('HERCULES') AIRCRAFT ON SEA ICE NEAR HALLETT
STATION

(US Navy photograph)

one at Marble Point, McMurdo Sound, and the Australians have investigated
a possible airfield site on the ice-free area of the Vestfold Hills. (The British have
constructed an airfield for light aircraft on volcanic ash at Deception Island.)
The alternatives remaining are sea ice, ice shelf, or continental ice.

The airfield at McMurdo (Williams Naval Air Facility) is a highly complex,
elaborately equipped installation. During October and November it acts as a
busy airport, receiving aircraft from Christchurch and despatching flights to
Byrd, Amundsen–Scott and Hallett Stations as well as providing for survey
flights and missions in support of field parties and scientific projects. Up to 500
men are used in these operations.

This airfield is situated on semi-permanent bay ice in McMurdo Sound. The
ice is about 6 to 10 m thick and is normally covered with a layer of snow.
Two airstrips are provided at right angles to each other, the principal one being

2000 m long and lying in the direction 070° and 250°. The snow is cleared by bulldozers and pushed onto heaps at the sides of the runways. The surfaces of the runways are then prepared by planing, grading, dragging and rolling. Hollows and pot holes or other defects in the surface are patched by filling with chipped ice and fresh water and allowing them to freeze solid. A 'pulvimixer' then chips off the ice surface and leaves a layer of fine ice fragments which are 'dragged' to produce an even layer about three inches deep over the basic ice of the runway. This pulvimixed ice provides a grip for aircraft tyres and allows normal running and braking instead of the slewing and skidding that would occur on smooth ice. Two men with a pulvimixer and a drag can maintain 1,000 m of runway per day.

After each blizzard the drift snow must be cleared from the runways and this takes extra work. In summer, melting of the ice causes the surface to deteriorate, and much 'patching' (by freezing ice chips and fresh water together in the depressions) must be done. In 1961 and 1962 such techniques enabled the airfield to be used right through the summer until February.

The weight of the bulldozed snow banks on each side of the runway, which reach a height of 6 m and a width of 30 m causes the sea ice beneath them to slump and the centre of the runway to hump upwards, producing a crack longitudinally down the centre. These are some of the many problems which face the United States authorities at McMurdo in carrying out their air transport programme.

The numerous facilities which must accompany a large airfield (accommodation for men, meteorological and radio facilities, landing and navigational aids, workshops, refuelling equipment, mapping and briefing facilities, etc.) are elaborate and complex and are housed in some thirty buildings. Everything on the sea ice at Williams Field must be ready to be moved at short notice if the ice shows signs of breaking up. Mounted on sledges, the buildings can be moved at any time. In fact, each summer one or two minor moves must be made as melting causes deterioration around the huts, and for the winter period the whole facility is packed up and transported three kilometres to the land at McMurdo, to be re-established the following spring.

Sea ice has also been successfully used by the Australians, who flew aircraft at Mawson from fast ice in the harbour from 1956 until 1960 between the months of April and November. Operations ceased during the summer when the ice broke up and moved out. The British have, since 1960, been using sea ice runways along the coast of Graham Land for flights for vertical aerial photography and the support of field parties, in addition to the supply of Fossil Bluff Station in George VI Sound.

On ice shelf, ski-equipped planes find excellent surfaces and almost unlimited expanses of suitable névé for all-year operation. However, until now no-one has succeeded in preparing such a surface to provide a suitable runway for wheel-equipped aircraft. The Russians have used the ice shelf at Lazarev station for landing ski-equipped transport planes which visit this station from Mirnyy.

Continental ice has been used mainly by the Americans, Russians and Australians. At Mirnyy a satisfactory strip on the mainland ice adjacent to the station has been maintained since 1956. It requires little attention but suffers somewhat from the slopes, both longitudinal and transverse. Aircraft may land or take off on either skis or wheels. Inland at Vostok and Pionerskaya, Russian ski planes land on the relatively smooth plateau névé. At Byrd and Amundsen–Scott, the Americans maintain airstrips on the plateau névé for receipt of summer air traffic on skis.

Ten miles inland from Mawson, on the hard blue ice of the coastal ablation zone at an altitude of 500 m, the Australians established an airfield in 1960 for use during the summer months when the sea ice at Mawson was not available. Aircraft could use either wheels or skis. However, a hurricane in December 1960 destroyed the DC-3 and Beaver aircraft moored there and the field has not been used since, except by Russian aircraft in transit between Mirnyy and Lazarev.

Hangar protection for aircraft is rare in Antarctica. The first hangar to be built was that erected at Mawson in 1956. Aircraft from Mawson were able to operate throughout the winter as a result of the protection afforded by the hangar. Later, a similar one was built by the New Zealand expedition at Scott Base but the loss of the New Zealand aircraft soon after left it largely unused. A new hangar to house two Otter aircraft was completed by the British at Deception Island in February 1962. At McMurdo and Mirnyy, aircraft are tied down on the ice in the open. Four aeroplanes have been lost at Mawson, two at an Argentine base, two at Mirnyy and one at Oazis as a result of the effect of strong winds on moored aircraft. The tethering of aircraft in the open on the plateau constitutes a major engineering problem.

In all operations where it is possible to land on them, wheels are preferred to skis because of the smoother landing characteristics and the smaller drag in the air. Ski-wheel combinations are often used, with which an aircraft can take off on skis and land on wheels, or vice versa. For flights from Australia or New Zealand to Antarctica such dual landing gear is desirable. The largest aircraft yet equipped with wheel-skis are the United States Hercules and the Russian AN-10.

American aircraft first linked New Zealand with Antarctica in December 1955, and Russian aircraft made their first flight to Antarctica, also via New Zealand, in December 1961. Two Argentine DC-3 aircraft linked South America with the Pole in January 1962.

Surface Transport

A wide variety of vehicles is used for surface transport in Antarctica, ranging from primitive man-hauled sledges to the heavy tractor trains of the Russians and Americans. Man hauling is still sometimes carried out, but not if dogs are available. The dog sledge remains the safest and often the only means of surface transport over crevassed plateau or weak sea ice. As early as 1956 the Australians used aircraft to land dog teams, sledges and men to carry out survey work in remote mountain areas. A dog team accompanied Fuchs's Trans-Antarctic Expedition as far as the Pole, and New Zealand expeditions have made fine use of this form of transport, often assisted by aircraft ferrying, in carrying out extensive exploration of the mountainous areas on the western side of the Ross Sea. Dog sledging remains the traditional and highly successful means of travel for British teams in Graham Land. Apart from its association with aircraft, dog sledging techniques differ little from those of Amundsen's day, except that adequate supplies of concentrated dog rations now make it unnecessary to regard the dogs as expendable during a journey.

The first really effective over-snow mechanized vehicle was the 'Weasel'. Powered by six-cylinder Studebaker engines and fitted with full tracks and

FIG. 12 SNO-CAT AND ROLLI-TRAILER AT MCMURDO SOUND
The huge tyres on the trailer each contain 2000 litres of fuel.
(*US National Science Foundation photograph*)

cabins, Weasels were designed for use during World War II. They were first used in polar work by the French in Greenland and later, in 1950–2, by the Norwegian–British–Swedish Antarctic Expedition. The French started using them in Terre Adélie in 1950 and the Australians at Mawson in 1954. However, weaknesses in the suspension and track-driving mechanisms made them far from satisfactory and, although much useful work was obtained from these vehicles by various expeditions, the expenditure of manpower on maintenance was out of all proportion to the mileage obtained. Further, they broke up rapidly when asked to tow heavy loads (for which they were not designed). An improved Weasel recently designed by the Japanese gives vastly superior performance.

Another light snow vehicle which became well known was the Sno-cat. This was used by the French, by the British (Trans-Antarctic Expedition) and the United States Operation Deep Freeze, the latter being responsible for the development of a much heavier and greatly improved vehicle. In general, though, the Snocat, like the Weasel, has not proved robust enough for the demanding work on the Antarctic plateau, where heavy loads must be hauled over hard sastrugi ridges. But as a light scout car it is excellent.

The Americans, Russians and Australians early developed the use of heavy caterpillar-tracked vehicles and these, designed for heavy duty haulage, gave superior performance at economical costs. The various types of tractors deserve detailed description, for they are in advance of any other type of over-snow

FIG. 13 KHARKOV TRACTOR AT MIRNYY

(ANARE photograph by J. Béchervaise)

vehicle in current use. However, they are particularly vulnerable in crevassed areas because of their weight.

The Americans use Caterpillar D-8 tractors, modified by fitting longer and wider tracks. The Australians use Caterpillar D-4 tractors with the widest standard tracks available from the manufacturers. The Russians have developed what is at present the most useful over-snow vehicle in Antarctica, the giant Kharkov tractor (Fig. 13). Each of these is adequate for the purpose for which it is used, but no one vehicle is universally adequate and a great amount of compromise is required when matching the available vehicles against the special difficulties of terrain and the transport demands which have to be met. If it is assumed that these tractors provide the answer for long, heavy haulage across desolate, crevasse-free plateau, then there still remains a need for other types of vehicles—light, fast scout cars, medium-weight all-purpose transports and amphibious carriers for use over treacherous sea ice.

The low ground pressure (L.G.P.) Caterpillar D-8 tractor exerts a flywheel power at sea level of 191 h.p. and has a maximum speed of 8·4 km/hr. With fuel its total weight is 32 metric tons. Its tracks are 137 cm wide and have a ground contact area of 111,000 cm², giving a ground pressure of 290 gm/cm². Its approximate overall dimensions are: length 760 cm, width 510 cm, height 325 cm. Its fuel consumption is about 30 litres/hr.

The smaller D-4 Caterpillar has 63 h.p. and a top speed of 10 km/hr. Its total weight is 8·2 tons. Its tracks are 61 cm wide and have a ground contact area of 22,500 cm², giving a ground pressure of 370 gm/cm². Its overall dimensions are: length 406 cm, width 245 cm, height 254 cm. Its fuel consumption is 11·4 litres/hr.

The Russian 'Kharkovchanka' is powered by a twelve-cylinder 500 h.p. engine and has a cruising speed (hauling a 50-ton sledge on the plateau) of 8 km/hr. Its weight is 33·5 tons. Its tracks are 130 cm wide and give a ground pressure of 400 gm/cm². Its overall dimensions are: length 850 cm, width 410 cm, height 420 cm. The tractor body provides living and working accommodation for eight men but no cargo is carried as this is towed on sledges behind. There are eight compartments in the cabin—driver's compartment, work room, radio room, kitchen, toilet, drying room, service compartment and entrance porch. Eight sleeping berths are provided, two of which are in the driver's compartment. The kitchen is electric, as also is the heating. Navigation aids include a gyro-compass, an astrocompass and a potentiometric distance compass.

Other vehicles which are being tried out for various purposes are the several models of Robin–Nodwell vehicles, the Porsche Snow-Trac (Fig. 14), the Russian Penguin (Fig. 15), and the Eliason motor toboggan (see Fig. 56). The larger Nodwell vehicles show promise of rivalling the more conventional heavy tractors but have not so far undergone sufficient tests. We must not forget the Ferguson tractor, which has proved a useful vehicle over the rock outcrops at Mawson and Davis and, fitted with full tracks, performed so splendidly for Hillary with the Trans-Antarctic Expedition.

Finally, some mention might be made of the possibilities of using vehicles of the Hovercraft type. From a number of points of view these should be parti-cularly suited to Antarctic conditions. Over the flat plateau and over sea ice they would obviate the hazards of crevasses and weak ice respectively. It remains to be seen how they will perform on heavy sastrugi and side slopes and in high winds. Perhaps some compromise vehicle, such as a vehicle on sledge runners using the Hovercraft principle merely to reduce the ground pressure, might be more effective?

With all vehicles there are metallurgical problems to be solved. At the low temperatures experienced on the high plateau, steel and other metals become brittle and fractures of metal parts such as chassis, springs and tracks become too common to be dealt with by routine maintenance. Difficulties of starting, of

FIG. 14 PORSCHE SNOW-TRAC AT MAWSON

(ANARE photograph by G. Newton)

FIG. 15 'PENGUIN' AT MIRNYY

(ANARE photograph by Phillip Law)

lubrication, of electrical systems, of rubber and synthetic rubber and plastic accessories all need smoothing out. On the high plateau, above 3000 m, diesel engines need to be supercharged to maintain efficiency.

The main difficulties, apart from mechanical ones, associated with surface travel on the Antarctic plateau are the dangers of hidden crevasses, the rough surfaces caused by high sastrugi, and the delays caused by white-out, drift and blizzard. Australians in the Mawson region in summer report that travel on the plateau is only possible on an average of one day out of every three because of these delays.

Crevasses are dealt with in several ways; the United States tractor train opening up a route from Little America V to Byrd used electrical crevasse detectors and manual probing to discover the crevasses, which were then exposed by blasting. Bulldozers pushed snow into them to form deep, solid bridges over which the trains could proceed. Most expeditions probe manually in treacherous areas, then weave and twist to discover safe tracks through the crevasses, flagging their paths as they go. The crevasse detector, an electrical instrument pushed in front of a vehicle on an extensive outrigger frame, is an effective but not perfect instrument which has a number of supporters. Further work in this field is needed. Living conditions on the trail have improved considerably with the advent of the mechanical vehicle, where weight is not as serious a limitation as on a dog sledge. Men still live on hard rations (pemmican and biscuits) and sleep in tents when running with dog teams, but in a tractor train they live almost luxuriously. As with the camping motorist, the tent has been displaced by the caravan. Caravans designed for special uses can be hauled behind the tractors to provide sleeping accommodation, cooking and eating space, scientific laboratories, etc., while more normal rations comprising tinned and frozen foods can be carried. The propane gas cooker or electric stove has replaced the kerosene stove, and electric light is provided. In the Kharkov tractor and the large modified Sno-cat, living quarters, radio room and scientific laboratory are all included in the tractor cabin. The Kharkov even has an electric kitchen and shower cubicle. Such trains can move continuously in fine weather, with drivers working in shifts and others sleeping as the train moves forward. Heavy equipment can be hauled, such as powered ice drills for seismic shooting and the elaborate seismic recording equipment. Such trains can transport sufficient fuel to be self-supporting, but air-dropped caches of fuel along their routes are commonly provided.

An interesting technique is that of the Americans (see Fig. 12), who use giant rubber wheels (rolli-tankers) to carry fuel, often linking four such fuel wheels with axles and a tray to form a rolling carrier for general cargo. Each wheel has a capacity of 2000 litres (500 gallons). This is a lighter and more convenient method of transporting fuel than carrying drums on sledges. As the fuel is used it is replaced by compressed air.

Station Construction

The stations maintained by the different nations in Antarctica exhibit a wide variety of techniques, according to the types of terrain upon which they are established. It is much more difficult to build permanent establishments on ice or névé than on rock, although the former offer certain advantages in sanitation and water production. Examples of rock-based stations are McMurdo, Mirnyy, Dumont d'Urville, Syowa, Mawson, Davis, Wilkes, Scott, Hallett, and the numerous stations of the United Kingdom, Chile and Argentine in Graham Land. Snow-based stations are Amundsen–Scott, Byrd, Vostok, Ellsworth, General Belgrano, Halley Bay, Lazarev, Norway and Roi Baudoin.

Where rock sites are available, huts are dotted around rather haphazardly,

FIG. 16 DUMONT D'URVILLE – A COMPACT STATION
(*ANARE photograph by Phillip Law*)

according to the availability of suitable sites on the irregular rock surfaces, and are generally separated from each other in order to diminish the risk of fire. The disadvantage is, of course, that men must expose themselves to the weather to move from one hut to another (see Fig. 17).

It is interesting to note that United States, Russian and Australian expeditions quite independently arrived at the same style of hut construction, namely flat-topped box-like huts made by clamping prefabricated wall panels together, supported on bearers resting on wooden stumps or scaffold piping, and firmly tied down to the rock by cables rigged to roof brackets. Panels are of plywood or aluminium, 10 to 15 cm in thickness, with an insulating core of rock-wool, foamed plastic or layered paper and reflecting foil. The Australian huts have aluminium-clad panels held together by long rods which run through the centres of the panels and have bolts at each end which screw onto the rods to cramp the sections tightly together. Gaskets of 'rubazote' are provided at each joint. Six men can erect a fair-sized hut in two days, complete with in-built partitions, furnishings, heating system and electrical fittings. Flat roofs in windy areas are cleared of snow by the wind. The British and Norwegians have used more conventional timber-framed buildings, while the French at Dumont d'Urville have used prefabricated, pressed steel huts with low-pitched gable roofs. Care must be taken in using conventional building methods with wooden materials. The extremely dry atmosphere causes warping of solid wood, which also becomes splinter dry and, in windy areas, is eroded by snow blast. At Mawson's 1912 station at Cape Denison one can see 4 cm of wood worn from a memorial cross, and tongue-and-groove boards eroded to resemble venetian blinds.

FIG. 17 MAWSON – AN OPEN STATION

The prime advantage of a compact station is ease of access to all facilities in any weather. The disadvantages (avoided in open stations) are great fire risk, difficulties in providing large foundation rafts and overcrowding of equipment, particularly exterior fittings

(*ANARE photograph by G. Newton*)

Although a rock-based station may become drifted over by snow in winter, it will as a rule melt clear again in summer, so that regular maintenance on huts is possible and the station has a permanence that is not attainable with a snow-based station. With good siting of huts it is possible to keep drifting to a minimum and in windy areas like Mawson the station remains practically snow-free right through the winter.

At a rock-based station the disposal of waste (sewage, waste water, garbage) poses a problem. Sewage and garbage are most generally collected in drums and deposited on sea ice or dumped into the sea itself, although at Mawson a neat technique of burning sewage in the latrine is used. Waste water has to be collected in drums and carried away. At McMurdo, waste water is allowed to run out over nearby rocks where it freezes to form 'glaciers'. These are periodically removed by bulldozers. It is an advantage, though, to have rock sites for dumps of fuel where drums cannot become permanently buried in ice. The erection of radio masts and the provision of electrical 'earthing' is much simpler on rock. It is not to be wondered at, then, that most of the good coastal rock sites have already been snapped up by expeditions looking for suitable places for permanent stations.

Considerable efforts must be directed towards keeping such stations free from accumulated rubbish. All sorts of discarded trash—paper, packing materials, pieces of rope and wire, timber, etc.—tend to be dropped into and buried by

FIG. 18

NEW BYRD STATION

Peter Snow Miller ejecting stream of snow as it completes a length of tunnel

(*US Navy photograph*)

snow during the year, only to reappear after the spring thaw to disfigure the station.

The main disadvantage of a station built on névé or ice is its impermanence. Such ice is constantly, even though imperceptibly, moving; plateau ice is generally moving, glacier fashion, towards the coast; ice shelf is likewise moving seawards; and bay ice is the least stable of all. Such movement of the exact position of a station is a serious disadvantage for observatory work (see for instance p. 466), but that is not the main difficulty. More serious is the tendency of buildings to sink gradually into the névé and for snow drift to become heaped over them, so that after a year the whole station is irretrievably buried, never again to emerge. Men then live unenviably underground, like rabbits. As time proceeds, the pressure of the surrounding ice or névé and the subsidence of foundations causes walls and roofs to cave in and floors to buckle upwards. At the end of three or four years such stations are beyond redemption. Little America V the deserted U.S. station established in 1956 on the Ross Ice Shelf, has now sunk 8 m below the surface, while the British Halley Bay Station, set up in 1956 on ice shelf, is covered by some 10 m of snow.

The United States Byrd Station suffered so seriously from deformation that Operation Deep Freeze 62 has rebuilt it to a new design. The technique, originally developed by the Americans at Camp Century in Greenland, consists of digging and roofing deep trenches and building the huts in these so that no névé is in contact with the walls or roofs. High stumps, broadly based, support the

FIG. 19 NEW BYRD STATION — INSTALLATION OF ARCHWAYS
OVER TRENCHES

(*US Navy photograph*)

buildings around the edges only, so as to avoid 'hogging' of the centres of the floors.

A special machine, the Peter Snow Miller, is used to excavate the trenches. This 18-ton machine has hydraulically driven rotor blades which can cut a swathe through névé 3 m wide, 1 m deep and 100 m long in half an hour, throwing the pulverized snow into a chute which blows it high up to one side out of the trench (Fig. 18).

The new Byrd Station, which was occupied in February 1962, has a main trench 200 m long and 5 m wide at the top, undercut to 7 m at the bottom. Several side branches lead off this main trench on each side, of which the largest (100 m × 12 m wide × 11 m deep) is to house the vehicle workshop and diesel power station. Arched galvanized iron sections are bolted together to form the roofs of the trenches, which then are covered by snow to the level of the surrounding terrain. In other tunnel branches the normal T5 type United States polar prefabricated buildings have been erected, leaving 1½ m clearance between the walls and the sides of the trench. Should the walls show signs of encroaching inwards upon this space they will be shaved off periodically to preserve the clearance (Figs. 19-21).

Underground stations of this kind have certain advantages. Sheltered from the wind, the huts need not be as strongly built nor as heavily insulated and they can therefore be of cheaper design. Much storage space can be provided by the

FIG. 20 NEW BYRD STATION – ARCHWAY VIEWED FROM ABOVE
(*US Navy photograph*)

tunnels themselves, without special buildings, and this also saves expense. Movement to and fro between sections of the station is simple in all weather, whereas in an exposed station men must haul themselves laboriously along blizzard lines connecting the separated huts when strong winds blow. As will be mentioned later, the greatest danger facing an underground station is that of fire.

There is an alternative method of solving the problem of deterioration due to distortion of buildings built on névé and covered by drift snow. It is to raise the huts on stilts so that the floors are 2 to 3 m above the snow surface. Drift will then blow unimpeded through the supports and the snow surface around the huts will not drift up. So far no-one has tried this design of station, which would raise its own set of special problems.

Some further points about the new Byrd Station are of interest. In the early stages it will be powered by four 150 kw diesel generators, but later it is planned to install a nuclear energy reactor. Water will be obtained from 'Rodriguez wells': a live steam jet is directed downwards into the névé and, as the snow melts, the water is pumped out. A deep shaft is thus drilled until a layer of impermeable névé or ice is reached, usually at a depth of 70 to 100 m. Ice melted by the steam collects here and the steam melts out a broad chamber surrounding the shaft, so that the well finishes up as a bulbous cavern anything up to 70 m in diameter and 30 m deep. Heat from the steam jet keeps the water from freezing and it can be pumped up as required.

Sewage will be conveyed by heated sewer mains to abandoned, empty Rodriguez wells. Garbage will be burnt in a deep pit and the heat of combustion will tend to melt the remnant refuse deeper into the ice. Space heating will be by hot air produced by oil burners and ventilation will be by circulating fans.

The fuel required for such a station will be considerable and the transport of drummed diesel oil 1300 km from McMurdo will pose a major logistic problem. (It has been estimated, for example, that a gallon of oil costing 12 cents in the USA is worth $5 by the time it reaches Byrd Station.) It can be seen, therefore, that the development of nuclear power stations in Antarctica is essential if the development of installations inland is to pass beyond a very limited stage.

A novel hut for an inland station was designed for use by Expéditions Polaires Françaises at Charcot. The hut, 8 m long, was semi-circular in cross section and 4 m wide. For transport it was divided into three and each section was mounted on a sledge to form a caravan. The sledges were towed to Charcot and there a long pit was dug to accommodate the building. The sections were placed in the pit and bolted together, then drift covered them to restore the original level of the snow surface. The hut was occupied in 1957 and 1958 but has not been visited since.

Huts exposed on the surface must be strongly constructed and well anchored to withstand hurricane winds. Windows are double or treble glazed to decrease heat loss and avoid condensation on the inside, while the spaces between the panes are often sealed and filled with dried air or carbon dioxide so that fogging on the inside surfaces does not occur.

Each hut is fitted with an entry porch which acts as a trap to prevent entry of wind and snow or loss of heat from the hut when the door is opened. Such porches are often uninsulated so that they remain cold; snow-sprinkled external clothing hung in such porches does not thaw and become wet.

Huts must have emergency exits in case of fire and, where huts become drifted over in winter, trapdoors must be provided in roofs to allow entry without the labour of digging drifts away from the main doors.

The commonest source of heat and power is diesel oil. Most stations use diesel-electric generators of size varying from 15 kVA to 150 kVA, sometimes arranged in banks and connected in parallel, to provide 3-phase alternating current which is reticulated by standard distribution methods throughout the station. Difficulties are often experienced in earthing and shielding generators and distribution lines so that they do not produce 'noise', which interferes with radio and scientific electronic equipment. The adequate stabilization of voltage and frequency, particularly when loads fluctuate, is a further problem.

There are two main alternatives for reticulating power lines at rock-based stations: one can string them up in aerial array on robust poles, or lay them along the ground. The first has the advantage of accessibility at all times, but generally involves 'catenary' suspension from steel cables to prevent the wires blowing down in high winds. The use of 'pyrotenax' cables laid on the rock is coming into favour, with protection by concrete or by steel pipes where vehicles must cross them. In an ideal station all problems such as siting of huts, reticulation of power lines, water pipes, telephone lines and heating ducts, and the routing of vehicular traffic would be dealt with in the planning stage before construction commenced; this, however, rarely happens—stations grow from small beginnings by the rather haphazard addition of extra facilities year by year.

The use of wind as a source of power has not been fully exploited, although in many areas the winds are strong and constant enough to be harnessed for this purpose. A number of expeditions has used wind as an auxiliary source of power and the Australians have used wind generators of 1·5 kW power to charge the batteries which drive the automatic weather stations at Chick and Lewis Islands. The main objection to this type of power generation is the intermittent nature of the operation and the consequent necessity for banks of large storage cells to provide constancy of voltage. Conversion from d.c. to a.c. is also required for many purposes. However, the use of wind power for heating offers possibilities, as various forms of simple heat reservoirs can be designed which could be charged when the wind blew and later could release this heat in periods of calm. The melting of snow for water would be an excellent application of such a technique and, together with the use of wind power for general lighting purposes, would save much fuel. The use of alternators with rectifiers where required instead of d.c. generators would increase reliability and general performance. The French in 1962 investigated the power potentially available from the wind at Dumont d'Urville using special recording instruments.

One difficulty is the size, and hence the vulnerability in high winds, of the propeller required to turn a wind generator of large power; another is the gustiness of the hurricanes which attain speeds exceeding 70 m/sec. Some form of automatic device to decrease the pitch of the propeller as the speed of the wind increases would be of value under these conditions, the blades being finally 'feathered' for winds in excess of, say, 40 m/sec.

A type of wind generator experimented with in France and England might have practical advantages in Antarctica. Its blades are hollow, with vents at the tips, where the Venturi principle causes a decrease in pressure as the blades rotate. Air is therefore sucked through the hollow blades from a pipe connected to an air turbine at ground level. This design has the advantage of removing the heavy generator from the mast and of reducing the problem of speed control.

No Antarctic station ever seems to have enough electric power. Estimates made when a station is built invariably have to be doubled or trebled a few years later. There is no doubt that, if Antarctica is ever to be exploited industrially for mining or other purposes, nuclear energy must be used, for the transport of the large quantities of liquid or solid fuel required would be out of the question. (One might, of course, use the local high-grade coal if one's business happens to be within a reasonable distance of such reserves!)

The heating of an Antarctic station is a major problem. The simplest, cleanest and safest way is to use electric power, but it is rare for a station to have electricity to spare for this purpose. A variety of other methods is therefore seen at the different stations, ranging from ducted hot air heated by oil or coal burners and oil-fired hot-water systems down to simple coke-fired stoves. The distribution of hot air or hot water from a central furnace is difficult in a station where huts are separated, although systems used in Greenland (where hot-water pipes surrounded by boxed insulation pass from house to house throughout a village) could probably be adopted successfully. For under-snow stations the distribution of hot air from a central source seems to be the most practicable method. Whatever system is used, consideration of the fire hazards involved is of the greatest importance.

Fire is the greatest single hazard in Antarctica. Most of the buildings are wooden; the exceptionally dry climate dehydrates the materials and contents of huts; a considerable amount of internal heating is used; high winds are prevalent; many huts are not occupied for the full 24 hours a day; electrical wiring is sometimes poorly installed; and there is a temptation, for convenience and comfort, to connect separated buildings by passageways and tunnels which aid the spread of any fire which may start. An expedition which is burnt out of its living quarters during an Antarctic winter is indeed in a desperate plight. Although all stations are organized so that emergency food, clothing, power and radio are provided against such an emergency, considerable hardship would be involved for a party even if life were not endangered by a major fire, and of course scientific programmes would be completely disrupted.

Firefighting in Antarctica can be greatly complicated by circumstances. For example, if the station is buried in snow, smoke may drive the occupants out onto the snow surface above, from which they would have little chance of fighting the fire. Strong winds may make it impossible to direct fire extinguishers onto the seat of the fire. Wind may drive the flames rapidly along beneath floors or through corridors. Water is always in short supply.

The best action is prevention. Men must be trained to be highly fire conscious and station discipline in anti-fire precautions must be raised to the highest level. Next, buildings and installations should be designed with due regard to fire hazards; the lay-out of a station and the choice of fire-proof building materials can materially decrease such risks. Finally, adequate provision of fire alarm systems and suitable extinguishers, both manual and automatic, is essential.

Various systems have been tried for firefighting. In some powerhouses automatic flooding by carbon dioxide in case of fire is used; in others, automatic water sprinklers attached to 'dry-pipe' systems connected to water tanks in warmed huts are installed; and in some coastal places pumps are arranged to bring sea water to hydrants placed at strategic points in the station. No precautions, however, can eliminate the danger due to human carelessness.

Inadequate ventilation in buildings, tents or vehicles can subject the occupants to the risk of carbon monoxide poisoning. This is a very common danger and there have been numerous close escapes from death by this cause. Carbon monoxide is produced when the process of normal combustion does not proceed to completion and is more likely to occur when the temperatures of the air and metal surfaces surrounding a combustion process are very low. Produced normally in quantities too small to be dangerous, carbon monoxide may build up to toxic proportions if allowed to accumulate because of poor ventilation. Inadequate ventilation is common in an environment where the external air is bitterly cold, where a hot comfortable 'fug' is preferred to draughts in a hut, and where drift snow will enter through the smallest crack. The design of ventilating systems has exercised many brains and some excellent methods are available; however, the blocking of hut vents by snow during blizzards or the deliberate sealing of tents and vehicles by occupants trapped in a storm can produce conditions favourable to the accumulation of this highly poisonous gas. It is now common practice to provide stations with test meters which, used in shelters or vehicles, will show the percentage of carbon monoxide present in the air.

Some specialized buildings provided in Antarctica for scientific programmes deserve mention. Most common is the balloon release shelter, with its associated balloon-filling equipment, required by meteorologists for launching balloons to obtain upper air data. Launching large-diameter balloons carrying fragile instruments in high and gusty winds is a difficult business and success depends largely upon the design and siting of the balloon release shelter. It must have large 'garage type' doors 4 to 5 m high and should be sited on high ground where the slope falls away on the leeward side. It is difficult to design large sliding or tipping doors which can be easily opened when drift snow lies piled up outside but which can be perfectly sealed against fine powder snow. To avoid the tendency of balloons to dip after release in turbulent conditions and dash their delicate cargoes against the ground, the Russians have designed a tower shelter in which the balloon, inflated at ground level, rises 7 m to a large exit occupying the top half of one wall of the tower. This exit faces down wind and the balloon, allowed to stream out through this door, is caught by the wind and whipped away.

Electronic devices, such as radar or 'rawin' recorders, require elaborate aerials of the 'dish' or 'yagi' type and these must be housed in non-metallic shelters which are symmetrical about the rotating aerial inside. The commonest type of hut is a truncated, flat-based sphere made of fibre glass, about 5 m in diameter, which can be adequately sealed and insulated while still preserving the required transparent qualities for the radio signals.

Glaciological laboratories must be kept cooled well below freezing point so that snow and ice samples can be handled without their melting. While this is simple to achieve in winter, it may require insulation and refrigeration of a hut on a rock site in summer. At Mirnyy the glaciogical laboratory was established in the top of a crevasse and cold air to keep the temperature low in summer was pumped up from lower down in the chasm.

A novel cosmic ray hut was built at Mawson. Its walls were designed to have an average density approximating that of air and, while insulated, to be heat-conducting on the inside surface and to provide electrical shielding for the equipment inside. The walls were made of plywood, with corrugated paper insulation in the middle of the panels and bonded aluminium sheeting on the inner surfaces.

Auroral observatories present difficulties. The Americans use Perspex-domed towers, erected on stilts to avoid drifting up. Hot air must be used inside to prevent fogging of the transparent Perspex, while icing up and abrasion by wind-blown snow necessitate frequent attention to the external surfaces of the domes. Where sealed recording instruments can be designed, it is better to leave their optical heads unshielded by any dome, but where a human observer is to make records some shelter is obviously essential.

Cooking facilities vary greatly from station to station. The large kitchen at McMurdo, with meals *à la cafeteria*, is provided with large oil-fired ranges, while the small one at Davis has an electric stove and a gas stove. Some stations have Primus kerosene stoves, others slow-combustion coke stoves. Generally, limited generation of electric power precludes the use of electric stoves. Slow combustion stoves have a number of advantages, but suffer from the disadvantage that many bags of coke must be lumped by manual labour to provide their fuel. Bottled gas has revolutionized cooking in Antarctica both at stations (where it is used generally to fuel auxiliary small stoves) and in the field (where small gas burners are rapidly replacing the older Primus kerosene stoves).

But nowhere has the revolution been as great as in food. For some years now Antarctic expeditions, supplied by modern ships with refrigerated storage capacity, have been able to avail themselves of fresh meat and deep-frozen vegetables. Frozen fresh meat has been the greatest boon, for tinned meats suitable for hot meals have always been limited in variety and rather unsatisfactory in quality.

However, until now the men in the field, particularly those who were limited by weight considerations, have been forced to make do mainly with pemmican, perhaps eked out by a few tinned meats. A major development has just occurred – the evolution of accelerated freeze drying as a process for preserving foods. Now, in packaged form, concentrated meats of light weight are available which need only a few minutes soaking in water to convert them to attractive fresh meat. Moreover, they do not require to be transported or stored in refrigeration. Vegetables also are available in this form but, as dehydrated and tinned vegetables have always been reasonably satisfactory, the benefit is not as great as in the case of meats. A sledge ration now may contain chicken, minced pork and beef steaks with weights which show a useful advantage even over pemmican. It will not be long before tinned meats cease to occupy a place in the larder of an Antarctic expedition.

Clothing

A whole separate treatise could be written about Antarctic clothing. Here a break-through is imminent but it has not yet occurred, in spite of the development of many new, synthetic fabrics. Basically the method used has been the same for fifty years, namely to clothe the body with a number of layers of warm material of a cellular, permeable type and to cover these externally with a light, windproof envelope. The method has two disadvantages: first, regulation of temperature is clumsy, involving the removal of the external windproof garments and adjustment of the number of layers beneath before replacing the windproofs again; secondly, in extremely cold conditions the number of warm layers required becomes so great that movement is restricted by the clumsy thickness of material, particularly at the joints.

To conquer the former one needs the equivalent of a set of louvres which can be opened or closed at will; for the latter, the development of artificially warmed clothing is required. The Russians have experimented with warmed clothing at their inland stations where temperatures below $-75°C$ are experienced in winter. Electrically heated suits have been tried, in which the wearer trails a long lead from a source of power inside his hut when he ventures out into the vicious cold; they have also experimented with thermal pads, chemically heated, which can be strapped onto the body beneath the clothing. Something of this sort is obviously required if man is to work exposed to outside conditions in temperatures below $-50°C$, and some satisfactory solution to this technical problem will be a major contribution.

For the milder conditions experienced around most of the coast of Antarctica in winter or on the high plateau in summer, where temperatures reach about $-40°C$, the normal methods of clothing first described have proved adequate, even in strong winds.

Reverting to the question of temperature regulation, it should be understood that clothing must be designed to protect a man over a wide range of physical exertion, from the passivity of an observer standing for long periods almost motionless beside some instrument he is reading to the strenuous activity of a man skiing vigorously uphill or engaged in heavy physical labour. In general a man must avoid sweating, otherwise his undergarments become damp and their insulating qualities deteriorate; also the evaporation of sweat from the skin produces chilling. To avoid such dangers a man must either increase ventilation about the body or decrease the amount of clothing worn when working hard. Clothing in general is made permeable so that water vapour transpired from the skin can escape.

The Eskimo had the right approach to this problem. In brief, a tent-shaped garment made of warm fur and tied at the neck trapped body-heated air and kept him warm. Opening the garment at the neck allowed the warm air to escape, and the ventilation could be further increased by opening draw strings at the bottom of the garment and the ends of the sleeves if desired. This system worked because the Eskimo wore no other garments underneath his furs. It will not work with our multi-layer system and our ideas of hygiene and underclothing which must be regularly changed. Our one attempt at improving ventilation has been the development of 'string' underclothing which, worn against the skin, holds the normal underclothing away and allows space for evaporation.

The ventilation problem is complicated by condensation and icing. Imagine an insulating section of material, be it clothing, sleeping bag or hut panel, which is maintained at nearly body temperature on one side and exposed to bitter cold on the other. There is a gradient of temperature through the section from, say, $+30°C$ at one side to $-40°C$ on the other. At some intermediate point in the material the temperature will fall past $0°C$, the freezing point of water. If water vapour is being transpired through the section, it will freeze to form ice or hoar frost at about this layer of the material. (To avoid such ice formation in the walls of huts, the panels are either filled with solid impermeable insulating material or else a 'vapour barrier' of impermeable sheeting is incorporated immediately behind the inner wall surface.) It was this process which caused the sleeping bags of early explorers to ice up. In Eskimo clothing such frost occurs at the base of the hairs (the furs are worn with the hairs next to the skin) and when the Eskimo returns to his igloo he simply turns the garment inside-out and shakes out the ice. The problem is not as serious for a man moving around in the open air in the wind as for one sleeping in still air inside a cold tent in a sleeping bag, for the frost will tend to evaporate again and pass out through the semi-permeable windproof outer. However, this frost layer is a matter that must be watched in clothing design for extremely low temperatures.

An interesting application of the vapour barrier principle is provided by the US 'thermal' boot. Footwear has always been a problem in Antarctica. Feet tend to sweat heavily and wet socks, with their insulation destroyed, can produce frostbite. This problem can be overcome by keeping the insulation of the foot covering dry. The thermal boot incorporates a layer of insulation, coated both on the outside *and* the inside with impermeable rubber. The sweat of the foot cannot escape through the vapour barrier, therefore the feet become wet. However, the insulation in the boot itself remains dry and effectively conserves the body heat, so the foot and the sweat remain warm. Only one pair of socks is used, mainly to avoid chafing, and this pair is changed and washed each night. A certain amount of psychological adjustment is needed to accustom oneself to the sensation of walking about with wet feet, but once one realizes that, though wet, one's feet are *warm* there is no great difficulty. These boots are equally effective in both dry cold, down to $-50°C$, and in wet cold and slush. What a boon they would have been to Nansen and Peary in their Arctic sledging over slushy summer sea ice!

Once one passes from general principles in clothing to the design of actual garments one becomes involved in numerous details which depend largely upon personal taste – the looseness of a parka, the placing of pockets and draw strings, the relative merits of various materials, the design of a suitable hood, and so on. Here no unanimity can be expected.

There is one important consideration, however, with regard to underclothing and socks. Where large numbers of men are concerned and water is short, a community laundry, with washing machines, is inevitable. In such a system ordinary woollen clothing suffers severely and shrinkage soon makes the garment useless. In small stations, reasonable care with hand laundering overcomes this difficulty. The US Operation Deep Freeze has moved from wool to cotton and synthetic materials to avoid shrinkage problems, but there is no doubt that wool is by far the warmest material for underwear. Not only is it warmer when dry, but it is the only material which is still reasonably warm even when damp with sweat. Recent developments by CSIRO in Australia have resulted in a process by which woollen garments can be made shrinkproof, even to the point where blankets can be boiled without shrinking or felting. The application of such a process to woollen underwear and socks for Antarctic use should be a considerable step forward in improving the conventional clothing.

Communications

The problem of adequate communications is still one of the greatest which confronts modern Antarctic expeditions. Nowhere in the world are radio conditions more difficult. The noise-to-signal ratio is high, fading is prevalent, and frequent 'blackouts' frustrate the efforts of operators. Most of these difficulties arise from the fact that communication paths must pass along or through the auroral zone, where ionospheric disturbances associated with auroral displays and magnetic storms are common. Other problems are caused by the 'static' produced when drift snow blows across aerials during blizzards, by the problems of maintaining aerials and masts in the teeth of hurricanes up to 80 m/sec, by interference caused by other electrical and electronic equipment at the stations, and by the difficulty of establishing adequate 'earth' connections on dry hard rock or on snow and ice. Often sheer non-availability of space prevents the distribution of aerial masts and equipment in the most desirable array.

At the larger stations great improvements have been made during the last few years. Directional aerial systems, mostly rhombic arrays, have been erected; teletype circuits have been installed; transmitters and receivers have been adequately separated; high power transmitters have been installed; and facsimile equipment is coming into greater use.

No solution to the 'blackout' problem seems possible with the present system of high frequency radio communication, but three future developments ('forward scatter' techniques, radio satellites, and ultra-long wave transmissions) offer some hope. In the meantime, communications within Antarctica are aided by a system whereby strategically situated 'mother' stations with adequate facilities collect and disseminate weather and general information from smaller, less favourably equipped stations. Communications from Antarctica outwards to other continents are best where the transmission route lies across rather than along the auroral zone, thus traversing as short a path as possible through the disturbed region. Thus McMurdo–Wellington is a better circuit than Mawson–Sydney.

The level of electrical interference at a station is, however, a very serious problem. The difficulty of adequately earthing equipment makes this problem more serious than elsewhere, while the conflicting requirements of various sections of the station – power generation, radio communications, and electronic scientific observations – complicate matters unbelievably. Mutual interference is

FIG. 2I NEW BYRD STATION – PREFABRICATED COMMUNICATIONS
BUILDING IN COMPLETED TUNNEL
The structure stands about one metre above the snow tunnel floor. Note the cable runners suspended from the archway

(*US Navy photograph*)

greatest between ionospheric recorders and radio equipment, and some compromise is required in the arrangement of recorder times and radio schedules to limit this annoyance.

By far the greatest amount of traffic is that associated with the exchange of meteorological data. First, mother stations must collect data from all Antarctic stations and, via one or two central stations, transmit it to the International Weather Analysis Centre in Australia. Secondly, various stations are interested in regional and, in some cases, continental weather and require to collect data accordingly. All this means an elaborate network of radio channels and a highly organized system of time schedules and allotted frequencies. The Antarctic

Treaty nations and SCAR are both working at present towards a rationalization of existing circuits.

Teletype equipment greatly simplifies this sort of exchange of meteorological data. A mother station can record incoming messages from daughter stations on teletype tape and play the tape through transmitters to send it on again. However, teletype equipment can only operate when conditions are reasonably good and, as the noise-to-signal ratio rises, the manual radio operator must come back to the job. At present a great deal depends upon his persistence and attention to duty to maintain communications in difficult periods.

Other important aspects of the communication picture are: – the maintenance of listening watches on emergency frequencies to pick up distress calls; the operation of ground-to-air communications and navigation aids for aircraft; and the station–field party–aircraft three-way channels that must be worked when traverse or exploration parties backed by air support are operating in the field.

All-in-all, communications in Antarctica present the most complex and difficult problems of all the logistic support programme and it will be a number of years before some satisfactory pattern emerges.

Technical developments in Antarctica, as we have seen, have been tremendous and logistic support for scientific operations is reasonably satisfactory. But there is a long way to go before Antarctica can be opened up for development and exploitation. Sea transport can be improved and harbours must be constructed; permanent airfields are needed; new principles in clothing must be evolved; nuclear energy must be developed at stations; communications must be improved; and better methods of over-snow transport are needed. Finally, provision must be made for families to live at Antarctic establishments before it can be considered that normal human habitation of this desolate continent has been achieved.

CHAPTER THREE

The Mapping
of Antarctica

J. HOLMES MILLER, *Wellington*

Introduction

The past decade has witnessed the passing of an era; the age of geographical discovery is closed. This age, which began with the wanderings of Marco Polo in the thirteenth century, has stage by stage unfolded to European eyes the darkest corners of the globe. The challenge offered by the unknown was accepted by men like da Gama, Magellan, Drake and Cook; by Speke, Livingstone, Nansen and Peary; until by the middle of this century Antarctica alone could hold surprises. And now even this continent has yielded her secrets. The blank spaces on the map of Antarctica have all but disappeared. This large continent of 14 million square kilometres has been completely scrutinized by the aerial camera; 150,000 kilometres of surface traverse have crisscrossed the inland plateau. It remains for the cartographer to compile in the manner best suited to the area the charts of the last unmapped area of the earth.

Man had long conjectured the existence of a southern continent. The ancient Greek philosophers had propounded the essential idea of such a land by virtue of the demands of symmetry. Later thinkers, however, postulated if not a Southern Hemisphere with the same land masses as the Northern Hemisphere then surely a land mass to balance the void of the Arctic Ocean.

Why then did others believe in a *terra Australis* occupying all of the Southern Pacific and Indian Oceans almost to equatorial latitudes? We may attribute this to the Renaissance cartographers who, while accepting a spherical earth, yet dared not allow of more water than that which had been proved navigable. Not until two or three centuries later did man reject the Mediterranean premise that all was land until proved water. (The Orontius map of the Southern Hemisphere of this time, 1531, is an example of Renaissance cartography. Faithfully shown in Figure 22 is the southern shore of Africa after Diaz, and most surely the Straits of Magellan, but note Tierra del Fuego stretching to the Pole and twice as far beyond northwards to the Tropic of Capricorn in the eastern Indian Ocean.) Then began the wearing down and pruning back of the imaginary continent as Drake, Hartog and Tasman in turn made their severances. Drake separated the Americas from *terra Australis incognita*; Hartog blundered into western Australia, but it was Tasman who separated present-day Australia yet still left New Zealand a possible shore of the unknown.

There were those who journeyed – Bouvet and Bougainville – and those who wrote – de Brosses in France and the recalcitrant Dalrymple in England. Dalrymple's writings were based on fact and on much hard experience. Luckily for the project he propounded to the Royal Society, namely the observation in the South Pacific of the transit of Venus, the Royal Navy made the perfect choice of leader. By that choice, and with the successful conclusion of James Cook's first voyage, the great Antarctic *incognita* was threatened. For in 1772 Cook was despatched to solve the mystery of the southern continent.

The story of the exploration of Antarctica is *ipso facto* the chronicle of the cartography of that southern continent and its surrounding seas. Exploration without mapping for topographical, geological or purely navigational reasons is not exploration at all. Travelling and voyaging without the end result of a plotted course from which a map may be constructed is adventuring *per se*; inasmuch as the tracks of the earliest polar travellers were recorded, so with their explorations began polar cartography. The veil of ignorance of *terra Australis nondum cognita* was lifted little by little as the navigators wore down the barriers of latitude which had preserved the Antarctic regions from man's discoveries.

The Navigators

None would have disputed the claim of Captain James Cook, had he made one, to have been the first Antarctic explorer. It was he who carved great masses from the unknown but suspected continent. Those masses which were dissected by him outweighed many times that which was eventually proved to exist. In what has been called by J. C. Beaglehole 'probably the greatest voyage ever made', Cook proved that if land did exist then it lay in latitudes higher than 60° S, along which parallel he made his circumnavigation in 1772–5. In many places he pushed much further south, crossing the Antarctic Circle in the summer of 1772–3 and twice in the summer of 1773–4. His penetration to 71° 10′ S off what was later named as Thurston Island (or Peninsula) was not exceeded in that particular longitude until the summer of 1959–60 when two United States icebreakers forced their way past the island and into the Bellingshausen Sea. Cook found no land south of 60° S, though he deserved to do so. That there would be land he was certain but he predicted that when land was discovered it would provide no habitation for man nor means for his subsistence.

Cook's circumnavigation of the Southern Ocean, completed in February 1775, narrowed the area of search considerably (Figure 23). Although he was not followed immediately by any other polar explorer, he did usher in the era of south polar navigation which was to extend right up to the end of the nineteenth century, when man finally began to establish himself on the continent. Forty-five years were to elapse before Thaddeus von Bellingshausen was despatched by Emperor Alexander I of Russia to find the southern continent. Bellingshausen was as redoubtable a navigator as Cook and in the years between 1819 and 1821

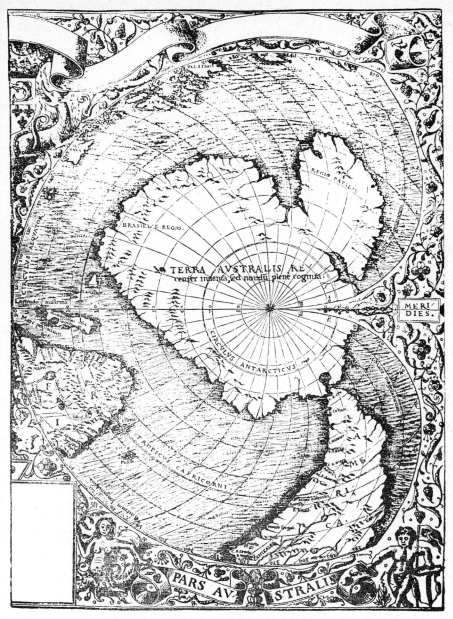

FIG. 22 SOUTHERN HEMISPHERE – MAP OF ORONTIUS 1531

he sailed his *Mirnyy* and *Vostok* completely round Antarctica in latitudes between 60° and 65° S with penetrations to 69° S in two places. He was the first to discover land south of the Antarctic Circle when he found and named Peter I Øy, and most authorities agree that he was the first to view the continent itself (although he did not recognize it as such) right on the meridian of Greenwich. His sighting of Alexander Island in Latitude 68° S, although almost a year later than the sightings by Bransfield and Palmer 5° further north, is surely not less meritorious. Not until 1940 was this proved to be the largest island in proximity

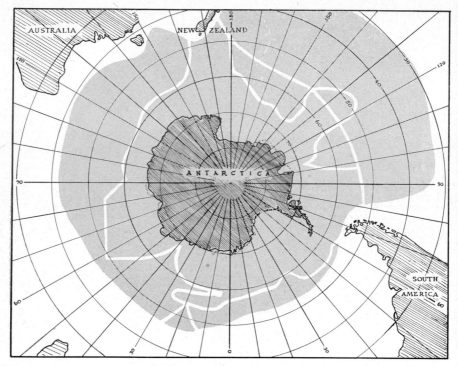

FIG. 23 JAMES COOK'S ANTARCTIC VOYAGES
The previously uncharted area is shown in dark shading

to the continent, while the findings of Bransfield and Palmer proved to be the northern extremities of Graham Land and truly continental.

With Palmer the period of seal-hunting voyages was entered and the notable discoveries between 1820 and 1840 were due to the resources and fortitude of their captains. The influence of the firm of Enderby at this time cannot be overlooked, for while the captains in the company's employ were expected to pursue the economic purpose of their voyages, they were also encouraged to record their findings. Thus we are indebted to masters such as James Weddell (Fig. 5) whose exploits in the Weddell Sea have never been repeated, and Briscoe who made a circumnavigation in 1831-2, discovering and naming

Enderby Land. With the passing of the next decade, and the proof that land found in high latitudes did not enrich the fur seal industry, activities continued to flourish only in the Subantarctic islands. Enderby Brothers made their last contribution to Antarctic exploration in 1839 with John Balleny's discovery of the islands subsequently named after him.

Science led the next period of activity which, in many ways, was the most remarkable of the nineteenth century. The pursuit of the South Magnetic Pole followed the fixing of the North Magnetic Pole by James Clark Ross (Fig. 2). Gauss had computed a position for the southern pole some 25° in latitude south of Tasmania. Three nations sent out expeditions to prove the fixing by actual observation at the pole. Figure 24 illustrates the general contemporaneity of the expeditions. Despatched by the French Ministry of Marine in the southern

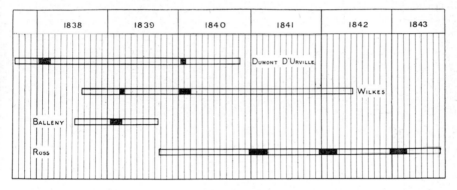

Note.—Each vertical column represents a month ; the horizontal bands show the duration of the expeditions by the number of months they run through ; the time spent south of 60° S. is indicated in solid black.

FIG. 24 THE VOYAGES OF THE EARLY VICTORIAN NAVIGATORS

Each vertical column represents a month; the horizontal bands show the duration of the expeditions; the time spent south of 60° S is indicated in solid black

(From *The Siege of the South Pole*, by Hugh R. Mill)

summer of 1837–8, Dumont d'Urville carried out a season's work near Graham Land before returning to the Antarctic in the Australian sector in the 1839–40 season, to find his way blocked by ice and land which he named Terre Adélie. In the previous season Charles Wilkes (Fig. 8), leading the United States Exploring Expedition, had split his squadron at Tierra del Fuego; in December 1839 the squadron re-formed, returned to the Antarctic and charted a series of landfalls along the coast of Wilkes Land. His fixings were questioned by Ross, who claimed to sail over his areas of land a year later. But time and research have awarded Wilkes his due recognition as a discoverer of the sizeable portion of the coastline of Antarctica, still known by his name.

Captain James Clark Ross, under the auspices of the Admiralty together with the British Association and the Royal Society, was in Hobart in 1840. Here he learnt of the discoveries by Balleny and of the land found by both d'Urville and

Wilkes, and of their inability to approach the South Magnetic Pole in the longitudes south of Australia. Ross set out in *Erebus* and *Terror* to try to make southing
on a more easterly meridian. This led to one of the most astonishing penetrations
of all. He sighted land near Cape Adare, landing on Possession Islands. Pushing
southward through the pack ice, he found and named Victoria Land and entered
the Ross Sea. In this and the following season, when he again entered the Ross
Sea, he charted the Victoria Land coast, Ross Island, the edge of the Ross Ice
Barrier (now Shelf) and skirted the coast, after Wilkes, westward to about 140° E.
By his fortuitous entry into the Ross Sea he had opened a gateway for some of
the most profitable of all Antarctic endeavour. But not for almost sixty years
was this amazing opportunity to be exploited.

The second half of the nineteenth century was notable for the absence of
continued south polar activity despite the initiation of an International Polar
Year in 1882–3. There was some activity in the Subantarctic, but Dallman from
Germany in 1873–4 and Nares from Great Britain in the *Challenger* in the same
year were the only men to approach the continent proper until Kristensen and
Bull landed on the Possession Islands and Cape Adare in January 1895. There
had been occasional visits to the northern tip of Graham Land, such as that by
Smyley of the United States in 1841–2. Figure 25 illustrates the known land at
the end of the nineteenth century.

The age of the navigators closed right at the end of the century with a Belgian
expedition in the *Belgica* under de Gerlache. This expedition was sponsored by
government grants and private contributions for a broad programme of scientific
observations. De Gerlache Strait was discovered and charted as the ship moved
southward to within sight of Alexander Island where the vessel was beset, and
the ship's company became the first to experience a south polar night.

Up to this time such maps and charts as were published were those accompanying reports, narratives and scientific papers. In fact, this practice was to continue
well on into the twentieth century. It was not until the first twenty years of the
twentieth century that the coastline of the continent began to take shape. In this
the contribution of the navigators had been considerable. But their work is most
appreciated when one considers the knowledge they amassed of the oceans, and
the scores of Subantarctic islands which they added to the map. A summary
of these accomplishments would be dull reading but mention should be made of
some.

South Georgia, strategically placed in the South Atlantic, was visited and
mapped to some degree by many British, Russian and United States expeditions,
notably by Bellingshausen whose charts of the southern coastline were accepted
up to 1930. French expeditions from 1773 onwards added surveys of Îles de
Kerguelen and Îles Crozet. Bligh added the Bounty Islands in 1788, Vancouver
the Snares in 1791, Waterhouse the Antipodes in 1800, and Hasselborough in
1810 added both Campbell Island, named for his employers Campbell and Co.
of Sydney, and Macquarie Island, named for the Governor of New South Wales.
It is an indication of the thorough manner in which the captains of the small

sealing craft of the early nineteenth century scoured the ocean to discover seal rookeries, that as early as 1810 they had placed on the map of the South Pacific every one of the Subantarctic islands now known to exist.

The South Shetland, South Sandwich and South Orkney Islands were paid much more attention than any other group of islands in the Southern Ocean as ships from almost every participating nation from 1820 onwards called for commercial or other reasons. While sailing from Boston to Melbourne in 1853 Captain Heard of the United States discovered Heard Island, upon which the

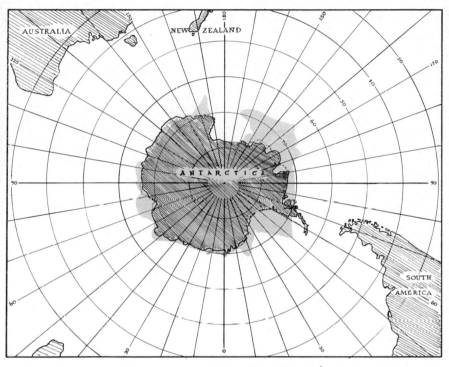

FIG. 25 ANTARCTICA AT THE END OF THE 'AGE OF THE NAVIGATORS', 1898
The unvisited area is shown in dark shading

first landings were made by his compatriots Rogers and Smith in 1855. At this time the first map of the island was produced. Heard was the third discoverer of this small island, the first of whom was an Enderby captain, Peter Kemp, in 1833. A combination of whaling, sealing and charting was responsible for the many voyages of C. A. Larsen of Norway from 1892 onwards, first along the eastern tip of Graham Land, and ending with his captaining of the ship during Nordenskjöld's 1901 expedition to the same area. The new century brought a new approach in man's attitude to Antarctica. With it came the first attempts to win a foothold and to move inland from the coast.

Footholds on the Continent

The new attack upon the continent made by land-based parties brought new methods of survey but not for many years any systematic methods of mapping. The use of the aeroplane was still almost thirty years ahead, so that meanwhile any mapping accomplished was that done by ground parties, travelling by man-hauling or dog team.

It is difficult to trace the first compilations of the many scattered maps which had accumulated during the nineteenth century, but atlases of the early part of this century show a continent vaguely defined with the only established coastlines in the areas of Graham Land, the Ross Sea and scattered portions along the large sector of the South Atlantic and Indian Oceans.

During the nautical period, charting was by such hydrographic means as was afforded by the equipment carried by the vessel. The variations of running surveys from ships are only to be expected when latitude fixes are subject to scattered opportunity and the excessive refraction of a Sun at low altitude. Longitude fixes are likewise affected, with the added uncertainty of chronometer regulation during years of absence in those pre-radio days.

Land-based parties had many immediate advantages. The theodolite replaced the sextant, and solar or astro-fixes could be made by deliberate repetition at the same station. Dead reckoning courses by sledgemeter and compass, whether sun-compass or magnetic compass, were probably more reliable than dead reckoning at sea during long periods of overcast and in total ignorance of drift due to tide and currents. Thus, although large scale mapping was still a long way ahead, the advent of land-based expeditions added a considerable element of accuracy to charting.

Naturally enough, the transition from shipborne to land-based expeditions was not a sudden event. The expeditions of the first decade of this century were notable for a combination of both methods of exploration. While Scott's greatest achievements were on land, some credit must be reserved for the achievements of his ships, *Discovery*, *Morning* and *Terra Nova*. Another to map by sea and land was Charcot. In 1903–5 he led a shipborne expedition in the *Français*, with many coastal forays; and in 1908–10 in the *Pourquoi Pas?* he led an expedition, which, while it did move well into the Bellingshausen Sea, west of Alexander Island, also established winter quarters ashore on Petermann Island. On this expedition Marguerite Bay and Charcot Island were discovered and charted, and short journeys made onto Graham Land.

As late as the thirties of the twentieth century shipborne expeditions were probing for the coastline in many parts of the southern oceans. Mawson's BANZARE expedition sponsored by the governments of Great Britain, Australia, and New Zealand sailed in the *Discovery* from Capetown in October 1929. During the ensuing summer, with the aid of an aeroplane, the MacRobertson and Kemp Coasts were sighted and charted. Again in the following summer of 1930–1 out of Hobart the Banzare Coast was added to the map. The many

voyages of the *Discovery II* from 1929 through to 1938, while primarily oceanographic in purpose also achieved a considerable return in the surveying field.
It was customary to set aside a period of approximately one month in each cruise
to be spent in running surveys of coastline either of the continent proper or
adjacent island groups. By such means more accurate charting was gained of the
South Sandwich Islands in early 1930, the South Shetlands in December 1930,
the South Orkneys in early 1933 and the Balleny Islands in February 1936 and
again in January 1938.

The first party ever to winter ashore was the British party led by Borchgrevink, a purely scientific expedition which established quarters on Ridley
Beach, at Cape Adare, in 1899 (see Fig. 7). No great amount of mapping was
achieved due to the difficulty of getting inland from Robertson Bay. Many
landings were made during the following summer as the ship *Southern Cross*
picked up the party and moved around the Ross Sea via Coulman Island, Wood
Bay, Franklin Island, Cape Crozier and the Ross Ice Shelf, where dog team
parties pushed sufficiently far south to establish a record southing. Unfortunately
this record appears to have become more the prime objective than the acquisition
of knowledge, either scientific or geographical. Not so, however, with the
National Antarctic Expedition entrusted to Robert Falcon Scott, from 1901–4.
Few expeditions since have made such notable advances towards knowledge of
the continent. The reports of this expedition, and the maps appended to them,
are due testimony of the dedication of the whole party to the true aims of
exploration in the widest sense. For the first time there appeared on maps the
western shore of the Ross Ice Shelf as far south as the Nimrod Glacier, the
course of the Koettlitz Glacier, the Ferrar (and Taylor) Glacier and the whole
of Ross Island. Shackleton's British Antarctic Expedition of 1907–9 extended
mapping south from the Nimrod Glacier up the mighty Beardmore Glacier to
the Polar Plateau. The journey of David, Mawson and McKay up the coast
of Victoria Land beyond the Drygalski Ice Tongue made notable additions to
the detail of that coast. The second Scott expedition, 1910–13, produced maps
with considerably more detail in such areas as Granite Harbour, and other
localities in McMurdo Sound.

Not until the expeditions by New Zealand parties from 1956 onwards were
any amendments or additions made to the maps of Victoria Land from Cape
Adare to and beyond the Beardmore Glacier (see Fig. 28). The compilations
and issues before 1956 repeated the information gained up to 1912; of this
information it must be said that errors later found in it were those of longitude
and not latitude. It should be remembered that in 1912 radio was in its infancy
and time signal checks still many years ahead.

Shackleton's Trans-Antarctic Expedition of 1914–17 closed the so-called
'heroic era' which included Amundsen's Norwegian expedition, the Japanese
expedition under Shirase and Mawson's Australasian expedition 1911–14. It is
regrettable that Amundsen left so little record in map form of his travels. The
best contribution of his expedition is the work of Prestrud who travelled over the

unknown southeasterly portion of the Ross Ice Shelf. Japan has left its mark with such names as Okuma Bay and Kainan Bay, on the Ross Ice Shelf. Mawson's endeavours in the scientific fields of his expedition are well known and this can also be said of his geographical work. While geology and physics (terrestrial magnetism in particular) may have been his first pursuits his mapping was not neglected. At this time we see mapping beginning to assume its true place in Antarctic exploration, that of providing the means for the illustration of other sciences, notably geology. Figure 26 shows our knowledge of the Antarctic Continent at the end of the 'heroic age'.

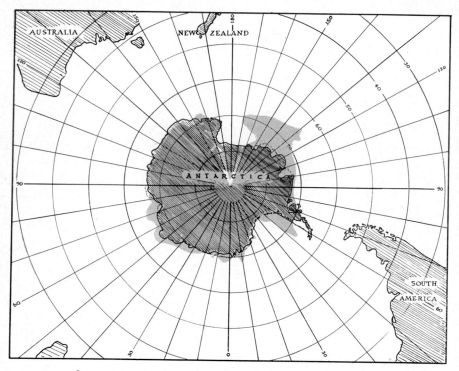

FIG. 26 ANTARCTICA AT THE END OF THE 'HEROIC AGE', 1917
The unvisited area is shown in dark shading

The Advent of the Aeroplane

The aeroplane arrived in the Antarctic as an aid to survey in 1928, thus introducing the most efficient of all ancillary tools at the service of the cartographer. The speed of flight compared with land travel is one asset, the aid to reconnaissance is another, but by far exceeding both is the use of the aeroplane in providing a platform for the aerial camera. Photogrammetry, as the carefully planimetrically and vertically controlled application of the aerial photograph for cartographic purposes, had not yet arrived but with the aeroplane it was on its way. Wilkins flew the length of the Graham Land peninsula on 20 December 1928. Two months later Byrd was flying all his three planes from Little America I in the Ross Sea.

Wilkins' first flight led him into a serious cartographic error. He reported and charted Stefanson Strait which purported to sever Graham Land from the continent. This error was only corrected when Rymill of the British Graham Land Expedition travelled over the ground in 1936. This incident is related to indicate the importance of ground reconnaissance in the interpretation of the aerial photograph and even more important, to provide the essential planimetric and vertical control.

It was the aircraft in association with the hand-held camera in those early days which began to lift the veil so rapidly from the face of the frozen wastes. The controlled photograph was still some way off, at least in Antarctica. Not until the U.S. Operation High Jump in 1947 and its follow-up Operation Windmill in 1948, was aerial photography in the full-scale trimetrogon pattern carried out. Byrd's intervening expeditions in 1933 and 1939 made increasing use of the aeroplane, yet even so the best mapping results were the products of the dog team journeys of Black to the Robert Scott Glacier and of Moulton, Berlin and Bursey to the Hal Flood Range in Marie Byrd Land, journeys comparable with that of Gould to the Queen Maud Range in 1929–30. Conventional methods with light aircraft support were used to advantage by the British Graham Land Expedition 1934–7, under Rymill. King George VI Sound was largely the result of a flight to the extreme range of the small aircraft, but the many additions and corrected errors were the result of overland journeys. The trans-Antarctic flight from Dundee Island to Bay of Whales by Ellsworth and Hollick-Kenyon from 23 November to 5 December 1935 was an epic adventure and gave the first indications of the interior of the Marie Byrd Land. Air reconnaissance and photography played an important part in the geographical discoveries of the several voyages promoted by the Norwegian whaling magnate Lars Christensen. Figure 27 illustrates the knowledge of the continent at the end of World War II.

Modern Mapping

From 1945 onwards those nations interested in Antarctica began to produce maps and charts on more extensive and intensive scales. Before the IGY at least three nations compiled a general map of the Antarctic Continent. The map produced by Australia as early as 1939 on a scale of 1 : 7,500,000 was in two sheets. A compilation of a revised addition of this map on a scale of 1 : 10,000,000 was published in one sheet in 1953. New Zealand also produced a general 'Map of the Antarctic Regions' on a scale of 1 : 16,000,000. Perhaps the most important general map of the continent in this period was that of the American Geographical Society (1955), drawn in four sheets at a scale of 1 : 3,000,000 although a single sheet coloured edition was published at a scale of 1 : 6,000,000. Even before this map had reached publication the information on which it was based was used by Kosack of Germany to produce his four-sheet map of 1 : 4,000,000, which was published in 1954. Recent discoveries by members of

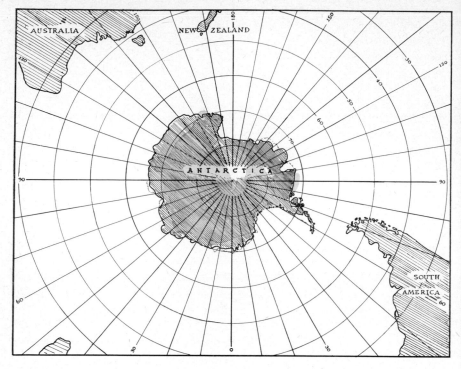

FIG. 27 ANTARCTICA AT THE BEGINNING OF THE 'MODERN AGE', 1946
The unvisited area is shown in dark shading

Falkland Islands Dependencies Surveys were included in his map, even those
of only one year's standing.

In the field of mapping on a larger scale the most important contribution or
aid at this time was undoubtedly the photo coverage by Operation High Jump.
In the summer of 1946–7, 65,000 photos were taken by twelve aircraft of the
United States Navy over most of the coast between Longitudes 15° E and 170° E
and between 95° W and 130° W. In the following summer 'Operation Windmill', equipped with helicopters, established ground control for a considerable
proportion of this aerial photography in the coastal regions, principally between
Longitudes 90° E and 110° E. This photography was made available to many
nations and mapping on a large scale was carried out from it. Examples of this
are the maps of the coast of Terre Adélie in four sheets at a scale of 1 : 100,000
and one sheet of 1 : 500,000 published by France in 1955. Norway produced an
Atlas of Parts of the Antarctic Coastal Lands, constructed from the aerial photographs obtained by the Lars Christensen expedition of 1936–7. The atlas
consisted of twelve sheets extending from Longitudes 21° E to 82° E, all on a
scale of 1 : 250,000. Norway was also responsible for the mapping programme of
the 1949–52 Norwegian–British–Swedish Expedition. An area of 60,000 square

kilometres was triangulated, while from the main base of Maudheim, aircraft of the Swedish Air Force obtained aerial photographs over the mountain regions of Dronning Maud Land. Undoubtedly some of the most consistent effort was that provided by the Falkland Islands Dependencies Survey which from 1945–55 carried out topographic and hydrographic surveys from bases at Stonington Island, Hope Bay and Deception Island. Between 1948 and 1950 eleven sheets were published covering the mainland and offshore islands of Graham Land, with three further separate sheets of the Subantarctic regions of South Georgia, South Sandwich Islands and South Orkney Islands.

Argentine and Chile had also produced maps of the Graham Land area as early as 1946. Thus, by 1955, when plans were crystallizing for the International Geophysical Year and its attendant operations, several areas of Antarctica had been quite well mapped. When IGY operations on the grand scale commenced it is probable that most use was made of the $1 : 1,000,000$ series published as the United States Air Force Aeronautical Charts. While these Aeronautical Charts conveyed little new in mapping, the uniformity of the series, which was of 43 sheets to cover the whole continent, made them a most valuable aid to all field operations during the years from 1956 onwards. During the whole of this IGY period, eleven nations participated in widespread mapping of the continent particularly in the areas of ice-free rock and other identifiable detail.

At this stage electronic measuring equipment began to be a valuable aid in the planimetric control of aerial photography in Antarctica. The use of this type of equipment was not without its serious problems in the cold temperatures and many trials were undertaken to solve the problems arising. Between 1957 and 1959 the United States Navy obtained mapping photographs of some 400,000 square kilometres of the coastal and inland land masses south of 70° S. The stage had not yet been reached when the surveyor was able to go into the field with the photographs of his area in his hand – this was still to come. But at this time, there began the fixing of control points for aerial mapping as the photographs began to become available. It is most difficult to separate the mapping which was done during the two years of the International Geophysical Year from that which was done later when most nations found that they were able and anxious to continue in Antarctic endeavour. Many nations pursued photogrammetic methods in their mapping programmes. Argentina, Australia and the United States of America carried out aerial photography on the trimetrogon system; other nations such as the USSR and Japan used wide-angle photography, and New Zealand oblique photography.

The obvious problem, of course, was the task of providing ground control for satisfactory mapping from this photography. In the early stages there was no escape from ground traverse parties using such means of transport as was available. New Zealand and the United Kingdom in particular persisted with the use of dog teams. This method was also used by parties in Australian, Belgian and Japanese expeditions where the topography excluded the use of mechanized aids. Once in the field the method of controlling photography was immediately obvious – that of obtaining astronomical fixes of identifiable points. When once these fixed points were plotted and an attempt made to cover the intervening areas with detail, considerable difficulty was met in attempting to hold the points as fixed. It was very quickly obvious that as most of these determinations had been by fixes of the Sun during the Antarctic summer, astronomical refraction with its obvious irregularities when observed at low altitude was very much the main contributing cause of the difficulty in holding the fixes as computed. Displacement of as much as 5 km, indicating anomalies in the observations in altitude of up to three minutes of arc were frequently apparent. To overcome this problem it was fairly clear that despite the bright Antarctic Sun an attempt would have to be made to carry out daylight star observations and this course has now been put into practice by all or most of the participating nations. Most have precomputed tables for the quick finding of stars in southern latitudes and it is possible to carry out paired observations at a high altitude and so reduce the effect of the irregularities of astronomical refraction to a minimum. Such methods have resulted in a great advance in the accuracy of the control plots. It has frequently been possible to link such astronomically determined positions by small isolated nets of triangulation and also to control the net by measurement of the baseline.

Tremendous strides were taken from 1957 onwards with the mapping of the Antarctic Continent and the surrounding ocean. Figure 28 indicates the extent of the detail provided by New Zealand sledging parties between 1957 and 1963 in the Victoria Land section of the Trans-Antarctic Mountains. This degree of transformation is common to many parts of the continent where other nations have effected equivalent additions. It is impossible to list the hundreds of maps and charts produced in recent years. The proper guide to these is the *Catalogue of Topographic Maps, Aeronautical and Hydrographic Charts of Antarctica* compiled on behalf of the Scientific Committee on Antarctic Research and published by the Division of National Mapping, Department of National Development, Canberra, Australia. In 1959 the SCAR Working Group on Cartography issued fourteen recommendations about Antarctic mapping, among which were the following specific recommendations.

8. That the metric system should be used in all Antarctic mapping.
9. That a 500 metre contour interval, with supplementary contours at closer intervals when required, is suitable for maps at scales smaller than 1 : 1,000,000.
10. That the International Spheroid should be used for all Antarctic mapping.
11. That maps at a scale smaller than 1 : 1,000,000 should be on the polar stereographic projection, with standard parallel at 71°.
12. That, in maps and charts at the scale of 1 : 1,000,000 ICAO specifications for projections at that scale should be used, and also the common ICAO, IMW sheet lines along parallels and optional meridional limits. (ICAO – International Civil Aviation Organization; IMW – International Map of the World.)

13. That, in maps and charts at scales larger than 1 : 1,000,000 sheet lines should normally subdivide 1 : 1,000,000 sheet lines and a conformal projection should be used.

14. That the 1 : 1,000,000 scale should be adopted for hydrographic charting for scientific purposes and general coastal navigation.

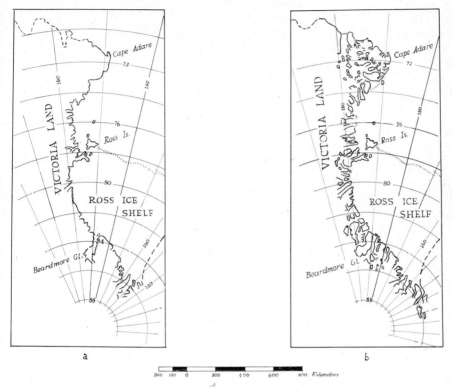

FIG. 28 THE MAPPING OF VICTORIA LAND

Map *a* shows the situation in 1957 and map *b* the improvement effected by 1963

Projection and Spheroid

While cartography remained an independent responsibility of the particular nation undertaking mapping in its own assumed territory, there was complete freedom as regards representation; firstly in the choice of projection, and secondly in the choice of spheroid, that is the actual mathematical dimensions of the regular figure of the Earth chosen as best fitting the geoid for the region concerned. This second consideration is a matter which will assume greater importance as the accuracy of mapping and control surveys develops and as the survey systems of the various nations begin to interlock. These matters were systematized at international level by the SCAR Working Group on Cartography, but prior to 1959, and while as many as twelve or more nations were separately representing their mapping in many scattered localities, many choices of both projection and figure were made. In some cases the easiest solution to the problem was grasped by replacing the spheroid by the sphere and plotting on a polar equidistant-azimuthal projection. To such a solution there could be no objection while the field mapping methods were haphazard and poorly controlled. Many general continental maps of Antarctica were plotted in just such a manner.

This is not the place to exhaust the subject of the best choice of projection for polar latitudes. Let it be said that such a projection should be orthomorphic – that is preserving true bearings around every point on the projection; that it should be polar and that the choice of scale standard should be such that scale distortions are held to a minimum. While the property of orthomorphism is common to many projections, among them the transverse Mercator and the conics (in particular the Lambert orthomorphic with one or two standard parallels), only the stereographic projection meets all requirements. Falling also into the division of the perspective projections, it may be pictured accurately as the projection providing that representation on a plane surface of the curved surface of the sphere or spheroid as viewed from the diametrically opposite point and when the plane surface is tangential to the curved surface so projected. Any required parallel of latitude of the polar stereographic may be held as the scale standard – that is the line (in this case arc) along which scale is correct. At all other points on the projection the scale is either enlarged or reduced according to whether the point is further from or nearer to the pole. When in 1956 the writer recommended that for New Zealand's purposes in Antarctica the stereographic projection be employed, the parallel of 80° S was selected as the scale standard, it being centrally placed in the areas which it was known would be covered in the following two years. However, this was changed to 71° S after 1959 to conform to the SCAR recommendation of that year.

The matter of a selection of suitable spheroid will arise again below when mention will be made of modern techniques of geodetic measurement with relation to Antarctica.

The Geoid in Polar Areas

The recommendations of the SCAR Working Group in Cartography (see above) included one that the International Spheroid be adopted as the figure of the Earth for Antarctic mapping. This prescribes fixed radii for the elliptical section of the spheroid and thereby a fixed degree of flattening at the poles. The adoption of the International Spheroid is now many decades past and this spheroid has not been proved to be seriously in error for most Northern Hemisphere and many Southern Hemisphere systems. However, modern advances will make it possible to put this figure to the test in the Antarctic regions. Prior figures of the Earth were arrived at by the method of arc measurement as furnished by the analysis of chains of triangulation on a trans-continental scale. Fundamentally the method has not changed; the dimensions of an arc of the geoid must still be measured.

It is certain that the Antarctic Continent will never be crisscrossed with chains or nets of triangulation; this will be replaced by traverse lines measured by tellurometer or electrotape. That these traverses will cover thousands of miles is beyond question and may span the whole continent. The staggering success of those brilliantly executed operations, Topo North and Topo South, by teams from the US Geological Survey which in 1961–2 spanned 1300 km (followed by the further 1100 km of Topo's West and East in 1962–3), point to the possibility of a rapid survey control of the whole continent. Primarily of course this type of control is aimed at providing planimetric control for photogrammetric mapping but geodetic data are a by-product. Already it is known that the determination of a station position at the head of the Beardmore Glacier by a New Zealand party using daylight star observations differs only by a few metres from the position obtained by connection through the measured lines of Topo South from a carefully observed origin datum at McMurdo Sound. The comparison of such astronomically fixed positions with the geodetic or controlled fix will, when other anomalies are allowed for, give the A — G (Astronomical minus Geodetic) value from which dimensions of the geoid may be obtained.

This work, however rapid, may be overtaken by a further development in intercontinental connection using suitably orbiting satellites. Such a method envisages a satellite in polar orbit transmitting at prescribed intervals a signal of a type suitable for reception at prepared stations by electronic means. The accumulation of such simultaneous observations leads to a determination of absolute geodetic position. This method has yet to be used in any latitudes although sufficient is known of the problem to ensure its success.

Deflection of the Vertical

The major part of the A — G value is that produced by the effect of local land masses on the plumb-line, the so-called Deflection of the Vertical. This means that the normal to the surface of the geoid differs from the normal to the surface of the spheroidal or theoretical figure. Gravity is not pulling directly towards the assumed centre of the Earth. Neglecting any consideration of isostatic compensation, it will be seen that astronomically determined positions, dependent as they are on observations of elevation (altitude to the surveyor) which in turn are dependent on the accuracy of a level bubble settling at a normal to the plumb-line, are affected by any deviation of the plumb-line from the true vertical to the spheroidal surface. In a discussion of the anomalies produced by aberrations in astronomical refraction above it could have been said that it was suspected that a further contributing cause of the misfit of plots based on astrofixes was a deflection of the vertical. This has been most apparent to New Zealand parties working east and west of and through the Victoria Land Mountains. In this area, with the Ross Sea graben or depression on the one side and the 150 km width of the uplifted Victoria Land chain on the other, the stage is set for the full effect of plumb-line deflection to be displayed. The computation of the amount of this deflection will require a close study of the A —G values, together with an analysis of gravimetric observations over a wide field. In the past two years geodetic considerations have been more and more concerning those responsible for Antarctic mapping; among these considerations is the determination of gravity for the purpose of utilizing the data for geodesy as well as for the study of the Earth's crust. As well as absolute determination of gravity by pendulum apparatus, relative determinations by various types of gravimeter furnish data for determining the Earth's figure entirely independently of the arc methods previously discussed. From the observed variation of gravity with latitude the polar compression or flattening may be computed. Such measurements therefore will give the form but not the absolute dimensions of the spheroid. All nations participating in Antarctic research have been conducting gravity surveys for many years and have been urged to extend the areas of these observations.

Antarctic Place-names

Place-naming authorities to adjudicate on the naming of Antarctic features have been set up by all participating nations. In New Zealand this is carried out by a New Zealand Antarctic Place Names Committee which is in fact the New Zealand Geographic Board augmented by Antarctic specialists. In Australia, the United States and Great Britain, the place-naming authorities are peculiarly Antarctic. Inevitably, duplication and overlapping occur in the allotting of place-names, but every effort is made to reach mutual agreement upon all decisions.

PART TWO

The Southern Ocean

> And now there came both mist and snow,
> And it grew wondrous cold:
> And ice, mast-high, came floating by
> As green as emerald.
> S. T. COLERIDGE

CHAPTER FOUR

Oceanography

J. W. BRODIE, *New Zealand Oceanographic Institute*

Introduction

The essential unity of the Arctic Ocean has never been in doubt, but a curious divergence of view has arisen on the geographical nature of the seas surrounding Antarctica. On one hand some geographers and hydrographers consider each of the Pacific, Atlantic and Indian Oceans to extend south to the margins of the Antarctic Continent, and on occasions these views have been very strongly expressed. On the other hand the concept has been advanced that, both from geographic and hydrological viewpoints, such an approach ignores basic geographic and hydrological entities. The use here of the term Southern Ocean accords with the latter view and is one customarily adopted by British scientists. The northern limit of the Southern Ocean is undefined; Herdman and his co-authors in 1956 proposed the Antarctic Convergence as the northern boundary but themselves adopted an arbitrary limit at Lat. 52° S in discussing the names of sea floor features.

If the name Southern Ocean is to be synonymous with 'Antarctic' Ocean then the Antarctic Convergence, as the northern limit of Antarctic Surface Water, is an acceptable boundary on the grounds of hydrological consistency. However, in terms of ocean circulation, the predominantly eastward-moving circumpolar currents that flow in the zone north of the Antarctic Divergence in Lat. 65° S occupy a large proportion of the Southern Ocean.

This dominantly eastward movement persists further north, through the Antarctic Convergence and indeed to the Subtropical Convergence in Lat. 40° S. The definition used here is that which accepts the parallel of 52° S as an approximate useful northern boundary.

In the late eighteenth century little was known of the Southern Ocean. The tracks of Spanish, Portuguese, Dutch and English navigators were all so located as to leave still the possibility of the existence of a great southern continent in middle latitudes. The voyages of Cook removed this possibility and clearly defined the existence of the circumpolar ocean. Thereafter discoveries by explorers and whalers had by the middle nineteenth century demonstrated the general southern limits of the ocean at the Antarctic continental margin.

Up to the beginning of 1955 when initial activity in the International Geophysical Year programmes commenced, more than forty substantial voyages of exploration and discovery had been undertaken in Antarctic seas, and innumerable commercial voyages had been made either on great circle passages or in pursuit of whales and seals – voyages that had made the Southern Ocean familiar waters to many thousands of seafarers. Many of the voyages had a partial objective of scientific enquiry (Ross in 1840 and 1841 and Scott in 1901–4 for example) in addition to their aim of simple geographic discovery; others pursued no scientific objectives. On the other hand, the comprehensive observations made from RRS *Discovery II* over two decades up to 1950 have furnished a mass of scientific data that has enabled the broad details of ocean circulation to be worked out and has provided an unrivalled accumulation of material for studies of the marine life of the Southern Ocean.

This stage of scientific knowledge of the Antarctic seas has been reviewed by Fleming and by Dell (1952) in the forerunner of this present volume.

We now see that the International Geophysical Year marked a turning point in scientific activity in Antarctica. Out of a projected limited manning of temporary observing sites, a continuing occupation of stations on the Antarctic mainland and on the islands of the Southern Ocean has emerged. In no field has the initial IGY activity and its continuation over the succeeding five years had more impact than in oceanography. The bulk of transport to the continent is by sea and few if any of the nations concerned have not taken the opportunity of securing oceanographic data on their routine supply voyages to the southern bases. A proportion of the countries participating have as well carried out active programmes in various fields of oceanography.

As a major over-simplification it can be assumed that there are two principal groups of problems in all the major disciplines of oceanography. One of these contains the simple problems of distribution, whether it be of sediments, of sea floor features, water temperature and salinity, of currents or of marine animals in the plankton or on the sea bottom. The other is the study of correlations between these distributions, the study of mechanisms and causes, and of the fundamental problems thus brought to light. The first study because of its simplicity is often merged by the individual scientist with its logical extension under the second head. It is one of the remarkable developments of oceanography in the last decade, that the very great deficiency of measurements and observations of marine variables grew to be recognized as the major stumbling block to further progress: so that in many areas, not least the Antarctic, considerable emphasis has been placed on the need for regional surveys in general, and on the need for synoptic hydrological data. These activities require many ships and oceanographers at sea, a requirement that is now being met. Full and early utilization of the results now accumulating requires equal emphasis on their analysis and interpretation.

In reviewing the progress that has been made in the last ten years, therefore, it is desirable to outline briefly and to discriminate between the activities that have accumulated facts and those that have explained them. Each has played its useful part in advancing our knowledge of oceanography.

Oceanographic Observations in the Last Decade

To assess the significance of the contributions that have been made to Antarctic oceanography in the last ten years, their particular nature has to be considered.

Observations of temperature both by bathythermograph and at the sea surface, sampling for surface salinity, and collections of surface plankton, have been made as routine activities on the base-supply vessels of the USA, USSR, France, Japan, Australia and New Zealand, to list but a few of the countries concerned. A lesser number of these ships (principally those of the United States) have been equipped to take routine deep echo soundings as well. In many cases no oceanographers have been involved in this work at sea.

In a specialized category has been the work carried out from a number of United States and some Argentine and New Zealand ships. Here, groups of oceanographers sailed on the supply voyages and during week-long periods specifically allocated to the work have carried out a comprehensive programme of oceanographic observations. The ships in these instances were normal vessels carrying some modifications such as heavy winches, booms and gallows and small laboratories to fit them for part-time oceanography. A notable contribution to the accumulating data has been made in this way by the United States Navy Office of Oceanography (latterly with help from the National Science Foundation) in collecting hydrological data, samples of marine plankton and bottom living animals and bottom sediment, with its oceanographers working from navy and coast-guard icebreakers.

The largest contribution has understandably been made from research vessels. In 1950 RRS *Discovery II* made her last circumnavigation of the Antarctic Continent, adding considerably to the store of physical measurements of the Southern Ocean. During the IGY years the USSR research ship *Ob* carrying up to fifty scientists made comprehensive surveys of all aspects – physical, geological and biological – of a wide extent of Antarctic waters. In post-IGY years the RV *Vema* of Lamont Geological Observatory has carried out studies of the oceanic geological structures principally in the Drake Passage region and RV *Argo* of the Scripps Institution has carried out physical and geological measurements far to the south in the Pacific Sector. The Tokyo University of Fisheries RV *Umitaka Maru* has made extensive observations particularly of temperature and salinity in the Indian Ocean sector (Ishino *et al.*, 1958) and the New Zealand Antarctic Programme has included an oceanographic cruise on a New Zealand naval vessel each year since the 1955–6 Antarctic season. On these cruises studies were carried out initially of the hydrology of the Antarctic Convergence region, and latterly of the distribution of benthic animals and of the shape and nature of the sea floor in the sector south of New Zealand.

The achievements of these research vessels were anticipated by those of a little known but none the less significant expedition. This was the voyage of the *Brategg* which sailed from Norway in October 1947 to return six months later having made an extensive examination of the temperature, salinity and plankton distribution in the area from Longitudes 90° W to 150° W between Lat. 55° S and the ice edge.

The latest additions to this brief summary of research cruises are those of the newly commissioned United States National Science Foundation vessel USNS *Eltanin* which has already made cruises in the South American sector on which work has been undertaken that ranges from cosmic physics to marine biology.

This activity at sea has by no means been distributed uniformly around the Southern Ocean. Extensive exploration of the sea around eastern Antarctica out to about 200 km offshore has been carried out by the United States naval ice-breakers and the Russian vessel *Ob*. Much less ocean has been traversed in the western sector but two notable end-of-season voyages were made by the ice-breakers USS *Glacier* and USS *Burton Island* to the Bellingshausen Sea and Eights Coast in February 1960, and by *Glacier* to the Hobbs Coast around Long. 130° W in February 1962. On both these cruises, almost unexplored seas were penetrated and the oceanographers on board obtained unique series of measurements.

Many ship tracks traverse the Southern Ocean in the sector between longitudes 140° E and 170° W south of Tasmania and New Zealand that includes the supply routes to the Australian and French bases and to the United States and New Zealand bases in McMurdo Sound and the Ross Sea. Another concentration of ship tracks occurs in the sector 10° E to 80° E south of Africa and the western Indian Ocean, for here the area includes the supply route between Cape Town and Russia's Mirnyy Base, and along this eastern Antarctic coastline there has been a concentration of land bases – Lazarev 13° E, Roi Baudouin 23° E, Syowa 40° E, Mawson 63° E, Davis 78° E, Mirnyy 93° E, Wilkes 110° E and Dumont d'Urville 140° E. A lesser concentration crosses Drake Passage principally to the Weddell Sea area. Elsewhere tracks are sparsely spread.

The number of tracks is a relative index of activity in measuring sea water temperatures and collecting samples for salinity determinations. While the hydrological measurements are relatively easy to make, sampling of the sea bottom for sediments and animals is time-consuming and therefore much less has been done in these fields.

Sediments of the Southern Ocean

The first attempt to describe the sea floor sediments in the Southern Ocean came as a result of the investigations made during the voyage of HMS *Challenger* between the years 1872 and 1876. As in so many other fields of marine work the syntheses then made have endured in broad outline. The sediment distribution in high southern latitudes charted by Murray and Renard in 1891 based on the *Challenger* data, shows a circumpolar belt of terrigenous deposits extending north to Lat. 60° S from the Antarctic Continent boundary; between approximately Latitudes 50° and 60° S lies a belt of Diatom ooze succeeded northward by Globigerina ooze in intermediate depths with red clay in the abyssal areas and terrigenous sediments close to land masses and around islands (See Fig. 29a).

Their generalizations were based on eleven stations south of Lat. 50° S, and on the very few earlier samples.

The available data on Antarctic sediments increased slowly over the succeeding half-century: successive expeditions added their quotas, and Neaverson, in 1934, was able to discuss three hundred sediment samples principally from the Atlantic sector and around Graham Land that had accumulated in the *Discovery* collections.

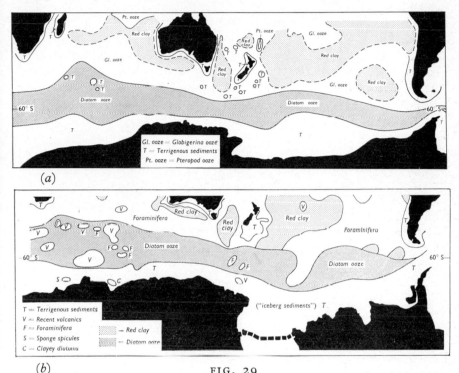

(*a*)

(*b*)

FIG. 29

(*a*) Sea floor deposits in the Southern Ocean between the Cape and Drake Passage (after Murray and Renard, 1891);

(*b*) The same (after Lisitzin, 1962)

Layering in Antarctic sediments as seen in short cores had been commented on by Phillipi as early as 1912, and further short cores were obtained by Edward Roos on the second Byrd Expedition in the Ross Sea in 1933 (Roos, 1937; Stetson and Upson, 1937). A notable advance was made however when, during the US Operation High Jump a series of longer cores was secured, again in the Ross Sea, by Hough (1950). During the IGY and subsequent operations, substantial numbers of surface sediment samples and cores were taken, many from the Ross Sea, a large number from the USSR expeditions on the *Ob* (Lisitzin and Zhivago, 1960) and a few from other operations in the South American and New Zealand – Ross Sea sectors.

THE GLACIAL SEDIMENTS

The patterns of distribution of surface sediment types on the floor of the Southern Ocean is a function of a diversity of controlling factors. We can readily appreciate that, under the present glacial environment, there is a northern limit to the area of sea floor on which the continental glacial moraines (ranging from muds to large boulders, 30 cm and more in diameter), fall when released from melting icebergs.

Hough (1956) found that the northern limit of dominant glacial marine deposits (a term first used by Philippi in 1912 when describing the sediments obtained from the *Gauss*) coincided with the average northern maximum extension of pack ice. On his chart this boundary lies at roughly Lat. 65° S in eastern Antarctica. Through Drake Passage and in the South Sandwich area north of the Weddell Sea, the northwards projection of Graham Land, its effect on ocean currents, and the glaciological regime in the Weddell Sea all combine to produce a northerly extension of the area of glacial marine sediments towards the South Atlantic Ocean. The northern boundary of the glacial deposit is the junction with the diatom zone. In the superficial waters, substantial diatom production extends south of this boundary but because of a northward component of transport and the larger volume of glacial debris deposited, diatoms do not there dominate in the sediment.

The data available to Lisitzin in 1962 (400 sediment samples including cores up to 16 m long) have enabled him to show more precisely the boundaries of the major sediment zones particularly those south of the Indian Ocean (See Fig. 29b). He has discovered on the shelf small patches of 'clayey diatoms' and bryozoan and shell bottom within the 300–900 km wide glacial deposit zone. These patches are analogous in some respects to the barnacle plate bottom found at several localities in the northern Ross Sea by Bullivant (1959) where dredge hauls from several stations consisted almost entirely of barnacle plates. The lack of present-day deposition of terrigenous glacial material in some areas in the Ross Sea is perhaps in part due to local increases in current velocity. In the inner near-shore portion of the glacial zone a low rate of deposition prevails for here there is little melting of the icebergs in which the glacial debris is transported. There are many localities where filter-feeding animals cover the entire bottom and where deposition of all grades of clastic sediments must be low. The glacial deposits are found predominantly on the outer shelf and on the slope, away from the continental margin. The finer grades are found in the northern part of the zone. Glacial deposits are derived from a continent on which subaerial chemical weathering of the rocks is effectively non-existent and where the total seaward transport of rock fragments is by ice. The marine sediments that result include muds, fine and coarse sands and large and small boulders: the dominant colour of the finer sediment grades is greenish-grey.

Under the present climatic regime, with its indications of local climatic ameliorations, the total sediment load carried out over the Antarctic margin may well be very much less than that which produced the present distribution of glacial sediments still dominant at the surface of the sea floor.

The Russian work reported by Lisitzin (1960, 1962) has shown that the mineralogy of glacial sediments (his 'Iceberg Sediments') makes it possible to establish several mineral provinces in this sediment zone south of the Indian Ocean. The proportions of heavy minerals (density more than $2 \cdot 7$ gm/cm^3) range from 1 to 20%, with maxima occurring off the Knox and Discovery Coasts. For the eastern part of the shelf he was able to establish provinces characterized by a dominance of groups of minerals – garnet–ilmenite–amphibole (Depot Bay and Davis Sea); garnet–ore (Shackleton Shelf); ore minerals and limonite (Knox Coast); amphibole–limonite–zircon with orthoclase (Sabrina Coast); and amphibole–epidote–zircon (Banzare Bank). With suitable assumptions of the probable paths of icebergs into these areas the nature and properties of the terrigenous source rocks can be deduced. Thus from the nature of the sediments direct evidence can be obtained of the character of the continental rocks hidden beneath the ice. Pollen and spore studies on sediment samples from areas adjacent to the coasts have shown that sediments have been derived from Carboniferous, Permian, Triassic, Jurassic, Cretaceous, and Tertiary rocks in which spores of ferns and pollens of birch, alder and Myrtaceae occur. These deductions provide substantial support for the paleogeographic interpretations that can be made from the relatively small area of outcrop of rocks on Antarctica itself.

THE DIATOM OOZE ZONE

The 1000–2000 km wide zone of diatom ooze consists mainly of diatom frustules that have settled out of surface waters. It contains also the tests of planktonic Foraminifera and according to its distance from the Antarctic Continent or volcanic islands, a varying but small proportion of mineral particles. The ooze is creamy yellow.

The northern limits of the diatom ooze zone in the Southern Ocean are controlled by two factors, a diminution in absolute abundance of diatoms in the warmer waters north of the Antarctic Convergence and an increase in the production of Foraminifera. It might be expected that the northern boundary on the sea floor would be some distance to the northward of the Antarctic Convergence and Lisitzin's 1962 chart bears this out (see Fig. 29b).

The Russian work on sediment distribution has utilized both seismic studies of sediment thicknesses on the one hand and analyses of the amount of suspended particulate matter in the water on the other. The principal contributions to the present discussion however come from core and echo sounder data. Within the diatom ooze zone, many sites of geologically late vulcanism are located. A proportion of ash is found in most of the diatomaceous sediment, and around the island eruptive centres up to 70% of volcanic ash has been found in surface sediments.

In the Indian Ocean sector Lisitzin (1960) has recognized three large areas of

Recent, mainly basaltic volcanic sediments. One of these, over 1,000,000 km² in area, lies north of Enderby Land. Here submarine volcanoes rise up to 2500 m above the sea floor and extensive ash deposits are found at depths down to 5000 m. In this area one core showed ash bands in a layer 4·4 m below the sediment surface and for long distances the echo-sounder traced from two to five layers in the sediments that were ascribed to volcanic horizons.

South of Africa, in an area of volcanic cones 1000 to 2000 m high, vesicular lava, lapilli and ash (this last sometimes up to 60–70% of the total sediment) have been collected from the sea floor. East of Trals Island at depths of 4600–5500 m the surface layer of the sediment is volcanic sand.

Near the Balleny Islands volcanic sands that include black uncrystallized ash and basaltic glass are found in the surface sediments. In these areas where ash now dominates in the superficial sediment, this Quaternary vulcanism has undoubtedly occurred at a very late date.

The topographic highs in the diatom ooze tend to have a sediment cover of foraminiferal ooze. The most southerly occurrence according to Lisitzin is on Gunnerus Bank in Lat. 68° S where about 60% of the sediment is composed of Foraminifera.

North of the diatom ooze zone, foraminiferal 'Globigerina ooze' predominates in middle depths beyond the northern limits of the Southern Ocean. In the Atlantic and Indian Oceans the deep basins with red clay sediment mostly lie north of 40° S but in the Pacific sector the Tasman Basin and Southwestern Pacific Basin and smaller deep areas west of southern Chile that project into the Southern Ocean are floored with red clay where they are deeper than the carbonate solution depth.

THE INFLUENCE OF PAST CLIMATES

The question whether the observed distribution of sediment on the surface of the Antarctic floor is in balance with the present scale of sediment distributing processes, has not been determined and somewhat more refined concepts of both sedimentary processes and glaciological changes may well be needed before this problem can be resolved. However, it is possible by examining, in sediment cores, the lithological changes that have taken place in the sediments deposited at one spot, to formulate some views as to the changes in the sedimentation environment that have taken place in later Quaternary times. Such studies are still in elementary phases but when developed might well contribute further to an understanding of the glacial chronology of Antarctica.

Philippi in 1912 and Schott in 1939 deduced that climatic changes were indicated by the alternation of sediment types in the short cores available to them. The materials examined by Hough (1950) and Thomas (1959) allowed recognition of alternations of glacial and non-glacial sediments. The problem of determining a Pleistocene chronology of sedimentation was emphasized by Ewing and Heezen (1956) in directing attention to the outstanding problems of Antarctic submarine geology.

It may be presumed that during low temperature glacial stages of the Pleistocene, zonal ocean circulation patterns prevailed that were broadly similar to that
existing at the present day. The effects of glaciation can then be simply viewed as
a northwards shift of the circum-Antarctic isotherms. Not only was the water at
a given latitude colder than at present, but there may have been substantial increases in the widths of the cooler water zones south of the Subtropical Convergence. Thus in colder periods the bulk of icebergs would drift further north
before melting and the maximum of diatom production associated with upwelling
of nutrient-rich water at the divergence between the east and west wind belts
and the area of dominant foraminifera production, would both be found further
to the north.

The sedimentary materials obtained subsequently have shown that in long

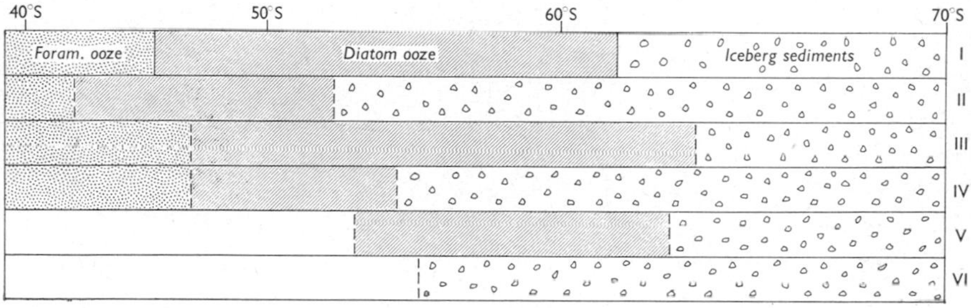

FIG. 30

Variations in Quaternary sediment zone widths and distribution around
Antarctica as interpreted by Lisitzin (1962), from core data. The successively
older lithologic horizons III and V show similar distributions of iceberg sediments, little different from that of the present. Horizons II, IV and VI indicate
cooler stages

cores (Lisitzin, 1962) repeated alternations of sediment types can be traced,
reflecting the northward and southward migrations of climate-controlled sediment zone boundaries during the climatic fluctuations of the Quaternary. The
maximum geographic shift is assessed at 1000 km and six main 'lithologic
horizons' (variations of position and width of circumpolar sediment zones)
equated with corresponding climatic circumstances, have been deduced (Fig. 30).

Rates of sedimentation from radium and ionium dating of glacial sediments
are 0·3 to 30 cm per 1000 years; for diatom oozes, 0·5 to 2 cm; and from C^{14}
dating of Foraminifera 0·3 to 2·6 cm per 1000 years. Some of the cores studied
penetrated into Tertiary sediments and repeated climatic ameliorations and
worsenings can be interpreted.

Extensions of studies of these and similar materials will it is hoped provide the
basic detailed chronology and reference points with which our understanding of
the climatic regime of the Antarctic can be advanced.

The Sea Floor

The morphology of the Antarctic sea floor was first depicted in bathymetric charts by Murray (1895) that included data from soundings made by Sir James Clark Ross in addition to those of other Antarctic navigators and as well, the *Challenger* Expedition results. A gradual improvement in the delineation of the sea floor features took place as further soundings accumulated, but a significant advance commenced in 1925 when the *Meteor* Expedition, equipped with deep water echo sounder made considerable additions to knowledge of the shape of the sea floor in the Atlantic sector. An interpretation of the soundings now available is presented on the chart used by Nudelman (1960) and for the Pacific sector on the chart of the Pacific Ocean (Udintsev, 1963).

The land margins of Antarctica are fringed with a continental shelf that is everywhere narrow except in the two large embayments occupied by the Weddell and Ross Seas and their associated ice shelves. The Antarctic continental shelf is notable for the great depth at which the break in slope lies. Four to six hundred metres is a not unusual value and in the Ross Sea depths of up to 800 m are reached before the shelf ends and the continental slope begins. Where it occurs, the shelf width is some tens of kilometres, but Herdman, Wiseman and Ovey (1956) point out that in many places it does not appear to exist at all.

With small exceptions, the continental slope descends simply to depths of at least 3000 m all round Antarctica. The areas that show some complexity are off the north end of Graham Land, the Scott Island–Balleny Islands area north and west of the Ross Sea; and, in Long. 70° E, the Kerguelen Ridge. In the latter two areas the sea floor rises rapidly again a relatively short distance away from the foot of the slope, while the Graham Land peninsula extends beneath the sea as a linear area of irregular topography (some of the highs emerging as islands) that forms the southern limb of the Scotia Ridge. Nevertheless the marginal escarpment of the Antarctic Continent is a strongly developed feature.

North of the escarpment of the continental slope the circum-Antarctic sea floor is of two types—either broad ridge or deep basin. The most extensive features are the basins. From near Scott Island in Lat. 68° S, Long. 180° the Pacific–Antarctic Basin trends eastward as an elongated triangular area bordering the Antarctic Continent and extending to Southern Chile. In the north it is bounded by the Pacific–Antarctic Ridge and the South-eastern Pacific Plateau in Lat. 40° S. Its central area 1600 km long is more than 5000 m deep and a maximum sounding of 6414 m has been reported at the western end.

Two further large basins border the Antarctic Continent. One stretches from the Scott Island–Balleny Islands area west to the Kerguelen Ridge – the Eastern Indian–Antarctic Basin. Its greatest depth is 5455 m in Lat. 54° 33′ S and Long. 123° 05′ E (Herdman *et al.*, 1956). West from the Kerguelen Ridge in Lat. 70° E the largest of the three basins, the Atlantic–Indian–Antarctic Basin, encircles the remainder of the Antarctic Continent to the Scotia Ridge. Its greatest depth is 5872 m in Lat. 58° 40′ S, Long. 29° 30′ E, a sounding taken by SS *Thorshavn* in 1933.

Three major ridges, whose crests lie in less than 3000 m and whose general trend is circumpolar, form the northern limits to the basins. The Atlantic–Antarctic Ridge lies in about Lat. 52° S and extends from mid-Atlantic towards the Kerguelen Ridge.

The Indian–Antarctic Ridge extends from the mid-Indian Ocean in Lat. 50° S to the Balleny Islands area. Finally the Pacific–Antarctic Ridge (also referred to as the East Pacific Rise) extends from the vicinity of Scott Island north and east towards Easter Island. Three north-trending ridges separate the three major basins, Scotia Ridge in the Atlantic sector, Kerguelen Ridge in the Indian Ocean sector and Macquarie Ridge in the Pacific sector, the last linking the Balleny Islands area with New Zealand (see Fig. 31). All appear to be complex structures.

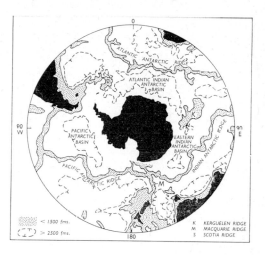

FIG. 31

OCEAN RIDGES AND BASINS
AROUND ANTARCTICA
(After Ewing and Heezen, 1956)

The charts show a number of lesser irregular ridges, one of the most substantial being that extending southeastwards for some 800 km from the Prince Edward Islands, paralleling the Kerguelen Ridge. Numerous traverses by the *Ob* have defined this feature.

Our commentary has been limited so far to the broad morphology of these very substantial submarine features. Though significant advances have been made in sounding and charting in particular areas, yet on the whole the density of echo-soundings that controls the bathymetric interpretation is very slight. A great deal of work has yet to be done to produce a satisfactory record of the shape of the whole Southern Ocean floor. However advances have been made that permit an analysis of the morphological character of the submarine relief. Zhivago (1962) has recognized three large, genetically different divisions: abyssal plains of marine accumulation; elevations and ridges with superstructures of volcanic relief forms; and expanses of abyssal, mainly also volcanic, relief.

The abyssal plains usually occur at depths of 3700 to 5000 m and form a nearly continuous zone around the continent at the foot of the continental slope. The plains vary in width from 100 to 600 km with an observed maximum of 900 km in the meridian of Easter Island. Large near-flat areas of deep sea floor are found between the Balleny Islands and Victoria Land and separate Kerguelen Island from the Gaussberg area. The surface of accumulation is flat or slightly undulating with gentle scarps. Zhivago believes that turbidity currents originating near the margins of Antarctica have supplied the sediment that has built the plain surfaces. However there is still insufficient data to determine the source of the sediments with precision. This was one of the problems advanced by Ewing and Heezen in 1956, and relatively few soundings close to the continent that might have detected submarine canyons have been made; and only a limited number of precision sounding traverses have been carried out across the abyssal plain areas.

The plains occupy the southern parts of the great basins that fringe the continent. Bordering the plains to the north is a zone of volcanic relief. This is expressed in a variety of forms. The highest portions emerge as islands such as Bouvet, the Prince Edward Islands, Crozet, Kerguelen, Heard, the Balleny group and Scott Island. Some of the volcanic outpourings form superstructures on upwarped structural highs, and some occur as isolated cones truncated to appear as banks or seamounts, and some (for example the Balleny Islands area) are grouped as volcanic masses. The relief is variable and where it is low the volcanics can appear as the hummocky floors of basins. These diverse forms make up the second and third of Zhivago's major divisions of the sea floor. He emphasizes that our concept of the Pacific–Antarctic Ridge as a narrow feature is inappropriate. It is more properly a wide stretch of mountainous relief diversified with volcanic forms that are probably of Quaternary age. To the south, this relief merges with the hummocky floor of the northern part of the Pacific–Antarctic Basin.

THE MID-OCEAN RIDGES

In discussing the morphology and the genetic divisions of the sea floor an important further aspect of the ridge systems needs consideration. Ewing and Heezen (1956) have summarized the views that have been developed by the Lamont Geological Observatory workers on the nature of the oceanic ridge systems of which the Southern Ocean ridges are part. The mid-Atlantic Ridge is the most studied of any oceanic ridge system. Its form is well known from a multiplicity of echo-sounding traverses made across it. It is characterized by a median rift zone located on the crest. The ridge coincides with a belt of earthquake epicentres: many extinct volcanoes are located on the flanks of the Ridge but are outside the earthquake belt. The earthquakes are associated with continuing movements along the faults of the rift.

Ewing and Heezen have shown the probable pattern of ridges (Fig. 31). The mid-Atlantic Ridge extends through the South Atlantic and then east halfway between Africa and Antarctica (the Atlantic–Antarctic Ridge); it turns north-east to loop into the Indian Ocean then south-east to a course midway between Australia and Antarctica (the Indian–Antarctic Ridge); to the Balleny Islands–Scott Island area. Here one line branches northward through Macquarie Island towards New Zealand (the Macquarie Ridge); recent bathymetric surveys by the NZ Oceanographic Institute from HMNZS *Endeavour* have shown it to be essentially continuous from Macquarie Island to the Campbell Plateau just south of New Zealand.

From the 180° meridian the main line of ridge extends north-east (as the Pacific–Antarctic Ridge) to join the South Pacific ridge systems, one branch extending to the Chilean coast, one reaching westwards and the most substantial extending northwards (as the East Pacific Rise) into the Northern Hemisphere.

Some of this continuity is inferred, and some based on the distribution of epicentres. However, studies from Lamont's RV *Vema* showed the median rift to extend into the Indian Ocean and Zhivago has been able to show on his geomorphic chart (1962) a median rift along the Atlantic–Antarctic Ridge and along part of the eastern portion of the Indian–Antarctic Ridge. Menard in his study of the East Pacific Rise (1960) did not find evidence of the median rift in the Southern Hemisphere portion. Ewing and Heezen point out that the ridges that show continuity are active seismically but that substantial highs such as the Kerguelen Ridge that extend into ocean basins are seismically inactive and may be considered as a second category. Both these ridge types exhibit normal oceanic basaltic vulcanism.

In contrast the igneous rocks of the Scotia Ridge are andesitic and granitic. The arc has a foredeep on the eastern (convex) side and an associated earthquake belt and a structural relationship that resembles the West Indian arc system. The Macquarie Ridge (Balleny Islands to New Zealand) should probably be placed in the first category for there is seismic activity along the whole of its length and basaltic volcanoes are at least present, if not everywhere dominant.

One of the most substantial features of the Pacific–Antarctic Ridge shows as a north-west trending right lateral displacement of the bathymetric contours centring on a position in Lat. 55° S, Long. 135° W. This displacement of the ridge has been interpreted by Menard as a probable fracture zone analogous to the series of such zones that extend from the eastern Pacific margin several hundred kilometres into the Pacific. These fracture zones (for example the Mendocino and Murray in the North Pacific) separate large areas of sea floor lying at different depths. More soundings are needed from the Pacific–Antarctic Ridge before such a feature can be associated with the displacement of isobaths, but soundings available at present show that this is not improbable. The work done from Scripps Institution of Oceanography and reported by Menard suggests that the crust under the ridge can be interpreted as thinner than that under the adjoining ocean floor, a circumstance that upwards directed large scale convection currents located there could produce.

E

CAMPBELL PLATEAU

52° 27' S
175° 02' E

a

SOUTHWESTERN
PACIFIC BASIN

b

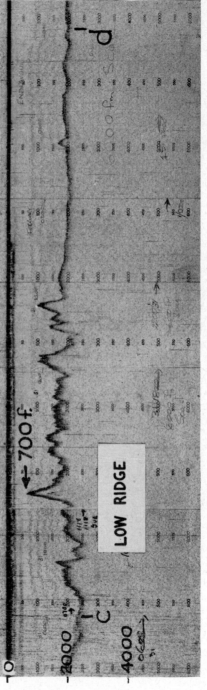

FIG. 32 Continued overleaf

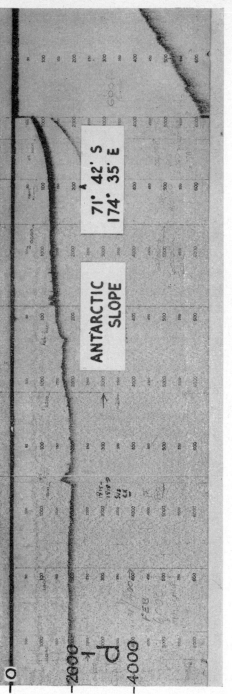

FIG. 32 ECHO SOUNDINGS ALONG THE 175° E MERIDIAN

Taken from HMNZS *Endeavour*, January 1963. The track crosses the Ross Sea shelf edge west of Scott Island, then continues north over a low ridge crest, across the South-western Pacific Basin and up on to the Campbell Plateau. The smooth slope and abyssal area of sedimentation at either end contrast sharply with the hummocky topography of the southern part of the South-western Pacific Basin and the rugged relief in the Ridge area south of the Basin

THE ANTARCTIC SHELF

The Antarctic Shelf has already been noted as narrow, where it exists at all and anomalously deeper at its edge than the common depth of 150 m. The shelf is most extensively developed in the Ross Sea and Weddell Sea and in the former, the shelf edge is at nearly 800 m. Roos (1937) describes the discovery from the *Bear of Oakland* of Iselin Bank that rises to 400 m from depths of more than 3000 m. Iselin Bank typifies the highly irregular slope that bounds the shelf in the north-western portion of the Ross Sea, where the whole slope below the shelf edge and down to 3000 m is indented with valleys between high ridges, that might equally be the effects of ice gouging or adventitious vulcanism. In the south-eastern area of the Ross Sea soundings are fewer and features thus appear smoother when isobaths are drawn. There are here several major re-entrants in the slope and shelf edge that strongly suggest localized, but large-scale, glacier action. On the surface of the Ross Shelf, Pennell Bank, rising to 100 m, has been suggested to be a huge terminal moraine (Taylor, 1930) and the broad depressions and rises and the generally irregular topography found elsewhere on the shelf support the view that direct glacial action in times of extended ice cover and the consequent residual moraines, shape the surface of the shelf.

This ice load has no isostatic effect on the shelf that is now covered with water. However, the gross load of ice on the whole continental mass may well have caused a depression of the continent as a unit as Dietz (1952) has suggested. Thus if the shelf were being shaped by ice in a Pleistocene glacial stage then the ice-rock interface may well have been lower with respect to present sea-level than the shelf surface is today. The shelf edge is therefore unusually deep because of the extent to which it was carved by outwards moving ice in the glacial maximum; a process that would be facilitated by the lowered sea level. It is thus not an analogue of the temperate shelf, depressed by a present or unrelieved loading. Subsequent eustatic withdrawals of the sea probably have not brought the outer shelf level again within reach of the waves. At the inner shelf margins there are some indications that, despite the protection afforded by sea ice in minimizing wave action, later low stands of sea-level have left a record of small wave-cut platforms, now submerged to 80 metres. One such platform has been described from Franklin Island and adjacent banks in the Ross Sea (Brodie, 1959).

Zhivago (1962) has charted a narrow (20 km wide) depression that extends more than 3000 km from the Davis Sea to Victoria Land. The depression lies approximately in the middle of the shelf, separating a hillocky inner shelf from smoother outer areas of accumulation. A maximum depth of the depression of about 1600 m has been found near King George V Coast and Victoria Land. Zhivago ascribes its origin to peripheral faulting caused by changing Pleistocene ice loads on the continent.

STRUCTURAL RELATIONS

The tectonic connections of the Antarctic Continent with other Southern Hemisphere land masses have been the subject of much speculation. The bulk of

Eastern Antarctica is made up of Precambrian shield rocks and overlying relatively undeformed sedimentary series that have been correlated with the Australian and Brazilian shield areas (Fairbridge 1952).

Western Antarctica on the other hand is an area of extensively folded rocks, the oldest being Paleozoic and the structures Alpine in character. These have been visualized as linking with the Andean belt of South America through the Scotia Arc, and in the opposite direction through the Eastern Australian and New Zealand geosynclinal areas. The modes of linking postulated have varied from 'circum-Pacific fold chains' to continental drift.

There has been some increase in the geophysical data available from the Southern Ocean and Antarctica that throws some light on the crustal character-istics of the continent and its surrounding ocean basins and ridges.

Seismic studies of natural earthquakes have shown that the crust under Eastern Antarctica is 35–40 km thick and that under Western Antarctica 30 km thick (Evison *et al.*, 1960; Kovach and Press, 1961). From gravity data Bentley *et al.* (1960) showed that the crust was approximately 30 km thick beneath the Ross Sea. The available information shows that the crust beneath the Indian sector is 5–10 km thick. The measurements so far made do no more than outline the major differences between oceanic and continental crusts and are not yet applicable to smaller scale problems. Measurements of the Earth's magnetic field at sea (e.g. Adams and Christoffel 1962) are not yet numerous enough to display regional patterns.

On morphological grounds Zhivago (1962) has emphasized the distinctive character of the Southern Ocean structures and their topographic isolation from the continental mass. His zone of volcanic relief represents a structural province of considerable magnitude whose character is purely oceanic. The oceanic ridge systems themselves are a cohesive, self-consistent group of earth forms. Their geography suggests little linkage with the structural patterns of the Antarctic Continent.

Circulation in the Southern Ocean

The pattern of circulation in the Southern Ocean that results from the combina-tion of wind-driven and gradient currents can be described from a number of viewpoints, dependent on the differing aspects which separate investigators have chosen to emphasize.

From the simplest point of view it is possible to consider the distribution of one variable – temperature – at the ocean surface. It is apparent that there are abrupt changes of gradient that disturb the orderly spread of isotherms with latitude. The northernmost abrupt change in temperature gradient is at the Subtropical Convergence in about Lat. 40° S, north of the Southern Ocean. North from this boundary Subtropical Water occupies the surface layer of the ocean, and south of it, some 4° C cooler, is Subantarctic Surface Water. In latitudes 55°–60° S another major temperature drop of several degrees marks the Antarctic Convergence, to the south of which at the surface, lies Antarctic

Upper Water. The average temperature change here is $3°$ C. These two boundaries separate three major zones of surface water in the Southern Hemisphere – Antarctic, Subantarctic and Subtropical.

ANTARCTIC DIVERGENCE

It has been recognized that in the zone of Antarctic Upper Water, between the continent and the Antarctic Convergence, there is an area of divergence of surface waters and consequent upwelling that coincides with the boundary between the easterly and westerly wind belts. The position of this Antarctic Divergence (US Hydrogr. Office, 1957) and the occurrence and strength of divergent motion are both variable, and dependent at any one time on the prevailing meteorological circumstances (Ivanov, 1961). Under the influence of the wind and the Earth's rotation the ocean surface water on each side of the divergence moves in a direction to the left of the wind direction. The divergence lies to the north of the pack ice and 5 to 10 degrees of latitude south of the Antarctic Convergence.

ANTARCTIC UPPER WATER

In winter the Antarctic Upper Water is cooled and its salinity increases as a result of ice formation. Temperatures vary from near-freezing at the southern limit to about $1°$ C at the Convergence. As summer progresses this water becomes overlain with warmer, less saline water, as the temperature rises and melting of ice occurs. This uppermost layer averages 50 m thick. The total thickness of Antarctic Upper Water averages 200 m but is less than half this figure in the area of the Antarctic Divergence.

SUBANTARCTIC SURFACE WATER

In the Subantarctic Surface Water that lies between the Antarctic and Subtropical Convergences, the meridional gradient of temperature is relatively uniform. It has been noted however by Burling (1961) that in the area south of Australia and New Zealand a frontal zone can be recognized in Lat. $52°$ S, north of which the salinity is more than $34\cdot5°/_{oo}$. Two types of Subantarctic Surface Water can thus be recognized – Australasian Subantarctic Water having this higher salinity and occurring between Longitudes $100°$ E and $167°$ E and Circumpolar Subantarctic Water to the south and in the remaining sectors of the Southern Ocean.

MERIDIONAL WATER MOVEMENTS

The existing data collected by earlier expeditions and the observations taken from RRS *Discovery II* formed the basis for a broad synthesis of Southern Ocean circulation dynamics by Deacon (1937). The results of Deacon's work and of preceding and later studies by Sverdrup (1942) have been utilized many times to present a schematic view of the Southern Ocean water movements in a meridional section from Antarctica to the Subtropical Convergence (see Fig. 33). It has to be realized that mass transport in a meridional direction represented in such descriptions is less than transport in the zonal Circumpolar Current.

From the Antarctic Divergence near Lat. 65° S some of the upwelled water mixed with surface water moves south and west in the easterly wind belt. In the winter the salinity of the cooled surface and deep waters increases by loss of fresh water to form ice. In specific places – the Weddell Sea in particular but perhaps in the Ross Sea and other areas also – local circumstances lead to formation of very cold high density water that sinks at the continental margin and with some mixing forms Antarctic Bottom Water. This spreads out northwards and eastwards over the sea floor as a relatively homogeneous mass, with temperatures less than 0·5° C, occupying the lowest levels below about 4000 m. It is found all round the Antarctic Continent and even beyond the Equator in the Atlantic Ocean but is of more limited extent in the Pacific and Indian Oceans.

Immediately above this layer is one of higher temperatures – the Warm Deep Current or 'Deep Water' that is formed in the North Atlantic and perhaps in the northern Indian Ocean by the cooling and sinking of high salinity water. This Deep Water moves southward, is modified on the way, and ultimately spreads into most of the world's oceans. In the Southern Ocean it forms the south-moving layer up to 2000 m thick that overlies the Bottom Water. In the Atlantic and Indian Ocean sectors Deep Water that approaches the surface near the Antarctic continent and south of the Antarctic Convergence upwells to take the place of divergent surface water that has moved either south as described above or north towards the Antarctic Convergence. There is some doubt that Deep Water forms in the North Pacific Ocean. Deep Water of Atlantic origin is modified by highly saline Mediterranean water and in the Southern Ocean can be specifically recognized as 'Upper Deep Water'. It is best developed in the Atlantic sector.

In the South Pacific, the warm Deep Water does not everywhere move southward and indeed the meridional circulation balance may require northwards movement in this sector.

THE ANTARCTIC INTERMEDIATE CURRENT

Part of the water that upwells at the Antarctic Divergence near Lat. 65° S moves northward as does the winter-cooled water immediately beneath. Where these cold dense components of Antarctic Upper Water meet the warmer lighter Sub-antarctic Surface Water near Lat. 60° S, they sink beneath the surface and continue northward, mixing with the water above and below but acquiring a set of properties that enable Antarctic Intermediate Water to be recognized with certainty over a wide extent of the world's ocean. Deacon (1937) has suggested that Antarctic Intermediate Water spreads northwards along two paths, one visible in a vertical section as a layer of minimum salinity, the other (corresponding to the cold sub-surface layer of Antarctic Upper Water) as a deeper layer of minimum temperature. However Midttun and Natvig (1957) support the view that a single core of movement lies between these two minima. Later work (Burling, 1961) reinforces earlier suggestions that sinking of surface water to form Antarctic Intermediate Water occurs as well, over a broad zone north of the Antarctic Convergence. The attitude and values of the isohalines in a section between Macquarie Island and the Campbell Plateau obtained by Russian workers from RV *Ob* suggest that convergent movement, with sinking of southern water, is taking place up to those latitudes. In any case from the Convergence latitude north, a salinity minimum considered the 'core' of Antarctic Intermediate Water lies at depths of 500 m in the south and commonly at about 1000 m in Subantarctic and temperate latitudes. The body of Antarctic Intermediate Water has a temperature range from $3°-7°$ C. In the New Zealand region the core temperature is about $5°$ C.

The meridional flow is often described as if it were composed of discrete sharply bounded layers. It is as well to recall that this is far from the case and that in the distribution of water characteristics it is principally maxima and minima of temperature and salinity that can be recognized. Temperature and salinity limits given to particular water types are arbitrarily imposed and the 'boundaries' are in fact almost totally gradational.

The main movements of water in the Southern Ocean are zonal and from west to east. The meridional northward transport may be considerably less in the surface layers though Kort's figures (1962a) suggest comparable transport in the bottom waters. The northward or southward deviations of zonal flow as a response to the influence of bottom topography themselves are likely to be greater than the upper meridional components of thermohaline flow.

A third fact that should qualify any consideration of meridional flow is the range of variation that exists in the location of major boundaries both around the Antarctic Continent and with time. One diagram can only represent a very arbitrary mean position.

THE ANTARCTIC CONVERGENCE

The Antarctic Convergence forms one of the major fundamental boundary zones of the world's oceans. The principal property by which its location can be mapped is the steep temperature gradient at the sea surface (Mackintosh, 1946). Across the Convergence the temperature change in summer is from $4°$ C to $8°$ C and in winter from $1°$ to $3°$ C. Below the surface the Convergence marks the area in which Antarctic Upper Water sinks beneath and mixes with the warmer south-moving Subantarctic Surface Water.

The Convergence position has been regarded by Deacon (1937) as fixed by the thermohaline circulation and to coincide with the area in which warm Deep Water rises over Antarctic Bottom Water as the continent is approached. The Convergence position and properties in the near-surface water can be considered as controlled by the wind stress at the surface. This view has been elaborated by Wyrtki (1960) who described the distribution of divergent and convergent motion at the surface of the Southern Ocean under varying conditions of the westerly winds – with strong westerlies a zone of convergence will develop

north of the axis of maximum westerlies and a zone of divergence south of this
axis. As the wind maximum shifts north or south so do the parallel zones of
convergence and divergence.

One of these particular cases, that of strong westerlies lying well to the south,
can be applied to the circulation model discussed by Deacon (1937). In this case
the wind maximum lies just to the south of the Antarctic Convergence position
and divergent movement is found to the south, thus coinciding with the area of
upwelling and northward movement of Antarctic Upper Water: the convergent
situation lying to the north of the wind maximum similarly coincides with the
Antarctic Convergence and the area of sinking to the north. Wyrtki (using the

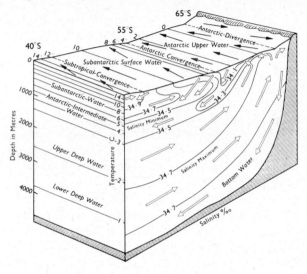

FIG. 33

Schematic diagram of the meridional and zonal flow in the Southern Ocean
(adapted from Sverdrup, 1942). The diagram represents summer conditions;
average positions of Convergences and Divergence are shown

The Upper Deep Water is best developed in the Atlantic sector. The south-
going component in Lower Deep Water is weak or reversed in the Pacific

term Antarctic Polar Front for the Antarctic Convergence in the sense that has
been used in the preceding pages) points out that if the zone of maximum westerlies lies in a northerly position then the accompanying divergence and convergence zones will also be found further northward. The Polar Front – the area of
steep surface temperature gradient – then becomes an area of divergence. This
case was that elaborated by Wexler (1959) as an explanation of the occurrence of
cold water cores (seen in temperature profiles from bathythermograph data)
which he ascribed to upwelling, just south of the Convergence (see Fig. 34).
In the case of weak westerly winds Wyrtki finds reason for a divergence to occur
north of the Convergence and for no zone of convergence to develop. Complexities of local weather will induce comparable complexities in detail super-

imposed on these broad 'climatological' situations. Many meridional temperature sections of the top 250 m show similar distributions to that illustrated (Fig. 34). The northern isolated patches of cold water can well indicate disruptive effects as the zone of mixing and sinking of Subantarctic Surface Water is approached from the south. A great deal more energy would have to be expended to lift water as cold as the patches described by Wexler (−1° C) from water of appropriate temperature at depth than to derive it from the adjacent sinking Antarctic Upper Water that is at this temperature and only a few miles to the south. In any case no appropriate source of such water of low enough temperature (taking account of the very small adiabatic cooling that can occur) exists at depth.

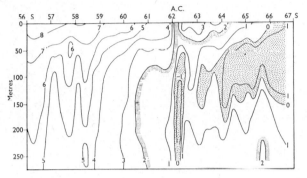

FIG. 34

Longitudinal section across the Antarctic Convergence (AC) at 177° E from bathythermograph observations from HMNZS *Hawea* in December 1956 (Burling, 1961). The area of water colder than 2°C is enclosed within hatched isotherms. Water less than 0°C is shown stippled

Ivanov (1961) suggests that a Subantarctic Divergence is needed between the Subtropical and Antarctic Convergences to satisfy the principle of continuity. Though absolute values for meridional water velocities in the surface layers are not known, yet relative velocities could quite well be such that continuity could be satisfied by a divergence north or south of both convergences. In fact, as remarked above, the front developed in Lat. 50° S that Burling (1961) associated with the southern limit of his Australasian Subantarctic Surface Water exhibits convergent properties.

RADIO CARBON MEASUREMENTS

The principal parameters used in analyses of Southern Ocean circulation and dynamics have been temperature and salinity. Some useful data have latterly been obtained from determinations of the C^{14} activity of dissolved carbon in ocean waters, made on large samples (Garner, 1958; Burling and Garner, 1959). On the simplest of assumptions, the longer a parcel of sea water has been removed from a position at the sea surface and therefore shielded from the atmosphere, the more depleted will its C^{14} activity become. Ignoring the effects of mixing, a very broad inverse relation of activity with time can be inferred. It was found from surface and subsurface samples that the activity of water at the surface in the region of the Antarctic Divergence at Lat. 64° S was very low and consistent with upwelling, and that even when this upwelled water had reached the Antarctic Convergence at Lat. 61° S and commenced to sink its activity had not regained equilibrium with the atmosphere and was still low. The results also raise the possibility that both Antarctic Intermediate Water and Deep Water south of Lat. 30° S in the western Pacific may have very different histories from the equivalent water masses north of this latitude.

THE ANTARCTIC CIRCUMPOLAR CURRENT

One of the earliest attempts to make a quantitative estimate of the flow of water in the Southern Ocean was made by Sverdrup (1942) based on expedition results and observations from *Discovery II*.

The main water movement is the vast east-flowing Antarctic Circumpolar Current, that is primarily driven by the westerly winds. The Circumpolar Current involves the whole depth of water in the Southern Ocean and Sverdrup's calculations showed that between the surface and 3000 m depth 120 million cubic metres per second were transported eastwards past the section between Antarctica and South Africa, 150 million across the section between Antarctica and Tasmania and 90 million through Drake Passage between Antarctica and South America.

During the IGY efforts were made to improve these estimates (Kort, 1962a). His calculations showed that the mass transports across these sections were more nearly the same – 190, 180 and 150 million cubic metres per second – than the earlier work had suggested. The differences from section to section show the effects of loss to and gain from the northern oceans. The largest loss is of 40 million cubic metres per second into the Tasman Sea.

The region of maximum eastward flow coincides with the Antarctic Convergence and that of minimum flow with the Antarctic Divergence. In two areas at the Antarctic coastline westward-flowing counter currents are developed – strongly in and east of the Weddell Sea and less substantially in the Bellingshausen and Amundsen Seas. Kort found that the total northward transport of bottom waters away from the Antarctic Continent was 800 million cubic metres per second or five times the total zonal transport. The rate of flow is not five times as great, however, because of the larger area of cross section across which the transport is taking place. This outflow is balanced by southward movement in the warm Deep Water. From these figures and water temperatures and the atmospheric gain and loss, the annual heat exchange figures can be derived. Kort (1962a, b) assesses the incoming heat at 10×10^{21} gm cal of solar energy plus 30×10^{21} gm cal from warm Deep Water (a total of 40×10^{21} gm cal); the outgoing heat is 34×10^{20} gm cal lost to the atmosphere and 5×10^{21} gm cal carried north in bottom waters (a total of 39×10^{21} gm cal). The heat brought in towards Antarctica from the northern oceans is utilized to warm the cold Antarctic air masses. The larger loss of Southern Ocean water into the Tasman Sea and East Pacific makes the Pacific Ocean slightly cooler than the Indian Ocean and a great deal cooler than the Atlantic.

The topography of the sea floor has a substantial effect on the flow of the Circumpolar Current. Stream lines show that over rising bottom the current is deflected to the north, and as the sea floor deepens the current is deflected to the south.

One of the questions that remains to be determined is the degree of variation in the values and distribution of the water properties of the Southern Ocean from year to year. Answers to this problem may well enable future long range forecasts of climate to be made.

Bibliography

ADAMS, R. D., and CHRISTOFFEL, D. A. 1962: Total Magnetic Field Surveys between New Zealand and the Ross Sea, *J. Geophys. Res.* **67:** 805–13.

BENTLEY, C. R., CRARY, A. P., OSTENSO, N. A., and THIEL, E. C. 1960: Structure of West Antarctica, *Science* **131:** 131–6.

BRODIE, J. W. 1959: A Shallow Shelf around Franklin Island in the Ross Sea, Antarctica, *N.Z. J. Geol. Geophys.* **2:** 103–19.

BULLIVANT, J. S. 1959: An Oceanographic Survey of the Ross Sea, *Nature* **184:** 422–3.

BURLING, R. W. 1961: Hydrology of Circumpolar Waters South of New Zealand, *N.Z. Oceanogr. Inst. Mem.* **10.**

BURLING, R. W., and GARNER, D. M. 1959: A Section of C^{14} Activities of Sea Water Between 9° S and 66° S in the South-west Pacific Ocean, *N.Z. J. Geol. Geophys.* **2:** 799–824.

DEACON, G. E. R. 1937: The Hydrology of the Southern Ocean, *Discovery Rep.* **15:** 1–123.

DELL, R. K. 1952: Marine Biology, Simpson, F. A., ed. *The Antarctic Today*, pp. 129–50, Reed and NZ Antarctic Society, Wellington.

DIETZ, R. S. 1952: Some Pacific and Antarctic Sea-floor Features Discovered during the US Navy Antarctic Expedition 1946–1947, *Proc. 7th Pac. Sci. Congr.* **3:** 335–44.

EVISON, F. F., INGHAM, C. E., ORR, R. H., and LE FORT, J. H. 1960: Thickness of the Earth's Crust in Antarctica and the Surrounding Oceans, *Geophys. J.* **3:** 289–306.

EWING, M., and HEEZEN, B. C. 1956: Some Problems of Antarctic Submarine Geology, *Geophys. Monogr.* **1:** 75–81, Amer. Geophys. Union.

FAIRBRIDGE, R. W. 1952: The Geology of the Antarctic, Simpson, F. A., ed. *The Antarctic Today*, pp. 56–101. Reed and NZ Antarctic Society, Wellington.

GARNER, D. M. 1958: The Antarctic Convergence South of New Zealand, *N.Z. J. Geol. Geophys.* **1:** 577–94.

HERDMAN, H. F. P., WISEMAN, J. D. H., and OVEY, C. D. 1956: Proposed Names of Features on the Deep-sea Floor: 3. Southern or Antarctic Ocean, *Deep-Sea Res.* **3:** 253–61.

HOUGH, J. L. 1956: Sediment Distribution in the Southern Oceans around Antarctica, *J. Sed. Pet.* **26:** 301–6.

HOUGH, J. L. 1950: Pleistocene Lithology of Antarctic Ocean-bottom Sediments, *J. Geol.* **58:** 254–60.

ISHINO, M., MORITA, Y., and SAOTOME, Y. 1962: Note on the Oceanographical Surveys in the Indian Ocean and the Southern Ocean, *J. Tokyo Univ. Fish.* (Special Edition) **1:** 103–230.

IVANOV, YU. A. 1961: Frontal Zones in Antarctic Waters, *Okeanologicheskiye Issled. 1961,* **3:** 30–51.

KORT, V. G. 1962a: The Antarctic Ocean, *Scientific American* **207:** 113–28.

KORT, V. G. 1962b: On Heat Exchange of the Antarctic Waters, *Geophys. Monogr.* **7:** 163–7, Amer. Geophys. Union.

KOVACH, R. L. and PRESS, F. 1961: Surface Wave Dispersion and Crustal Structure in Antarctica and the Surrounding Ocean, *Annal. Geofisica* **14:** 211–24.

LISITZIN, A. P. 1960: Bottom Sediments of the Eastern Antarctic and Southern Indian Ocean, *Deep-Sea Res.* **7:** 89–99.

LISITZIN, A. P. 1962: Bottom Sediments of the Antarctic, *Geophys. Monogr.* **7:** 81–8, Amer. Geophys. Union.

LISITZIN, A. P., and ZHIVAGO, A. V. 1960: Marine Geological Work of the Soviet Antarctic Expedition 1955–1957, *Deep-Sea Res.* **6:** 77–87.

MACKINTOSH, N. A. 1946: The Antarctic Convergence and the Distribution of Surface Temperatures in Antarctic Waters, *Discovery Rep.* **23:** 179–212.

MENARD, H. W. 1960: The East Pacific Rise, *Science* **132:** 1737–46.

MIDTTUN, L. and NATVIG, J. 1957: Pacific Antarctic Waters, *Sci. Rep. Brategg Exped. 1947–8,* **3:** (*Pub. Christensens Hvalfangstmus. 20*)

MURRAY, J. 1895: A Summary of the Results, *Rep. Voy. Challenger 1872–6,* London, HMSO.

MURRAY, J., and RENARD, A. F. 1891: Deep Sea Deposits, *Rep. Voy. Challenger 1872–6,* London, HMSO.

NEAVERSON, E. 1934: Sea Floor Deposits, *Discovery Rep.* **9:** 295–350.

NUDELMAN, A. V. 1960: *Soviet Antarctic Expeditions 1958–60,* Moscow, Acad. Sci., 106 pp. chart.

PHILIPPI, E. 1912: Die Grundproben, *Rep. Deutsche Südpolar Exped. 1901–3,* **2:** 431–4.

ROOS, S. E. 1937: The Submarine Topography of the Ross Sea and Adjacent. Waters, *Geogr. Rev.* **27:** 574–83.

SCHOTT, W. 1939: Deep Sea Sediments of the Indian Ocean, Trask, P. D., ed. *Recent Marine Sediments,* Tulsa, Amer. Assn Petrol. Geol.

STETSON, H. C., and UPSON, J. E. 1937: Bottom Deposits of the Ross Sea, *J. Sed. Pet.* **7:** 55–6.

SVERDRUP, H. U., JOHNSON, M. W., and FLEMING, R. H. 1942: *The Oceans*, New York, Prentice Hall.

TAYLOR, T. G. 1930: *Antarctic Adventure and Research*, New York, Appleton.

THOMAS, C. W. 1959: Lithology and Zoology of an Antarctic Ocean-bottom Core, *Deep-Sea Res.* **6:** 5–15.

UDA, M. 1961: Deep Circulation in the Antarctic Ocean, *Antarctic Record* **11:** 111–5.

UDINTSEV, G. B. 1963: A New Relief Map of the Pacific Ocean, *Okeanologiya* **3:** 169–75.

US NAVY HYDROGRAPHIC OFFICE, 1957: Oceanographic Atlas of the Polar Seas. Part 1 Antarctic, *H.O. Pub.* **705,** Washington, Hydrographic Office.

WEXLER, H. 1959: The Antarctic Convergence – or Divergence? Bolin, B., ed., *The Atmosphere and the Sea in Motion; Scientific Contributions to the Rossby Memorial Volume*, pp. 107–20, New York, Rockefeller Inst. Press.

WYRTKI, K. 1960: The Antarctic Circumpolar Current and the Antarctic Polar Front, *Deut. Hydrogr. Zeitz.* **13:** 153–74.

ZHIVAGO, A. V. 1962: Outlines of Southern Ocean Geomorphology, *Geophys. Monogr.* **7:** 74–80, Amer. Geophys. Un.

CHAPTER FIVE

Marine Biology

R. K. DELL, *Dominion Museum, Wellington*

Introduction

Ten years ago the writer attempted to give an outline of the broad features of marine biology in Antarctic and Subantarctic seas. Since the great outbursts of scientific exploration in the eighteenth and nineteenth centuries there can seldom have been a comparable explosive development of activity in the biological field as has taken place in the Antarctic in the last decade. Biologists of many nations have contributed in many separate areas to such an extent that the writer's conclusions (Dell, 1952, pp. 148–9) in which he rather tentatively attempted to indicate probable future developments have nearly all been rendered obsolete.

At the present time, however, any writer attempting a general survey of marine biology in the Antarctic must suffer from an intense sense of frustration. Research in the physical, geophysical, geological and to a certain extent oceanographical sciences is such that preliminary results can appear comparatively rapidly. In biological fields, especially in an area where the fauna and flora are not well described or documented, results depend upon team work where the very mechanics of determining names for the animals concerned means a considerable time lag. Thus it is that although an unexampled amount of field work has been carried out, the published biological results are only beginning to appear. At any moment scientific papers on Antarctic marine biology may appear from Japanese, Russian, French, Australian, British, Belgian, Norwegian, American, Argentinean, Chilean, South African and New Zealand sources. Extensive collections of Antarctic animals are in the hands of workers from all the countries mentioned and many others. In five years' time the major parts of these will undoubtedly have been recorded; at present the published information is little more extensive than what was available ten years ago.

The four inescapable conclusions that must be drawn from the above discussion are:

First, the Antarctic invertebrates are not well known or documented. In spite of all the animals which have been described in the scattered reports of expeditions of many nationalities and in the scientific periodicals of the world, there are very few groups for which an up-to-date monograph of the Antarctic species exists. Fell (1961) has recently published such a monograph for the Ophiuroidea or Brittle Stars of the Ross Sea. With such a work most biologists could identify their own material. Failing such monographs a biologist must seek the aid of a specialist worker who is not only capable of identifying Antarctic material but who is willing and able to do so in the foreseeable future. It is common knowledge among biologists that such specialists are rare.

Thus the second conclusion must be that specialists on the systematics of Antarctic animals are insufficient in number and cannot cover the whole range of animals represented. There are groups of animals which cannot at present be identified because there is no trained person to do this work. Such an important group in the Antarctic benthos as the Polyzoa is in this category.

Thirdly, until recently there has been too little financial support for that group of biologists known as systematists – those scientists who at the lowest level of their work identify animals and prepare reports upon them. Many able workers in this field have no technical assistance or the very minimum assistance with the primary mechanics of their task. Money has been found to finance the very expensive collection of material and the study of animals in the field and laboratory, but it has seldom been forthcoming to determine just what animals are being studied.

Fourthly, biological studies and especially marine biology have received the least attention of the sciences in the Antarctic. There is no doubt that the major efforts have been directed into the geographical, geological, physical and geophysical sciences and into the physical and chemical aspects of oceanography. The marine biologist requires a ship as a working base for his most productive work, especially in such an area as the Antarctic; and the uses of ships in the Antarctic have usually been controlled with the priorities of logistics first and foremost, then for other scientific investigations, then for oceanography with marine biology fitted in as opportunity offered. Only now is it becoming possible to plan a biological programme as such and hope to achieve it. One result of such a development has been that the physical and chemical environment in which the animals live has been well documented.

The difficulties caused by such deficiencies are readily apparent when it is realized that ecologists and physiologists cannot publish their results until they can record the names of the animals with which they are concerned. With these apologias firmly in mind we can consider what recent activity in the Antarctic has produced.

Phases of Biological Exploration

The biological exploration of Antarctic and Subantarctic waters can be considered to fall into three definite periods.

1. Early expeditions to the area investigated the fauna and flora, usually of a relatively restricted area. Such activity initiated the cataloguing phase, a purely descriptive stage. Organisms were collected, preserved and taken home to be described by specialist workers. An immense literature was gradually built up, in the main describing the plants and animals obtained and recording their distribution. With most expeditions such biological investigations were incidental

to the main purpose. Exceptions include the *Challenger* Expedition (which worked in some Subantarctic areas but did not visit the Antarctic proper), the German South Polar Expedition 1901–3, the *Terra Nova* Expedition, 1910–13, and the Australasian Antarctic Expedition, 1911–14. In the course of these, and to a lesser extent of other expeditions, definite and comparatively extensive biological programmes were instituted.

2. From 1925 until 1939 biological work in the Antarctic was overshadowed by the activities of the Discovery Committee. The investigations sponsored by this committee were at first confined to the South American quadrant and were primarily concerned with whales and whaling. The growth of oceanic whaling saw a gradual expansion of the committee's field to embrace the oceanography of the Southern Ocean. War interrupted this development and in 1949 the Discovery Investigations were taken over by the National Institute of Oceanography. (Since this time the area of activity of British oceanography has shifted completely from the south.)

The chief characteristics of the Discovery Investigations during this period were the institution of a continuous programme and the study of the Southern Ocean as a single unit. A primary result of the work was the elucidation of a general pattern of the physical and chemical characteristics of the Southern Ocean. An immense amount of biological work was also accomplished and much of this was interpreted on the same broad scale. Results of this work are still appearing regularly. This phase may be considered one of broad primary interpretation. Many other expeditions contributed to the advance of biological knowledge of the Antarctic during this period but for over a decade the Discovery Investigations were an Antarctic institution rather than an expedition.

3. A hiatus period after the end of World War II was terminated by the increasing tempo of national interest in the Antarctic largely initiated by the United States. The culminating explosion of international activity during the IGY, the continuing programmes of many of the participating nations since and the active functioning of SCAR in recent years seem the preludes to a phase of intensive investigation. At first, energy was concentrated upon other sciences but there are now abundant signs that biology will receive increasing backing and impetus.

Pelagic Organisms

For a number of reasons biological investigations in the Antarctic during the second phase from 1925 to 1939 centred around life in oceanic waters.

In the first place, the Discovery Investigations were initiated to study whales, and whales are oceanic animals. Practically all the factors influencing the life of whales must be studied in the ocean waters, e.g. distribution, migration and migration routes, the breeding cycle, food and feeding habits. In fact, an investigation of whales must lead to an intensive programme of physical and biological oceanography.

Secondly, the waters of the Southern Ocean present remarkably uniform and regular features. No conspicuous land masses apart from the Antarctic Continent affect the circulation of water masses and it has been found possible to map a number of uniform and rhythmically repetitive features as regards the physical characteristics and dynamics of the southern waters. Investigations on the associated organisms have shown similar uniformity and regularity, in most cases in strict correlation with the general physical pattern. This has made possible a broad investigation of the distribution of animals and plants, their seasonal migrations, life histories and inter-relationships on a scale unknown in other regions of the world. The Southern Ocean has presented a field in which broad principles of marine ecology may be investigated with some hope of success and for this reason much attention has been directed towards them.

It appears to be well accepted that the number of species of organisms present in Antarctic waters is few, but that each species occurs in countless numbers, whereas in tropical waters the reverse is the case.

In the sea, as on land, animal life depends for its ultimate sustenance on vegetation. The vegetation of the open sea consists of microscopic floating plants collectively termed phytoplankton. In the presence of sunlight these small plants can utilize directly the nutrient salts such as nitrates and phosphates dissolved in sea-water. The work of *Discovery II* has shown that concentrations of phosphates and nitrates much in excess of those noted elsewhere are associated with the immense quantities of phytoplankton in the Antarctic. In fact, phosphates and nitrates appear to be always in excess of requirements. This abundant source of food has many consequences and ultimately supports all the larger animals of the area. The actual steps involved may be followed through in a few cases.

Hardy (1935) showed that the local distribution of Blue and Fin Whales could be predicted from the distribution of the phosphates in the water. This is really a short-circuiting of a food chain commencing with dissolved nutrient salts and culminating, though not terminating, in whalebone whales. Dependent upon the phytoplankton are shoals of a crustacean known as 'krill'. In these waters the species is *Euphausia superba*, and these crustacea, some eight centimetres long, are the sole Antarctic food of the Blue and Fin Whales. The availability of food supply for the phytoplankton will therefore determine the relative abundance of *Euphausia* which will in turn influence the numbers of whales and their distribution.

Another food chain includes squids. These molluscs are dependent ultimately on the phytoplankton and probably feed on the 'krill' and other crustacea. Unfortunately squids are among the most difficult of marine animals to collect and though the remains of their beaks found in the stomachs of larger animals such as whales, sea-birds and seals indicate that their numbers are large in southern waters, relatively few have been examined. It is likely that crustacea form as large a part of the food of squids in Antarctic seas as they do in other waters. Squids form a very large part of the food of petrels, toothed whales (especially Sperm Whales) and some seals. For example, it has been estimated that

100,000 Elephant Seals (*Mirounga leonina*) frequent South Georgia and their food appears to consist solely of Cephalopods (Matthews, 1929).

In addition, fish and some seals and petrels feed directly on the 'krill' and other crustacea. The Emperor Penguin (*Aptenodytes forsteri*) and the Crabeater Seal (*Lobodon carcinophagus*) feed almost entirely on species of *Euphausia*, at least for part of the year. The same species form a large portion of the food of the Gentoo Penguin, and large numbers of Nototheniid fish are often observed feeding on the shoals of crustacea.

DIATOMS

The dominant constituents of the phytoplankton in Antarctic seas are the diatoms – minute single-celled plants usually not visible to the naked eye except when present in immense numbers when they may stain the sea-water brown. The usual colour of the individual diatom is brown and is caused by a pigment, diatomin, which conceals the green colour of the chlorophyll. Their outstanding characteristic is a siliceous 'shell' built on the principle of a pillbox, and often highly ornamented.

A typical cold-water diatom flora occurs south of the Subtropical Convergence. There are marked seasonal fluctuations in population densities of diatoms in southern seas. The lowest concentrations are recorded during the winter months, June to August. During October a marked increase occurs and in the northern part of the Antarctic water mass a peak is reached in November. This fluctuation may be correlated, largely, with duration of sunlight. Many Antarctic diatoms have a very wide geographical range, apparently because of a tolerance for a comparatively wide variation in physical conditions. Hart (1937) has shown that one species, *Rhizosolenia curvata*, is a biological indicator of the southern limit of Subantarctic Surface Water. Its presence to the south of the Antarctic Convergence is postulated to be a good indication that mixing of surface waters has recently taken place.

Hart (1942), dealing with Antarctic phytoplankton, reiterated the generalization that one of the outstanding characteristics of the Antarctic is the overwhelming predominance of diatoms and the negligible quantity of dinoflagellates. Hart has also found it necessary to subdivide the waters of the Antarctic Zone (at least 30,000,000 km² in extent) into a number of regions. In the areas to the south of the Atlantic, Indian and Pacific Oceans, the Antarctic Zone may be divided into three regions, which Hart names the Northern, Intermediate, and Southern Regions respectively. In addition there are a number of 'special areas'.

Where the Antarctic Convergence lies comparatively far to the south, these regions are telescoped and Hart advocates their designation as special areas. The two localities most affected are to the south-west of South America and to the south of New Zealand (north of the Ross Sea). There are also other areas where the presence of land and peculiar local conditions, such as pertain in South Georgia and the Scotia Sea, call for individual treatment. In the area to the north of the Ross Sea, for example, Hart in 1942 had only fifteen observations upon which to base his conclusions.

His main oceanic biogeographical areas in the Antarctic Zone are as follows: –

1. *The Northern Region*, between the Antarctic Convergence and a line 330 miles (about 530 km) south of it, all round the world, excepting the special areas between Longitudes 30° and 110° W, and between Longitudes 150° W and 170° E. It is never covered by continuous pack-ice and is invaded by loose pack or drift-ice only rarely in spring.

2. *The Intermediate Region*, between the southern limit of the above and the Antarctic Circle all the way round the world with the exception of the same complicated areas. The Antarctic Circle is an unavoidably arbitrary boundary. The area is largely covered by pack-ice in winter and spring, and mainly free during summer and late autumn.

3. *The Southern Region*, all seas south of the Antarctic Circle, excluding immediate coastal areas. It is largely covered by pack-ice throughout the year and free only in summer, the new ice frequently forming in March.

These divisions are based upon the interaction of the two most important factors bearing upon the productivity of the phytoplankton – light intensity and the distribution of the pack-ice.

ZOOPLANKTON

The term 'zooplankton' is used to indicate those animals that float in the oceanic waters at the mercy of currents. The chief characteristics of Antarctic zooplankton appear to be:

1. Almost complete absence of any larval forms of bottom-living animals except crustacea.

2. Vertical migration of comparatively long duration is a noteworthy characteristic of the more important species of zooplankton.

3. Forms inhabiting the surface layer are poor in species but rich in individuals.

4. Many forms migrate to the surface at night and sink during daylight hours.

Many zooplanktonic forms are confined to comparatively narrow circumpolar belts of surface waters. There has been much speculation on the methods by which such floating forms, which are capable of vertical movements only, maintain their distribution.

Mackintosh (1937) has studied the vertical seasonal distribution of the major planktonic forms in 80° W and has had access to sufficient data from the rest of the Antarctic seas to indicate that certain methods of planktonic circulation are probably of universal application in southern seas. With a knowledge of the circulation of deeper water masses and by plotting the depths at which maximum numbers of each species occur across a section along 80° W, we find the following patterns emerging:

1. The three species most important numerically in this area, *Rhincalanus*

gigas, *Eikronia hamata* and *Calanus acutus*, perform an annual vertical migration. During the summer they drift towards the north in the surface waters. During the winter they descend to the very deep southward-flowing water mass. In this way, by a vertical range of between 400 and 600 m they maintain a latitudinal position by means of a circular drift. The main drift of both surface and deep water masses is also towards the east so there is also a constant longitudinal shift. Since concentric belts of water in the Southern Ocean have essentially the same characteristics right around the Earth, this longitudinal drift presents no problems.

2. Some species have an energetic daily but no annual migration. These appear to adjust their distribution by daily migration to deeper water.

3. A number of species, some of irregular occurrence, have no obvious method of maintaining themselves in the appropriate ecological niche.

Fraser (1936) has shown that *Euphausia superba* probably passes through a similar series of movements, though correlated in this case with stages in the life history. Fraser's evidence shows that the earlier developmental stages congregate chiefly in the southward-flowing warm deep water. Upward movement causes a constant replenishment of adolescent *Euphausia* at the ice edge, the later stages flowing northwards in the Antarctic surface waters.

The distribution of planktonic organisms in relation to water masses is well shown by the southern species of *Euphausia*. Mackintosh (1960) has recently published a revised figure showing the zones occupied by these species. The total ranges of some of these species overlap considerably but the area of concentration for each species falls into a remarkably discrete zone. Much the same kind of distribution has been demonstrated for species of the arrow-worm, *Sagitta*, by David (1958).

Benthic Fauna

While the position of the Antarctic Convergence has proved a most useful line of division between an Antarctic and a Subantarctic fauna for pelagic and to some extent for bathypelagic plants and animals and for animals such as the seals and petrels which prey upon pelagic animals, it is not necessarily the best division for benthic animals. Many workers have attempted to use the position of the Antarctic Convergence to limit an Antarctic benthic region but in most cases this appears to be an artificial boundary. The use of the Antarctic Circle as a faunal boundary has fallen into disuse for it cuts the outer limits of the Antarctic Continent proper in a number of places and no marine biologist could admit that this logical, geographical but by no means biological line could divide two faunal entities.

The zone to the north of the Antarctic Convergence and south of the Subtropical Convergence, known to oceanographers as the Zone of Subantarctic Waters, has suffered a number of changes in nomenclature when considered by biogeographers. Islands which fall inside this zone, such as Prince Edward and Marion Islands, Gough, the Falklands, the Bounties, Antipodes, Aucklands,

Campbell and the Crozets, have usually been known as Subantarctic islands. Those which fall on one or other of the convergences, such as Macquarie, Kerguelen and Tristan da Cunha have been discussed as borderline between one zone and the next or as showing influences from both zones. But no recent worker has proposed that the east coast of the South Island of New Zealand, nor the coast of Argentina, Juan Fernandez nor the coast of Chile should be termed Subantarctic. There have been a number of attempts to find more apt descriptive terms for the Subantarctic Zone. Ekman (1953) proposed the term Antiboreal in contrast to the Boreal of the Northern Hemisphere. A discussion on the biology of this zone held under the auspices of the Royal Society used the term Cold Temperate, in contrast to the Warm Temperate to the north and the Antarctic to the south. This is the usage followed by Knox (1960).

As a contrast to divisions based upon hydrological, geographical or meteorological premises, what can be termed the 'provincial' concept has been developed. Based primarily upon faunal composition and relationship the Subantarctic (Southern Temperate, Cold Temperate or Antiboreal) has been divided into a large number of provinces. Provinces have also been defined by local workers for southern South America, South Africa, Australia and New Zealand. Powell (1951) outlined the development of divisions of the Antarctic Zone and named a new province, the Georgian for the South Georgia area and Shag Rocks. Knox (1960) gave a figure which summarized all the previously named provinces and proposed two subprovinces of the Antarctic, a Rossian and a Scotian Subprovince. Knox, however, discussed such provinces only for the littoral and this is rather a different concept from biogeographical provinces as such. Provinces should be based upon faunal analysis but it is perhaps true to state that in any area, provinces are the more easily defined, the less one knows of that fauna. In any case the concept of an enormous area such as the Southern Ocean divided into provinces gives an impression of rather more clear-cut distinctions than in fact exist. The land masses of the Subantarctic and Antarctic Zones (apart from the Antarctic Continent itself) are either extensions of continents such as South America, South Africa or Australia, or transition zones affected by several faunal influences such as the islands of the Scotia Arc and the southern islands of New Zealand, or are small, completely isolated islands or island groups such as Heard and Kerguelen. The faunas of the southern extensions of the southern continents are all influenced by the continental faunas themselves. Those of the isolated land masses owe their present biota to varied sources, some at least largely accidental. Such areas as the Scotia Arc seem best interpreted as transition zones rather than as forming several separate provinces. Attempts to link the isolated island groups into provinces are attempts to link unique faunas on the basis of one or other of the fortuitous elements held in common.

Even the apparent faunal differences usually quoted between the benthos of the Antarctic and the so-called Subantarctic prove to be largely based upon invalid comparisons. The bottom fauna in Antarctic seas is essentially a deep water fauna. Littoral faunas on the Antarctic Continent are almost non-existent.

A shelf is developed in very few localities and the restricted shallow water fauna, when present, seems obviously derived from the surrounding archibenthal fauna (which latter is what is usually maintained to be the typical Antarctic fauna). The faunal elements which are usually quoted as typical of the 'Subantarctic Islands' are essentially littoral and shallow water forms. The deeper water and archibenthal faunas of the 'Subantarctic Islands' are practically unknown. The distinctions usually quoted are therefore between a littoral and shelf Subantarctic fauna and an Antarctic archibenthal fauna. Perhaps the Subantarctic would be better defined as an area which has a littoral fauna!

The provincial concept, as used so far, does not therefore appear to have assisted much in understanding the relationships of the Antarctic fauna. A strictly faunal approach seems the only useful basis for biogeographical sub-division and discussion. This would entail comparatively complete knowledge of the latitudinal, longitudinal and benthic distribution of animals around the Antarctic Continent and in contiguous areas. We are lacking sufficient knowledge to undertake any such analysis.

There is no doubt that faunal elements are being added to the Antarctic through the Scotia Arc. Such a survey as that outlined above would indicate those species which have only recently arrived in the South American sector of Antarctica and which have probably been derived through this route. All other species occurring around the Antarctic Continent could then be considered truly Antarctic species, and their distribution northwards would then indicate the true limits of the Antarctic Province. Such evidence as we have in this matter indicates that various elements extend to various of the southern islands and land masses and that the Antarctic fauna is not quite so clear cut as Ekman (1953, p. 221) has stated. At the same time it is apparent that a large proportion of the Antarctic fauna as defined above is confined to the seas surrounding the Antarctic Continent and the islands of the Scotia Arc as far north as South Georgia, but excluding the Falklands and the Magellanic region. It is this region, comprising the whole Antarctic Continent, and the island groups of South Shetlands, South Orkneys, South Sandwich Islands, South Georgia and probably Bouvetøya which will be discussed as the Antarctic benthic region in this section. It must be obvious that the Antarctic benthos must be investigated very thoroughly before biogeographical relationships in the Southern Ocean can be adequately discussed.

Mackintosh (1960) has published a map of the Southern Ocean showing the position of the 500- and 2000-metre contours. It is obvious from this map that except in the Weddell, Bellingshausen and Ross Seas there is a relatively restricted area of shelf and continental slope around the Antarctic Continent. If Antarctic benthic animals are confined to the shelf, this would be a very clearly defined area in the sense that Ekman considered it. Too little evidence is available to be dogmatic but it is obvious that the benthic animals usually considered to be typically Antarctic are by no means confined to the shelf but extend into deeper water. More complete analysis of more adequate collections may demonstrate that an appreciable proportion of the benthic fauna is confined to the slope but there seems little possibility at present of defining a separate shelf fauna.

One of the major contributions to knowledge of the bottom fauna of Antarctic waters has come through the work of the New Zealand Oceanographic Institute

FIG. 35

Photograph of sea floor at New Zealand Oceanographic Station A518, off Beaufort Island, Ross Sea, in 75 metres, showing ophiuroids, starfish, gorgona-cean, holothurians, algae, bryozoa and the mollusc *Neobuccinum eatoni*

(*Photo. J. S. Bullivant, N.Z. Oceanographic Institute*)

in the Ross Sea. In January and February 1959, twenty-three stations were established in the Ross Sea using trawls and/or grabs in depths from 64 to 2195 metres (Bullivant, 1959a). In addition, at four stations photographs of the sea bed in both black and white and colour were obtained (Bullivant, 1959b). In the first two months of 1960 additional stations were established and more bottom photographs obtained. These photographs (see Figs. 35, 36) illustrate with

direct evidence the wealth of fixed animal life in many areas, thus amplifying
the evidence from bottom hauls. Four different types of bottom fauna were
shown:

1. Gorgonacea, Polyzoa and Porifera

FIG. 36

Photograph of sea floor at New Zealand Oceanographic Station A468, east
of Beaufort Island, Ross Sea, in 110 metres, showing growth of large sponges
(*Rosella* sp. ?) with gorganacean, starfish and pycnogonid

(Photo. J. S. Bullivant, N.Z. Oceanographic Institute)

2. A bivalve (*Limatula hodgsoni*) plus an asteroid (*Odontaster validus*).
3. Porifera.
4. Polyzoa, Polychaete and Ophiuroidea.

The abundance of fixed filter-feeding forms is well illustrated by the series of
photographs.

In addition as the fauna from stations at which bottom photographs were obtained is analysed, important deductions on aspects of the biology of some of the animals become possible. Fell, for example, has been able to deduce methods of feeding for some species of ophiuroids as well as the relative density of some species.

Most of the biological material obtained during these investigations has been distributed to specialists for report but little has so far been published. It is, however, already apparent that the belief that the Ross Sea was a relatively impoverished area as regards bottom animals is totally unfounded. Many expeditions have visited the Ross Sea area in the past and many reports have been written on the collections obtained. But the results indicated that no such wealth of life was present as has been demonstrated by Australian expeditions and the German Antarctic expedition in neighbouring areas. It is now, however, obvious that during the majority of expeditions to the Ross Sea marine biology was in practice the Cinderella amongst the sciences, especially as far as it involved the use of the expedition ships. Much of the material obtained was collected from ice-edge stations or through holes maintained in sea ice under appallingly difficult conditions. Biologists in these earlier expeditions were often involved in practical logistics during the summer months or were largely occupied studying penguins and seals. The dedicated maintenance of a winter programme of marine collecting in spite of every imaginable difficulty could not make up for the lack of summer facilities. The results obtained by the use of trawls, dredges and grabs from ships has demonstrated the eventual futility of much of this early endeavour.

Some Constituents of Antarctic Benthos

The Foraminifera are the main Protozoa so far recorded from Antarctic Seas, and apparently the major number have arenaceous tests. Nemertine worms and Pycnogonids are characteristic members of the Antarctic benthos. The Pycnogonids in particular are very well represented but no recent review is as yet available. Previous accounts are mainly concerned with systematics. The hydroid fauna cannot be considered to be prolific although some species are commonly represented. Octocorals are comparatively numerous.

SPONGES

Sponges make up a very substantial proportion of the benthic biomass. The majority of the forms represented are siliceous, the long, excruciatingly sharp, fine, glassy spicules being a constant threat to the hands of all biologists who sort samples of bottom material. Broken remnants of these spicules are common in the sorted tubes and jars containing the animals collected by many Antarctic expeditions. Burton (1932) showed that Antarctic waters support a more abundant sponge fauna than do those of the Indian Ocean, Australia or the West Indies. In the Southern Ocean, the Recent is as much the Age of Sponges as was the Cretaceous.

CRUSTACEA

Only eight species of the order Decapoda are so far recorded from the Antarctic and some of these are pelagic or bathypelagic rather than benthic in habit. All of them belong to the Natantia (shrimps), no Reptantia (crabs and crayfish) having as yet been recorded. The lack of reptant Decapoda is therefore a characteristic of the Antarctic fauna. In contrast the Amphipoda and Isopoda are very well represented. In the latter group the Serolidae is a characteristic family comprising some comparatively large forms. This development of large isopods achieves its climax in *Glyptonotus antarcticus* which reaches a length of up to 12 cm.

OPHIUROIDS

Fell (1961) has recently published a comprehensive account of the Ophiuroidea of the Ross Sea, in the course of which some 3000 specimens from sixty-seven Ross Sea stations between 30 and 1375 m in depth were examined. This is one of the first substantial systematic accounts of an animal group to appear, based upon the mass of newly collected material, and is perhaps indicative of what we may expect for other groups in the not too distant future. The ophiuroid fauna of the Ross Sea closely resembles that from West Antarctica, at least half the species recorded from the Ross Sea also occurring in the opposite sector. The composition of the ophiuroid fauna indicates isolation of these groups in Antarctic waters (or waters of comparable physical conditions) for a long period and the absence of any apparent benthal migration route to, or from, New Zealand or Australia. The group is distinguished by the development of a number of relatively stenothermal genera such as *Astrohamma*, *Astrochlamys*, *Glaciacantha*, *Ophiosparte*, *Ophiodaces*, *Euvondrea*, *Ophioperla* and *Theodoria*. For all these genera South Georgia is the northern limit of range. Some otherwise Antarctic genera do extend through the Scotia Arc to the Magellanic region.

Judging by the richness of material in collections and the evidence of bottom photographs it is obvious that the group forms a significant part of the Antarctic benthos. A very widespread characteristic, especially of ophiuroids but marked also for other echinoderms, is the incidence of viviparity and either direct development or an abbreviation of the planktonic stage in such echinoids as possess it.

Mainly from study of bottom photographs it has been possible to determine a number of interesting features of the biology of some of the ophiuroids, especially in regard to feeding habits. *Ophioceres incipiens*, for example, appears to be in the habit of climbing the tubes of tube worms and the stems of colonial hydroids, and while grasping the substrate with two arms to extend the others into the surrounding water in a fishing attitude. In the case of *Astrotoma agassizii* it is suggested that the arms sweep the surrounding water, transferring food particles to the mouth. *Ophiurolepis gelida* thrusts the arms through the detritus layer on more open substrates suggesting that it is a selective detritus feeder.

MOLLUSCA

The year 1951 saw published three major works on the mollusca of the Antarctic and Subantarctic regions. Powell produced a large report, based mainly on the Gastropoda of the *Discovery* collections, described new species, revised classification and discussed the relationships of the fauna. Soot-Ryen gave a complete critical account of the bivalves of Antarctica, based upon Norwegian collections and study of literature. Carcelles and Williamson presented a comprehensive check-list of the mollusca of the Magellanic region, thus supplying valuable information for discussing the relationship of the Antarctic fauna. Since 1951, the molluscan sections of the results of the Lund University Expedition to Chile (shelled Gastropoda not yet issued) have supplied additional evidence. In most cases the authors of these reports have critically examined the systematics of forms which also occur in the Antarctic or Subantarctic. Powell has published on the mollusca of the BANZAR Expedition (1957, 1958) and recently (1960) produced an extremely valuable checklist of all Antarctic and Subantarctic mollusca. The writer (Dell, 1959) has published an account of the BANZAR Expedition Cephalopoda, has reported upon the *Discovery* collections of Bivalvia, Amphineura and Scaphopoda (Dell, in press) and is currently studying the collections of mollusca from the Ross Sea. As a result of all this recent work, not only is this well-represented group becoming well known, but it is becoming well documented (Fig. 37).

There can no longer be any doubt that the molluscan fauna of Antarctic waters (in the sense used in this paper) is particularly restricted. Some ninety-one families are represented, containing 154 genera and 309 species. Each family therefore contains on the average 1·7 genera and 3·4 species. Each genus contains on the average two species. If such a molluscan fauna is compared with that of such a restricted and isolated geographical region as New Zealand the paucity of forms in the Antarctic is obvious. New Zealand has some 160 families of marine inter-tidal or benthic mollusca, containing 552 genera and 1759 species. Each family contains on the average 3·4 genera and eleven species, and each genus contains on the average 3·2 species.

But the extremely restricted composition of the Antarctic molluscan fauna is even more strongly demonstrated when it is realized that fifty of the families contain only one Antarctic genus, sixteen have two genera, five have three genera, six have four, four have five, one has seven, one has eight, and one family has ten genera. Twenty-eight families are represented by only one species, and fifty-six families are represented by three species or less. Only five families are represented by more than 11 species (the average for New Zealand families). Many of these Antarctic families contain only minute representatives or less typical genera and many of them are genera which elsewhere are considered deep water forms. For example, the only representative of the family Mytilidae is the small deep water genus *Dacrydium*. Similarly the family Arcidae is represented only by *Bathyarca*.

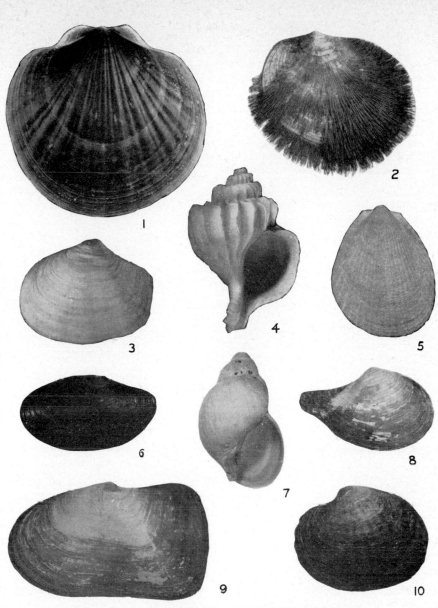

FIG. 37 SOME TYPICAL ANTARCTIC MOLLUSCA

1. *Adamussium colbecki* (Smith) (87 × 84 mm)
2. *Limopsis marionensis* Smith (45 × 40 mm)
3. *Thracia meridionalis* Smith (28 × 22·5 mm)
4. *Trophon longstaffi* Smith (42 × 28 mm)
5. *Limatula hodgsoni* Smith (28 × 34 mm)
6. *Yoldia* (*Aequiyoldia*) *eightsi* (Couthouy, in Jay) (46 × 26 mm)
7. *Neobuccinum eatoni* (Smith) (41 × 26 mm)
8. *Cuspidaria tenella* Smith (36 × 22 mm)
9. *Laternula elliptica* (King and Broderip) (53 × 34 mm)
10. *Cyclocardia astartoides* (von Martens) (42 × 33 mm)

One of the characteristic groups of animals living on the sea floor in the Antarctic is that of the eledonid octopods. The systematics of these animals is still poorly known but all members of the Octopoda from Antarctic waters have the suckers on the arms arranged uniserially, that is, there is only a single row of suckers on each arm instead of the double row as developed in typical *Octopus*. Most of the species are relatively small but Taki (1961) has recently described *Megaledone senoi* with a total length of 460 mm and a mantle width of 143 mm, making it a comparative giant. The higher classification of the eledonids cannot be said to be finally settled but twelve species, grouped in three subfamilies, are now known from the Antarctic. This then is undoubtedly another group which shows the phenomenon of explosive radiation in the Antarctic. Two other species of octopods and eight species of squids have been recorded. All the squids so far known are pelagic in habit.

The writer has recently completed a review of Antarctic bivalves. The Arctic bivalve fauna is now well known as a result of investigations by Norwegian, American and particularly Russian workers. Undoubtedly the Arctic fauna is better known than that of the Antarctic and subspecific and varietal names are in use for many Arctic forms whereas no subspecific categories are at present recognized for Antarctic forms. If the subspecific forms in the Arctic are ignored there are reasonable grounds for believing that a faunal comparison between the two polar regions is valid.

From such a comparison it is obvious that the Arctic fauna is much richer in families, genera and species.

	Families	Genera	Species
Arctic	31	51	118
Antarctic	25	36	66

Six of the Antarctic families do not occur in the Arctic and twelve Arctic families do not occur in the Antarctic. Fourteen genera are common to both areas, and the larger part of these are genera which are often found in deep water. Nevertheless amongst the families held in common there are some striking similarities. Many have a similar or identical number of genera represented in both polar regions although there tends to be a greater number of species in many of the Arctic genera. At the higher taxonomic levels there is a marked similarity between the two faunas.

The writer believes that there is ample evidence that many molluscan families are steadily invading Antarctic waters and that the major migration route is from southern South America through the islands of the Scotia Arc. Many families do not extend further south than southern Chile and Argentina. No less than seventeen families reach their limit on the Falkland Islands and some of these are widely distributed in other parts of the world. They include such well known families as the Acmaeidae, Nassariidae, Thaisidae, Anomiidae, Lucinidae, Mactridae, Cardidae, Teredinidae, Corbulidae, Myidae, Chitonidae, and Acanthochitonidae. In addition such widely distributed genera as *Calliostoma*,

Photinula, *Lamellaria*, *Typhis*, and *Pachysiphonaria* do not extend further south than the Falklands or Tierra del Fuego in this sector. Five additional families, the Retusidae, Calyptraeidae, Veneridae, Tellinidae and Hiatellidae are not represented south of South Georgia, while between South Georgia and the Falklands the Olividae reach their limit of extension. Two families, the Leptonidae and the Chaetopleuridae do not reach the Antarctic Continent although they may occur on one or other of the South Shetlands, South Orkneys or South Sandwich Islands. Five families, the Patellidae, Gaimardiidae, Hanleyidae, Ischnochitonidae and the Mopaliidae extend to the Antarctic Continent only in the Weddell Sea, Graham Land and Bellingshausen Sea area. It seems highly probable that other forms have earlier reached the Antarctic by this route and have since been more widely dispersed around the continent.

FISHES

Rofen and DeWitt (1961) have published a checklist of the shore fishes of the Antarctic Continent (south of Lat. 60° S including the South Sandwich Islands but excluding South Georgia, Bouvet, Kerguelen, Macquarie and the Falklands). Sixty-six species are listed representing nine families. However, four families, the Nototheniidae (Antarctic cods), Bathydraconidae (Antarctic dragon fishes), Chaenichthyidae (ice fishes) and Harpagiferidae (plunder fishes) include over 95% of the total fish fauna (Fig. 38). The Nototheniidae alone comprise over 50% of the total fish fauna. These four families are combined to form a compact group known as the Nototheniiform fishes, a group which is predominantly Antarctic in distribution. They do give off northern branches such as the family Bovichthyidae which occurs in South Australia, Tasmania, New Zealand, St Paul, Tristan da Cunha, the Falklands and southern South America as far north as Chile and Argentina, and the genus *Eleginops* which ranges from the Falklands to northern Chile and Rio de la Plata. Other members of the Nototheniidae form a strong element in the southern islands of New Zealand, even reaching the South Island of New Zealand, and in the fish fauna of the Magellanic region. Much inquiry is therefore being directed at the group of Nototheniiform fishes to determine general classification and speciation patterns. The realization that members of the Chaenichthyidae are 'bloodless' and some members of the Nototheniidae are partially bloodless has stimulated research into these aspects of fish physiology. Blood from these fishes shows no detectable haemoglobin or erythrocytes (Ruud, 1958) or very reduced quantities (Tyler, 1960). Studies of methods of oxygen transport and metabolism will undoubtedly follow on from these discoveries.

Wohlschlag has been engaged in studies of metabolic rate and degree of cold adaptation of some Antarctic fishes at McMurdo Sound. Preliminary results indicate that both metabolic rate and degree of cold adaptation for a nototheniid are exceptionally high and that Antarctic fishes have high growth rates. Miller has studied feeding habits of some of the commoner species in the Ross Sea, but results from this work are not yet available. An American group of

F

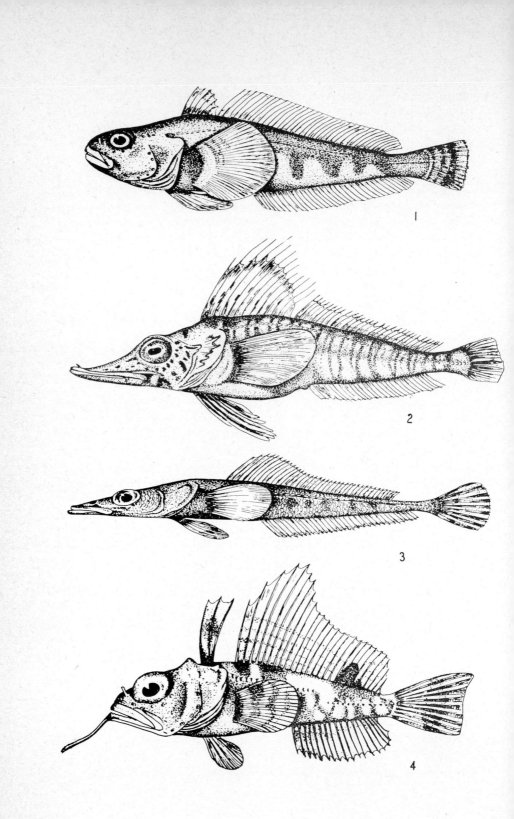

1

2

3

4

ichthyologists based upon Stanford University are attempting to monograph the fishes of the Antarctic.

A Russian group associated with Andriashev and collecting mainly from the vessel *Ob* has amassed a very large collection of Antarctic and Subantarctic fishes numbering more than 2700 specimens of eighty-five to ninety species from south of the Antarctic Convergence. A monograph of Antarctic fishes considering taxonomic, zoogeographic and ecological aspects is in preparation.

The fishes of Antarctica thus present a number of interesting features. Specific endemic families appear to have evolved in the Antarctic although members of these families now extend to various northern areas. These families and in fact the vast majority of Antarctic fishes belong to one group of fishes, the Notothenii-formes which are predominantly southern in distribution and presumably in origin. It would appear that this group once established in the Antarctic encountered little competition from other invading families and has radiated to fill many of the ecological niches available. In doing so these fishes have adapted themselves morphologically and physiologically to the requirements of many varied habitats. The majority are bottom fishes but some are pelagic in habit and have acquired some of the morphological characteristics of pelagic species.

On the other hand a considerable number of the fishes other than the Noto-theniiformes belong to families, the vast majority of whose members are normally found in temperate or tropical seas. A unique opportunity therefore exists not only to study a family group of fishes which is predominantly Antarctic but also to compare the Antarctic members of the 'temperate-tropical' families with their more 'normal' representatives.

On the whole the majority of Antarctic fishes are of medium size with comparatively large heads and mouths. A few remnants of very large fishes have been recorded, usually as mutilated remains in seal holes. A complete specimen has now been obtained and is still being studied.

MARINE ALGAE

Papenfuss (1961) summarized the present state of our knowledge of the marine algae of Antarctica showing the need for a systematic catalogue of the species which have already been recorded from the area. He also demonstrates much of what has already been recorded needs to be re-collected and re-assessed. Much confusion exists in the literature concerning the identity of many of the species already recorded, and some of the largest of the Antarctic algae such as the endemic genera *Ascoseira*, *Himantothallus*, *Phaeoglossum* and *Phyllogigas* cannot even be assigned to families. A large number of the genera recorded from the

---

FIG. 38 SOME TYPICAL ANTARCTIC FISHES

1. *Trematomus hansoni* (Boulenger). Family Nototheniidae. (After Boulenger.)
2. *Pagetopsis macropterus* (Boulenger). Family Chaenichthyidae. (After Boulenger.)
3. *Bathydraco macrolepis* Boulenger. Family Bathydraconidae. (After Boulenger.)
4. *Histiodraco velifer* (Regan). Family Harpagiferidae. (After Regan.)

Antarctic are endemic to the area and a very high percentage are monotypic. Papenfuss concludes that, 'the knowledge which will accrue about some of the marine algae from the Antarctic is certain to contribute significantly to our understanding of the inter-relationships and evolution of some of the major groups of algae'.

Distributions and Relationships of the Antarctic Benthos

There are enormous gaps in our knowledge of the geographical distribution of marine benthic organisms in the Antarctic. The best collected areas are those around Graham Land and the islands of the Scotia Arc, the Ross Sea and the shores of the Antarctic Continent from roughly 70° E to 170° E. If species are known from both eastern and western areas, it may be presumed that they have a circum-Antarctic distribution. As our knowledge becomes more precise it becomes obvious that a high percentage of each group of animals has a circum-Antarctic distribution. Of seventy-five species of Bivalvia, Amphineura and Scaphopoda found in Antarctic waters proper at least thirty (or 40%) are known from both eastern and western Antarctica. Fell has listed thirty-three species of ophiuroids from the Ross Sea and of these, nineteen, or 57%, are probably circum-Antarctic.

On the other hand many species are still known only from one locality. It is, of course, not possible to be certain if such records are the result of gaps in collections or truly represent extremely local development of species. The islands of the Scotia Arc undoubtedly act as relatively efficient stepping stones by means of which the truly Antarctic fauna can extend its range to southern South America, and in reverse the South American fauna can extend into the Antarctic. The evidence for molluscan traffic in this latter direction has already been discussed. It would appear that forms which have a wide distribution in Antarctic waters but which extend to varying degrees to the north and which have no obvious close relatives in other areas are in fact Antarctic forms which are spreading northwards. The subgenus *Aequiyoldia* of *Yoldia* which is an endemic southern subgenus is found as far north as the Falklands and Southern Chile but also occurs at Kerguelen. *Dentalium* (*Fissidentalium*) *majorinum* similarly extends as far north as the Falklands and the Magellan region. *Adacnarca* which is again a genus endemic to the Antarctic region reaches its northern limit at South Georgia. *Cyamiocardium*, which is widely spread in Antarctic seas, has one species off the coast of Chile, while *Pseudokellya* extends to South Georgia and Kerguelen Island. A number of other endemic Antarctic genera such as *Submargarita*, *Leptocollonia*, *Ovirissoa*, *Trichoconcha* and *Lorabela* appear to reach their northern limits at South Georgia while others such as *Antimargarita*, *Antitrichotropis*, *Discotrichoconcha* and *Notoficula* occur around the Antarctic Continent and on one or other of the adjacent island groups of the South Shetland, South Orkney, South Sandwich or Bouvet Islands.

In many groups the limits of distribution of the Antarctic species proper can be traced as far north as South Georgia in the region of the Scotia Arc. The seas between South Georgia and the Falklands certainly act as a faunal barrier to an appreciable number of forms. In addition to the mollusca mentioned above, Fell has listed eight genera of Ophiuroidea which are confined to the Antarctic Continent and the islands of the Scotia Arc but which do not reach the Falklands.

At the same time this barrier is by no means a universal one. Some very specific Antarctic forms of mollusca and three genera of Antarctic Ophiuroids extend to the Falklands and southern Chile. The probable colonization of the Antarctic by species using the islands of the Scotia Arc as stepping stones has already been discussed.

General Characteristics of the Antarctic Fauna

One of the striking characteristics of Antarctic invertebrates is the relatively large percentage of species which are ovoviviparous or which brood the young. Similarly in the Arctic, large-yolked eggs and abbreviated life histories with suppression of free-swimming larval stages are commonly encountered. The habit has been noted for many of the bivalves, ophiuroids and echinoids. At the same time many of these ovoviviparous forms are amongst the commonest and most widely distributed members of the fauna. In the case of the bivalves a high percentage of these forms are usually attached by means of a byssus to fixed substrates such as algae, colonial coelenterates, sponges or bryozoa or even to motile animals such as some of the echinoids. The fixed adult habit and lack of motile larval stages does not appear to have inhibited the powers of dispersal. It must therefore be presumed that when such attached forms are carried to a new area as the substrate breaks off and is carried passively by currents, it is of decided advantage for establishment if the animal can produce a quantity of developed young, ready formed. A single example of some of the quite small bivalves for example, about 0·6 cm in diameter, has been shown to contain up to 400 developing young.

It has been noted, again amongst the bivalves, that nearly all the species considered to be old inhabitants of the Antarctic region are ovoviviparous. At the same time there is a large number of Antarctic animals for which no details of breeding mechanisms are yet recorded.

From the evidence of the wealth of such material brought up in hauls of dredges and trawls it has been long surmised that in many parts of the Antarctic the bottom is coated with a thick layer of living, sessile, branching colonial animals. The more direct evidence of bottom photographs from the Ross Sea area amply confirms this supposition. It appears that in places the mat of living organisms of this sort may be 75 cm or more in height. The development of such a carpet of fixed organisms may be partially explained by a number of environmental factors. The regular supply of fine sediments in most of the areas surrounding the Antarctic seems particularly meagre. At the same time an abundant shower of the remains of planktonic organisms undoubtedly occurs especially during the summer when the development of plankton is at a maximum. Competition for such food will give quite considerable advantages to those animals which can cover a wide area with a feeding network of one kind or another and hence forms with a habit of this kind will tend to be favoured. Advantage will also accrue to a species which can reach above its fellows. The species comprising this mat will in turn provide food material for many specialized carnivores. Other forms which can maintain themselves by various means high up on this canopy will also gain a selective advantage. On these grounds the development of so many small attached bivalves with filter-feeding mechanisms is easily explicable. Fell (1961) has shown from the evidence of bottom photographs that some species of ophiuroids feed on canopy organisms while others have evolved feeding habits which allow them to make use of fishing techniques to avail themselves of the food in the plankton shower.

Mollusca on the whole have thin, rather colourless shells, many of which become badly eroded even in life. The large endemic pectinid *Adamussium colbecki* (Fig. 37) has a purple shell which contains so little calcium that the shell is slightly flexible in life. Other invertebrates are quite highly coloured as the colour plates published by Fell (1961) and the generalized bottom photographs published by Bullivant (1959a) amply demonstrate. Some of the colonial coelenterates are also relatively highly coloured.

The Origins of the Antarctic Fauna

On faunal grounds three main elements may be distinguished amongst those Antarctic groups which have been analysed from this point of view.

1. An old Antarctic group composed supposedly of forms which survived the latest onset of glacial conditions and whose ultimate origins are obscure. Amongst these groups are probably to be found those animals which are best adapted to the peculiar Antarctic conditions. These will include the fishes of the Nototheniiformes, such mollusca as *Adamussium colbecki*, *Thracia meridionalis*, *Astarte*, *Laternula elliptica*, *Adacnarca*, *Pseudokellya* and *Cadulus dalli antarcticus*, and the glacial genera of ophiuroids.

2. A large group derived from the faunas of contiguous deep-water basins in the South Indian, South Pacific and South Atlantic oceans. Many of these species live in Antarctic waters, in conditions which are essentially similar, ecologically, to more usual deep-water habitats. Such forms will include the Nuculanids, *Limopsis*, *Dacrydium*, *Thyasira*, *Pholadomya*, *Poromya*, *Cuspidaria*, *Leucosyrinx*, *Pleurotomella* and *Pontiothauma* amongst the mollusca.

3. A group which has been derived from South America through the islands of the Scotia Arc. This includes *Nuttalochiton*, *Philobrya*, *Cyclocardia*, *Gaimardia*, *Margarella* and *Amauropsis* in the mollusca.

Powell (1960, p. 122) summarizes the position for the mollusca as follows and these remarks probably apply also to other groups:

> Summarized the present Antarctic fauna can be viewed as being in an active stage of colonization effected by the proximity of the South American Continent continued through the islands and archipelagos of the Scotia Arc to the Antarctic Continent at Grahamland.

The Subantarctic west-wind drift affords means of dispersal in that zone to the westward and around the Antarctic Continent the prevailing east-wind drift operates in a reverse direction.

As already mentioned the deep basins afford yet another means of entry to the region and in the Subantarctic cross ridges and connecting basins provide means for lateral dispersal.

All this is superimposed upon an older fauna of few surviving members.

Bipolarity

A great deal of scientific energy has been expended in the past in discussions of bipolarity, the occurrence of identical or very similar species in Arctic and Antarctic waters. More critical systematics has shown that some of the supposed identical species are distinct in each area but undoubted closely allied species pairs do exist in the two opposite polar regions. In some groups there are very strong faunal similarities. Powell (1951) has shown that some supposed bipolar genera actually do occur in tropical waters at comparatively great depths. The evidence for bipolarity will be much more validly based when faunal revisions taking into consideration the recently collected material are concluded. Until the taxonomy is critically re-examined further discussions on the problem are largely futile. Much of the evidence previously marshalled can be interpreted in other ways. Many of the Arctic benthic animals are characteristic deep-water forms and the same is true of many Antarctic species. Faunal comparisons at the generic level based upon such records have little validity in a discussion of bipolarity.

Bibliography

BULLIVANT, J. S. 1959a: An Oceanographic Survey of the Ross Sea, *Nature* **184:** 422–3.

BULLIVANT, J. S. 1959b: Photographs of the Bottom Fauna in the Ross Sea, *N.Z.J. Sci.* **2:** 485–97.

BURTON, M. 1932: Sponges, *Discovery Rep.* **6:** 237–392.

CARCELLES, A. R., and WILLIAMSON, S. I. 1951: Catalogo de los Moluscos Marinos de la Provincia Magallanica, *Rev. Inst. Nac. Invest. Cienc. Nat. Zool.* **2:** 225–383.

DAVID, P. M. 1958: The Distribution of Chaetognaths of the Southern Ocean, *Discovery Rep.* **29:** 199–228.

DELL, R. K. 1952: Marine Biology, Simpson, F. A., ed., *The Antarctic Today*, pp. 129–50. Reed and NZ Antarctic Society, Wellington.

DELL, R. K. 1959: Cephalopoda, *B.A.N.Z.A.R. Exped. Rep.* **B8:** 89–106.

DELL, R. K. (in press): Antarctic and Subantarctic Mollusca: Bivalvia, Amphineura and Scaphopoda, *Discovery Rep.*

EKMAN, S. 1953: *Zoogeography of the Sea*, Sidgwick and Jackson, London.

FELL, H. B. 1961: The Fauna of the Ross Sea, Pt. I, Ophiuroidea, *N.Z. Dept. Sci. Ind. Res. Bull.* **142.**

FRASER, F. C. 1936: On the Development and Distribution of the Young Stages of Krill (*Euphausia superba*), *Discovery Rep.* **14:** 1–192.

HARDY, A. C. and GUNTHER, E. R. 1935: The Plankton of the South Georgia Whaling Grounds and Adjacent Waters, *Discovery Rep.* **11:** 1–456.

HART, T. J. 1937: *Rhizosolenia curvata* Zacharias an Indicator Species in the Southern Ocean, *Discovery Rep.* **16:** 413–46.

HART, T. J. 1942: Phytoplankton Periodicity in Antarctic Surface Waters, *Discovery Rep.* **21:** 261–356.

KNOX, G. A. 1960: Littoral Ecology and Biogeography of the Southern Oceans, *Proc. Roy. Soc.* **B.152:** 577–624.

MACKINTOSH, N. A. 1960: The Patterns of Distribution of the Antarctic Fauna, *Proc. Roy. Soc.* **B.152:** 624–631.

MATTHEWS, L. H. 1929: The Natural History of the Elephant Seal, *Discovery Rep.* **1:** 233–56.

PAPENFUSS, G. F. 1961: Recommendations concerning Future Research on Antarctic Marine Algae, *Nat. Acad. Sci. Nat. Res. Council* Publ. **839:** 77–80.

POWELL, A. W. B. 1951: Antarctic and Subantarctic Mollusca : Pelecypoda and Gastropoda, *Discovery Rep.* **26:** 47–196.

POWELL, A. W. B. 1957: Mollusca of Kerguelen and Macquarie Islands, *B.A.N.Z.A.R. Exped. Rep.* **B6:** 107–49.

POWELL, A. W. B. 1958: Mollusca from the Victoria-Ross Quadrants of Antarctica, *B.A.N.Z.A.R. Exped. Rep.* **B6:** 165–215.

POWELL, A. W. B. 1960: Antarctic and Subantarctic Mollusca, *Rec. Auck; Inst. Mus.* **5:** 117–193.

ROFEN, R. R. and DEWITT, H. H. 1961: Antarctic Fishes, *Nat. Acad. Sci. Nat. Res. Council* Publ. **839:** 94–112.

RUUD, J. T. 1958: Vertebrates Without Blood Pigment: A study of the Family Chaenichthyidae, *Proc. 15 Int. Coryr. Zool. London 6*, paper **32:** 526–8.

SOOT-RYEN, T. 1951: Antarctic Pelecypods, *Sci. Res. Norw. Ant. Exped. 1927–8 et seq.* No. 32.

TAKI, I. 1961: On Two New Eledonid Octopods from the Antarctic Sea, *J. Fac. Fish. Anim. Husband. Hiroshima Univ.* **3:** 297–316.

TYLER, J. C. 1960: Erythrocyte Counts and Hemoglobin Determinations for Two Antarctic Nototheniid Fishes, *Stanford Ichthyol. Bull.* **7:** 199–201.

CHAPTER SIX

Birds and Mammals

B. STONEHOUSE, *University of Canterbury, New Zealand*

Introduction

The rocks and ice blanket of the southern polar continent offer bare hospitality to animal and plant life. Land vegetation is sparse, restricted by cold, aridity and lack of soil to a meagre assembly of small plants. Algae, mosses and lichens are the characteristic plants of Antarctica; only two genera of flowering plant are known from the 14 million square kilometres of the continent. Land animals are limited in species to a few invertebrates of soil, vegetation and fresh water; protozoa, mites, tardigrades, nematodes, rotifers, and primitive insects are the only creatures which have so far been found on the continent itself. (See Chapters 13 and 14).

Antarctic seas are by contrast a teeming reservoir of life, comparable in yield per acre to the finest pasture land. At the height of summer their surface waters, although seldom more than one or two degrees above freezing point, contain rich accumulations of microscopic plants and animals which support, directly or indirectly, huge stocks of seals, whales and sea birds. Debris filtering downward from the surface supports an extensive fauna of sponges, echinoderms, molluscs and other creatures on the ocean floor. Only the intertidal zones of Antarctica are empty of animal and plant life, except in islands north of the region of fast winter ice (e.g. South Georgia); the continental shores with their persistent ice blanket offer little or no encouragement to the highly specialized forms which elsewhere gain a footing on wave-washed rocks and beaches.

The number of species of animals capable of living in polar conditions is small; abundance in the sea arises from the vast numbers of individuals by which each species is represented, and even on land or in fresh water surprising accumulations of animals of single species may develop in favoured places. Fresh-water lakes may teem with rotifers for a few days in each year, small rocks may be black with a dense cover of mites, and hundreds of acres of raised beach may be covered with penguin nests. Land-bound animals tend to be small – the largest animal capable of living entirely on land in Antarctica is considerably smaller than a housefly. At sea a large volume is advantageous to the warm-blooded creatures which dominate the food chains; the world's greatest seals and sea birds are found in Antarctic waters, and the Blue Whale, the largest animal the world has ever known, grows fat on the summer abundance of food in southern waters.

Marine birds and mammals make only sparing use of the Antarctic Continent; with few exceptions they spend more of their time at sea than on land, and feed entirely in the water. Sea birds roost and breed on the shore and coastal peaks. Some may breed far inland; thus Snow Petrels and McCormick Skuas have been found in small colonies at 2000 m in the mountains of Dronning Maud Land, 300 km from the sea. One species, the Emperor Penguin, breeds mainly on off-lying islands or even on the sea ice itself. The seals of Antarctica produce their young on shore, or more frequently on sea ice; two species, Ross and Crabeater seals, live almost exclusively on floating pack ice and are seldom seen on or near land.

Whales are entirely aquatic, but some species show a tendency to gather in sheltered inshore waters where, often enough, plankton is locally enriched. Like many of the seals and sea birds, whales migrate southward in spring and summer, when the surface waters of Antarctica provide their greatest abundance of food. They winter in lower, warmer latitudes, where food is usually scarce but heat losses from the body are smaller. Unlike seals and birds, whales produce their young in the warmer part of their range, and the summer excursions to high latitudes are periods of feeding and fattening rather than of breeding.

Forty-three species of birds and six species of seals breed in the area generally defined as the Antarctic region (i.e. on islands and coasts within the bounds of the Antarctic Convergence: see p. 121). Only twelve species of birds and four species of seals breed on or near the shores of the Antarctic Continent. Of the factors which combine to restrict the number of species in the far south, isolation has probably played an important role throughout the geological history of the continent. At present the narrowest gap separating Antarctica from the rest of the world is the Drake Passage, a 650 km stretch of deep and tempestuous water which forms a likely barrier to colonization by modern plants and animals. Land bridges may have spanned the gap (possibly through the islands of the Scotia Arc) at intervals during early and middle Tertiary times, when the climate of Antarctica was less rigorous than at present. The continent supported temperate or subtropical plant life and insects in the past, but no fossil remains of amphibia, reptiles, or land birds and mammals have been found. The only vertebrate fossils so far recorded are of Tertiary penguins and whale-like mammals, sea creatures akin to those which inhabit Antarctica at present; it is possible that the vertebrate fauna of the continent has always been restricted to animals which could reach it by flying or swimming. The sea birds and seals of today owe much of their success to Antarctica's isolation, for they flourish in the complete absence of large mammalian land predators.

Penguins and seals probably spend more than half their lives in cold water, an exacting environment for which they are well equipped. Their ability to live on the coldest continent follows almost incidentally, for adaptations to the one environment confer benefit in the other. Marine animals generally, and the warm-blooded vertebrates in particular, are more abundant in cold than in warm water, for cool seas (including the cold water masses and currents which penetrate toward the tropics from polar and temperate latitudes) are richer in food. To take advantage of food resources in cold water, warm-blooded animals need the means of reducing heat losses between their bodies and the sea. The dense, water-repelling plumage of penguin and petrel, the thick, tough skin of whale and seal, the fur borne by some of the seals of temperate and low-Antarctic latitudes, the sub-cutaneous fat or blubber common to all warm-blooded marine vertebrates, are devices for reducing the flow of heat between warm animal and cold sea. Compactness and size are further adaptations in the same cause. The extremities of seals and penguins are generally short and bony; muscles are concentrated in the body mass, so that little blood need circulate in the periphery. Largeness is itself an asset, for large animals have a low ratio of surface to volume and can therefore conserve heat more efficiently than smaller animals. Some animals, notably the whales, have a heat exchange system in the blood vessels of the skin, whereby cooled blood flowing inward from the skin is warmed by arterial blood flowing outward. Seals and sea birds capable of living in freezing water are apparently undismayed by air at very much lower temperatures, possibly because of the lower conductivity of still air. A cold, windy spell of weather in Antarctica sends seals rapidly back into the sea and may delay by a few days the onset of breeding in some birds; to this extent the animals are clearly responsive to cold. They are capable, however, of tending their young through blizzards lasting several days, and rarely seem to die of cold when food is plentiful. Young birds are more vulnerable than adults, and a single blizzard may give rise to heavy losses in a colony containing nestlings.

The warm-blooded animals of Antarctica seldom experience extreme cold. Most of them keep away from the continent during the coldest months; only the Emperor Penguin remains to breed in the depths of winter. In thinking of Antarctic conditions man takes the biased view of a mammal accustomed to living in temperate regions. Poorly adapted for polar life, he experiences hardships and difficulties which few Antarctic animals have to share.

Visiting continental Antarctica only in summer and living near the coast, where mean temperatures are ameliorated by the warmth of the sea, most southern sea birds and seals avoid the extreme conditions which man encounters on barrier and inland ice. Few birds fly inland; in their summer wanderings they are unlikely to encounter temperatures as low, for instance, as those met every winter by birds of eastern and central North America. Their own winters are spent among the pack ice or in warmer regions beyond; only when mean monthly temperatures are approaching or rising above freezing point will they return to breed in the region of the continental coast. Their environmental temperatures in summer are in any case higher than climatic records show, for the warming effects of sun on rock, and sheltered conditions near the ground, affect considerably the micro-climate in which they live during their months in Antarctica. Seals also miss many of the conditions which men encounter, for they lie in sheltered positions on the sea ice and return to the comparatively warm sea when temperatures are low or winds strong.

The continuing success of Antarctic mammals and birds, their numbers and wide distribution about the continent, above all their many remarkable adaptations for their environment, make them subjects of particular interest to biologists. The recent spate of scientific activity in Antarctica has provided many opportunities for their study, and the present account is an attempt to summarize some of the more important findings of research in the last quarter-century.

TABLE I

THE BREEDING BIRDS OF ANTARCTICA AND THEIR NESTING RANGES[1]

Order Sphenisciformes

1. *Aptenodytes patagonica.* King Penguin. Heard, Kerguelen, northern Scotia Arc and Subantarctic islands.
2. *Aptenodytes forsteri.* Emperor Penguin. Coast of Antarctic Continent only.
3. *Pygoscelis papua.* Gentoo Penguin. Heard, Kerguelen, Scotia Arc and northern Graham Land, and Subantarctic islands.
4. *Pygoscelis adeliae.* Adelie Penguin. Antarctic Continent, southern Scotia Arc, Bouvetøya and Peter I Øy.
5. *Pygoscelis antarctica.* Chinstrap or Ringed Penguin. Northern Graham Land, Scotia Arc, Bouvetøya and Peter I Øy.
6. *Eudyptes cristatus.* Rockhopper Penguin. Heard Island, Kerguelen and the Subantarctic islands.
7. *Eudyptes chrysolophus.* Macaroni Penguin. Scotia Arc, Bouvetøya, Heard, Kerguelen, and some Subantarctic islands.

Order Procellariiformes

8. *Diomedea exulans.* Wandering Albatross. South Georgia, Kerguelen and Subantarctic islands.
9. *Diomedea melanophris.* Black-browed Albatross. South Georgia, Kerguelen and Subantarctic islands.
10. *Diomedea chrysostoma.* Grey-headed Albatross. South Georgia and possibly Kerguelen; Subantarctic islands.
11. *Phoebetria palpebrata.* Light-mantled Sooty Albatross. South Georgia, Heard and Kerguelen, and Subantarctic islands.
12. *Macronectes giganteus.* Giant Petrel. Antarctic coast, Scotia Arc, Bouvetøya Heard, Kerguelen and Subantarctic islands.
13. *Daption capensis.* Pintado Petrel or Cape Pigeon. Antarctic coast, Scotia Arc, Bouvetøya, Heard, Kerguelen and Subantarctic islands.
14. *Fulmarus glacialoides.* Silver-grey Fulmar. Antarctic coast, Scotia Arc, Bouvetøya and Kerguelen.
15. *Halobaena caerulea.* Kerguelen Island and Subantarctic islands. Possibly Scotia Arc.

[1] I am grateful to Dr R. A. Falla for helpful comments on this table.

TABLE I—*contd.*

16. *Pachyptila desolata.* Dove Prion. Antarctic coast (Cape Denison), Scotia Arc, Heard, Kerguelen and Subantarctic islands.
17. *Pachyptila belcheri.* Thin-billed Prion. Kerguelen and Subantarctic islands.
18. *Pachyptila crassirostris.* Fulmar Prion. Possibly Kerguelen, Subantarctic islands.
19. *Thalassoica antarctica.* Antarctic Petrel. Coast of Antarctic Continent only.
20. *Adamaster cinereus.* Black-tailed Shearwater. Kerguelen and Subantarctic islands.
21. *Procellaria equinoctialis.* Shoemaker. South Georgia, Kerguelen and Subantarctic islands.
22. *Pterodroma macroptera.* Kerguelen and Subantarctic islands.
23. *Pterodroma lessoni.* White-headed Petrel. Kerguelen and Subantarctic islands.
24. *Pterodroma brevirostris.* Kerguelen Petrel. Kerguelen only.
25. *Pterodroma mollis.* Soft-winged Petrel. Subantarctic islands, possibly Kerguelen.
26. *Pagodroma nivea.* Snow Petrel. Antarctic coast, Scotia Arc, Bouvetøya.
27. *Oceanites oceanicus.* Wilson's Petrel. Antarctic coast, Scotia Arc, Heard and Kerguelen.
28. *Fregetta tropica.* Black-bellied Storm Petrel. Scotia Arc, Bouvet, Kerguelen, and Subantarctic islands.
29. *Garrodia nereis.* Grey-backed Storm Petrel. South Georgia, Kerguelen and Subantarctic islands.
30. *Pelecanoides georgicus.* South Georgia Diving Petrel. South Georgia, Kerguelen and Macquarie Islands.
31. *Pelecanoides urinatrix.* Australasian Diving Petrel. Heard, Kerguelen and Subantarctic islands.

Order Pelecaniformes

32. *Phalacrocorax verrucosus.* Kerguelen Cormorant. Îles de Kerguelen only.
33. *Phalacrocorax atriceps* Blue-eyed Cormorant. Graham Land, Scotia Arc, Heard Island.

Order Anseriformes

34. *Anas eatoni.* Kerguelen Pintail. Îles de Kerguelen only.
35. *Anas georgica.* South Georgia Pintail. South Georgia only.

Order Charadriiformes

36. *Catharacta skua.* Brown Skua. Northern Graham Land, Scotia Arc, Bouvetøya, Heard, Kerguelen and Subantarctic islands.
37. *Catharacta maccormicki.* McCormick's Skua. Southern Graham Land and Antarctic coast.

TABLE I—*contd.*

---

38. *Larus dominicanus.* Southern Black-backed Gull. Antarctic coast, Scotia Arc, Heard, Kerguelen and Subantarctic islands.
39. *Sterna vittata.* Antarctic Tern. Antarctic coast, Scotia Arc, Heard, Kerguelen and Subantarctic islands.
40. *Sterna virgata.* Kerguelen Tern. Île de Kerguelen only.
41. *Chionis alba.* Sheathbill. Northern Graham Land and Scotia Arc.
42. *Chionis minor.* Lesser Sheathbill. Heard, Kerguelen and Subantarctic islands of the Indian Ocean.

Order Passeriformes.

43. *Anthus antarcticus.* South Georgia Pipit. South Georgia only.

The Birds of the Antarctic Region

Forty-three species of birds breed within the Antarctic Convergence; their names and principal breeding grounds are listed in Table 1. Twenty-four of the species are petrels, seven are penguins and seven belong to the order Charadriiformes. The remaining species include two of pintail ducks (species endemic respectively on South Georgia and Kerguelen), two of cormorants, and a single passerine restricted to South Georgia.

The heavy preponderance of ocean-feeding species (penguins and petrels) is characteristic of the region. Birds which feed on shore or in shallow water (gulls, terns, cormorants and sheathbills) are fewer both in species and in numbers of individuals. Only the single species of passerine appears to feed entirely on land, although it has been recorded on floating fronds of *Macrocystis* immediately offshore, where it may take crustacea or other small marine animals. Brown Skuas and Sheathbills feed largely on land during the summer, when they respectively parasitize and scavenge on colonies of penguins, but they also take food in the intertidal zone of the more northerly islands. The two species of pintail feed among the grasses and seal wallows of South Georgia and Kerguelen, but may occasionally feed along the shore. The Kerguelen Tern is mainly a land bird in summer, when it catches large quantities of insects; it also feeds offshore in summer and presumably feeds only at sea in winter when insects are scarce on land.

Nearly half the species listed in Table 1 breed over a wide range in the Subantarctic, penetrating southward only as far as the fringing islands of northern Antarctica (Heard, Kerguelen and South Georgia). Only a dozen of the listed species breed on the shores of continental Antarctica below the latitude of southern Graham Land; five additional breeding species of more northerly range reach the continent on the Graham Land coast but do not breed further south. Only three species (Emperor Penguin, Antarctic Petrel and McCormick Skua) breed exclusively on the continental coast, reaching their northern limits in

Graham Land (Table 2). Most Antarctic breeding birds may therefore be regarded as species of the Subantarctic which have extended their summer range southward into the rich waters and tranquil breeding grounds below the Convergence. Their pattern of distribution suggests strongly that the Scotia Arc and Graham Land have provided an important route from north to south, while the prevailing westerly winds and ocean currents may have assisted dispersal eastward from this region.

Species of the far south tend to be circumpolar in distribution and morphologically unvarying throughout their range. Thus the three which breed

TABLE 2

THE BREEDING BIRDS OF CONTINENTAL ANTARCTICA

Species	Breeding on	
	Antarctic Coast, including Graham Land south of 68th parallel	Graham Land north of 68th parallel
*Aptenodytes forsteri	+	—
Pygoscelis papua	—	+
Pygoscelis adeliae	+	+
Pygoscelis antarctica	—	+
Macronectes giganteus	+	+
Daption capensis	+	+
Fulmarus glacialoides	+	±
Pachyptila desolata	+	±
*Thalassoica antarctica	+	—
Pagodroma nivea	+	+
Oceanites oceanicus	+	+
Phalacrocorax atriceps	—	+
Catharacta skua	—	+
*Catharacta maccormicki	+	+
Larus domicanus	+	+
Sterna vittata	+	+
Chionis alba	—	+

+ Breeding.
± Breeding probable but unconfirmed.
— Not recorded as breeding.
* Breeding exclusively in continental Antarctica.

exclusively on the continent and others which share their habitat cannot readily be divided into geographical races. Emperor and Adelie Penguins from Ross Island have so far proved indistinguishable from their fellows breeding on the coasts of Terre Adélie or Graham Land. The more northerly breeding species often give rise to subspecies, particularly among the island groups which spread in an east–west line across the central and northern reaches of the Southern Ocean. Species which breed both on the continent and on the islands tend either to be uniform and without subspecies, or to give rise to a single continental form (often circumpolar) and a number of more northerly subspecies. Giant Petrels and Pintado Petrels, whose breeding ranges spread from the continental shore to New Zealand's southern islands, have not yet been divided satisfactorily into sub-species; nor has the Dominican Gull, whose breeding range extends from southern Marguerite Bay in Lat. 68° S to the coast of northern Peru. Cormorants and skuas, Wilson's Petrel, the Dove Prion and the Antarctic Tern are among the more variable species. The Blue-eyed Cormorant may be divided into three distinct subspecies which respectively occupy Heard Island, South Georgia and the southern islands of the Scotia Arc with Graham Land; Antarctic Terns are similarly divisible into subspecies, a southern circumpolar form appearing at points on the continent as far apart as Gaussberg and Graham Land, and separate northern subspecies appearing on South Georgia and in the Kerguelen–Heard region. Dove Prions and Wilson's Petrels give rise to southern representatives with long wings, and northern island forms with shorter wings, but few other species obey so clearly definable a rule.

Species which breed in northern Antarctica but not in the far south usually have a wide distribution also in the Subantarctic. They may give rise to northern and southern forms, but the line dividing the breeding ranges of their subspecies seldom coincides with the Antarctic Convergence. Thus the northern form of the Wandering Albatross is restricted to islands of the Tristan da Cunha group, while the southern form breeds on Antarctic and Subantarctic islands on either side of the Convergence. The northern subspecies of the Gentoo Penguin by contrast straddles the Convergence from the Falkland Islands to South Georgia, while the southern form breeds only on the islands and mainland coast in the Graham Land region. The status of Gentoo Penguins breeding elsewhere in their extensive range is unknown.

The feeding ranges of most species widely overlap breeding ranges. Only a few sedentary species, notably the cormorants and land-feeding species, tend to feed close to their breeding grounds. Oceanic feeders, although probably restricted to within a thousand kilometres of their nest sites during the breeding season, wander considerably during non-breeding periods. Giant Petrels banded as nestlings in South Georgia and southern islands of the Scotia Arc are frequently recovered as juveniles in their first and second years on the subtropical coasts of Africa, Australia and South America; their travels during the early years of life may take them several times round the world in the belt of westerly winds. Other species may be expected to make similar movements of dispersion before breeding. Banding evidence at present suggests that breeding birds tend to return to their nest sites of previous years, although long migrations may be the rule between seasons. Wilson's Petrels are believed to migrate regularly into Arctic and Subarctic regions during the southern winter. McCormick Skuas have been captured in the Northern Hemisphere, and Pintado Petrels in large numbers appear off the whaling stations of New Zealand and South Africa each year. Birds of northern Antarctica similarly find their way south; the light-mantled Sooty Albatross, which breeds only on the northern Antarctic islands and in the Subantarctic, has been recorded as far south as the Bay of Whales (77° 50′ S), and Wandering Albatrosses are frequently recorded in the region of the polar circle. Particular species are associated with the zones of ice-free water and pack ice which encircle the Antarctic Continent. Thus Giant Petrels, White-headed Petrels, the smaller albatrosses and prions, are numerous over open water immediately south of the Convergence; Silver-grey Fulmars and Antarctic Petrels appear in quantity as the pack ice is approached. Snow Petrels almost invariably indicate the presence of pack ice nearby, and among the pack are found the species which breed along the continental coast. Unfortunately little is known of the winter distribution of birds in the pack ice; the records of the *Belgica* and *Endurance* expeditions provide most of our meagre information on this neglected but interesting aspect of Antarctic biology.

Numbers and distribution of breeding species in the Antarctic region probably depend largely on two important factors – the availability of food and the presence of suitable nest sites and materials. These in turn are controlled by climatic and geographical factors, the effects of which are most clearly seen in the South American sector of Antarctica where island chains extend between the northern and southern edges of the region.

For many purposes the Antarctic Convergence serves well as a northern boundary to Antarctica. Islands lying to either side of it differ markedly in climate, vegetation and avifauna, although as we have already seen it does not necessarily provide a geographical dividing line between subspecies. The effects of cold Antarctic water on the flora and fauna of islands below the Convergence are well illustrated in a comparison between South Georgia and the Falkland Islands. Although only 1500 km apart and separated by less than three degrees of latitude, the Falklands and South Georgia show respectively the main characteristics of Subantarctic and Antarctic islands. The Falklands are mild, windy, and free of sea ice throughout the year. Monthly mean temperatures remain above freezing point and the annual temperature range is slight. Insects and fresh-water animals are plentiful, and the islands support nearly 150 species of flowering plants. Moorlands, swamps, sheltered harbour shores and creeks, pastures and mud flats provide a variety of habitats for land and marine birds; approximately two-thirds of the sixty-five breeding species of birds feed entirely on land. South Georgia by contrast is glaciated and surrounded by cold Antarctic water throughout the year. Mean monthly temperatures in winter fall below freezing point and the annual mean is 4° C lower than in the Falklands.

The vegetation includes only sixteen species of flowering plants, among which tussock grasses and small recumbent shrubs predominate. Shore, fresh-water and insect life is scarce, and feeding and nesting habitats are less varied than those of the Falkland Islands. South Georgia supports only two true land-feeding birds (the endemic pintail and pipit) among its twenty-five breeding species, although the Sheathbill and Brown Skua also feed mainly on land in summer.

Within Antarctic waters the mean northern limit of pack ice provides another important boundary affecting the distribution of sea birds. Islands which lie within the pack in winter suffer a continental type of climate, for the surface of the pack has many of the insulating and reflecting properties of land ice. The islands of the southern Scotia Arc (South Orkney, South Shetland, and the southernmost islands of the South Sandwich chain) have harder and longer winters than South Georgia. Their flora is much reduced; the tussock grasses are among the many prominent species which fail to survive below the northern limit of pack ice. Ten species of breeding birds are lost between South Georgia and the South Orkney Islands, and of these at least eight depend on the food, cover, or nesting sites which tussock associations afford. Thus the Shoemaker and Diving Petrel, which breed in holes dug in the soil of tussock banks, the Grey-backed Storm Petrel, which usually nests among tussock roots, the pipit and pintail, which forage among the dense, damp vegetation, and the albatrosses, which seem to prefer nesting on grass-covered slopes or cliffs, are all absent from the southern islands. Wandering Albatrosses and King Penguins may have other good reasons for avoiding islands below the northern limit of pack ice, for both maintain their chicks throughout winter and require a milder, more oceanic type of climate than the southern islands provide. King Penguins penetrate to the northern islands of the South Sandwich chain, where the effects of the pack ice may be felt only slightly, but do not breed on the more southerly islands which are engulfed by ice for several months each year. It would be of particular interest to know whether their breeding routine on the South Sandwich Islands varies from the complex pattern which the mild climate of South Georgia allows.

The southern islands of the Scotia Arc are in summer climatically similar to the west coast of the Graham Land peninsula, and many species extend their range southward to the edge of the continent in this area. Gentoo Penguins and Sheathbills, both of which breed widely in the Subantarctic, reach their southern limits about the 65th parallel in western Graham Land; Giant Petrels, Dominican Gulls, Brown Skuas, Blue-eyed Cormorants (all species which breed over a wide range north of the Convergence) penetrate as breeding birds below the 67th parallel in Marguerite Bay. Although much of the Antarctic coast is lined with thick ice for ten or more months of the year, local conditions along the western side of Graham Land provide small areas in which the sea may remain open for all but a few days in the coldest months. Sea birds are thus able to reach open water even in mid-winter, and winter populations of cormorants and Giant Petrels may be found well below the Antarctic Circle in this region. Elsewhere, much of the Antarctic coastline lies on or about the Circle; although open water in winter has been recorded from many points, even as far south as McMurdo Sound (77° S), birds tend to leave the coast after the end of their breeding season and return only in spring and early summer. Species which breed on the Antarctic coastline generally congregate in areas where open water may be expected early in the season. The presence of a large penguin colony in a particular area is usually a safe indication that the sea ice nearby is unstable or likely to break several months before the dispersal of the main sheet.

The importance of food in determining the distribution of Antarctic birds has yet to be fully studied. Most birds of the region eat crustacea, squid and fish from the surface waters; these in turn feed on smaller creatures, and the base of the food pyramid is the vast abundance of diatoms which occurs every year from October onward. Antarctic surface waters in summer are between five and fifty times richer in food than tropical waters; the richest areas of all are found at the Convergence, in the East Wind Drift (the easterly flowing current which encircles continental Antarctica close inshore) and in the westerly flowing Weddell Current, which emerges by the tip of Graham Land and spreads across the southern Atlantic Ocean toward Tristan da Cunha. The peak of plant production is reached in November near the Convergence, from December to February in regions further south. The peak of production of animal life may follow a few days or weeks behind. Birds of the northern Antarctic region begin breeding earlier than those of the far south, although the difference in any widely ranging species is slight. Thus Adelie Penguins at Cape Royds, McMurdo Sound, the southern limit of their range, lay only two to three weeks later than those of the South Orkney Islands, 2000 km nearer the Equator at the northern edge of the breeding range.

The laying season in Antarctica is generally short, and breeding cycles are hurried; even in the most favourably situated colonies the birds appear to be racing against time to rear their chicks and complete their own post-nuptial moult during the brief summer abundance of food. Eggs lost are not usually replaced, and most species rear only one or two chicks in a single annual brood. The late arrival of spring or the early onset of cold weather in autumn can affect very seriously the year's crop of young, and the effects of climate may be just as severe toward the northern end of a species' range (where winds and heavy snow predominate) as in the colder but sunnier conditions of the far south.

The life cycles of many Antarctic birds, together with details of their taxonomy, measurements, etc., will be found in the two volumes of R. C. Murphy's *Oceanic Birds of South America*. Published in 1936, this work remains the most important single source of information in the field of Antarctic ornithology. Other major contributions to the study of Antarctic birds include R. A. Falla's report on the birds of the BANZAR Expedition (1937), and reports by Holgersen (1945, 1950, 1957) and by Bierman and Voous (1950) on birds studied in the course of whaling voyages. Species studies, particularly of penguins, have been prominent among biological reports of the last quarter-century. Emperor Penguins, first visited at a Ross Sea colony by members of the *Discovery* expedition in 1902, have now been watched through their annual cycle in colonies in Graham Land and Terre Adélie (Sapin-Jaloustre, 1952; Stonehouse, 1953; Prévost, 1961). Adelie Penguins have also received attention from French and British workers (Sladen, 1955, 1958; Sapin-Jaloustre, 1960), and are at present being studied in detail on a number of colonies in the Ross Sea area (Reid, 1961; Taylor, 1962; Stonehouse, 1963). At the northern edge of Antarctica King Penguins on South Georgia were made the subject of a year-round study by Stonehouse (1960). Gentoo and Chinstrap Penguins were earlier studied by Bagshaw (1938) and Roberts (1940b). Breeding of Gentoo, Rockhopper and Macaroni Penguins on Heard Island has been studied by Gwynn (1953), and notes on many of the other species of this interesting island have been compiled by Downes *et al.* (1959). Species other than penguins have on the whole received less detailed treatment, although reports are available on the Brown Skua in South Georgia (Stonehouse, 1956), the McCormick Skua on the coast of the polar continent (Eklund, 1961; Caughley, 1961; Young, 1963a, b), the Dove Prion on the South Orkney Islands (Tickell, 1962) and Wilson's Petrel in Graham Land (Roberts, 1940a). The Giant Petrel has recently been studied on Macquarie Island (Warham, 1962).

The bibliography at the end of this chapter includes many references to recent work, including banding programmes, physiological studies, and other aspects of avian biology which have received attention in Antarctica in recent years.

The Mammals of the Antarctic Region

Eight species of seals and more than a dozen species of whales are found regularly in Antarctic waters. Six species of seals breed and spend much, or all, of their lives below the Convergence; most of the whales, if not all of them, make regular migrations from cold to warm water each year, breeding toward the northern end of their ranges. Land mammals are also present in Antarctica; both Reindeer (*Rangifer arcticus*) and Brown Rats (*Rattus norvegicus*) flourish among the tussock grasses of South Georgia, where they were introduced respectively by whalers and sealers, and farm animals and domestic pests have been liberated on Kerguelen with varying measures of success. Rats and mice were from time to time reported at occupied land whaling stations in the southern Scotia Arc, but did not survive after the stations were abandoned. For notes on reindeer and rodents in Antarctica see papers by Lönnberg (1960), Olstad (1930) and Bonner (1958) listed in the bibliography.

The six species of seals which breed in Antarctic waters represent two families (Otariidae, Phocidae) of the three into which the order Pinnipedia is divided: the third family (Odobenidae, the walruses) is confined to the Arctic region. Seals of the family Otariidae, the 'eared' fur seals and sea lions, are prominent on islands and continental coasts in the Subantarctic. For over a century they formed the basis of an important industry and periodically suffered near-extinction. At present they appear to be recovering their numbers and returning to some of the localities from which they have long been absent. The Southern Fur Seal

Arctocephalus tropicalis gazella, the Antarctic representative of the family, is found on Bouvetøya, Kerguelen, South Georgia, the northern islands of the South Sandwich group, South Orkney and South Shetland. The nominate subspecies lives north of the Convergence on Marion, Gough, and Amsterdam Islands (possibly also on Prince Edward and the Crozets). A form generally regarded as a separate species *Arctocephalus australis* breeds in the Fuegian–Falkland Islands region, and races of a further species *Arctocephalus forsteri* are distinguished in New Zealand and Tasmania.

The Phocid seals are more widely distributed in Antarctica. Five species of separate genera inhabit the seas south of the Convergence. *Mirounga leonina*, the Southern Elephant Seal or Sea Elephant, breeds mainly on the fringes of the Antarctic region; South Georgia, supporting about half the total population of the species, is by far the largest breeding station. Large concentrations are found also on Kerguelen and Heard Island below the Convergence, and on Macquarie, Marion, the Falklands and Crozets, Antipodes, Auckland and Campbell Islands in the Subantarctic. Smaller breeding colonies are known on the islands of the southern Scotia Arc, and there is evidence that the species is at present expanding to reoccupy many of its old haunts. Like Fur Seals, Elephant Seals suffered widespread destruction during the nineteenth and early twentieth centuries; their oil was valued highly on world markets before mineral oils came into common use.

The remaining Phocid species breed only in the Antarctic, mostly within the northern limit of the pack ice. Weddell Seals (*Leptonychotes weddelli*) are most frequently recorded in high latitudes off the continental coast, but breed also in the southern Scotia Arc and in a single bay of South Georgia. They may reach their northern limit of breeding on Heard Island. Weddells are by far the commonest seals of the mainland coast, and have been taken as food for dogs and men by many Antarctic expeditions. Ross Seals (*Ommatophoca rossi*) are rare by comparison; they appear to spend most of their life in the pack ice and are seldom found either near the continental shore or on the northern islands of the Antarctic region. Crabeater Seals (*Lobodon carcinophagus*), which feed almost entirely on planktonic crustacea, and Leopard Seals (*Hydrurga leptonyx*), which hunt penguins, fish and other seals, are also creatures of the pack ice. While Crabeaters are seldom seen away from the pack, Leopard Seals are often encountered near the Convergence and wandering specimens are known from as far north as the tropics. Leopard and Ross Seals are usually solitary; other seals of the Antarctic region are more or less gregarious and fur and elephant seals form large breeding groups which may cover many miles of beach and rocky coast.

Of the whales which inhabit Antarctic waters, by far the best known are the large, commercially important rorquals, which for over half a century have supported a considerable industry on the threshold of the Antarctic Continent. Smaller species, which may be restricted in their distribution to narrow zones of water on the outer fringes of the region, have received less attention from whalers and scientists, and little is known of their biology. Largest of all is the Blue or

Sulphur-bottom Whale *Balaenoptera musculus*; both vernacular names derive from the yellow film of diatoms which covers the skin and imparts a blue-grey or yellow tint to the black epidermis. The largest Blue Whales measure over 30 m long and weigh about 150 tons. Specimens over 25 m long are commonplace in certain parts of the southern ocean. They belong to the sub-order Mysticeti, and make their living by filtering krill or whale-food (mostly crustaceans of the genus *Euphausia*) from the sea. Huge filters of baleen or whalebone hang from the roof of their mouth; enormous jaws and pleated, expansible throats enable them to take in massive gulps of water as they swim through the sea. Blowing out surplus water through the side of the mouth, they retain the krill on their baleen and transfer it to the gullet by movements of the muscular tongue. Other Mysticete whales include the Fin Whale (*Balaenoptera physalus*) and Sei Whale (*B. borealis*), which average in length respectively 20 m and 15 to 17 m, and the Little Rorqual, Piked or Minke Whale (*B. acutorostrata*) which seldom exceeds 10 m in length. Whales of this group are fast moving, with pleated throats and a small dorsal fin. Carrying only short baleen plates only a metre long, they sink after harpooning and were therefore of little value to early whalers, who hunted from open boats and required their whales to stay afloat long enough to be towed back to the station or factory ship. More valuable were the so-called 'right-whales', slow-moving Mysticetes with whalebone measuring 3 to 4 m in length, which remained afloat on harpooning. The Southern Right Whale (*Balaena glacialis*), like its counterparts in northern seas, was hunted almost to extinction during the nineteenth century and is now extremely rare. The Humpback Whale (*Megaptera nodosa*), another slow-moving Mysticete, suffered intensive hunting during the revival of southern whaling early in the present century. Once plentiful about South Georgia and the South Shetland Islands, in Antarctica they are now restricted almost entirely to deep water.

Toothed whales (of the sub-order Odontoceti) are less important to whalers in Antarctica and less is known of their biology. They are generally smaller and less valuable than Mysticetes; the largest bull Sperm Whale is only half the length of a large Blue Whale, and the smallest Antarctic Odontocetes (dolphins of northern Antarctic waters) only 2 to 3 m long. Killer Whales (*Orcinus orca*) are by far the commonest. Males measure up to 10 m, females seldom exceed 5 to 7 m. Both are distinguished by a tall dorsal fin, which stands about one and a half metres above the spine, and by vivid black and white patterning on sides and abdomen. Killer Whales are active predators, taking seals and dolphins and even attacking larger whales on occasions. Sperm Whales (*Physeter catodon*) feed almost entirely on cephalopods. Only unaccompanied bulls are found in Antarctic waters, and they seldom penetrate far into the ice.

Dolphins or small toothed whales are not easy to distinguish at sea, and confusion is likely among the many species which have been reported from Antarctica. Bottle-nosed Dolphins (*Hyperoodon rostratus*) are one of the best authenticated species; specimens have been identified well within the pack ice along the Antarctic coast, and also in warmer waters close to the Convergence.

Dusky Dolphins (*Lagenorhynchus obscurus*), well-known in New Zealand waters, Hour-glass Dolphins (*L. wilsoni*), first described by Edward Wilson from the deck of *Discovery* and subsequently named after him, and possibly other species of the same genus, are more commonly found between the outer edge of the pack ice and the Convergence. Dolphins of the genera *Lissodelphis* and *Cephalorhynchus* have also been reported from northern Antarctic and Subantarctic waters.

Both seals and whales show a range of remarkable adaptations for life in cold water; seals in addition are well equipped for the periods which they spend on land or on floating ice. Phocid seals are at the same time more highly aquatic and better protected against cold than Otariids. Their short, meagre covering of hair contrasts strangely with the dense, layered pelage of the fur seal, but may be more practical for animals which emerge wet from the sea and lie on ice at temperatures well below freezing point. They are generally larger than fur seals and sea lions, with short flippers, abdominal testes and thicker blubber.

The long, flat limbs of Otariids, which are admirable for rapid movement through tussock and over rocks and beaches, expose too great a surface for economy in colder regions. Their reduction to the Phocid pattern requires a very marked change in methods of moving both on land and in water. Otariids row through the water with their fore-flippers, using tail and hind-flippers as an additional unit of propulsion: on land they walk quadrupedally, supporting most of their weight on the powerful forequarters. They are surprisingly agile on land, negotiating rocks and rough ground at speed. Phocids move on land and in water by undulating the muscles of their trunk; they slither effectively over ice and snow in a movement which much resembles their swimming, and the faster-moving species (Leopard and Crabeater) can outpace a man without difficulty on soft snow. Elephant Seals, largest and most widely ranging of the Antarctic Phocids, remain agile in spite of their enormous bulk. Males measuring 7 m in length and almost as much in girth fight actively on the harem beaches, rearing the front half of their body almost vertical to crash down on their adversaries.

Whales are more completely committed to aquatic living. Their streamlined shape, stabilizing fore-limbs and dorsal fins, absence of hind limbs (even, in many species, of pelvic girdle elements), combined with large brains and specially developed senses, place them far out on a limb of the mammalian evolutionary tree. They mate and give birth to their young in water: while some species of Phocid seals court and mate in water, all, so far as is known, emerge onto land or ice to produce their pups. Whales die, usually of sunstroke or internal damage to thorax and abdomen, if stranded for more than a few hours on a beach.

Living in a medium denser than air has enabled whales to increase their body size beyond the range of most terrestrial mammals; the smallest are 1 to 2 m long and a few weigh less than 50 kg. Size has given them dominance and comparative freedom from predators in the ocean, and has also helped to combat losses of heat through the skin, allowing them to live in very cold water. Maintaining a large bulk, and a high body temperature of the order of 35° C to 38° C, requires constant activity and abundant food, and the annual journeys to polar seas give the large whales access to the ocean's richest food supplies. In summer the southern stocks feed abundantly, laying in stores of fat in the cold, rich waters below the Convergence. In winter, when food is scarce in Antarctic surface waters, they return to warmer tropical seas. In warmer water their heat losses are slighter, and conditions are more favourable for producing their calves, although food is far from plentiful. Only Sperm Whales and Humpback Whales are known to feed during their months in the tropics; rorquals killed at the northern end of their migratory range and during the journey south are usually both empty of food and low in reserves of oil.

Seals and whales have thick, waterproof outer skin, well vascularized to prevent overheating when the animal is active, but capable of being almost completely isolated from the main blood circulation by the contraction of arterioles. Skin temperatures can therefore be regulated critically and reduced when necessary almost to freezing point. The inert, oily tissues under the skin prevent rapid heat losses, as would occur if highly vascular muscle lay directly under the dermal sheet, but thin blubber on the whale's tail and the seal's flippers allows their surfaces to be used as radiators when necessary. Whales carry sensory organs in their skin. The few hairs on the face of Mysticetes are tactile and may inform the whale when it is swimming through shoals of food; other areas of the body are sensitive to touch. Seals are probably much less sensitive on the surface; they sleep soundly on angular rocks and suffer appalling wounds from fighting with little apparent ill-effect. Bull Elephant Seals may lose much of the hair on shoulders and thorax from the accumulation of scar tissue.

Seals hunt mainly by sight; their eyes are large, and some species possess a tapetum or reflecting layer behind the retina to make as much use as possible of dim light. The lens is almost spherical for underwater vision, and the pupil contracts to a slit for sharp focusing in air. They hear well in air and may also use their ears under water; Weddell Seals make an astonishing range of underwater noises, and their large ear bullae suggest the use of sonar in hunting under the ice. The passage of the outer ear is closed by muscular action when the seal submerges. For their size whales have small eyes, set well back on the sides of the head and allowing little or no forward vision. Dolphins make use of reflected sound impulses for determining the position of underwater obstacles and prey a faculty which may be well developed in all cetaceans but has not so far been demonstrated in seals.

The nostrils of both whales and seals close automatically under water and the lungs are bounded by an oblique muscular diaphragm and built to resist compression. Both kinds of animal contain rather more blood per unit of volume than other mammals, and their muscles are rich in the respiratory pigment myoglobin. The blood system of seals is remarkably specialized for diving. A muscular sphincter in the diaphragm tightens when the seal is under water, cutting off from the heart the venous system of the lower trunk. Circulation is thus brought almost to a standstill in all but the important cardiac and cephalic vessels. Rate of heartbeat falls to about one-tenth of its normal value, and the muscles work for long periods under anaerobic conditions.

On surfacing the seal respires rapidly and efficiently, dispersing the accumulated toxins from its muscles and restoring blood circulation to normal. Elephant Seals can remain submerged for half an hour, smaller species possibly for less. Weddell Seals may find that their diving helps them survive under large sheets of sea ice: they are often heard breathing under pressure ridges well inshore from the edge of the winter ice sheet, and can travel considerable distances under the ice between breathing holes in search of new feeding grounds. They are known to dive for up to twenty minutes.

Whales as a group are less highly adapted for deep diving. Their blood systems, with complex retia, are remarkably labile and capable of dealing with wide variations of pressure, but only two Odontocete species, the Sperm Whale and Bottle-nosed Dolphin, are known to take their food at great depths and to show modifications (e.g. small lungs) for deep diving. Mysticetes have no obvious respiratory or circulatory specializations for swimming at depths; their adaptations are rather for maintaining steady swimming for long periods on or near the surface, as would be expected from their method of feeding. However, much physiological research remains to be done on whales, which are far from ideal laboratory or experimental animals.

Seal teeth are generally small and unspecialized: they often fit loosely into their sockets and are lost easily during life. The teeth of some Antarctic seals show interesting specializations. Elephant Seals have huge canines which grow persistently throughout life. Their roots lie almost horizontally in the jaw, displacing the roots of neighbouring molars. The crown is sharp and pointed, and is used for slashing and cutting in fights. Canines reach their greatest development in the large harem bulls, but the cows also make use of enlarged canines in defence. The teeth grow by the addition of dentine at the interior surface of the pulp cavity: material is added at differing rates and densities throughout the year and none is withdrawn, so that the tooth furnishes a record of the animal's life and may be used to assess its age.

Weddell Seals use their teeth for maintaining openings in the ice, and also for cutting steps in the sides of the holes by which they emerge. The canines, smaller than those of the Elephant Seal, are often badly worn and broken in old animals. This species too keeps a record of age and condition in its canine teeth. Leopard Seals have long tooth rows, with sharp molars appropriate to a predatory carnivore; the roots of the teeth are long and firmly embedded, and the canines are well developed. The lobed teeth of Crabeater Seals intermesh to form a sieve, by which Euphausid crustaceans and other animals of the plankton are filtered from the sea. Ross Seals have sharp, pointed teeth suitable for holding squid. Fur seals have comparatively unspecialized teeth, which may enable them to tackle a wide range of food species. They are said to eat fish and penguins, but their feeding habits and biology have yet to be studied in detail. Mysticete whales have vestigial teeth in embryonic life but resorb them before birth. Odontocete whales usually have small peg teeth suitable for holding fish; in Sperm Whales only those of the lower jaw develop. In Killer Whales the teeth form a sturdy, formidable mechanism for catching and biting large prey.

The life histories of Antarctic whales and seals have so far been studied almost entirely from the point of view of conservation; the best known species are those with present or future commercial importance. Unfortunately hunting in many cases preceded research, so that we have little or no knowledge of stocks as they were before man's predation began. Southern Right Whales today are clearly only a small remnant population of the enormous stocks which once roamed the Southern Ocean. Between 1804 and 1817 nearly 14,000 are believed to have been taken annually; now only a few are seen each season. Fur Seals and Elephant Seals suffered similar depredations during the nineteenth century and are only now beginning to build up their stocks to former levels. Even controlled predation has a pronounced effect on the social structure and size of exploited populations; fewer of the largest sizes of the Blue Whale appear in the commercial catches each year, and considerable differences are found in breeding habits and social life between exploited and unexploited populations of Elephant Seals (see below). Hunting has, however, provided much information which would not otherwise have become available; anatomy and physiology both of whales and seals is better understood because of its commercial significance, and our knowledge of whale migrations and movements is due almost entirely to records of markers recovered on the flensing platform.

Elephant Seals, the only Phocids at present of commercial interest, have been studied recently on the South Orkney Islands, South Georgia and Macquarie Island. Valuable reports by Laws, Carrick and others are listed in the bibliography. They are by far the most accessible of Antarctic seals, and long-term marking has provided data for analyses of their population structure. They breed gregariously, the females forming harem groups in September and October. Bulls contest for possession of the harems, which may include as many as 1000 to 1200 cows or as few as 50. The larger harems are divided between several bulls, and sections of the harems change ownership from time to time as individual bulls gain and lose dominance. Only large mature bulls, aged fourteen years and over, are likely to hold a portion of a harem for any length of time; younger bulls of six to thirteen years may attempt breeding, but are seldom allowed long in the vicinity of a harem if the owners remain alert. The cows produce their single pups four or five days after joining the harems, feeding them on milk for about three weeks. Oestrus occurs either a few days before or shortly after the pups are weaned, and the cows leave for the sea soon after copulation. The fertilized cell lies dormant for four months in the uterus before developing. During their stay of four weeks on land the cows remain without food and yet manage to satisfy the demands of their rapidly growing pups. The pup's birth weight of 40–50 kg is trebled during the three weeks of maternal care. Harem bulls remain ashore without feeding for even longer periods, threatening, fighting and copulating frequently during the spell of greatest activity in September and October.

At weaning the pups wear a thick layer of blubber, which they live on for a further three or four weeks before entering the sea. They grow little during their first year of independence, but increase in length from about $1\frac{1}{2}$ to 2 m during their second to fourth years. From the third or fourth year onward males grow faster than females. By the eighth year females on South Georgia average less than 3 m while males exceed 4 m in length; Macquarie animals are apparently slightly smaller. On South Georgia nearly all cows pup in their third year, but on Macquarie Island the average age of first pupping is about six years. This striking difference may be due to differences of population structure and density brought about by human interference. There is evidence to suggest that the unexploited population on Macquarie Island has reached its natural limiting size; its members are therefore subject to keen intrasexual competition for food and living space. The South Georgia population, from which 6000 to 8000 young bulls are removed annually, and which may not in any case have recovered completely from the slaughter of earlier years, remains in a state of unbalance which favours the young females and allows them to breed early.

Breeding success in this species is high, at least 40% of either sex surviving into their fourth year. Fighting in adolescence may account for heavy mortality among males in their fourth to eighth years, but those which survive may live twenty years or more. Females maintain a higher rate of survival to their sixth year, but the rate thereafter declines fairly rapidly and few live longer than ten years. The only important natural predators known to affect this species are Killer Whales, whose toothmarks are occasionally seen on young animals of intermediate size ranges. Immature Elephant Seals range widely throughout the Antarctic region, appearing occasionally as far north as New Zealand and Australia, and moulting alone or in herds of ten to 400 on the shores of the Antarctic Continent.

Weddell Seals have been described by naturalists of many overwintering expeditions, but only in recent years have attempts been made to study their biology in detail. Reports by Lindsey, Bertram, Sapin-Jaloustre and Mansfield are listed in the bibliography. Weddell Seals are most plentiful along the inshore ice of the Antarctic Continent. The most southerly breeding groups form in McMurdo Sound and the Bay of Whales, in the Ross Sea sector of Antarctica. Weddell Seals are semi-gregarious, groups of ten to fifty or more in the same area often being associated with a single hole or crack in the ice. They seldom lie more than a few yards from a point of access to water. Holes are kept open by gnawing, although tidal and other movements of inshore ice usually provide an ever-changing pattern of cracks and holes which allow the seals to breathe under the ice sheet even in winter. More seals are visible along the coast in summer than in winter; while some are known to spend their winters inshore (where they may be heard under the ice) others may migrate away in late summer and autumn when the inshore ice disperses.

Little is known of social organization within populations of Weddell Seals. In the South Orkney Islands and Graham Land males begin to haul out on the ice in July, and pregnant females appear in late July and August. From late August to September the pups are born, usually among pressure ice or close to islands with easy access to enclosed water. Weighing 30 to 35 kg, the pups are covered with long, fleecy hair which is lost from the second or third week onward; they enter the water after a week, but are suckled for six to seven weeks. As in other seal species, the milk dentition is resorbed during foetal life and the complete set of permanent teeth is ready for action by the time the pup is weaned. At weaning the pup has trebled its birth weight. Oestrus probably occurs when lactation ceases, and copulation takes place in the water. Early embryos are seldom found before January. Implantation is therefore delayed about two months. At the southern edge of their range the breeding cycle begins and ends three to four weeks later; thus at the Bay of Whales pupping begins in early or mid-October, the young leave their mothers toward the end of November, and the first embryos are found in late January and February.

Weddell Seals are smaller than Elephant Seals, and males tend to be smaller than females at maturity. Fully grown animals of either sex measure 3 m in length. Although some fighting occurs among males during the rutting season, there is no evidence of harem formation. Females normally become pregnant at the beginning of their third year, and may live for nine or ten years. The species is at present being studied in some detail in McMurdo Sound.

Crabeater Seals spend most of their life in and about the pack ice; they are probably more numerous than any of the other Antarctic seals, but their floating home is seldom invaded by biologists and they are comparatively little known. Wandering animals are seen from time to time in New Zealand, Australia and South America, and at the southern edge of their range Crabeaters have a reputation for wandering inshore and losing themselves far inland among the mountains. Several mummified specimens were found above 1000 m by members of Scott's expeditions, and carcases discovered recently in dry glacial valleys of Victoria Land have been shown by carbon dating to be well over 2000 years old. Crabeaters are apparently both gregarious and migratory. Large herds are seen from time to time, both in the water and afloat at the edge of the pack ice; a herd of over 3000 young animals, stricken by a fatal disease, was recently reported off the east coast of Graham Land. Crabeaters feed largely on krill, which they filter through their lobed teeth. The stomach often contains grit and gravel, which may help to grind up the food in the absence of flattened, grinding molars. Small fish also form part of the diet.

Little is known of the breeding behaviour of Crabeater Seals. The pups are born on pack ice, probably in September or October. Very few newly born pups have been seen, but one taken shortly after birth in western Graham Land had a long, silky coat, with closely packed finer hairs forming an underpelt. It measured over one and a half metres from nose to tail, i.e. almost two-thirds the length of a mature animal and rather longer than most Weddell pups. Young animals tend to move inshore during their first year, possibly to avoid the attention of Killer Whales, and there is some evidence that females become pregnant at the beginning of their second year. Most older animals bear long, parallel gashes inflicted by Killer Whales, which must account for large numbers of this species throughout the year. Crabeater Seals are extremely lithe and active on snow, moving with lateral swimming strokes of the tail and hind flippers. They are distinguishable from Weddell Seals by their pale, unspotted coat, which fades almost to white in summer; they are also more slender than Weddells, and more likely to take avoiding action when approached by man. Very few are seen inshore during winter, although in Graham Land some are believed to spend at least part of the winter under the fast ice close to land. Their food at this time descends into deep water, and Crabeaters killed close to land in winter usually have empty stomachs.

Leopard Seals are also creatures of the pack ice, although part of their year may be spent in open water near islands where food is plentiful. At Heard Island, where the species has been studied for several years, over seven hundred Leopard Seals make use of the beaches for hauling out in winter. Between October and December numbers decrease substantially, the breeding population moving out to produce pups and mate among the pack ice; only adolescents and old males remain on the island during the breeding season. Adults reappear from late December onward, males tending to return before females, and from June onward pups of the year also join the herds. A captive female Leopard Seal gave birth at Heard Island in mid-November; the pup measured 160 cm in length and weighed 30 kg, but died at or shortly after birth.

Leopard Seals are also met frequently in South Georgia, the Scotia Arc, Kerguelen, Macquarie, and at certain points along the Antarctic coast, and are fairly common on the southern islands of the Subantarctic. They are usually solitary, and individuals may associate for weeks or months at a time with a particular stretch of beach or penguin colony. In South Georgia they take toll of King, Macaroni and Gentoo Penguins, patrolling the waters close to the colonies and catching birds as they come in to land. At Cape Crozier in the Ross Sea Leopard Seals are found in October, catching Emperor Penguins on their way to and from the famous colony; they may spend part or all of the winter among disturbed ice in the vicinity. In the Falkland Islands they have a reputation for attacking small boats; curiosity often impels them to make a close inspection of rowing boats and their occupants, but there are few substantiated cases of aggression. Their silver-grey dappled coat is prized by sealers but has no commercial value.

Ross Seals are the least known of all the Antarctic seals. Fewer than fifty specimens had been seen up to 1940; with the advent of powerful icebreakers and the invasion of dense concentrations of pack ice, more of their haunts have been disclosed in recent years. Their sharp, curved incisor and canine teeth are adapted for feeding on cuttlefish. Molars are much reduced. Ross Seals are solitary and, even in their heaviest concentrations form less than 1% of the total seal population in the pack ice.

Southern Fur Seals, like Elephant Seals, breed gregariously on islands toward the northern edge of the Antarctic region. Several thousands breed on islands off the western end of South Georgia, and Bouvetøya has a breeding population numbered in hundreds. Small colonies of breeding animals have become established, apparently during the last decade, on the South Sandwich and South Shetland Islands, and breeding may also have started on Kerguelen, Heard Island and the South Orkney Islands. On South Georgia harems form in October and November; the pups, a little over a foot long at birth, are covered with dense woolly fur and are probably suckled for several months longer than any of the Phocid seals. Mature males are about 2 m long, breeding females averaging about a third of a metre shorter. The species is at present under survey in South Georgia.

The breeding and life cycles of whales have been studied mainly on post-mortem evidence; best known are those of the larger rorquals, which form the bulk of the annual whale catch in Antarctic waters. The biology of Blue, Fin and Sei Whales is in many respects similar. All are found in every ocean of both hemispheres, concentrating toward the poles in summer and spread over the broader tropical waters in winter. Fin Whales of the Northern Hemisphere are from 5 to 10% shorter than southern stocks and yield only half as much oil, probably because of poorer feeding in the Arctic; otherwise northern and southern stocks are very similar and there is no justification for placing them in separate species.

Blue Whale calves are 8 m long at birth. They grow remarkably quickly during the first weeks of life, living on milk supplied by their mothers. During October and November the Southern Hemisphere stocks move southward, and the calves are weaned among the rich food of Antarctica. Fin and Sei Whales, born slightly later than Blue Whales, tend to arrive later in Antarctic waters and to leave earlier in the autumn. While Blue Whales penetrate in large numbers into the far south, the smaller species are more numerous north of the pack ice; Sei Whales are seldom found below Lat. 60° S. Blue Whales yield about twenty tons of oil each; being the most economical to catch, they stand in greatest danger of overfishing at present. Fin Whales yield only half as much oil per head but are probably about four times as numerous: Sei Whales have a much smaller yield and are worth taking only when other species are scarce. Minke Whales, among the smallest of the Mysticetes, are numerous along the continental shore of Antarctica in summer. They occasionally swim under fast ice, poking their sharply pointed heads through small holes and tide cracks to breathe. Although hunted commercially in other seas, they have seldom been taken in Antarctic waters except for food; their meat is considered a delicacy in the mess-rooms of the whale factory ship.

Female Mysticetes are usually both heavier and longer than males. The largest of all are found in the richest feeding grounds, which lie in the southern Atlantic Ocean east of South Georgia and below the tip of South Africa. Other rich areas occur in the Indian Ocean south-west of Australia, in the corners of the Pacific

Ocean below New Zealand and south-west of Cape Horn, and in the waters immediately surrounding the Antarctic Continent. Here the densest accumulations both of krill and of Mysticete whales are found. The greatest abundance of food is provided by the waters of the Weddell Current, which flows from the Weddell Sea past South Georgia and on toward the tip of South Africa. Eastward from this region, even in the most favoured areas of the Indian and Pacific Oceans, Blue Whales and other Mysticetes are fewer, their yield of oil per carcase is lower, and the proportion of unsaturated fatty acids within the oil decreases.

Whales may be marked by small stainless steel darts, which are fired from a modified shot-gun and remain in the blubber until the animal is caught and flensed. Marking has shown that some individual whales return year after year to the same parts of the southern ocean; several have been killed only a few kilometres from where they were marked a number of years previously. Others have been recovered hundreds of kilometres east or west of their marking point. During their annual north and south movements they carry a range of parasites and commensals on their skin from one zone to another, and the migration may help to rid them of some undesirable guests; thus most whales caught in the Antarctic bear the scars of lampreys and other ectoparasites, which attack them in warmer water but fall off as the colder regions are approached.

Humpback Whales tend to migrate close inshore where coastlines lie near their route, and are therefore particularly vulnerable to capture from shore stations both in the Antarctic region and along their migration routes. Stations in South Africa, Australia and New Zealand have taken many Humpbacks on migration, and for years the shore stations on South Georgia and other islands in the Scotia Arc made up the bulk of their catch from this species. Averaging 11 to 14 m long, Humpbacks provide a high yield of oil for their size. In tropical waters they feed on shoaling fish; like the rorquals they calve in warm seas, and marking suggests that the five main feeding grounds in Antarctica may support populations which seldom intermix even in the tropics.

Southern Right Whales, slow moving, with long baleen and a high yield of oil, were the ideal catch for open-boat whalers in Subtropical and Subantarctic waters. Although seldom found in the far south, this species was occasionally taken at South Georgia and the South Shetlands early in the present century, and Southern Right Whales with their distinctive double spout are occasionally reported among the ice today. They breed in warmer latitudes, apparently close to the continental and island shores rather than in deep water, and are at present rigorously protected by international whaling agreement.

Killer Whales, which hunt in packs, have a reputation for savagery and fearlessness; they are one of the more successful of the world's hunters and their intelligence may be formidable. Southern stocks are apparently identical with those of the tropics and northern oceans: although a prominent species, little study has been made of their biology. Males average 8 to 10 m in length, females are seldom longer than 7 m. Sperm Whales show a similar sexual dimorphism: as in seals, the phenomenon is associated with polygamous breeding. Solitary males caught in Antarctica, representing the non-breeding surplus, average 16 m in length. Females caught at tropical stations seldom exceed 13 m.

The larger whales have gestation periods of eleven to twelve months (only half as long as the largest land mammals) and growth after birth is correspondingly rapid. Humpback Whales, almost 5 m long at birth, reach lengths of 7 to 8 m on weaning five to six months later: Sei Whales almost double their birth length in the same period. Growth after weaning is slightly slower, but most whales are ready to reproduce at the end of their second year or during their third. Rapid growth and speed of multiplying reflect the success and efficiency of whales in taking advantage of their food resources. They are the qualities which have allowed whales to withstand all but the most ruthless attacks of man, and are the basis of the large and efficient modern whaling industry.

Whaling is controlled by an international commission, which accepts advice from biologists and attempts to ensure, by the agreement of its members, that biological principles rather than industrial expediency be allowed to set limits to annual catches of the larger and more profitable species of whales. Half a century of research has provided a sound base for conservation measures, and many scientists in Britain, Holland, Norway and Japan are at present engaged in work on the commercial species to increase the efficiency and soundness of the advice which they can give to international legislators. The need for vigilance and continued research is fortunately recognized, for greed and biological ignorance have proved, many times in the past, more than a match for the most ebullient and successful species of animals, and stocks of whales are in danger for as long as they remain an object of commercial interest. Section 2 of the bibliography lists a number of recent research papers on both whales and seals; prominent among them will be found studies by investigators of the National Institute of Oceanography (*Discovery Reports*) and the Whales Research Institute, Tokyo. The whalers' 'newspaper' – *Norsk Hvalfangst-tidende*, published in Norwegian and English, is also a most useful source of up-to-date information on whaling research, annual catches, methods and other matters of interest connected with the industry. The papers presented at the first symposium on Antarctic biology have been published since this chapter was written (Carrick, R., Holdgate, M. W., and Prévost, J., eds. Symposium de Biologie Antarctique (1962), Hermann, Paris 1964, 651 pp.). They include important articles on birds and mammals of the Southern Ocean.

Bibliography

This bibliography is mainly concerned with research of the last quarter century and is by no means exhaustive. For references to earlier work on birds see Murphy (1936) and Roberts (1941), on seals see Bertram (1941) and Scheffer (1958), and on whales see Jenkins (1948) and Slijper (1962).

Section 1. Birds and Marine Biology

ARDLEY, R. A. B. 1936: The Birds of the South Orkney Islands, *Discovery Rep.* **12:** 349–76.

AUSTIN, O. L. 1957: Notes on Banding Birds in Antarctica, and on the Adelie Penguin Colonies of the Ross Sea Sector, *Bird Banding* **28:** 1–26.

BAGSHAWE, T. W. 1938: Notes on the Habits of the Gentoo and Ringed or Antarctic Penguins, *Trans. Zool. Soc. Lond.* **24:** 185–306.

BÉCHERVAISE, J. 1954: Birds of Heard Island, *Vict. Nat. Melb.* **71:** 71–2.

BIERMAN, W. H., and VOOUS, K. H. 1950: Birds Observed and Collected during the Whaling Expedition of the Willem Barendsz in the Antarctic 1946–47 and 1947–48, *Ardea Special No.:* 1–123.

BRYANT, H. M. 1945: Biology at East Base, Palmer Peninsula, Antarctica, *Proc. Amer. Phil. Soc.* **89:** 256–69.

BUDD, G. M. 1961: The Biotopes of Emperor Penguin Rookeries, *Emu* **61:** 171–89.

BUDD, G. M. 1961: Some Notes on Immature Emperor Penguins, *Emu* **61:** 204–8.

CAUGHLEY, G. 1960: The Cape Crozier Emperor Penguin Rookery, *Rec. Dom. Mus. Wellington.* **3:** 251–62.

CAUGHLEY, G. 1960: The Adélie Penguins of Ross and Beaufort Islands, *Rec. Dom. Mus. Wellington.* **3:** 263–82.

CAUGHLEY, G. 1960: Observations on Incubation and Chick Rearing in the Antarctic Skua, *Notornis* **8:** 194–5.

CENDRON, J. 1953: Notes sur les Oiseaux de la Terre Adélie (Pétrels et skuas), *L'Oiseau et R.F.O.* **23:** 212–20.

DELL, R. K. 1960: Sea Bird Logs between New Zealand and the Ross Sea, *Rec. Dom. Mus. Wellington.* **3:** 293–305.

DOWNES, M. C. 1952: Arctic Terns in the Subantarctic, *Emu* **52:** 301–10.

DOWNES, M. C., EALEY, E. H. M., GWYNN, A. M., and YOUNG, P. S. 1959: The Birds of Heard Island, *ANARE Reports Series B Zoology Melbourne.* **1:** 1–135.

DOWNES, M. C., GWYNN, A. M., and HOWARD, P. F. 1954: Banding of Giant Petrels at Heard and Macquarie Islands, *Emu* **54:** 257–62.

EALEY, E. H. M. 1954: Analysis of Stomach Contents of some Heard Island Birds, *Emu* **54:** 204–10.

EKLUND, C. R. 1942: Body Temperatures of Antarctic Birds, *Auk* **59:** 544–8.

G

EKLUND, C. R. 1945: Condensed Ornithology Report, East Base, Palmer Land, USAS Expedition 1939–41, *Proc. Amer. Phil. Soc.* **89:** 299–304.

EKLUND, C. R. 1959: Antarctic Ornithological Studies during IGY, *Bird Banding* **30:** 114–8.

EKLUND, C. R. 1961: Distribution and Life History Studies of the South Polar Skua, *Bird Banding* **32:** 187–223.

EKLUND, C. R., and CHARLTON, F. E. 1959: Measuring the Temperature of Incubating Penguin Eggs, *Amer. Scient.* **47:** 80–86.

ETCHECOPAR, R. D., and PRÉVOST, J. 1954: Données Oologiques sur l'Avifaune de Terre Adélie, *L'Oiseau et R.F.O.* **24:** 227–47.

FALLA, R. A. 1937: *British–Australian–New Zealand Antarctic Research Expedition 1929–31 Reports: Series B II Birds*, Adelaide, pp. 1–28.

FALLA, R. A. 1952: Antarctic Birds, Simpson, F.A., ed. *The Antarctic Today*, pp. 216–28, Reed and NZ Antarctic Society, Wellington.

FOXTON, P. 1956: The Distribution of the Standing Crop of Zooplankton in the Southern Ocean, *Discovery Rep.* **28:** 191–236.

FRIEDMAN, H. 1945: Birds of the US Antarctic Service Expedition, 1939–41, *Proc. Amer. Phil. Soc.* **89:** 305–13.

GIBSON-HILL, C. A. 1949: Notes on the Cape Hen *Procellaria equinoctialis*, *Ibis* **91:** 422–6.

GIBSON-HILL, C. A. 1949: The Gentoo Penguin, *Geogr. Mag.* **22:** 233–8.

GLENISTER, T. W. 1954: The Emperor Penguin *Aptenodytes forsteri* Gray: II. Embryology, *Sci. Rep. Falkland Islands Dependencies Survey* **10:** 1–19.

GWYNN, A. M. 1953: The Egg-laying and Incubation Periods of Rockhopper, Macaroni and Gentoo Penguins, *ANARE Reports Series B Zoology*, Melbourne, **1:** 1–29.

HAMILTON, J. E. 1934: The Subantarctic forms of the Great Skua (*Catharacta skua skua*), *Discovery Rep.* **9:** 161–74.

HAMILTON, J. E. 1954: The Emperor Penguin in the Falklands, *Ibis* **96:** 315.

HARDY, A. C., and GUNTHER, E. R. 1936: The Plankton of the South Georgia Whaling Grounds and Adjacent Waters, *Discovery Rep.* **11:** 1–456.

HARRINGTON, H. J. 1960: Adelie Penguin Rookeries in the Ross Sea Region, *Notornis* **9:** 33–8.

HARRINGTON, H. J., and MCKELLAR, I. C. 1958: A Radiocarbon Date for Penguin Colonisation of Cape Hallett, *N.Z. J. Geol. Geophys.* **1:** 571–6.

HART, T. J. 1942: Phytoplankton Periodicity in Antarctic Surface Waters, *Discovery Rep.* **21:** 261–356.

HOLGERSEN, H. 1945: Antarctic and Subantarctic Birds, *Sci. Res. Norweg. Ant. Exped. 1927–8 et seq.* **23:** 1–100.

HOLGERSEN, H. 1950: On the Birds of Peter I Island, *Proc. 10th Int. Ornith. Congress, Uppsala*.

HOLGERSEN, H. 1957: Ornithology of the Brategg Expedition, *Sci. Res. Brategg Exp. 1947–8 Bergen*, No. 4.

HOWARD, P. F. 1954: Banding of the Black-browed Albatross at Heard Island and Macquarie Island, *Emu* **54:** 256.

HOWARD, P. F. 1954: ANARE Bird Banding and Seal Marking, *Vict. Nat. Melb.* **71:** 73–82.

INGHAM, S. E. 1959: Banding of Giant Petrels by the Australian National Antarctic Research Expeditions 1955–58, *Emu* **59:** 189–200.

INGHAM, S. E. 1962: New Records for Australian Antarctic Stations, *Emu* **62:** 126–8.

JEANNEL, R. 1941: Au Seuil de l'Antarctique, *Museum National d'Histoire Naturelle, Paris. Publ.* **5:** 1–236.

KALNENAS, K. 1952: Ascorbic Acid Levels in the Plasma of some Antarctic Birds and Mammals, *Nature* **69:** 836.

KOROTKEVICH, E. S. 1958: Nablyndeniya nad Ptitsami vo Vremya Pervoy Zimovki Sovetskoy Antarkticheskoy Ekspeditsii, *Inf. Byull. Sov. Ant. Eksp.* **3:** 83–7.

LØVENSKIOLD, H. L. 1960: The Snow Petrel *Pagodroma nivea* in Dronning Maud Land, *Ibis* **102:** 132–4.

LOWE, P. R. and KINNEAR, N. B. 1930: Birds, *Brit. Ant. (Terra Nova) Exp. 1910–13 Zoology* **4:** 103–93.

MACINTOSH, N. A., and HERDMAN, F. H. P. 1940: Distribution of the Pack Ice in the Southern Ocean, *Discovery Rep.* **19:** 285–96.

MARPLES, B. J. 1953: Fossil Penguins from the mid-Tertiary of Seymour Island, *Sci. Rep. Falkland Islands Dependencies Survey* **5:** 1–15.

MARR, J. W. S. 1935: The South Orkney Islands, *Discovery Rep.* **10:** 283–382.

MARR, J. W. S. 1956: *Euphausia superba* and the Antarctic Surface Currents, *Norsk Hvalfangsttid, Arg.* **45:** 127–9, 132–4.

MATTHEWS, L. H. 1929: The Birds of South Georgia, *Discovery Rep.* **1:** 561–92.

MATTHEWS, L. H. 1951: *Wandering Albatross*, MacGibbon and Kee, London.

MOREAU, R. E. 1942: Giant Petrel at 8° S, *Ibis* **84:** 108.

MURPHY, R. C. 1936: *Oceanic Birds of South America*, Macmillan, New York. 2 vols.

MURPHY, R. C. 1947: *Logbook for Grace*, Hale, London.

MURPHY, R. C. 1947: A New Zonal Race of the Gentoo Penguin, *Auk* **64:** 454–5.

PARSONS, C. W. 1934: Penguin Embryos, *Brit. Ant. (Terra Nova) Exp. 1910-13 Nat. Hist. Rep. Zoology* **4:** 253–62.

PAULIAN, P. 1953: Pinnipèdes, Cétacés, Oiseaux des Îles Kerguelen et Amsterdam, *Mem. Inst. Sci. Madagascar, A8 : 111–234.

PERKINS, J. E. 1945: Biology at Little America III, the West Base of the US Antarctic Service Expedition 1939–41, *Proc. Amer. Phil. Soc.* **89:** 256–69.

PETTINGILL, O. S. 1960: Crèche Behaviour and Individual Recognition in a Colony of Rockhopper Penguins, *Wilson Bull.* **72:** 213–21.

PRÉVOST, J. 1953: Notes sur la Reproduction du Fulmar Antarctique *Fulmaris glacialoides, Alauda* **21:** 157–64.

PRÉVOST, J. 1953b: Notes sur l'Écologie des Pétrels de Terre Adélie, *Alauda* **21**: 205–22.

PRÉVOST, J. 1958: Note Complémentaire sur l'Écologie des Pétrels de Terre Adélie, *Alauda* **26**: 125–30.

PRÉVOST, J. 1961: Écologie du Manchot Empereur, *Exp. Polaires Françaises No. 222, Paris*: 1–201.

RANKIN, N. 1951: *Antarctic Isle*, Collins, London.

REID, B. E. 1961: Cape Hallett: Bird Banding and Nest Marking Report January 1959–January 1960, *DSIR Antarctic Division, Wellington*.

ROBERTS, B. B. 1940a: The Life Cycle of Wilson's Petrel *Oceanites oceanicus* (Kuhl), *Sci. Rep. Brit. Graham Land Exp. 1934–7* **1**: 141–94.

ROBERTS, B. B. 1940b: The Breeding Behaviour of Penguins, with Special Reference to *Pygoscelis papua*, *Sci. Rep. Brit. Graham Land Exp. 1934–7* **1**: 195–254.

ROBERTS, B. B. 1941: A Bibliography of Antarctic Ornithology, *Sci. Rep. Brit. Graham Land Exp. 1934–7* **1**: 337–67.

ROBERTS, B. B. 1959: The British Contribution to Antarctic Ornithology, *Ibis* **101**: 107–14.

ROBERTS, B. B., and SLADEN, W. J. L. 1952: Preliminary Note on Bird Ringing by the Falkland Islands Dependencies Survey 1945–51, *Ibis* **94**: 538–40.

ROUTH, M. 1949: Ornithological Observations in the Antarctic Seas 1946–47, *Ibis* **91**: 577–606.

SAPIN-JALOUSTRE, J. 1952: Decouverte et Description de la Rookery de Manchot Empereur (*Aptenodytes forsteri*) de Pointe Géologie (Terre Adélie), *L'Oiseau et R.F.O.* **22**: 143–259.

SAPIN-JALOUSTRE, J. 1960: Écologie du Manchot Adélie, *Exp. Polaires Françaises No. 208 Paris*: 1–208.

SIMPSON, G. G. 1946: Fossil Penguins, *Bull. Amer. Mus. Nat. Hist.* **87**: 5–99.

SIPLE, P. A., and LINDSEY, A. A. 1937: Ornithology of the Second Byrd Antarctic Expedition, *Auk* **54**: 147–59.

SLADEN, W. J. L. 1952: Arctic Skua in the Antarctic, *Ibis* **94**: 543.

SLADEN, W. J. L. 1955: Some Aspects of the Behaviour of Adelie and Chinstrap Penguins, *Acta XI Congressus Internationalis Ornithologici Basel*: 241–7.

SLADEN, W. J. L. 1958: The Pygoscelid Penguins. I. Methods of Study. II. The Adelie Penguin, *Sci. Rep. Falkland Islands Dependencies Survey* **17**: 1–97.

SLADEN, W. J. L., and FRIEDMANN, H. 1961: Antarctic Ornithology. Science in Antarctica. Pt. 1: The Life Sciences in Antarctica, *Nat. Acad. Sciences Washington. Publ.* **839**: 62–76.

SLADEN, W. J. L., and TICKELL, W. L. N. 1958: Antarctic Bird Banding by the Falkland Islands Dependencies Survey 1945–57, *Bird Banding* **29**: 1–26.

STONEHOUSE, B. 1953: The Emperor Penguin *Aptenodytes forsteri*: I. Breeding behaviour and development, *Sci. Rep. Falkland Dependencies Survey* **6**: 1–33.

STONEHOUSE, B. 1956: The Brown Skua *Catharacta skua lonnbergi* (Mathews) of South Georgia, *Sci. Rep. Falkland Islands Dependencies Survey* **14**: 1–25.

STONEHOUSE, B. 1958: Notes on the Ringing and the Breeding Distribution of the Giant Petrel *Macronectes giganteus*, *Ibis* **100**: 204–8.

STONEHOUSE, B. 1960: The King Penguin *Aptenodytes patagonica* of South Georgia: I. Breeding Behaviour and Development, *Sci. Rep. Falkland Islands Dependencies Survey* **23**: 1–81.

STONEHOUSE, B. 1963: Observations on Adelie Penguins (*Pygoscelis adeliae*) at Cape Royds, Antarctica, *Proc. 13th Int. Ornithol. Congr:* 766–79.

TICKELL, W. L. N. 1960: Notes from the South Orkneys and South Georgia, *Ibis* **102**: 612–4.

TICKELL, W. L. N. 1960: Chick-feeding in the Wandering Albatross *Diomedea exulans* (Linnaeus), *Nature*, **185**: 116–7.

TICKELL, W. L. N., and CORDALL, P. A. 1960: South Georgia Biologica Expedition 1958–59, *Polar Rec.* **10**: 145–6.

TICKELL, W. L. N., and SCOTLAND, C. D. 1961: Recoveries of Ringed Giant Petrels *Macronectes giganteus*, *Ibis* **103a**: 260–6.

TICKELL, W. L. N. 1962: The Dove Prion *Pachyptila desolata* Gmelin, *Sci. Rep. Falkland Islands Dependencies Survey* **33**: 55 pp.

TAYLOR, R. H. 1962: The Adelie Penguin *Pygoscelis adeliae* at Cape Royds, *Ibis* **104**: 176–204.

TAYLOR, R. H. 1962: Growth of Adelie Penguin (*Pygoscelis adeliae* Hombron and Jacquinot) Chicks, *N.Z.J. Sci.* **5**: 191–7.

WARHAM, J. 1962: The Biology of the Giant Petrel *Macronectes giganteus*, *Auk* **79**: 139–60.

WILKINSON, J. 1956: South Sandwich Islands – Bird Life, *Sea Swallow* (*Ann. Rep. Royal Naval Bird Watching Soc.*) **9**: 8–20.

WILKINSON, J. 1957: A Second Visit to the South Sandwich Islands, *Sea Swallow* (*Ann. Rep. Royal Naval Bird Watching Soc.*) **10**: 22.

WILLING, R. L. 1958: Feeding Habits of Emperor Penguins, *Nature* **182**: 194–5.

WILLING, R. L. 1958: Australian Discoveries of Emperor Penguin Rookeries in Antarctica during 1954–57, *Nature* **182**: 1393–4.

YOUNG, E. C. 1963a: The Breeding Behaviour of the South Polar Skua *Catharacta maccormicki*, *Ibis* **105**: 203–18.

YOUNG, E. C. 1963b: Feeding Habits of the South Polar Skua *Catharacta maccormicki*, *Ibis* **105**: 301–18.

YUDIN, K. A. 1958: Ornitologicheskie Sbory Sovetskoy Antarkticheskoy Ekspeditsii, *Inf. Byull. Sov. Ant. Eksp.* **3**: 89–90.

Section 2. Whales and Seals

ARETAS, R. 1951: L'Éléphant de Mer, *Mammalia* **15**: 105–17.

ARSENIEV, V. A. 1957: Distribution of the Whales in the Atlantic Sector of the Antarctic, *Trans. Inst. Marine Fisheries and Oceanography of the USSR* **33**: 76–95.

ASH, C. E. 1952: The Body Weights of Whales, *Norsk Hvalfangsttid. Arg.* **41:** 364–74.

BENNETT, A. G. 1931: *Whaling in the Antarctic,* Blackwood, London, Edinburgh.

BERRY, A. J. 1960: The Occurrence of a Leopard Seal (*Hydrurga leptonyx*) in the Tropics, *Ann. Mag. Nat. Hist.* **13:** 591.

BERTRAM, G. C. L. 1940: The Biology of the Weddell and Crabeater Seals, *Sci. Rep. Brit. Graham Land Exp. 1934–7* **1:** 1–139.

BONNER, W. N. 1955: Reproductive Organs of Foetal and Juvenile Elephant Seals, *Nature* **176:** 982–3.

BONNER, W. N. 1958: Notes on the Southern Fur Seal in South Georgia, *Proc. Zool. Soc. Lond.* **130:** 241–52.

BROWN, K. G. 1952: Observations on the Newly-born Leopard Seal, *Nature* **170:** 982.

BROWN, K. G. 1957: The Leopard Seal at Heard Island 1951–54, *ANARE Interim Reports* **16.** Melbourne.

BROWN, S. G. 1954: Dispersal in Blue and Fin Whales, *Discovery Rep.* **26:** 355–84.

BROWN, S. G. 1954: The Movements of Fin and Blue Whales in Antarctic Waters, *Norsk Hvalfangsttid. Arg.* **43:** 301–9.

BROWN, S. G. 1957: Whales Observed in the Indian Ocean; Notes on Their Distribution, *Mar. Obs.* **27:** 157–65.

BRYANT, H. M. 1945: Biology at East Base, Palmer Peninsula, Antarctica, *Proc. Amer. Phil. Soc.* **89:** 268–9.

CARRICK, R., and INGHAM, S. E. 1962: Studies on the Southern Elephant Seal *Mirounga leonina* (L.): I. Introduction to the Series, *CSIRO Wildlife Research* **7:** 89–101, Melbourne.

CARRICK, R., and INGHAM, S. E. 1962: Studies on the Southern Elephant Seal *Mirounga leonina* (L.): II. Canine Tooth Structure in Relation to Function and Age Determination, *CSIRO Wildlife Research* **7:** 102–18. Melbourne.

CARRICK, R., CSORDAS, S. E., INGHAM, S. E., and KEITH, K. 1962: Studies on the Southern Elephant Seal *Mirounga leonina* (L.): III. The Annual Cycle in Relation to Age and Sex, *CSIRO Wildlife Research* **7:** 119–60, Melbourne.

CARRICK, R., CSORDAS, S. E., and INGHAM, S. E. 1962: Studies on the Southern Elephant Seal *Mirounga leonina* (L.): IV. Breeding and Development, *CSIRO Wildlife Research* **7:** 161–97, Melbourne.

CARRICK, R., and INGHAM, S. E. 1962: Studies on the Southern Elephant Seal *Mirounga leonina* (L.): V. Population Dynamics and Utilization, *CSIRO Wildlife Research* **7:** 198–206, Melbourne.

CHITTLEBOROUGH, R. G., and EALEY, E. H. M. 1953: Seal Marking at Heard Island. *ANARE Interim Reports* **1,** Melbourne.

CLARIDGE, G. G. 1961: Seal Tracks in the Taylor Dry Valley, *Nature* **190:** 559.

CLARKE, R. 1956: Sperm Whales of the Azores, *Discovery Rep.* **28:** 237–98.

CSORDAS, S. E. 1958: Breeding of the Fur Seal *Arctocephalus forsteri* Lesson at Macquarie Island, *Aust. J. Sci.* **21:** 87–8.

DAWBIN, W. H. 1952: Whales and Whaling in the Southern Ocean, Simpson, F. A., ed. *The Antarctic Today*, pp. 151–94. Reed and NZ Antarctic Society, Wellington.

DEARBORN, J. H. 1962: An Unusual Occurrence of the Leopard Seal at McMurdo Sound, Antarctica, *J. Mammal.* **43**: 277.

EKLUND, C. R. 1960: Elephant Seals in Antarctica, *J. Mammal.* **41**: 277.

EKLUND, C. R., and ATWOOD, A. L. 1962: A Population Study of Antarctic Seals, *J. Mammal.* **43**: 229–38.

GIBBNEY, L. F. 1953: Delayed Implantation in the Elephant Seal, *Nature* **172**: 590–91.

GIBBNEY, L. F. 1957: The Seasonal Reproductive Cycle of the Female Elephant Seal *Mirounga leonina* Linn. at Heard Island, *ANARE Reports B*, **1**: 1–26, Melbourne.

GWYNN, A. M. 1953: The Status of the Leopard Seal at Heard Island and Macquarie Island 1948–50, *ANARE Interim Report* **3**, Melbourne.

GWYNN, A. M. 1953: Notes on the Fur Seal at Macquarie Island and Heard Island, *ANARE Interim Report* **4**, Melbourne.

HAMILTON, J. E. 1934: The Southern Sea Lion *Otaria byronia* (De Blainville), *Discovery Rep.* **8**: 269–318.

HAMILTON, J. E. 1939: The Leopard Seal (*Hydrurga leptonyx*), *Discovery Rep.* **18**: 239–64.

HAMILTON, J. E. 1939: A Second Report on the Southern Sea Lion *Otaria byronia* (De Blainville), *Discovery Rep.* **19**: 121–64.

HAMILTON, J. E. 1945: The Weddell Seal in the Falkland Islands, *Proc. Zool. Soc. Lond.* **114**: 549.

HARRISON, R. J., MATTHEWS, L. H., and ROBERTS, M. 1952: Reproduction in Some Pinnipedia, *Trans. Zool. Soc. Lond.* **27**: 437–50.

HYLEN, A., JONSGARD, A., PIKE, G. C., and RUUD, J. T. 1955: A Preliminary Report on the Age Composition of Antarctic Fin Whale Catches 1945–46 to 1952–53 and some Reflections on Total Mortality Rates of Fin Whales, *Norsk Hvalfangsttid. Arg.* **44**: 577–89.

INGHAM, S. E. 1957: Elephant Seals on the Antarctic Continent, *Nature* **180**: 1215–16.

IRVING, L., SOLANDT, O. M., SOLANDT, D. Y., and FISHER, K. C. 1935: The Respiratory Metabolism of the Seal and its Adjustment to Diving, *J. cell. comp. Physiol.* **7**: 137.

JEANNEL, R. 1941: Au seuil de l'Antarctique, *Museum National d'Histoire Naturelle, Paris. Publ.* **5**: 1–236.

JENKINS, J. T. 1948: A Bibliography of Whaling, *J. Soc. Bibliog. Nat. Hist.* **2**: 71–161.

JONSGARD, A. 1952: On the Growth of the Fin Whale (*Balaenoptera physalus*) in Different Waters, *Norsk Hvalfangsttid. Arg.* **41**: 57–65.

KANWISHER, J., and LEIVESTAD, H. 1957: Thermal Regulation in Whales, *Norsk Hvalfangsttid. Arg.* **46**: 1–5.

KELLOGG, W. N. 1961: *Porpoises and Sonar*. Univ. Chicago Press.

KING, J. E. 1957: On a Pup of the Crabeater Seal *Lobodon carcinophagus*, *Ann. Mag. Nat. Hist.* **10:** 619–24.

KING, J. E. 1959: The Northern and Southern Populations of *Arctocephalus gazella*, *Mammalia* **23:** 19–40.

KING, J. E. 1959: A Note on the Specific Name of the Kerguelen Fur Seal, *Mammalia* **23:** 381.

KING, J. E. 1962: Some of the Aquatic Modifications of Seals, *Norsk Hvalfangsttid. Arg.* **51:** 104–20.

KOROTKEVICH, E. S. 1958: Nablyndeniya nad tyulenyami vo Vremya Pervoy Zimovki Sovetskoy Antarkticheskoy Ekspeditsii, *Inf. Byull. Sov. Ant. Eksp.* **3:** 79–80.

LAWS, R. M. 1953: A New Method of Age Determination in Mammals with Special Reference to the Elephant Seal (*Mirounga leonina* Linn.), *Sci. Rep. Falkland Islands Dependencies Survey* **2:** 1–12.

LAWS, R. M. 1953: The Elephant Seal (*Mirounga leonina* Linn.): I. Growth and Age. *Sci. Rep. Falkland Islands Dependencies Survey* **8:** 1–62.

LAWS, R. M. 1956: The Elephant Seal (*Mirounga leonina* Linn.): II. General Social and Reproductive Behaviour, *Sci. Rep. Falkland Islands Dependencies Survey* **13:** 1–88.

LAWS, R. M. 1956: The Elephant Seal (*Mirounga leonina* Linn.): III. The Physiology of Reproduction, *Sci. Rep. Falkland Islands Dependencies Survey* **15:** 1–66.

LAWS, R. M. 1956: Growth and Sexual Maturity in Aquatic Animals, *Nature* **178:** 193–4.

LAWS, R. M. 1957: On the Growth Rates of the Leopard Seal *Hydrurga leptonyx* (De Blainville, 1820), *Saugetierk Mitt.* **5:** 49–55.

LAWS, R. M. 1959: The Foetal Growth Rates of Whales with Special Reference to the Fin Whale *Balaenoptera physalus* Linn., *Discovery Rep.* **29:** 281–308.

LAWS, R. M., and TAYLOR, R. J. F. 1957: A Mass Dying of Crabeater Seals *Lobodon carcinophagus* (Gray), *Proc. Zool. Soc. Lond.* **129:** 315–24.

LINDSEY, A. A. 1937: The Weddell Seal in the Bay of Whales, *J. Mammal.* **18:** 127–44.

LINDSEY, A. A. 1938: Notes on the Crabeater Seal, *J. Mammal.* **19:** 456–61.

MACINTOSH, N. A. 1952: The Marking of Whales, *Norsk Hvalfangsttid. Arg.* **41:** 236–40.

MACINTOSH, N. A., and WHEELER, J. F. G. 1929: Southern Blue and Fin Whales, *Discovery Rep.* **1:** 257–540.

MANSFIELD, A. W. 1958: The Breeding Behaviour and Reproductive Cycle of the Weddell Seal (*Leptonychotes weddelli* Lesson), *Sci. Rep. Falkland Islands Dependencies Survey* **18:** 1–41.

MARKOWSKI, S. 1952: The Cestodes of Seals from Antarctica, *Bull. Brit. Mus.* (*Nat. Hist.*), *Zool.* **1:** 125–50.

MATTHEWS, L. H. 1929: Natural History of the Elephant Seal, *Discovery Rep.* **1:** 233–56.

MATTHEWS, L. H. 1937: The Humpback Whale *Megaptera nodosa*, *Discovery Rep.* **17:** 7–92.

MATTHEWS, L. H. 1938: The Sperm Whale *Physeter catodon*, *Discovery Rep.* **17:** 93–168.

MATTHEWS, L. H. 1938: Notes on the Southern Right Whale *Eubalaena australis*, *Discovery Rep.* **17:** 169–82.

MATTHEWS, L. H. 1938: The Sei Whale *Balaenoptera borealis*, *Discovery Rep.* **17:** 183–290.

NISHIWAKI, M. 1950: On the Body Weight of Whales, *Sci. Rep. Whales Res. Inst., Tokyo* **4:** 184–209.

NISHIWAKI, M. 1950: Determination of the Age of Antarctic Blue and Fin Whales by the Colour Changes in Crystalline Lens, *Sci. Rep. Whales Res. Inst., Tokyo* **4:** 115–61.

NISHIWAKI, M. 1951: On the Periodic Mark on the Baleen Plates as a Possible Clue to Age in Whales, *Sci. Rep. Whales Res. Inst., Tokyo* **6:** 133–52.

NISHIWAKI, M., HIBIYA, T., and OSHSUMI, S. 1958: Age Study of Sperm Whales Based on Readings of Tooth Laminations, *Sci. Rep. Whales Res. Inst., Tokyo* **13:** 135–51.

NISHIWAKI, M., ICHIHARA, T., and OHSUMI, S. 1958: Age Studies Based on Ear Plug, *Sci. Rep. Whales Res. Inst., Tokyo* **13:** 155–69.

NORMAN, J. R., and FRASER, F. C. 1948: *Giant Fishes, Whales and Dolphins.* Putnam, London.

OGAWA, T., and ARIFUKU, S. 1948: On the Acoustic System in the Cetacean Brains, *Sci. Rep. Whales Res. Inst., Tokyo* **2:** 1–20.

OGAWA, T., and SHIDA, T. 1950: On the Sensory Tubercles of Lips and of Oral Cavities in the Sei and Fin Whale, *Sci. Rep. Whales Res. Inst., Tokyo* **3:** 1–16.

O'GORMAN, F. A. 1961: Fur Seals Breeding in the Falkland Islands Dependencies, *Nature* **192:** 914–6.

OLIVER, W. R. B. 1921: The Crabeating Seal in New Zealand, *Trans. Proc. N.Z. Inst. Wellington* **53:** 360.

OLSTAD, O. 1930: Rats and Reindeer in the Antarctic, *Sci. Res. Norwegian Antarctic Exp. 1927–8 et seq.* **4:** 1–20.

OMURA, H. 1953: Biological Studies on Humpback Whales in the Antarctic Whaling Areas IV and V, *Sci. Rep. Whales Res. Inst., Tokyo* **8:** 81–102.

PAULIAN, P. 1953: Pinnipèdes, Cétacés, Oiseaux des Îles Kerguelen et Amsterdam, *Mem. Inst. Sci. Madagascar,* **A.8:** 111–234.

PERKINS, J. E. 1945: Biology at Little America III, the West Base of the US Antarctic Service Expedition 1939–41, *Proc. Amer. Phil. Soc.* **89:** 277–81.

PÉWÉ, T. L., RIVARD, N. R., and LLANO, G. A. 1959: Mummified Seal Carcases in the McMurdo Sound Region, Antarctica, *Science* **130:** 716.

PLEHANOFF, P. 1933: The Determination of the Age in Seals, *Abst. Works. Zool. Inst. Moscow Univ.*: 88–91.

PURVES, P. E. 1955: The Wax Plug in the External Auditory Meatus of the Mysticeti, *Discovery Rep.* **27:** 293–302.

RAYNER, G. W. 1940: Whale Marking; Progress and Results to December 1939, *Discovery Rep.* **19:** 245–84.

RAYNER, G. W. 1948: Whale Marking: II. Distribution of Blue, Fin and Humpback Whales Marked from 1932 to 1938, *Discovery Rep.* **25:** 31–8.

RING, T. P. A. 1923: The Elephant Seals of Kerguelen Land, *Proc. Zool. Soc. Lond.*: 431–43.

RUUD, J. T. 1940: The Surface Structure of Baleen Plates as a Possible Clue to Age in Whales, *Hvalråd. Skri.* **23:** 1–24.

SAPIN-JALOUSTRE, J. 1952: Les Phoques de Terre Adélie, *Mammalia* **16:** 179–212.

SAPIN-JALOUSTRE, J. 1953: Les Phoques de Terre Adélie (suite et fin), *Mammalia* **17:** 1–20.

SAPIN-JALOUSTRE, J. 1953: L'Identification des Cétacés Antarctiques à la Mer, *Mammalia* **17:** 221–59.

SCHEFFER, V. B. 1950: Growth Layers in the Teeth of Pinnipedia as an Indication of Age, *Science* **112:** 309–11.

SCHEFFER, V. B. 1958: *Seals, Sea Lions and Walruses. A Review of the Pinnipedia.* Stanford Univ. Press.

SCHOLANDER, P. F. 1940: Experimental Investigations on the Respiratory Function in Diving Mammals and Birds, *Hvalråd. Skri.* **22:** 1–131.

SCHULTZ, L. P. 1938: Can the Weight of Whales and Large Fish be calculated? *J. Mammal.* **19:** 480–7.

SILVERTSEN, E. 1954: A Survey of the Eared Seals (family Otariidae) with Remarks on the Antarctic Seals Collected by M. K. *Norvegia* 1928–29, *Sci. Res. Norwegian Ant. Exp.* **3:** 1–76.

SLIJPER, E. J. 1948: On the Thickness of the Layer of Blubber in Antarctic Blue and Fin Whales, I, II, and III, *Proc. Kon. Nederl. Akad. Wetenschappen* **51:** 1033–45, **51:** 1114–24, **51:** 1310–16.

SLIJPER, E. J. 1962: *Whales.* Hutchinson, London.

SORENSEN, J. 1950: Elephant Seals of Campbell Island, *Cape Exp. Ser. Bull.* **6:** 1–31.

SYMONS, H. W. 1955: The Foetal Growth Rate of Whales, *Norsk Hvalfangsttid. Årg.* **44:** 519–25.

SYMONS, H. W. and WESTON, R. D. 1958: Studies on the Humpback Whale (*Megaptera nodosa*) in the Bellingshausen Sea, *Norsk Hvalfangsttid. Arg.* **47:** 53–81.

TURBOTT, E. G. 1949: Observations on the Occurrence of the Weddell Seal in New Zealand, *Rec. Auckland (N.Z.) Inst.* **3:** 377–9.

TURBOTT, E. G. 1952: Seals of the Southern Ocean. Simpson, F.A., ed. *The Antarctic Today*, pp. 195–215, Reed and NZ Antarctic Society, Wellington.

WILLIAMSON, G. W. 1961: Two Kinds of Minke Whale in the Antarctic, *Norsk Hvalfangsttid. Arg.* **50:** 133–41.

YAMADA, M. 1953: Contribution to the Anatomy of the Organ of Hearing in Whales, *Sci. Rep. Whales Res. Inst., Tokyo* **8:** 1–79.

CHAPTER SEVEN

Antarctic Pack Ice

JOHN A. HEAP, *University of Michigan*

Introduction

In 1683 one Abraham Cowley said that when blown well to the south of Cape Horn his crew were 'So extreme cold that we could bear drinking 3 quarts of Brandy in 24 hours each man, and be not at all the worse for it.' (Christie, 1951.) Despite this undeniable evidence of the cold nature of *terra Australis nondum cognita* James Cook in his first voyage was instructed by the Admiralty and the Royal Society to discover *terra Australis*, which was believed to be temperate, make contact with its inhabitants and 'with their consent' take possession in the king's name. Cook returned from his second voyage in 1775 saying that 'The risque one runs in exploring a coast, in these unknown and icy seas, is so very great, that I can be bold enough to say that no man will ever venture farther than I have done.' One has only to look at the exaggerated lithographs of Antarctic icebergs and pack ice drawn by Cook's surgeon, Forster, and compare them with his relatively subdued and accurate pictures of Cook's subsequent voyagings in the Pacific to know how awesome these ice masses must have seemed. (See, for instance, Figs. 3 and 4.)

Probably because of Arctic experience of contending with, and overcoming, problems of navigating small sailing vessels in sea ice (and because icebergs were comparatively rarely seen in the Arctic) the huge masses of ice, sometimes measured in miles, stimulated much greater interest in the early Antarctic explorers than the sea ice. It was only when Ross in 1841 penetrated the sea to which he gave his name and realized, sounding perilously near the ice front of the Ross Ice Shelf, that it was afloat and was the probable birthplace of the giant tabular bergs, that interest in icebergs abated.

Sixty years later the heroic age of Antarctic exploration began when expeditions struggled through the pack as best they could and, once on the continent, resolutely turned their back on the sea and faced the pole. Three expeditions under de Gerlache, Filchner and Shackleton spent winters drifting with the ice in the Bellingshausen and Weddell Seas but made little of the opportunities offered them for work on the morphology of the Antarctic pack when compared with the contemporary emphasis on sea ice work in the Arctic by Nansen and Malmgren. From that time until the present, the Arctic sea ice has been subject to ever-increasing study, largely because of economic and defence importance, while the study of Antarctic ice has remained in its infant stages.

Apart from the overriding interest in the continent rather than the surrounding seas the main reason for the lack of knowledge of Antarctic sea ice is the enormous area involved. In the Arctic most of the main problems concerned with the physics of sea ice have been worked out and these answers are, with little modification, applicable to the Antarctic. The outstanding problems in the Antarctic are concerned with the areal distribution of sea ice, seasonal and annual variations therein, and the closely related problems of the interaction between ocean, ice and atmosphere in the broad sweep of the Southern Ocean.

The continued existence after the IGY and IGC of a reasonable scatter of meteorological stations round the periphery of the continent, and the future possibility of plotting overall ice distribution from television satellite photographs means that the tools are now available to solve the large-scale problems of Antarctic sea ice regime. This article attempts briefly to sketch the present state of knowledge and, in so doing, outline the most important future requirements.

Seasonal Distribution

The major work on Antarctic sea ice distribution was published in 1940 by Mackintosh and Herdman. It remains, today, the only published atlas of one facet of Antarctic sea ice distribution, based on itemized and unequivocal evidence, which gives a circum-Antarctic picture. The study is purely of ice edge positions and is built up from the observations of the Discovery Committee's vessels, of whaling factory ships and of various expeditions. No attempt is made to plot ice conditions inside the ice edges but a fair indication is given of the average limits inside which ice of any concentration may be expected. What follows is largely based on their work.

At the end of the summer, in early February, the temperature begins to drop in the cold southerly parts of the Weddell Sea and ice forms. In the Bellingshausen Sea ice forms a little later and the slight movements of the pack in this region decrease. In the Ross Sea, which is much more open in its southern reaches than the Weddell Sea, ice does not form until March or the beginning of April.

From the Ross Sea westwards to the Weddell Sea there are areas of pack of all sizes forming a discontinuous fringe. When pack ice is present it is sometimes close to the coast but more often it is some way off, and the fringe may vary in width from 1 km to 200 km. As the air temperature drops towards winter, ice begins to form in sheltered bays and will slowly extend seawards. At the same time ice forms, more slowly, in the interstices of the pack lying off shore and will extend from these nucleii of old pack until it joins up with the ice along the coast to form an almost continuous belt. By August or September the pack will probably have reached its maximum extent.

During the build-up phase ice forms by the freezing of sea water and by the addition of superimposed snow. It is believed that snow contributes more to ice growth in the Antarctic than it does in the Arctic with the general result that Antarctic ice tends to be softer, for the same thickness, than Arctic ice. Although this should make the ice easier to break, the presence of large masses of snow in the water during icebreaking activities increases skin friction along the hull so much that the vessel may be brought to a standstill.

While the ice is building up it is liable to disruption by wave action, or pressure. Both factors are due to wind or, basically, to differences in atmospheric pressure between one region and another.

A patch of thin ice may be broken up by small waves and the pieces will jostle together, turning up the edges of each bit to form pancake ice. On the other hand it may be subject to pressure from the bigger floes to each side and will raft, bringing about a rapid increase in thickness. Pressure may continue until the bigger floes are thrown into pressure ridges up to 7 m high. Huge pressure ridges have a draught below the waterline which is between three and four times their height above the waterline. In the north-eastern part of the Weddell Sea in 1956 it was calculated that although the general thickness of undisturbed ice was about 2 m there would be an average of between 3 and 4 m if the excess ice from the tremendous pressure formations was evenly redistributed. (See Fig. 39.)

At the outer edge of the pack, until August or September, the ice is thinner and eventually feathers out to a sludge or slush of ice or sodden snow. The thin ice is continually broken up by waves and blown about by the wind but its edge is usually found between the $-1 \cdot 9°$ C and $-1 \cdot 5°$ C ocean surface isotherms. This is consistent with the freezing temperature of sea water. The outer edge of the pack in winter has, however, rarely been seen.

At the height of the winter the pack is relatively still as has been shown by the drifts of vessels in the Weddell and Bellingshausen Seas. But as spring wears on to summer the pack loosens up and new ice does not form in the interstices to keep it cemented together. As the whole mass becomes more mobile it will have a greater opportunity to spread or to compact. It may not be a coincidence that Shackleton's *Endurance*, having weathered the long winter with little difficulty, was finally crushed in October.

During the summer the ice melts first in the north and the decay progresses southwards. At the same time much of the heavy ice rots internally as small pockets of brine melt out adjacent ice first. It gives rotting ice the appearance, below the waterline, of Gruyère cheese.

By the end of January the circum-Antarctic ice belt is once more broken up, leaving large masses of ice only in the Bellingshausen and Weddell Seas.

Throughout the cycle of formation and decay the circum-Antarctic ice belt is generally moving. As has been suggested above, the movement is least during the winter and greatest during the summer. The movement is generally from east to west except for the clockwise circulation of ice in the Weddell Sea which, in the northern part of the sea, produces a west to east drift. This movement of ice is superimposed on a similar wind drift of water and is a function of the general atmospheric pressure and wind regime of the Antarctic.

In the Bellingshausen Sea the westerly drift is least marked. Gerlache in 1898–9 in the *Antarctic* drifted indeterminately throughout the winter, more generally east or west than north or south, but always slight movements. In the summer of 1899–1900 he was finally swept westwards and released well to the west of Peter I Øy. Nothing is known about the general ice drift in the Amundsen Sea but presumably it is to the west and contributes substantially to the ice tongue which bars the entrance to the Ross Sea in the early part of the summer. In the late summer, surprisingly unlike the Weddell Sea, the Victoria Land coast of the Ross Sea is largely clear of ice and the western extremity of the tongue of ice across the Ross Sea is retreating eastwards from 180°.

Round the remainder of the Antarctic coastline, from the Ross to the Weddell Seas, the ice drift is uniformly to the west under the dominance of the prevailing easterly winds.

In the Weddell Sea the drifts of the *Deutschland, Endurance* and *Theron* proved the existence of the strong clockwise circulation of ice. This circulation, from the time a piece of ice enters the sea off Kapp Norvegia to the time when it melts in the northern part of the sea, probably takes about two years.

For many years it has been thought that the clockwise circulation of the Weddell Sea produces a tongue of pack drifting from west to east between approximately 60° S and 65° S. It is also believed that this tongue of pack may drift as far east as Long. 40° E and that there is an area of open water lying between it and the westerly moving ice close to the continent. The records of vessels entering the Weddell Sea pack have shown no clear indication that the tongue exists as a perennially distinct feature. Despite the correlative evidence of the tongue of anomalously cold water in the same region as the supposed ice tongue, the inference of such a large-scale feature from extrapolation of the few pieces of spatially restricted evidence seems unwarranted.

Direct observational evidence does not exist to support statements about the average age of Antarctic sea ice, or of the seasonal change in the mass of ice present in the Southern Ocean. It has been suggested above that the Weddell Sea and Bellingshausen Sea ice masses are the largest to survive the summer and that round the remainder of the continent the ice belt is very much reduced and may disappear altogether along some coasts. It would appear that as a rough estimate, by the end of the summer the area of sea ice is reduced to between a half and a third of the maximum winter extent and there is a reduction in the thickness of the remaining ice. This means that the greater proportion of the sea ice is not more than one winter old. In the Weddell Sea much of the ice may be two years old and there is probably a little in the Weddell and Bellingshausen Seas which is older still. The fact that the ice is generally young in the Antarctic makes it a less severe navigational problem than the very old, tough, Arctic pack which may reach ages of up to seven years.

Annual Variations

The general pattern of the seasonal variation of ice is fairly well known. The main navigational problems arise when the usual does not happen. Ships are stopped when there is more ice than usual and coastal sledge parties are frustrated when fast ice fails to form.

A study has been made by the present writer of the distribution of sea ice in the Southern Ocean between Longitudes 7° W and 92° W. In this area very large variations in ice conditions have been found. In the period covered by the study, from 1898 to 1960, two types of variation have appeared. One is a long-term variation of the order of a decade and the other a short-period variation of between two and four years.

The long-term variation shows up most clearly in the ice and temperature records at Laurie Island in the South Orkneys (Prohaska, 1951; Argentina, 1951) which cover the period 1903–50. In the nine years from 1923–32 the annual temperature was consistently below the mean for the period of observation and the number of days each year during which fast ice lasted in Scotia Bay were consistently greater than average. The remainder of the record seems to suggest that this variation from normal is episodic in character rather than cyclical. There is evidence to suggest that the northern ice edge of the Weddell Sea pack lay well to the north of the South Orkney Islands during the early summer of these nine years. Ice edges near to South Georgia were reported in 1926, 1928 and 1930 and have not been seen so close since.

The only known marked peculiarity of these years was the enormous numbers of icebergs seen in the South Atlantic. It is difficult to be certain that this sudden excess of reported icebergs is not a result of the equally sudden appearance from 1925 onwards of people to report them. In 1925 Discovery Committee vessels began to work in the South Atlantic and it is upon their records that the suggested peculiarity of these years is based. Wordie and Kemp (1933) reported a number of sightings of monster bergs of which one probably measured at least ninety by thirty-five miles while Marr (1935) reported over 2000 icebergs in the immediate vicinity of the South Orkney Islands in 1933. If such a huge berg as that mentioned above were to melt it would be capable of cooling down by 1° C a volume of water 10 m thick and 1,000,000 km² in extent. In deciding the merits of this suggestion it is of interest to note two points: the first is that Towson (1859) and Findlay (1883, 1899 and 1920) have given evidence of similar iceberg swarms in the South Atlantic in the early 1850s and in the 1890s. The second is that ten-year running means of annual temperature for the Falkland Islands, South Georgia and the South Orkney Islands suggest that the cooling deviation from the normal over this decade was greatest in the South Orkney Islands, and decreased northwards. It is therefore probable that the causal factor lay within the Antarctic Convergence. It is worthy of note that Wexler (1959) in his study of recorded temperatures during this century in the Ross Sea area finds no evidence of variation such as that in the South Orkney Islands.

The short period variations also appear in both annual temperature and ice records. These variations were first noticed with reference to the accessibility of Marguerite Bay.

Since Marguerite Bay was discovered by Charcot in 1909, twenty-three attempts have been made to enter the bay, of which fifteen were successful. The remaining eight attempts failed at some time in the course of the first three months of 1930, 1941, 1949, 1953, 1954, 1955, 1959, 1960. In every case except 1955 the failure was not primarily because of unyielding ice in Marguerite Bay but because of an enormous mass of ice which lay to the west of the bay. Figure 40 shows the extent of this ice mass, as far as is known in 1959 and 1960. The thickness of some of this ice – up to 8 m – shows that the main mass could not possibly have formed *in situ*. Most of it must have formed over a number of years, well to the south, probably along the southern coast of the Bellingshausen

FIG. 39 'MAGGA DAN' IN VERY HUMMOCKY ICE, NORTH-EAST
WEDDELL SEA, 2 JANUARY 1957
(*Photo. Commonwealth Trans-Antarctic Expedition*)

Sea; it must then have broken away, drifted north and formed a nucleus for the growth of more ice which helped to keep it in position off the west coast of the peninsula. Evidence supporting this course of events is that in March 1958, when the last ships left the area, the seas to the west of Graham Land and to the north of the South Shetland Islands were clear of ice. Then, between April and May 1958, the mean temperature at Argentine Islands dropped from an above average mean for April of −3° C to −11·7° C in May, the third coldest May on record at this base. During May the Argentine Islands were invested with ice and at the end of the month *HMS Burghead Bay* attempted to reach Deception

Island and was stopped by close pack about 140 km north-west of Smith Island. The next greatest drop in temperature between April and May was from —4·6° C to —11·0° C in 1952 which was followed by the 1952–3 and 1953–4 seasons when it was impossible to enter Marguerite Bay.

Only the most tentative reasons can be put forward for the causes of these exceptional ice seasons around Graham Land. It is of immediate interest to note that, although these great severities are not, so far as is known, continent wide, the severity of the ice situation around the South Orkney Islands varies in phase with the conditions on the west coast of Graham Land. This suggests that the cause has a wide influence which straddles the peninsula. This, in turn, suggests some singularity in the atmospheric circulation as being the most likely cause. Figures 41 and 42, from the work of IGY meteorologists at Little America V, show, that in 1958, compared with 1957, there was a singular dominance of low pressure in the central Weddell Sea. Although there is considerable latitude for judgement in the preparation of Antarctic mean monthly pressure maps, if the maps present a true difference between 1957 and 1958 then the map of mean atmospheric pressure in May 1958 suggests a cause for the outbreak. Zubov (1947) showed that ice tends to drift along isobars calculated as means of ten days or longer. The arrangement of these isobars between Ellsworth Land and Graham Land in May 1958 would seem to be conducive to a drift of ice across the Bellingshausen Sea towards Graham Land. At the moment it has not been possible to test this hypothesis as there has not been a recurrence of an outbreak of ice from the Bellingshausen Sea.

Before 1957 the data with which to build even tentative mean isobaric maps did not exist and even now such maps are usually vague over the South Pacific for lack of observation in this area. It is interesting to note that Makerov (1959) has suggested a possible relationship between differing patterns of mean atmospheric pressure over the Weddell Sea and sea surface temperature anomalies in the westward drift from the Weddell Sea.

Future Problems

An attempt has been made to suggest that around Graham Land, at least, the most stimulating problems lie in the direction of trying to elucidate further the nature and causes of annual variations. At the moment the main barriers to further progress are that detailed studies of ice regime have not been carried out for the Antarctic apart from the sector between Longitudes 7° W and 92° W and that, of necessity, meteorological and oceanographical work has been aimed primarily at obtaining a true picture of the average condition. The result is that it is not yet possible to take a circum-Antarctic view of ice variations nor is it yet possible to do more than indicate a tentative relationship between ice variation and atmospheric pressure.

A first step towards solving these problems would be to make an analysis of ice distribution round the remainder of the Antarctic in order to give a continent-wide picture of annual variations. This will allow any subsequent analysis of

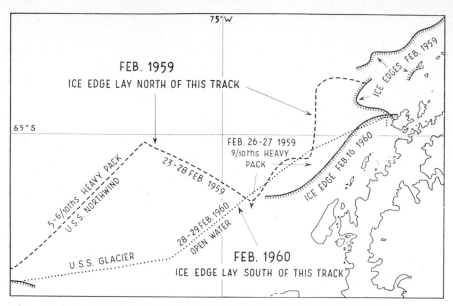

FIG. 40 ICE EDGES IN THE BELLINGSHAUSEN SEA, FEBRUARY 1959 AND
FEBRUARY 1960

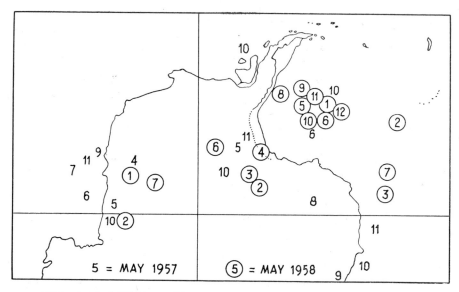

FIG. 41 MONTHLY MEAN POSITIONS OF CYCLONIC CENTRES
OVER WEST ANTARCTICA

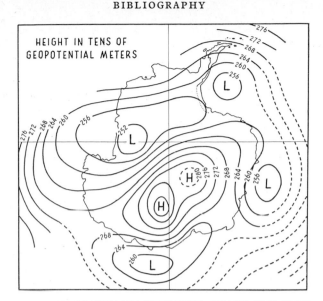

HEIGHT IN TENS OF
GEOPOTENTIAL METERS

FIG. 42 700-MB CONSTANT PRESSURE CHART FOR MAY, 1958
(From Alt, Astapenko and Ropar, 1959)

ice distribution from television satellites on pole-to-pole orbits to be analysed in the light of past experience.

To elucidate further the causes of sea ice variation requires long-range study of anomalous behaviour of both ocean and atmosphere over the Southern Ocean. Sea ice, sandwiched between the sea and the air is the vastly variable interface expressive of the complex interrelation of both.

Bibliography

ALT, J., ASTAPENKO, P., and ROPAR, N. J. 1959: Some Aspects of the Antarctic Atmospheric Circulation in 1958, *IGY General Report Series* **4**, U.S. Nat. Acad. Sci.

ARGENTINA 1951: *Datos Climatologicos y Geomagneticos. Islas Orcadas del Sur*, Argentina, Servicio Meteorologico Nacional, Ser. B 1, Pt 1.

CHRISTIE, E. W. HUNTER 1951: *The Antarctic Problem*, London, George Allen and Unwin, p. 41, footnote.

FINDLAY, A. G. 1883: 8, Ice. *Directory for the South Atlantic Ocean* (London), 9th ed., 127–38.

FINDLAY, A. G. 1899: *Directory for the South Atlantic Ocean* (London), Addenda to 9th ed., p. 8.

FINDLAY, A. G. 1920: 8, Ice. *Directory for the South Atlantic Ocean* (London), 10th ed., 172–87.

MACKINTOSH, N. A. and HERDMAN, H. F. P. 1940: Distribution of the pack-ice in the Southern Ocean, *Discovery Rep.* **19:** 285–96.

MAKEROV, YU. V. 1959: Godovyye i Mezhgodovyye Izneneniya Tempera-turnykh Usloviy Poverkhnostnykh vod Atlanticheskogo Sektora Antarktiki, *Trudy Gosudarstyvennogo Okeanograficheskogo Instituta* **46:** 5–27.

MARR, J. W. S. 1935: The South Orkney Islands. *Discovery Rep.* **10:** 283–382.

PROHASKA, F. J. 1951: Sobre el Estado de los Hielos en la Bahia Escocia (Islas Orcadas del Sur), *Meteoros* (Buenos Aires), Ano **1:** 216–18.

RASTORGUEV, V. I., and ALVAREZ, J. A. 1958: Description of the Antarctic Circulation Observed from April to November 1957 at the IGY Antarctic Weather Central, Little America Station, *IGY General Report Series* **1,** US Nat. Acad. Sci.

TOWSON, J. T. 1859: *Icebergs in the Southern Ocean: A Paper read Before the Historic Society of Lancashire and Cheshire on the 19th of November, 1857, and corrected from Reports of More Recent Dates. Printed for Private Circulation,* Liverpool, T. Brakell, Printer.

WEXLER, H. 1959: A Warming Trend at Little America, Antarctica, *Weather* **14:** 191–7.

WORDIE, J. M., and KEMP, S. 1933: Observations on Certain Antarctic Ice-bergs, *Geogr. J.* **81:** 428–34.

ZUBOV, H. N. 1947: Wind and Movement of Ice, *Dynamical Oceanology,* Gidrometeoizdat, Moskva/Leningrad, 1947. Chapter VIII, 336–53. [Trans-lated by L. G. Robbins, Technical Services Branch, Division of Oceanography, USN Hydrographic Office.]

PART THREE

The Antarctic Continent

Beyond this flood a frozen Continent
Lies dark and wilde, beat with perpetual storms
Of Whirlwind and dire Hail, which on firm land
Thaws not, but gathers heap, and ruin seems
Of ancient pile; all else deep snow and ice.

MILTON

CHAPTER EIGHT

The Ice Shelves

CHARLES SWITHINBANK, *Scott Polar Institute*, and JAMES H. ZUMBERGE, *Grand Valley College*

Introduction

More than one third of the coastline of Antarctica is fringed by icc shelves. The ice shelves are floating ice sheets. They have a level or gently undulating surface and flow under their own weight. Limited areas are aground. Ice shelves cover more than 1,400,000 km² in the Antarctic; the Ross Ice Shelf (530,000 km²) and Filchner Ice Shelf (400,000 km²) being the two largest (Fig. 43). Ice thickness

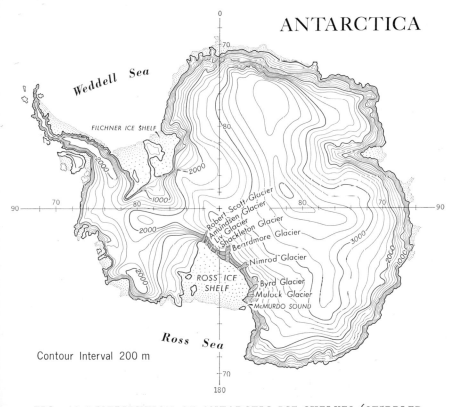

FIG. 43 DISTRIBUTION OF ANTARCTIC ICE SHELVES (STIPPLED AREAS)

varies from about 200 m at the ice front to as much as 1300 m at the junction
with land ice some hundreds of kilometres inland. In this chapter we outline
the physical characteristics and dynamics of the ice shelves as they are known
today.

Physical Characteristics

THICKNESS

Nourished by abundant snowfall and free to creep under its own weight in any
direction, an ice shelf would probably maintain an equilibrium thickness of
around 200 m. This is in fact the thickness of many tabular icebergs on calving
from their parent ice shelves. But most icebergs are inadequately nourished by

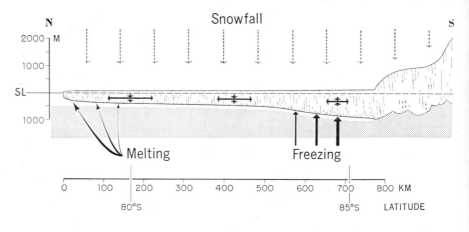

ROSS   ICE   SHELF

FIG. 44 GENERALIZED SECTION THROUGH ROSS ICE SHELF ALONG
THE MERIDIAN 168°W
(After Crary and Van der Hoeven, 1961)

snowfall and are consequently thinning. Except at the ice front, ice shelves are
generally confined by flanking arms of the inland ice sheet or of land. Free to
move in one direction only, their thickness increases with distance from the ice
front (Fig. 44) and varies with the configuration of the ice shelf boundaries.
In places where the ice is forced to converge in order to pass through a strait, it
may reach a thickness of up to 1300 m.

PHYSIOGRAPHY

The physiography of ice shelves is treated at length by Wright and Priestley
(1922) and Swithinbank (1957). In this section we summarize the main features
as they are described by these authors, adding references to recent contributions
and to features inadequately discussed in the earlier work.

(a) *Seaward margin*. The ice front forms a sheer cliff, normally about 30 m though in places anything from 2 m to 50 m in height.

Low ice fronts (Fig. 45) may be caused by rapid horizontal strain rates or by melting on the underside of the ice shelf, whereas high ice fronts (Fig. 46) may be due to the development of an underwater ram. In plan, the ice front

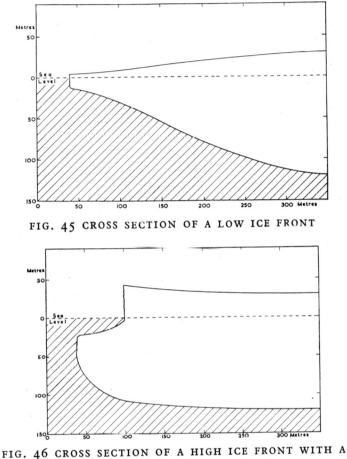

FIG. 45 CROSS SECTION OF A LOW ICE FRONT

FIG. 46 CROSS SECTION OF A HIGH ICE FRONT WITH A
SUBMERGED RAM

presents a rugged, seemingly random arrangement of inlets, promontories, bays and unbroken stretches of monotonously uniform ice cliff facing the sea along hundreds of kilometres of coast (see Figs. 50, 55). But the pattern of major inlets is related to the shape of each ice shelf and to the position of obstacles affecting its movement. The Bay of Whales has been a permanent feature of the Ross Ice Shelf since its discovery in 1841 and Vahsel Bay has been a permanent feature of the Filchner Ice Shelf since its discovery in 1912. Limited sections of an ice front may be grounded (see Fig. 53).

Periodically large portions of ice shelves break off and drift away to sea as tabular ice bergs. Most of these icebergs have horizontal dimensions between a few hundred metres and several kilometres, but icebergs 30 to 40 km long are not uncommon. The largest on record was 185 km long (Tofte, 1927, p. 464).

(b) *Surface*. The surface is for the most part flat (see Figs. 51 and 56), though series of undulations or depressions are quite common. Within 50 km of the ice front, there is commonly a series of depressions with a wave length of 1–4 km and a wave height of 5–20 m (Lunde, 1961). Robin (1958) suggests that this kind of depression is found where diverging flow is too great to be accommodated by spreading due to surface accumulation. Another kind of undulation is associated with areas of local grounding. These are apparently pressure waves caused by the damming action of the grounded ice and are confined, as would be expected, to the inland side of a grounded area. A third, quite different form of surface undulation has been encountered by every party approaching land along the western margins of the Ross Ice Shelf. Most run parallel with the land. They have a wave length of 1–3 km and a wave height of 10–20 m. Neuburg *et al.* (1959) report undulations having a wave height of 'several hundred feet' near the inland margin of Filchner Ice Shelf. This kind of undulation is evidently due in some places to the thrust of land glaciers flowing into an ice shelf, but elsewhere it appears to be a product simply of shearing along the boundary between floating and grounded ice.

Giant rifts trending parallel with the ice front have been encountered on both Filchner and Ross Ice Shelves. Neuburg *et al.* (*ibid.*) describe 'a gigantic rupture . . . Grand Chasm' in the Filchner Ice Shelf. The chasm is 100 km long, 400 m to 5 km wide and 53 m deep, and evidently represents a fracture extending from top to bottom of the ice sheet. 'Grand Chasm' is 80 km from the ice front. Similar rifts on the Ross Ice Shelf were first noted by Siple (1945) and have been seen and photographed by Swithinbank. There are three rifts between 60 and 100 km in length between latitudes 78° 30′ and 81° S and between longitudes 174° E and 180°. Each is some 10–20 m deep and varies in width from a single crevasse to a 400 m wide chaotic confusion of ice blocks. The origin of rifts is uncertain, though the initial fracture is probably due to stresses set up by differential movement resulting from the configuration of the ice shelf boundaries. Wilson (1960) goes so far as to suggest that the frictional drag of the strong westerly current in the Weddell Sea is largely responsible for the formation of 'Grand Chasm'.

Crevasses are rare. They are, however, found near the margins of ice shelves except where the direction of movement of the land ice is the same as that of the floating ice. Elsewhere, crevasses are associated with locally grounded areas and with rifts. Zumberge *et al.* (1960) discuss criteria for the formation of crevasses in the disturbed area of the Ross Ice Shelf near the Bay of Whales (Fig. 54).

Grounded areas can generally be identified by the crevasses that surround them as well as by the absence of crevasses in the centre of the grounded area. Large areas of ice resting on rock and surrounded by floating ice shelf are known as *ice rises*. No rock is exposed and there may be none above sea level. Ice rises generally have a dome-shaped surface and are anything from 1 km to more than 100 km in diameter. Roosevelt Island, the largest ice rise on the Ross Ice Shelf, measures about 65 by 155 km. The direction of flow is a criterion for distinguishing between locally grounded areas and ice rises. Ice may be deflected or even halted by grounded areas, but in ice rises, movement is independent of that of the ice shelf and, being in the main radial, may in places oppose it.

(c) *Inland margin.* The inland margin is marked by the start of the gentle upward slope of the land ice, and by a number of cracks in the surface caused, by the independent tidal rise and fall of the ice shelf. Known as strand cracks these have been encountered on most ice shelves including Filchner Ice Shelf (Neuburg *et al.*, 1959) and Fimbulisen (Lunde, 1961). Often the margin is also

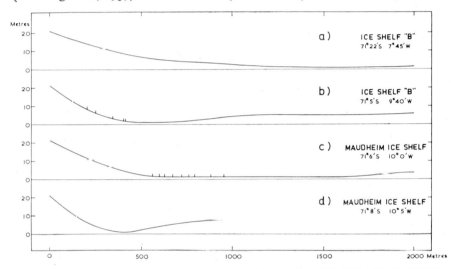

FIG. 47 CROSS SECTIONS OF THE DEPRESSION AT THE INLAND MARGINS OF TWO ICE SHELVES IN WESTERN DRONNING MAUD LAND
The vertical marks show the positions of strand cracks

marked by a wide and shallow depression running parallel with the boundary of the land ice. The depth of the depression is proportional to the slope of the land ice (Fig. 47). Most cross sections of the margin show a single depression, but a subdued series has been found in one place (Thiel and Ostenso, 1961).

Where an ice shelf moves generally parallel with the land rather than away from it, such as along the western margin of the Ross Ice Shelf, the depression gives way in places to discontinuous rifts similar to the rifts that have been encountered in the middle of ice shelves. In rare cases a continuous cliff separates an inland ice sheet from the ice shelf at its foot. Ice cliffs have been seen to mark the inland boundary of an ice shelf in western Dronning Maud Land, and Fuchs and Hillary quote Stratton's description of an 'ice wall' bordering Filchner Ice Shelf 'similar to the ice front'. Ice cliffs seem to be confined to areas in which a relatively thin inland ice sheet slopes steeply to its junction with an ice shelf.

LITHOLOGY

Ice shelves are made of snow, firn and ice. Each substance consists of ice crystals with intervening air spaces, though the amount of air decreases from top to bottom of the ice shelf. In the absence of melting, the mean crystal section area increases with depth from as little as <0.01 mm^2 in newly fallen snow (Liljequist, 1956) to 9.4 mm^2 in old ice at 100 m (Schytt, 1958). There is probably no generally preferred orientation of crystals between the surface and 100 m depth. Fabric diagrams show isolated maxima of c-axes that may be of sedimentary origin (*ibid.*, p. 143), while four separate maxima are sometimes centred about the pole to the theoretical shear plane (Reid, 1961). Ice shelves generally exhibit a conspicuous stratification. This is normally seasonal, though it can also be due to unusual weather conditions.

IMPURITIES

(a) *Gases.* Little is known of the chemical composition of the air entrapped in ice shelves. Studies of Greenland icebergs (Scholander *et al.*, 1961) suggest that in the absence of melting there may be very little contamination or alteration of air after its inclusion in glacier ice.

(b) *Liquids.* There is evidence that meltwater occasionally percolates through the uppermost few centimetres of some ice shelves (Schytt, 1958; Kotlyakov, 1961). There is no evidence of the penetration of sea water into the bottom layers of ice shelves of normal thickness (Ragle *et al.*, 1960), though a brine-soaked layer was found at a depth of 41 m in the Lazarev Ice Shelf (Dubrovin, 1960). Brine-soaked firn snow was found 4 m below sea level at 15 m depth in a core taken from a thin arm of the Ross Ice Shelf near Scott Base (Stuart and Bull, 1963).

(c) *Solids.* Ice shelves contain rock material derived from nunataks and from land over which the ice moves before it reaches the sea. But little is known of the amount of debris nor of the proportion remaining in the ice shelf at the time calving takes place. Voronov and Kruchinin (1961) found organic remains, together with pebbles and sand derived from metamorphic rocks, in a rift near the ice front on Lazarev Ice Shelf. Debenham (1920) describes the findings of gravel, marine muds, mirabilite and organic remains on the surface of the McMurdo Ice Shelf; but the area is exceptional in many ways and it cannot be compared with the main mass of the adjacent Ross Ice Shelf. Ragle *et al.* (1960) found 'aggregates of glassy, markedly angular material identified tentatively as volcanic ash' in a drill core from the Ross Ice Shelf at Little America V. Thiel and Schmidt (1961) were able to filter particulate matter including meteoritic spherules from water obtained from an ice core in the Ross Ice Shelf at 80° 26' S, 169° 35' E.

DENSITY

The density of the ice shelves lies between that of new snow at the surface (0.1 to 0.3 gm/cm^3) and pure ice (0.917 gm/cm^3) at the ice/water interface. Bender and Gow (1961) report on the only density measurements that extend

from top to bottom of an ice shelf. Their work refers to the 256 m thick Ross Ice
Shelf at Little America V (Fig. 48). Schytt (1958) and Robin (1958) discuss
density measurements down to 100 m in the 200 m thick ice shelf at Maudheim.
Aughenbaugh *et al.* (1958) record densities to a depth of 57 m in the 232 m
thick Filchner Ice Shelf at Ellsworth Station. The increase in density with depth
is due to compaction, recrystallization and expulsion of interstitial air in the
surface layers. Below the depth at which air interstices interconnect, density
increases through compression of the air bubbles. Zumberge *et al.* (1960)

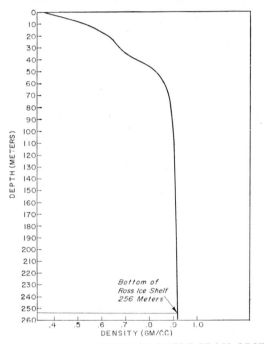

FIG. 48 THE DENSITY OF THE ROSS ICE SHELF FROM OBSERVATIONS IN
A DRILL HOLE AT LITTLE AMERICA V
(From Bender and Gow, 1961)

observe that some densification is produced by horizontal compression in the
Ross Ice Shelf near the Bay of Whales.

TEMPERATURE

The temperatures of ice shelves lie close to the mean annual air temperatures
near the surface and the freezing point of sea water at the ice/water interface.
The surface layers are subject to fluctuations approaching those of the ambient
air temperature. Bender and Gow (1961) report on the only temperature measurements that extend from top to bottom of an ice shelf. Their work refers to the
256 m thick Ross Ice Shelf at Little America V (Fig. 49). Schytt (1960) describes
temperature measurements down to 100 m in the 200 m thick ice shelf at Maudheim. Aughenbaugh *et al.* (1958) record temperatures to a depth of 57 m in the

232 m thick Filchner Ice Shelf at Ellsworth Station. Temperatures at a depth of 10 m vary from −9° C on the Shackleton Ice Shelf in Lat. 66° S to −31° C on the Filchner Ice Shelf in Lat. 82° S (*ibid.*). Figure 52 shows that 10 m temperatures on the Ross Ice Shelf vary from −23° to −29° C. The significance of the observed temperature profiles with respect to the ice regime is discussed by Robin (1955), Schytt (1958), Wexler (1960) and Crary (1961a). It is generally agreed that the temperatures suggest that there is considerable bottom melting near the ice front.

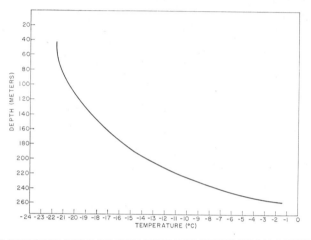

FIG. 49 THE TEMPERATURE OF THE ROSS ICE SHELF FROM OBSERVATIONS IN A DRILL HOLE AT LITTLE AMERICA V
(From Bender and Gow, 1961)

Nourishment

Ice shelves are nourished by the accumulation of snow on their surface, by ice discharged from land glaciers, by the products of sublimation and in some places by the freezing of sea water. No major part is played by drift snow swept from the land ice (Swithinbank, 1958b; Kotlyakov, 1961).

ACCUMULATION

Accumulation of snow is probably the principal source of nourishment of Antarctic ice shelves. Figure 52 shows that the total accumulation on the Ross Ice Shelf is 22 gm/cm² per year near the ice front; but it drops to between 18 and 19 gm/cm² at distances greater than 150 km from the ice front and maintains this amount even at points 650 km from the sea. Swithinbank (1958b) found a somewhat greater mean accumulation over the ice shelves of western Dronning Maud Land. Burton (1960) reports 38 gm/cm² for the ice shelf in the neighbourhood of Halley Bay, and Behrendt (1962) quotes 21 gm/cm² for the Filchner Ice Shelf at Ellsworth Station. Giovinetto (1961) reports a mean value of 18 gm/cm² for the whole Filchner Ice Shelf, while Lister (1960) gives 16

FIG. 50 AIR PHOTOGRAPH OF THE FRONT OF THE ROSS ICE SHELF
NEAR THE BAY OF WHALES

FIG. 51 AIR PHOTOGRAPH OF THE SURFACE OF THE ROSS ICE
SHELF, SHOWING SNO-CATS AND THEIR TRACKS

gm/cm² for the sector east of Berkner Island. Lunde (1961) calculates that the
mean accumulation over the period 1940–59 at Norway Station on Fimbulisen
was 50 gm/cm² per year. Tongiorni *et al.* (1962) record 38 gm/cm² per year
as a 5-year mean for Base Roi Baudouin in Dronning Maud Land. Kruchinin
(1961) reports 37 gm/cm² for the year 1959 on the nearby Lazarev Ice Shelf. The
highest figures are those of Kotlyakov (1961), who reports 65–70 gm/cm² on
the Shackleton Ice Shelf. From the available information he shows that the
amount of accumulation is related more to latitude than to any other factor.
Accumulation generally falls with increasing distance from the principal paths

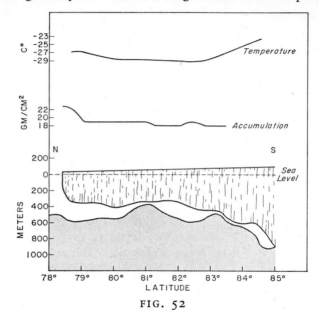

FIG. 52

Section through the Ross Ice Shelf along the meridian 168° W (Crary and Van
der Hoeven, 1961) showing mean annual accumulation as determined from
pit studies (Vickers, personal communication) and temperature at 10 metres
depth (after Crary, personal communication)

of cyclonic storms across the Southern Ocean. This indicates that the principal
source of accumulation is atmospheric precipitation. Schytt (1960) concludes on
the basis of temperature data that in addition to snowfall, the ice shelf at Maudheim receives 2·2 gm/cm² water per year, or at least 6% of the total accumulation, in the form of sublimation products. Kotlyakov (1961) also believes that
hoar-frost plays a significant part in the nourishment of ice shelves.

LAND GLACIERS

Little is known about the contribution of land glaciers to the nourishment and
survival of ice shelves, though isolated measurements have been made (Swithinbank, 1960; Wilson and Crary, 1961). Crary and Van der Hoeven (1961) believe
that the Ross Ice Shelf is nourished largely by the inland ice sheet along the

southerly parts of its eastern margin, and note that the 'nearly constant elevations along the western portions of the shelf are proof that the high plateau area
of Victoria Land contributes little to the shelf'. The principal valley glaciers
draining into the Ross Ice Shelf are shown in Fig. 43. At least three ice streams,
Slessor Glacier, Recovery Glacier and a larger unnamed ice stream, drain into
Filchner Ice Shelf (Behrendt, 1962). Lambert Glacier, perhaps the largest ice
stream in the Antarctic, drains into Amery Ice Shelf. Elsewhere, long stretches
of the margins of most ice shelves are fed by the inland ice sheet.

FIG. 53 AIR PHOTOGRAPHS OF THE SAME SECTION (NORSELBUKTA AND
MAUDHEIM IS-SHELF) OF THE ICE FRONT IN LONGITUDE 8° 40′ W
Upper photo: January 1952; *lower photo:* December 1958
The grounded ice front on the left has suffered no change, whereas the
floating tongues on the right have been deformed and truncated by calving
during the 7-year interval

H

BOTTOM FREEZING

There is little doubt that some sea water freezes on the bottom of the ice shelf in McMurdo Sound (Debenham, 1920) and it has been claimed (Debenham, 1949) that bottom freezing may play an important part in the nourishment of the Ross Ice Shelf. Whereas there is evidence of bottom melting near the ice front, bottom freezing could only take place where there is little circulation of sea water. However, the rock and ice bottom profile in Fig. 52 suggests that there may be bottom melting even near the southern limits of the Ross Ice Shelf. There is a distinct parallel between rises in the rock bottom and rises in the ice

FIG. 54 ICE ANTICLINES AND CREVASSES IN THE DISTURBED AREA
OF THE ROSS ICE SHELF NEAR THE BAY OF WHALES

bottom, indicating that the layer of circulating sea water may be able to maintain its thickness despite movement of the ice towards shallower water. It is evident that if there is little circulation of sea water along the line at which cold land ice goes afloat, bottom freezing may take place. All that can be said at present is that the amount of bottom freezing will decrease towards the ice front as shown diagrammatically in Fig. 44; that somewhere there is an equilibrium line where neither freezing nor melting takes place; and that bottom melting must increase progressively on the seaward side of this line.

Wastage

Loss by calving accounts for by far the greatest discharge to the ocean; it is followed in descending order of importance by bottom melting, the blowing of snow into the sea, evaporation and, in exceptional conditions, by surface run-off.

Beyond this general qualitative observation, one can say very little in terms of quantitative values for processes of ice shelf wastage.

CALVING

The origin of the huge tabular icebergs common to the Antarctic seas was proved by Sir James Ross during the nineteenth century when he penetrated to the edge of the ice shelf which now bears his name. Earlier, in 1774–5, Captain James Cook speculated on the source of the flat 'ice islands' which confronted him in high southern latitudes, and deduced an explanation remarkably close to the truth (Herdman, 1959).

In spite of the countless observations of tabular icebergs recorded in the logs of the many ships which have penetrated high southern latitudes, no attempts have been made to measure the volume of ice discharged from an ice shelf, except as reported by Korotkevich (1959), Shil'nikov (1960) and Crary (1961). Little is known of the mechanism involved in the calving process or of the timing of calving. Many segments of the seaward edge of an ice shelf break off when a downward bending movement is caused by bottom melting, but this does not explain the calving of enormous masses from the parent body. The origin of 100-km long icebergs in the Ross Sea is still unknown. Tsunamis, action of storm wave, and tidal movement are agents invoked by some writers to account for calving, while others attach greater significance to the character of the ice shelf margin itself: for example the presence of heavily crevassed areas and rifted zones that indicate grounding.

Another unanswered question is: when does the bulk of calving take place? Some segments of an ice shelf may yield icebergs at a more or less constant rate over a period of a few years, while other parts of the same shelf may experience only a single breakout in a decade or longer. The origin of such indentations as Okuma Bay, the Bay of Whales and Kainan Bay along the Ross Ice Shelf margin may be related to this very question. The Bay of Whales has undergone enormous changes in configuration since the turn of the century. Clearly, the whole problem of calving from ice shelves constitutes an area of investigation which needs more attention from glaciologists and oceanographers.

MELTING

Wastage by bottom melting of Antarctic ice shelves has been measured indirectly by Crary (1961) for the Ross Ice Shelf near Little America V, and Swithinbank (1962) for Maudheim Is-shelf. Wexler (1960) considered various theoretical temperature gradients through the Ross, Maudheim and Filchner ice shelves, and in making the theoretical curves fit the observed temperature gradients, concluded that bottom melting must have occurred. Because the borings in which the temperature measurements were made are all near the ice front, no analyses of the thermal regime can be made for bottom conditions far from the ice front where no bottom melting may occur at all.

Surface melting is not an important process of wastage on the Ross or Filchner ice shelves, but the McMurdo Ice Shelf shows marked evidence of a net loss by melting. Mellor and McKinnon (1960) imply that considerable surface melting occurs on the Amery Ice Shelf. Although some of this water originates through the melting of land ice which borders the shelf, it is possible that surface melt-water from the shelf escapes to the sea and must represent a loss to the regime.

DRIFTING SNOW AND EVAPORATION

These two ablation processes are the most difficult to measure by direct means. In snow pit studies or accumulation measurements from snow stakes, where net

FIG. 55 AIR PHOTOGRAPH OF NORSELBUKTA AND MAUDHEIM
IS-SHELF FROM 2800 METRES ABOVE SEA LEVEL

annual increments are measured, the loss by deflation and evaporation is included as emphasized by Mellor (1959).

Blowing snow streaming over the ice front into the sea is a common sight, and the countless miles of eroded snow surfaces seen from the air over the Ross Ice Shelf leave little doubt that vast quantities of snow are deflated from it. Crary (1961) measured a net loss of 2 cm of snow for the month of November 1957 at Little America V, and Mellor (1959), and Mellor and Radok (1960) attribute loss by drifting snow for the whole of Antarctica to be an important item in the mass budget.

Evaporation would seem less important on the low-lying ice shelves where the relative humidity is higher than on the elevated regions of the interior. Wade (1945) did not consider evaporational losses to be of any significance for the Bay of Whales region on the Ross Ice Shelf, and Swithinbank (1957) reached the same conclusion for Maudheim.

Movement

The mechanism of movement is essentially a spreading of the ice shelf in response to the accumulation of snow on its surface. The ice is able to compensate for varying amounts of snowfall by varying its rate of spreading. The result is that the altitude of the upper surface can remain more or less unchanged at a

FIG. 56 MOTOR SLEDGE PARTY ON THE ROSS ICE SHELF NEAR THE BEARDMORE GLACIER

given position. Another component of movement is contributed by the ice of land glaciers flowing into the ice shelf.

Very few measurements of absolute movement have been made. By comparing the 1902 *Discovery* survey of the ice front of the Ross Ice Shelf with the 1911 *Terra Nova* survey, Debenham (1923) computed a *minimum* rate of movement of 1300 m per year between the meridians of 179° E and 173° W. If this figure is correct, it is likely to be more representative of the bulk of the seaward portion of the Ross Ice Shelf than is any measurement made close to the land boundaries of the ice shelf. Estimates of movement in the Bay of Whales sector of the ice front have been collected by Wexler (1960), who quotes values between 322 and 458 m/yr. The area lies on the downstream side of Roosevelt Island, an ice rise; it cannot therefore be considered representative. The only available measurements elsewhere were made 50 km east of White Island, where the ice moves 844 m/yr (Stuart and Bull, 1963).

Astronomical observations have been made in recent years to determine the rate of movement of Filchner Ice Shelf, and the results indicate a northward component of movement of 1·3 km/yr at Ellsworth Station and 2·6 km/yr at General Belgrano Station (Behrendt, 1962). On the basis of a mass balance study Swithinbank (1958a) computed a rate of movement of 280 m/yr for the ice shelf at Maudheim.

Deformation studies can give information on the nature of the delicate balance that exists between net accumulation and the thickness of an ice shelf. Surface strain rate measurements can be used to extrapolate absolute movement figures for the purpose of mass balance calculations. Swithinbank (1958a) surveyed a pattern of stakes on the ice shelf at Maudheim and found the greatest strain rates in directions parallel with the ice front. This is probably an edge effect, for it is to be expected that where an ice shelf flows between flanking arms of land or land ice, maximum strain rates will be found parallel with the direction of movement. Crary (1961b) compares the principal horizontal strain rates at Maudheim: 138×10^{-5} and 55×10^{-5} per year, with the corresponding values from his own surveys at Little America V: 129×10^{-5} and 81×10^{-5} per year. Deformation studies have been made at Ellsworth Station on Filchner Ice Shelf (Aughenbaugh et al., 1958), and Crary (1961b) states that these also indicated a nearly 2 to 1 ratio of strain rates between directions normal to and parallel with the direction of flow.

Ice Shelves as Geological Agents

EROSION

Ice shelves can only erode when they are grounded or where they abut against a marginal land mass. There will be no erosion of hard rock unless the basal ice contains enough clastics to cause abrasion, or unless the bedrock is capable of being quarried. Basal ice debris is available from land ice flowing into the ice shelf or from unconsolidated clastics overridden by the ice itself. Some rock materials have been seen in old tilted icebergs, but generally these should be largely sediment-free because of bottom melting while they are still part of the ice shelf.

A unique mechanism of erosion by an ice shelf is the freezing of bottom sediment and organisms on to the bottom of the McMurdo Ice Shelf. This debris gradually works its way to the surface through continued freezing on the bottom and melting on the surface (Debenham, 1948). It is not known whether the process is peculiar to the McMurdo shelf or whether it occurs in other shelves covering shallow water.

TRANSPORTATION

The lack of visible moraine in ice shelves and the widespread occurrence of dirt-free icebergs suggests that little or no rock material other than eolian debris is transported by an ice shelf. Philippi (1912), Hough (1956) and Thomas (1960), imply that icebergs contribute ice-rafted materials to the sea bottom through melting, producing a so-called glacial marine sediment. If we assume that this is true, we are justified in suggesting that debris is shed from the bottom of the ice shelf in the zone of bottom melting. The source in the case of the Ross Ice Shelf must be feeder glaciers such as the Beardmore, Shackleton, Nimrod and others.

As long as the surface receives a net accumulation of snow, it is impossible for any imported debris to reach the surface. If there is also net accumulation on the bottom by freezing of sea water near the landward margin of the shelf, all of the debris contained in the ice must be transported seaward until it reaches the zone of net loss from the bottom through melting, where it is released and falls to the ocean bottom. This explains the lack of surface moraine in the Ross Ice Shelf and shows the need for borings in the shelf close to the landward margin.

SEDIMENTATION

The sediments of the Ross Sea have been classified as glacial marine by Philippi (1912). Hough (1956) describes glacial marine sediment as '. . . composed mainly of material which has been transported from the land or shallow water by ice-rafting, and has been dropped to the bottom when the ice melted. It is composed of a wide range of particle sizes, from clay (less than 0·004 mm in diameter) to gravel (greater than 2 mm in diameter)'. Hough further describes this material as having the general appearance of glacial till and notes that it may be unlaminated, the implication being that some of it *is* laminated. Glacial marine sediment from the Ross Sea contains diatom and foraminiferal tests, which Hough believes flourish in sea water in the pack ice. This is confirmed by the work of Burkholder and Sieburth (1961) who show that, in Antarctic waters, the most abundant phytoplanktons occurred in areas containing a high content of chlorophyll *a*. Sunlight is therefore necessary for the existence of the microscopic animals and it can be inferred that no organisms of this type can live in the dark waters beneath an ice shelf. Abundant remains of vertebrate and macroscopic invertebrate marine animals have been observed lying in the ablation zone of the McMurdo shelf. These remains presumably came from *beneath* the ice, which has been estimated to be at least 30 m thick and is known to be some 2 km from the open sea (Swithinbank et al., 1961).

We may draw some preliminary conclusions about the nature of the deposit derived from a floating ice shelf. This glacial marine sediment on the sea floor is till-like in appearance, contains no pelagic remains but may contain benthonic forms such as corals, sponge spicules, molluscs, brachiopods and even fish. In deeper waters such as those beneath the Ross and Filchner Ice Shelves where water depths in excess of 800 m below the base of the shelf have been measured by seismic methods (Crary et al., 1962; Thiel and Ostenso, 1961) benthonic remains would be less common or entirely absent.

The presence of a living bottom fauna beneath an ice shelf has not been directly proved, but indirect evidence from the McMurdo Ice Shelf strongly suggests that one does, in fact, exist in some places. Till-like Pleistocene deposits containing marine shells are known from the north-western coast of the state of Washington in the United States, and it is possible that these were laid down by an ice shelf attached to the continental ice of the North American cordillera. The absence of a pelagic micro-fauna in such deposits would lend further support to the hypothesis, because this criterion may be important in distinguishing between glacial marine sediments derived from waters infested with icebergs and pack ice as compared with sediments of similar physical appearance laid down beneath a continuous ice shelf. A further line of evidence helpful in separating the two would be the presence of eolian material such as volcanic ash layers which Thomas (1960) reported from Ross Sea cores. He is of the opinion that the interbedding of volcanic ash with glacial marine deposits precludes a continuous ice cover. However, the presence of deeply buried ash layers in the Ross Ice Shelf at Little America V (Ragle *et al.*, 1960) shows that materials of eolian origin are able to sink gradually in an ice shelf, and given sufficient time, would eventually melt loose from the bottom. Whether or not they would retain their volcanic characteristics is another matter, although if no other detrital materials were intermixed, the mineral composition should provide the necessary basis for identification of a volcanic origin.

Conclusion

The survival and extent of the ice shelves today depends not only upon adequate nourishment by ice flow and accumulation but also on the anchorage provided by flanking arms of land ice and locally grounded areas (Swithinbank, 1957; Thomas, 1960; Kapitsa, 1961). Evidence of grounding is to be found in works of Mawson (1942), Mason (1951) and Reece (1951). Without anchorage in some form, the ice shelves might break loose and drift bodily to sea. The salient characteristics on which this conclusion is based can be seen from Figure 43. The principal ice shelves fill in great bays between arms of land or land ice and generally smooth the outline of the continent. Nowhere do they stretch far to seaward unprotected. A line joining the northern extremities of the inland ice sheet and the outermost grounded areas conforms in remarkable degree with the present position of the ice front. This suggests that ice shelves, unless they are flanked by land or by inland ice sheets, may never extend far to sea beyond the outermost shoals which might ground them. It follows that the probable maximum seaward limit of an ice shelf during the Quaternary period could in many cases be established by soundings alone.

The ice shelves can be used to study some fundamental problems of glacier flow. In formulating a satisfactory flow law for ice it is necessary to take into account the temperature of the ice and the shear stress at the glacier bed. On land glaciers these things are hard to measure owing to the inaccessibility of the glacier bed. But on ice shelves the problem of ice flow is equivalent to that of a weightless material being compressed between frictionless plates. It is easy to measure the temperature at the upper surface, and the lower surface must be at the melting point of fresh-water ice in sea water. Because ice shelves occur within a wide range of air temperature and have a wide range of thickness, they serve in many ways as ideal model glaciers.

Studies of ice shelves have up to now been largely exploratory. While detailed measurements have been made, they refer only to small areas near the ice front. Three holes have been drilled to depths greater than 100 m, but the farthest was no more than 20 km from the ice front (Tongiorni et al., 1962). The need now is for a series of detailed studies, including drilling, along a line trending up-stream from an ice front. Field (1961) has discussed measurements that should be made. Most of the basic quantities involved in the mass balance are still unknown. What is the relative importance to the regime of ice flow from the land, of ice formed from local accumulation and of ice made by the freezing of sea water? How long does the ice reside over the sea? In which parts of the ice shelf is there melting from below; and how much is melted? These and other basic questions can only be answered by careful measurements of accumulation, strain rate, absolute movement and surface slope. Drill holes should be planned not only to study the ice structure and ice temperatures, but to go right through the ice shelf into the water below. Profiles of ocean temperature, salinity, current velocity and turbulent heat transfer are needed to establish melting or freezing at the bottom of the ice. The opportunity could be taken to study the possibly unique forms of life in the dark waters beneath, for biologists do not know whether, in the absence of photosynthesis, phytoplankton carried beneath an ice shelf by tidal currents can provide the basis for a life cycle at great distances from the open sea. Finally it must be said that a nuclear submarine could be an effective tool for the rapid exploration of the bottom surface of the ice shelves.

Bibliography

AUGHENBAUGH, N., NEUBURG, H., and WALKER, P. 1958: Ellsworth Station Glaciological and Biological Data 1957–58, *Ohio State University Research Foundation Report 825–1 Part I.*

BEHRENDT, J. C. 1962: Geophysical and Glaciological Studies in the Filchner Ice Shelf Area of Antarctica, *J. Geophys. Res.* **67:** 221–34.

BENDER, J. A. and GOW, A. J. 1961: Deep Drilling in Antarctica. IUGG Symposium on Antarctic Glaciology, Helsinki, 1960, *Int. Assn Sci. Hydrol. Publ.* **55.**

BURKHOLDER, P. R., and SIEBURTH, J. M. 1961: Phytoplankton and Chloro-phyll in the Gerlache and Bransfield Straits of Antarctica, *Limnology and Oceanography* **6:** 45–52.

BURTON, J. M. C. 1960: The Ice-Shelf in the Neighbourhood of Halley Bay. *Proc. Roy. Soc.*, **A256:** 197–200.

CRARY, A. P. 1961a: Glaciological Studies at Little America Station, Antarctica,

1957 and 1958, *IGY Glaciological Report* **5,** American Geographical Society, New York.

CRARY, A. P. 1961b: Glaciological Regime at Little America Station, Antarctica, *J. Geophys. Res.* **66:** 871–8.

CRARY, A. P., ROBINSON, E. S., BENNETT, H. F., and BOYD, W. W. 1962: Glaciological Regime of the Ross Ice Shelf, *J. Geophys. Res.* **67:** 2791–807.

CRARY, A. P., and VAN DER HOEVEN, F. G. 1961: Sub-Ice Topography of Antarctica, Long. 160° W to 130° E. IUGG Symposium on Antarctic Glaciology, Helsinki, 1960, *Int. Assn Sci. Hydrol. Publ.* **55.**

DEBENHAM, F. 1920: A New Mode of Transportation by Ice, *Quart. J. Geol. Soc. Lond.* **75** (part 2): 51–76.

DEBENHAM, F. 1923: Report on the Maps and Surveys. *British (Terra Nova) Antarctic Expedition 1910–13,* Harrison & Sons, London.

DEBENHAM, F. 1948: The Problem of the Great Ross Barrier, *Geogr. J.* **112:** 196–218.

DUBROVIN, L. I. 1960: Rassol v shel'fovom lednike Lazareva, *Inf. Byull. Sov. Ant. Eksp.* **22:** 15–16.

FIELD, W. O. 1958: Antarctic Glaciology, in *Science in Antarctica,* Part 2: 36–56. US Nat. Acad. Sci., Nat. Res. Council Publ. 878.

FILCHNER, W. 1922: *Zum sechsten Erdteil,* Ullstein, Berlin.

FUCHS, Sir V., and HILLARY, Sir E. 1958: *The Crossing of Antarctica,* Cassell, London.

GIOVINETTO, M. 1961: Mass Accumulation in West Antarctica. IGY Bull. 50, *Trans. Amer. Geophys. Un.* **42:** 386–9.

HERDMAN, H. F. P. 1959: Some Notes on Sea Ice Observed by Captain James Cook, R.N., during his Circumnavigation of Antarctica, 1772–75, *J. Glaciol.* **3:** 534–41.

HOUGH, J. L. 1956: Sediment Distribution in the Southern Oceans around Antarctica, *J. Sediment. Petrol.* **26:** 301–6.

KAPITSA, A. P. 1961: Dinamika i Morfologiya Lednikovogo Pokrova Tsentral'-nogo Sektora Vostochnoy Antarktidy, *Trudy Sov. Ant. Eksp.* **18:** 1–93.

KOROTKEVICH, Ye. S. 1959: Ledovyy Rezhim Morya Deyvisa, *Izvestiya Vsesoyuznogo Geograficheskogo Obshchestva,* 91 *Vyp* **2:** 152–5.

KOTLYAKOV, V. M. 1961: Pitanie Shel'fovykh Lednikov Antarktidyi i Neko-torye i Problemy ikh Proiskhozhdeniya, *Issledovaniya Lednikov i Lednikovykh Raionov* **1,** Izdatel'stvo Akademii Nauk SSSR. Moskva.

KRUCHININ, Yu. A. 1961: Dinamika Snezhnoy Poverkhnosti Shel'fovogo Lednika Lazareva, *Inf. Byull. Sov. Ant. Eksp.* **27:** 5–8.

LILJEQUIST, G. H. 1956: Halo-Phenomena and Ice Crystals, *Norwegian-British-Swedish Ant. Exp. 1949–52. Sci. Results II Part 2a,* Norsk Polarinstitutt, Oslo.

LISTER, H. 1960: Glaciology 1: Solid Precipitation and Drift Snow, *Trans-Antarctic Exp. 1955–58: Sci. Report* **5,** Trans-Antarctic Expedition Committee London.

LUNDE, T. 1961: On the Snow Accumulation in Dronning Maud Land, *Skr. Norsk Polarinst.* **123**, Norsk Polarinstitutt, Oslo.

MASON, D. 1951: The Larsen Shelf Ice., *J. Glaciol.* **1:** 514.

MAWSON, D. 1942: Geographical Narrative and Cartography, *Australasian Ant. Exp. 1911–14: Sci. Reports Ser. A1.*

MELLOR, M. 1959: Mass Balance Studies in Antarctica, *J. Glaciol.* **3:** 522–33.

MELLOR, M., and MCKINNON, G. 1960: The Amery Ice Shelf and its Hinterland., *Polar Rec.* **10:** 30–4.

MELLOR, M., and RADOK, U. 1960: Some Properties of Drifting Snow. Symposium on Antarctic Meteorology, Melbourne 1959: 333–46, Pergamon Press, London.

NEUBURG, H. A. C., THIEL, E., WALKER, P. T., BEHRENDT, J. C., and AUGHENBAUGH, N. B. 1959: The Filchner Ice Shelf. *Ann. Ass. Amer. Geogr.* **49:** 110–9.

PHILIPPI, E. 1912: Die Grundproben der Deutschen Südpolar-Expedition 1901–03. *Deutsche Südpol. Exp.* **2:** 415–616.

RAGLE, R. H., HANSEN, B. L., GOW, A., and PATENAUDE, R. W. 1960: Deep Core Drilling in the Ross Ice Shelf, Little America V, Antarctica, *Technical Report* **70**, US Army Snow Ice and Permafrost Research Establishment.

REECE, A. 1951: The Ice of Crown Prince Gustav Channel, Antarctica, *J. Glaciol.* **1:** 404–9.

ROBIN, G. de Q. 1955: Ice Movement and Temperature Distribution in Glaciers and Ice Sheets, *J. Glaciol.* **2:** 523–32.

ROBIN, G. DE Q. 1958: Seismic Shooting and Related Investigations, *Norwegian–British–Swedish Ant. Exp. 1949–52: Sci. Results V*, Norsk Polarinstitutt, Oslo.

SCHOLANDER, P. F., HEMMINGSEN, E. A., COACHMAN, L. K., and NUTT, D. C. 1961: Composition of Gas Bubbles in Greenland Icebergs, *J. Glaciol.* **3:** 813–22.

SCHYTT, V. 1958: A. Snow Studies at Maudheim; B. Snow Studies inland; C. The inner Structure of the Ice Shelf at Maudheim as shown by Core Drilling, *Norwegian–British–Swedish Ant. Exp. 1949–52: Sci. Results IV*: 1–151, Norsk Polarinstitutt, Oslo.

SCHYTT, V. 1960: D. Snow and Ice Temperatures in Dronning Maud Land. *Norwegian–British–Swedish Ant. Exp. 1949–52: Sci. Results IV:* 156–79, Norsk Polarinstitutt, Oslo.

SHACKLETON, E. 1920: *South*, Heinemann, London.

SHIL'NIKOV, V. I. 1960: Opyt Podscheta Ob"yema Aysbergov v Antarktike, *Problemy Arktiki i Antarktiki* **6:** 27–36.

SIPLE, P. 1945: Geographical Exploration from Little America III, *Proc. Amer. Phil. Soc.* **89:** 23 60.

STUART, A. W., and BULL, C. 1963: Glaciological Observations on the Ross Ice Shelf near Scott Base, Antarctica, *J. Glaciol.* **4:** 399–414.

SWITHINBANK, C. 1957: A. The Morphology of the Ice Shelves of Western

Dronning Maud Land; B. The Regime of the Ice Shelf at Maudheim as Shown by Stake Measurements, *Norwegian–British–Swedish Ant. Exp. 1949–52: Sci. Results III*: 1–75, Norsk Polarinstitutt, Oslo.

SWITHINBANK, C. 1958a: C. The Movement of the Ice Shelf at Maudheim. *Norwegian–British–Swedish Ant. Exp. 1949-52: Sci. Results III*: 79–96, Norsk Polarinstitutt, Oslo.

SWITHINBANK, C. 1958b: E. The Regime of the Ice Sheet of Western Dronning Maud Land as Shown by Stake Measurements, *Norwegian–British–Swedish Ant. Exp. 1949-52: Sci. Results III*: 123–44, Norsk Polarinstitutt, Oslo.

SWITHINBANK, C. 1960: F. Ice Movement Inland. *Norwegian-British-Swedish Ant. Exp. 1949-52: Sci. Results III*: 147–58, Norsk Polarinstitutt, Oslo.

SWITHINBANK, C. 1962: Maudheim Revisited: The Morphology and Regime of the Ice Shelf, 1950–1960, *Årbok, 1960*: 28–31, Norsk Polarinstitutt, Oslo.

SWITHINBANK, C., DARBY, D. G., and WOHLSCHLAG, D. E. 1961: Faunal Remains on an Antarctic Ice Shelf, *Science* **133**: 764–6.

THIEL, E. 1961: Antarctica, One Continent or Two? *Polar Rec.* **10**: 335–48.

THIEL, E., and OSTENSO, N. A. 1961: The Contact of the Ross Ice Shelf with the Continental Ice Sheet, Antarctica, *J. Glaciol.* **3**: 823–32.

THIEL, E., and SCHMIDT, R. A. 1961: Spherules from the Antarctic Ice Cap, *J. Geophys., Res.* **66**: 307–10.

THOMAS, C. W. 1940: Late Pleistocene and Recent Limits of the Ross Ice Shelf, *J. Geophys. Res.* **65**: 1789–92.

TOFTE, E. 1927: Odd I's tokt til Peter den Förstes Ø, *Norsk. Geogr. Tidsskr.* **1**: 462–72.

TONGIORNI, E., PICCIOTTO, E., BREUCK, W. De, NORLING, T., GIOT, J., and PANTANETTI, F. 1962: Deep Drilling at Base Roi Baudouin, Dronning Maud Land, Antarctica, *J. Glaciol.* **4**: 101–10.

VORONOV, P. S., and KRUCHININ, Yu.A. 1961: O Nakhodke Morskikh Osadkov na Poverkhnosti Shel'fovogo Lednika Lazareva, *Inf. Byull. Sov. Ant. Eksp.* **29**: 22–6.

WADE, F. A. 1945: The Physical Aspects of the Ross Ice Shelf, *Proc. Amer. Phil. Soc.* **89**: 160–73.

WEXLER, H. 1960: Heating and Melting of Floating Ice Shelves, *J. Glaciol.* **3**: 626–45.

WILSON, C. R., and CRARY, A. P. 1961: Ice Movement Studies on the Skelton Glacier, *J. Glaciol.* **3**: 873–8.

WILSON, G. 1960: The Tectonics of the Great Ice Chasm, Filchner Ice Shelf, Antarctica, *Proc. Geol. Assn, Lond.,* **71**: 130–8.

WRIGHT, C. S., and PRIESTLEY, R. E. 1922: Glaciology, *British (Terra Nova) Ant. Exp. 1910-13*, Harrison & Sons, London.

ZUMBERGE, J. H., GIOVINETTO, M., KEHLE, R., and REID, J. 1960: Deformation of the Ross Ice Shelf near the Bay of Whales, Antarctica, *IGY Glaciological Report* **3**, American Geographical Society, New York.

CHAPTER NINE

The Ice Sheet

ANTHONY J. GOW, *Cold Regions Research and Engineering Laboratory, Hanover, N.H.*

Introduction

During the last million years (Pleistocene Epoch) the world has experienced four major glaciations. For much of this time large portions of the Earth's surface were covered by ice sheets, but only those of Greenland and Antarctica persist at the present day.

The Antarctic land mass was first sighted in the 1820s, but it was not until 1903 that the inland ice was observed for the first time by members of Scott's Discovery Expedition in Victoria Land. Prior to World War I several sledging parties penetrated deeply into the interior of Antarctica, but these were concerned primarily with the attainment of geographical goals and not with detailed studies of the ice sheet itself. Nevertheless some important contributions to our knowledge of the ice sheet were made at various localities along its margin, and in some cases these studies were carried inland for several hundred kilometres. In particular should be mentioned the glaciological work of Wright and Priestley of Scott's 1910-13 British (*Terra Nova*) Antarctic Expedition (Wright and Priestley, 1922). Much valuable information is to be found in the reports of a number of other expeditions preceding World War I, but space does not permit a summarizing of their glaciological observations here.

These, and the more important glaciological results obtained by American and British expeditions in between the two world wars, and by American, British, French and Australian expeditions prior to the International Geophysical Year have been adequately summarized in English by Gould (1940, 1957) and Odell (1952), and in German by Klebelsberg (1948) and Kosack (1955). Perhaps the most notable contribution to Antarctic glaciology prior to the IGY was made by the combined Norwegian–British–Swedish Expedition of 1949–52 on the ice sheet of Dronning Maud Land. This expedition, the first truly international effort in Antarctica, achieved more in terms of basic results than any previous expedition, and more or less set the pattern of future glaciological research in Antarctica. (Swithinbank, 1957–9; Schytt, 1958; Robin, 1958.)

It might be fairly said that until quite recently our knowledge of the Antarctic Ice Sheet consisted largely of uncorrelated observations near its edge. Even as recently as 1955, Gould (1957) estimated that between 5,000,000 and 7,000,000 km² of the inland ice sheet had never been seen. Much of what had been seen had never been studied in detail, so that virtually nothing of the structure or behaviour of the vast inland ice sheet of Antarctica was known prior to the IGY. In fact the first wintering-over of a scientific group on the inland ice was only accomplished in 1956 by the Russians at Pionerskaya Station in East Antarctica. Now, only seven years after the commencement of IGY studies in Antarctica, the broad physical features of the ice sheet and much knowledge of the physical and mechanical properties of its ice and snow are beginning to emerge. This can be attributed largely to the combined efforts of a large number of nations, and their use of modern logistics, instrumentation and research methods.

Physical Characteristics of the Ice Sheet

Antarctica comprises a polar-centred land mass overlain by an ice sheet of variable form and thickness. With the exception of the tip of Graham Land and portions of the coast of Wilkes Land and Enderby Land the ice sheet lies wholly within the Antarctic Circle. The ice extends below sea level at many points, and the land beneath is not uniformly continental. The load of the ice sheet has caused considerable depression of the Antarctic land mass. In the event of complete melting of the ice sheet the land mass would 'isostatically recover' by an amount equal approximately to one-third of the thickness of the ice. Nevertheless it is now known that much of Antarctica would remain below sea level.

Geographically Antarctica can be divided into two distinctive regions: *West Antarctica* lying south of the Americas, and *East Antarctica* bounded by the Atlantic and Indian Oceans, and separated from West Antarctica by a line linking the southern extremities of the Ross and Filchner Ice Shelves. We now know that this subdivision has both geological and glaciological significance, glaciological in the sense that the geologic structures of East and West Antarctica are sufficiently contrasted to reflect upon the thickness and surface morphology of the ice sheet.

The Antarctic Ice Sheet covers approximately 98% of the land mass of Antarctica and comprises about 90% of the world's ice. It is seven times as extensive as the Greenland Ice Sheet and is at least comparable in size to the Laurentide Ice Sheet that covered a large part of North America less than 20,000 years ago (Flint 1957, p. 326). The area of the ice sheet is estimated to be almost 13,500,000 km², and has a maximum diameter of about 4500 km. Its marginal length is in excess of 20,000 km, and the ice sheet is in contact with the ocean along the greater part of this length.

The Antarctic Ice Sheet is veneered by a relatively thin blanket of snow that is slowly transformed into ice at depth. As a layer of snow is compressed under the ever-increasing burden of newly deposited snow at the surface, it 'densifies'. On polar ice sheets this process of densification is essentially a dry process (no melting), involving gradual elimination of the air trapped between grains of snow, and changes in crystal structure. Old compacted snow is generally referred to as *firn* (or nevé). It is a thoroughly porous material and its structure is somewhat analogous to that of a sponge. As the firn becomes more deeply buried it densifies still further, thereby causing the intercommunicating air spaces to diminish, until at a density of about 0·83 gm/cm³ the air spaces seal off to form bubbles. The firn still contains about 10% of air but it is no longer permeable. This corresponds to the firn→ice transition, i.e. the point at which firn transforms into true *glacier ice*. The depth at which this transformation takes place depends on both the temperature and the rate at which snow accumulates on the surface. Near the edge of the ice sheet the transformation takes place at depths between 40 and 60 m. At Byrd Station the transition depth is about 65 m, and it is estimated to occur at approximately 100 m at the South Pole. In the colder and more remote parts of the inland ice firn persists to even greater depth and according to Kotlyakov (1961) glacier ice is not encountered until 120 m depth at Pionerskaya and 164 m at the Pole of Relative Inaccessibility. Assuming an average transition depth of 100 m, and an average ice thickness over Antarctica of 2000 m, we find that approximately 95% by volume of the ice sheet in Antarctica is in fact true glacier ice.

GLACIER CLASSIFICATION

With respect to temperature the Antarctic Ice Sheet is a cold polar glacier characterized by sub-freezing temperatures to a considerable depth. It is even possible that the greater part of the ice sheet is frozen onto its bed, in contrast to the temperate glaciers such as those of New Zealand, which are at or very close to the melting point. Negligible melting occurs on the surface of the Antarctic Ice Sheet. Calving of icebergs, not melting, is the principal cause of glacier wasting in Antarctica, and it would require a very substantial warming of the climate over Antarctica to cause any appreciable melting of the surface of the ice sheet.

The ice sheet most probably originated by the coalescence of two ice sheets in East and West Antarctica which were themselves formed by merging of several highland ice caps. Although this ice sheet welds East and West Antarctica together, it can be readily subdivided into a vast interior portion, the *inland ice*, and a variety of marginal components which include the *ice shelves, valley glaciers* and *ice streams*, and their seaward extensions the *ice tongues*. The inland ice, up to 4000 m thick in some places, is usually thick enough to completely submerge the underlying land mass.

As the snow-formed inland ice flows out towards the edge of the continent it thins out considerably, and the subglacial relief exerts an increasing effect on the shape and movement of the ice. In East Antarctica much of the inland ice discharges directly into the sea along a broad front of heavily crevassed terraced sheets. Channelling of the ice into valleys and depressions leads to the formation of relatively fast-moving ice streams and outlet glaciers which may extend some distance into the sea as ice tongues. Exceptionally large tongues have formed in front of the Ninnis and Mertz Glaciers that debouch from King George V Land.

Rock-walled valley glaciers attain their maximum development along the 'Horst' Ranges of Victoria Land and southwards to the Queen Maud Range. From McMurdo Sound polewards the principal valley glaciers are Mulock, Byrd, Nimrod, Beardmore, Shackleton, Amundsen and Robert Scott. These glaciers discharge directly into the Ross Ice Shelf and all seven appear to drain appreciable quantities of ice from the polar plateau. Smaller glaciers include the Skelton, Darwin, Lennox-King, Liv and Axel Heiberg. North of McMurdo Sound, however, the largest valley glaciers discharge directly into the sea. These include the Mackay, Davis and Tucker Glaciers, and also the Mawson and David Glaciers and their prominent seaward projections, the Nordenskjöld and Drygalski Ice Tongues. About 150 km south of Cape Hallett the Lady Newnes Glacier discharges into the Lady Newnes Ice Shelf. This ice shelf and a number of other ice-embayed areas along the Victoria Land Coast possibly represent fragments of the Ross Ice Shelf when it extended much farther north than it does at the present day. Perhaps the largest valley glacier in the world is the Lambert Glacier that feeds into the Amery Ice Shelf of MacRobertson Land. (Mellor and McKinnon, 1960.) It is certainly a much longer and more extensive stream of ice than the 200 km long Beardmore Glacier which has often been referred to as the world's largest valley glacier. Another very large glacier has been observed discharging into Rennick Bay on the Oates Coast. Tentatively called the Rennick Glacier (Weihaupt, 1961) this stream of ice is thought to be at least 50 km wide and more than 260 km long.

In West Antarctica a large portion of the inland ice is fed into large floating ice shelves. These include the Ross and Filchner Ice Shelves, which occupy the two large embayments of the Ross and Weddell Seas respectively. The Ross Ice Shelf is approximately 500,000 km^2 in area, up to 800 km wide, and extends to within 500 km of the South Pole. Its thickness varies from about 200 m at its seaward edge to 700 m at its junction with the inland ice of Marie Byrd Land and at the foot of the Queen Maud Range. Although such great glaciers as the Mulock, Byrd and Beardmore discharge directly into the Ross Ice Shelf, along its southern margin, they collectively contribute but a small fraction of the total inflow. The Trans-Antarctic Mountains effectively block any massive flow of ice from the South Polar Plateau, and the principal contribution of land-borne ice is probably from the direction of Marie Byrd Land (see Fig. 76).

The Filchner Ice Shelf is now known to be much more extensive than previously thought. It covers an area of at least 400,000 km^2 and ranges in thickness from 200 m up to 1300 m.

Smaller ice shelves include the Getz and Larsen Ice Shelves in West Antarctica and the Amery, Shackleton and West Ice Shelves in East Antarctica. Both the Shackleton and West Ice Shelves appear to be supported on off-shore islands, but the others though locally grounded are essentially free-floating structures. Antarctic ice shelves are nourished also by snow accumulation on their upper surfaces and tend to spread out laterally under the additional weight. This action combined with the 'push' from the rear of the ice from the land results in a relatively rapid movement seaward. Ice shelves comprise more than 10% of the surface of the Antarctic Ice Sheet. They discharge along more than 30% of the Antarctic coastline and periodically calve off the giant tabular icebergs that are unique to Antarctica. Most of these icebergs vary in length from a few hundred metres to several kilometres and they can be as thick as 200 m. Icebergs 30–40 km long are not uncommon and the largest recorded iceberg was more than 180 km long.

SURFACE ELEVATIONS

Figure 43 illustrates the principal features of the surface topography of Antarctica. Generally the ice slopes are quite steep near the continental margin, but diminish quite rapidly toward the interior. In East Antarctica the form of the surface is similar to the equilibrium profile of the ideal ice sheet, but in West Antarctica the surface of the ice sheet is complicated by a more highly irregular subglacial terrain. Two highland areas with elevations of about 4000 m are both located in East Antarctica, but neither coincides with the geographic South Pole. The centrally located highland contains the Pole of Inaccessibility; the point farthest from the sea, which by virtue of its altitude and interior remoteness is considered to be the 'cold pole' of Antarctica. The mean annual temperature at the Pole of Inaccessibility, $-57°$ C $(-72°$ F), is approximately 6° C (11 °F) colder than at the South Pole. The mean elevation of Antarctica is approximately 2000 m, which makes it the loftiest continent on Earth. Although this great average elevation is due in large part to the ice sheet itself, ice thickness measurements in East Antarctica show that the high point of the ice sheet does in fact correspond to the maximum elevation of the land mass beneath the ice, between Sovetskaya and the Pole of Inaccessibility. The ice sheet has depressed the continent by about 600 m on the average, and the land mass would rebound isostatically by this amount if the ice sheet was completely removed. This would bring the average elevation of an ice-free East Antarctica into line with other continents on the Earth's surface, but West Antarctica would most probably emerge as an archipelago of scattered mountainous islands.

SNOWFALL

Despite its great size the Antarctic Ice Sheet receives a minimum of nourishment, but apparently enough to maintain it in a relatively healthy state. It is a particularly thrifty body and its large size is largely a function of its thrift. This coupled with extremely low temperatures will probably ensure maintenance of its glaciers for a long time to come. The *average* snow fall, about half that of Greenland, is 12–15 cm water per year, which is comparable to the rainfall of the semi-arid regions of the Earth. Generally speaking the snow accumulation is greatest on the ice shelves, and in the coastal regions where cyclonic precipitation is augmented by snow drifted in from the interior by katabatic (drainage) winds. Accumulation falls off rapidly towards the interior (see Figs. 57 and 113).

In the centre of the ice sheet where little precipitable moisture penetrates the accumulation rarely exceeds 6–7 cm water per year. Approximate values of mean annual snow accumulation at a number of widespread locations on the ice sheet are given in Table 3 (p. 253).

WIND

Local and regional variations of snow accumulation on the surface of the ice sheet are largely caused by wind action. This redistribution depends upon both the speed and direction of the wind. Both cyclonic and katabatic winds are capable of transporting loose snow considerable distances across the surface of the ice sheet. Katabatic winds are essentially shallow surface winds created by

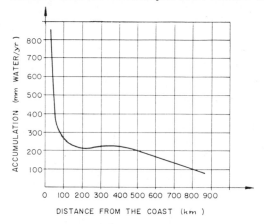

FIG. 57 VARIATION OF ACCUMULATION IN QUEEN MARY LAND
WITH DISTANCE FROM THE COAST
(After Vialov, 1958)

temperature inversions over the snow surface. They are generated over a considerable area of the Antarctic Ice Sheet, but in contrast to the ordinary pressure-controlled winds the katabatics are gravity winds. They tend to flow down the steepest slopes and are often characterized by extreme gustiness. The katabatic winds are thought by Wexler and Rubin (1961) to be responsible for the fierce but rather brief and localized Antarctic blizzards.

Much of the deep interior of the ice sheet experiences very light winds. At the South Pole for instance the average annual wind speed is only 8 m/sec, and gusts seldom exceed 30 m/sec. The strongest winds occur in regions where katabatic and cyclonic winds reinforce one another, and particularly where winds are funnelled into valleys and depressions, e.g. Cape Denison in the Commonwealth Bay area with an annual mean wind speed of 22 m/sec, and where gusts of up to 100 m/sec have been recorded (Mawson, 1915). Table 4 gives wind and temperature measurements at a number of locations on the ice sheet (p. 253).

TEMPERATURES

Antarctica is not merely a desert, it is a very cold desert, and sub-freezing temperatures persist all year around over 95% of its surface. In general the

temperatures along the Antarctic coastline tend to decrease with increasing latitude. In the ice-free valleys of McMurdo Sound, the East Antarctic 'Oases', and
Graham Land, summer temperatures are considerably enhanced by solar radia-

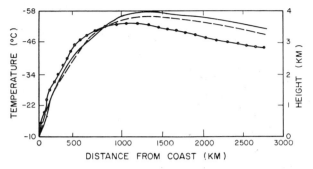

FIG. 58 SURFACE TEMPERATURE DETERMINANTS IN ANTARCTICA
The dotted line shows the elevation profile from the coast to the South Pole
between 93° and 107° E Longitude. The broken line is the curve of annual mean
air temperatures. These temperatures approximate very closely the temperatures
in the snow at 10 metres depth (solid line).
(After Rubin, 1962)

tion from exposed rock surfaces. Temperatures as high as 12° C (+53° F) have been
reported from Graham Land. On the other hand, windswept areas near the coast
may be somewhat cooler than the average for their latitudes. On the inland ice
sheet the surface temperatures are more closely related to changes in elevation

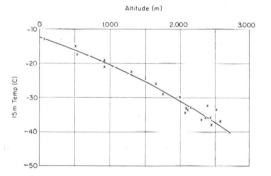

FIG. 59 VARIATION OF 15-METRE DEPTH ICE TEMPERATURE WITH
SURFACE ELEVATION (MACROBERTSON LAND)
(After Mellor, 1960)

than to latitude changes. These effects are illustrated in Figure 58. In East
Antarctica the mean annual temperature decreases by approximately 1° C per
100 metres increase in surface elevation (see Fig. 59). Mean annual temperatures
in East Antarctica are generally very much cooler than those of areas of
comparable latitude or distance from the coast in West Antarctica. Altitude

differences are important although it is very probable that the cyclones which frequent much of West Antarctica, but which rarely penetrate the deep interior of
East Antarctica, have an ameliorating effect on temperatures in West Antarctica.

TOPOGRAPHY

The surface of the Antarctic Ice Sheet is by no means featureless. It possesses a
great variety of surface relief forms which may be subdivided into (*a*) accumulation–deflation features formed at the surface as a direct result of wind, and which
we might refer to as the *microrelief*, and (*b*) large-scale surface structures related
to irregularities in the subglacial topography and to ice movement and which
may be conveniently referred to as the *macrorelief*.

The *microrelief* includes primary accumulation features such as snowdrifts and
dunes that are laid down during cyclonic snowstorms. These are somewhat
analogous to desert dunes on a small scale, even to the development of 'ripple
marks'. They tend to be packed by the wind into well-rounded forms that simulate whalebacks, or overturned canoes. During windstorms the dunes are cut
into a variety of jagged shapes that produce 'ridged', 'scalloped', 'terraced' and
other types of wind-sculptured structure called sastrugi. The long axes of sastrugi
tend to be oriented in the direction of the prevailing wind, and their size can
usually be correlated with wind speed. Sastrugi are only moderately developed
in the central regions of Antarctica, because of low accumulation and low
average wind speeds. They attain their maximum development in areas of
strong katabatic winds. According to Dolgushin (1961), dunes and sastrugi up to
100 m or more in length, and as high as 2 m are not uncommon in the katabatic
zone of East Antarctica. Since katabatic winds tend to flow down the steepest
slopes, sastrugi can be employed as very useful indicators of surface topography.

The most conspicuous features of the *macrorelief* are crevasses. These are
simply elongated open cracks that form wherever the ice sheet is stretched or
sheared beyond its breaking point. They are particularly common in areas of
relatively thin and highly deformed ice near the coast, e.g. on outlet glaciers and
ice streams, but they are also extensively developed on the ice shelves, especially
near the junction of shelf ice and land-based glacier ice, and in areas of grounded
shelf ice. They may be distorted by ice flow, rotated or even squeezed together,
but since they represent a response to flow crevasse orientations can serve as very
useful indicators of the direction of ice movement. Crevasses more than 30 m
wide have been observed but they probably do not exceed 100 m in depth. Great
rifts associated with crevasses arranged *en echelon* and more than 100 km long
have been observed on the Ross Ice Shelf. Much of the inland ice sheet is free of
crevasses because the ice is generally thick enough to contain the deformational
stresses deep in the ice, and thus prevent fracturing at the surface. However,
crevasses will form wherever peaks or ridges approach the surface or project
through it as isolated outcrops of rock called nunataks.

Precise barometric levelling and even visual observations have revealed the
existence of a considerable degree of surface relief over much of the Antarctic

Ice Sheet. Wade (1937) described huge terrace-like steps and broad terrace-like undulations on the slopes of the inland ice sheet of King Edward VII Land. There is not much doubt that these terrace structures represent broad but subdued reflections of the underlying bedrock relief, for Robin (1958) has since discovered by seismic sounding methods that 'steps' on the upper surface of the ice sheet in Dronning Maud Land correspond precisely with ridges in the glacier bed. As an example of surface relief on a more extensive scale we might mention the Sovetskoye Plateau. This vast tableland of ice located between Sovetskaya and the Pole of Inaccessibility in East Antarctica is thought by the Russians (Dolgushin, 1961) to reflect the existence of a huge range of mountains beneath the ice sheet. Similarly, a broad hollow on the surface of the ice sheet, extending more than 1000 km from Prydz Bay near the Amery Ice Shelf towards the Pole of Inaccessibility, is thought to represent the trace of a deep subglacial depression.

During the trans-Antarctic crossing in 1957–8 a large number of wave-like undulations, measuring between 5 and 30 km in wave length and about 20 m in amplitude were observed on the surface of the ice sheet (Nye, 1959a). Undulations of these dimensions are unlikely to be giant snowdrift features as they are not generally oriented in the direction of the prevailing winds (as sand dunes invariably are), and they are frequently located in areas of extremely low annual snow accumulation. Nye (1959b) believes that these surface 'waves' are most satisfactorily interpreted as subdued reflections of the subglacial topography. If the majority of surface undulations in Antarctica can be ascribed to this cause, then it would appear that a considerable bedrock relief exists beneath the Antarctic Ice Sheet.

Volume of Ice in Antarctica

The average thickness of grounded ice in Antarctica is now thought to exceed 2000 m (Robin, 1960). Novikov (1960) quotes a value of 2500 m. Bauer (1961) from hypsometric measurements, estimates the average thickness as 2300 m. These might be compared with pre-IGY estimates ranging from 600 m (Odell, 1952), to 1600 m or more (Sharp, 1956). Using a value of 2000 m for the average thickness of ice in Antarctica, including the ice shelves, we find that the volume of ice locked up in the Antarctic Ice Sheet works out at more than 27,000,000 km³. This is equivalent to nearly 24,500,000 km³ of water, or approximately 2% of the world's water budget. This represents nearly 90% of the total ice in the world, which if suddenly melted and the waters therefrom returned to the oceans, would raise mean sea level by about 60 m.

During the Pleistocene Epoch world sea level fluctuated with the waxing and waning of continental ice sheets. As ice sheets grew, sea level fell, but rose again as the ice sheets melted away during the relatively warm interglacial periods. Donn, Farrand and Ewing (1962) have used recent measurements of ice thickness in Antarctica, and other facts relating to previous extents of ice sheets, to compute ice volumes and sea level changes during the later part of the Pleistocene. They calculate that sea level was approximately 100 m lower than it is today, during the most recent glacial maximum (the Wisconsin or fourth glacial period), and that during the previous glacial maximum (Illinoian) sea level may have been as much as 159 m below present-day sea level. This would imply that during the period of maximum development of ice sheets on the Earth's surface during the Pleistocene, sea level fell by more than 200 m.

Nourishment, Wastage and the Mass Budget of Antarctica

One of the principal aims of current glaciological research in Antarctica is to determine the mass balance of the ice sheet, i.e. to determine whether the ice sheet is gaining or losing mass, or is in equilibrium. This requires measurement of both accumulation of snow on the surface of the ice sheet, and wastage, which occurs mainly at the edge of the ice sheet by calving of icebergs. Present indications are that accumulation exceeds wastage and the ice sheet should be getting thicker.

SNOW ACCUMULATION

The ice sheet is nourished almost exclusively by precipitation in the form of snow, the source of which is linked closely with the movements of low pressure systems (cyclones) around the periphery of Antarctica, and to their penetration inland. As already mentioned the bulk of the precipitation occurs in a narrow belt within two or three hundred kilometres of the coast. Accumulation falls off rapidly inland from this coastal zone, and in the centre of the ice sheet truly arid conditions exist. Since wind tends to redistribute freshly fallen snow unevenly over the surface of the ice sheet glaciologists must generally be content with measurements of the net accumulation rather than the actual precipitation. Of course in those areas where the amount of snow blown in equals the amount of snow blown away, the net accumulation will be equal to the precipitation. However, to obtain an estimate of the total annual precipitation over Antarctica, losses resulting from the drifting of snow over the edge of the ice sheet into the sea must be added to the net total accumulation.

The simplest way of measuring current accumulation is to plant stakes on the surface and measure changes in the height of the surface as the snow accumulates. Such measurements provide useful information on the seasonal distribution, and the variations in accumulation from year to year, at more or less permanently established bases. Elsewhere on the ice sheet, for instance along the routes of the oversnow traverse parties, stake measurements are obviously not feasible and other methods have to be used to determine the average annual snow fall. The simplest way of doing this is to dig a shallow pit in the snow to a depth of two or three metres, and measure the thickness and density of the annual layers exposed in the walls of the pit. As a rule the summer snow layers are softer, coarser grained and less dense than the winter snows. By carefully analyzing these differences in snow properties the glaciologist is able to count off the number of annual layers exposed in the wall of the snow pit. Figure 60 illustrates how this method was applied to the delineation of annual layers in three shallow snow pits at Byrd

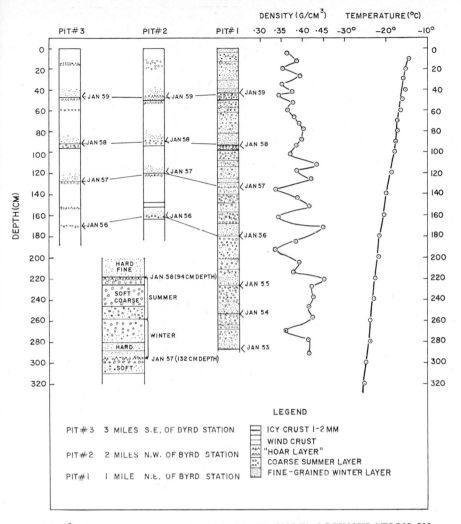

FIG. 60 STRATIGRAPHIC PROFILES OF SNOW ACCUMULATION IN
THREE SNOW PITS AT BYRD STATION, WEST ANTARCTICA
(After Gow, 1961)

Station. A photograph of part of the stratigraphy exposed in the wall of a snow
pit at the South Pole is shown in Figure 61.

The beauty of this type of analysis, called stratigraphic analysis, is that it can
be used most successfully to obtain past records of snow accumulation to considerable depths in the ice sheet. For example, in a hand-dug snow-mine at the
South Pole it was possible to count off annual layers to a depth of 27 m (Giovinetto, 1960). The snow at this depth was found to be 200 years old. Near Wilkes
Station in East Antarctica ice now at a depth of 35 m is estimated to have been

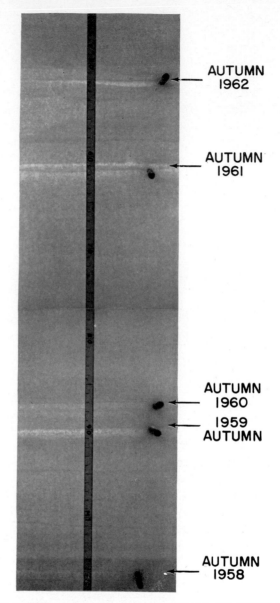

FIG. 6I A CLOSE-UP OF THE LAYERING IN THE WALL OF SNOW PIT AT
THE SOUTH POLE

The distinctive layers of depth hoar (marked with pegs) are formed each
autumn, and the thickness of snow between two such layers represents a year's
accumulation. The scale in the centre of the photograph is marked off in centimetres.

deposited on the surface as snow 175 years ago (Cameron *et al.*, 1958). At Little America annual layering could still be recognized at a depth of 48 m in cores from a deep drill hole. The firn at 48 m fell as snow on the surface of the Ross Ice Shelf about the year 1830. At Byrd Station it was possible to identify annual layering in deep drill cores to a depth of 89 m, which represents over 400 years of accumulation (Bender and Gow, 1961). The ice at the bottom of the drill hole (309 m deep) is estimated to be about 1700 years old. Figure 62 shows the variations in the year to year accumulation to a depth of 19 m in the snow at Byrd Station.

As a result of data obtained from pit studies at a large number of widespread localities upon the Antarctic Ice Sheet the general distribution of snow accumulation over the entire surface of Antarctica is now reliably known (Fig. 113). From a knowledge of the mean annual accumulation, average density of the annual

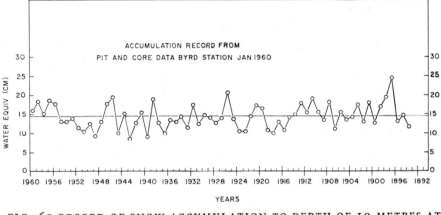

FIG. 62 RECORD OF SNOW ACCUMULATION TO DEPTH OF 19 METRES AT
BYRD STATION
(After Gow, 1961)

layer, and the total surface area of the Antarctic Ice Sheet, we can readily determine the volume of the net annual accumulation. With the information in Figure 113, the net accretion of snow on the surface of the ice sheet works out at $1 \cdot 7 \times 10^{18}$ gm water per year. This value agrees very closely with the result obtained by Mellor (1959b) from a study of meridional profiles of accumulation in East Antarctica. If we apply Mellor's estimate of 2×10^{17} gm water for the total amount of snow lost by wind-drifting off the edge of the Antarctic Ice Sheet each year to the net total accumulation, we obtain a value of $1 \cdot 9 \times 10^{18}$ gm water per year for the total surface precipitation. This is equivalent to laying down a sheet of water 14 cm thick each year over the entire surface of Antarctica.

In some parts of Antarctica recognition of annual layering has proved difficult, especially where erratic distribution of snow and generally low accumulation rates hinder sensible interpretation of snow stratigraphy. In deeper ice the stratigraphic method can not be used because of the gradual obliteration of annual layer structure by recrystallization. However, some recently developed dating procedures based on variations of the oxygen and hydrogen isotope concentrations in snow are available. Methods based on measurements of the radioactivity of snow contaminated with fallout from thermonuclear bombs are now being developed.

The oxygen isotope method depends upon the fact that the ratio $O^{18} : O^{16}$ of the snow varies significantly with the temperature, and hence with the seasonal distribution of snow. This method has been applied with considerable success for dating deep drill cores in Greenland (Epstein and Sharp, 1959). Results from Antarctica have not proved entirely satisfactory so far. Redistribution of snow by wind seems to be the major problem but Sharp (personal communication) believes that with more effective sampling the method should prove successful. Age determinations with tritium have been attempted but more recent work shows that the method cannot be generally applied to Antarctic snows because of possible time variations. According to Lorius (1961) seasonal variations in deuterium content in snow can be used to delineate annual layers in Antarctica. Stuart and Heine (1961) report that the results obtained by Lorius from deuterium analysis correlate almost exactly with stratigraphic interpretations of annual accumulation in several snow pits in Victoria Land.

Recently Marshall (1962) has shown that seasonal variations of particulate matter (terrestrial and cosmic particles) falling on the surface of the ice sheet can be used for estimating rates of annual snow accumulation.

Carbon-14 analyses of air trapped in glacier ice offer some possibility of absolute dating of samples from deep drill cores. However, sample sizes are critical, and even deep core drilling may not provide sufficient material for reliable analyses.

Other methods of measuring annual accumulation have been used. For instance Hoinkes (1962) used Sorge's law of snow densification (Bader, 1953) to estimate the average annual accumulation at the Little America III site on the Ross Ice Shelf. He obtained a value of 19 cm water per year for the period 1947–58, which is in almost perfect agreement with recently observed rates of snow accumulation near the edge of the Ross Ice Shelf.

WASTAGE OF ANTARCTIC ICE

Wastage takes place primarily at the edge of the ice sheet by calving of icebergs, but other processes are also involved. These additional forms of wastage include: ablation, transport of snow off the edge of the ice sheet into the sea, and melting of the undersides of ice shelves.

Ablation involves loss by both evaporation and run-off of meltwater at the surface. Significant evaporation of snow may occur in coastal areas subjected to strong and persistent katabatic winds, but elsewhere on the ice sheet evaporation is probably balanced by the reverse process of condensation of moisture onto the snow surface. Studies at Mirnyy (Kotlyakov, 1961), Terre Adélie (Loewe, 1956), MacRobertson Land (Mellor, 1958), and in Dronning Maud Land (Schytt, 1958) have shown that extensive surface melting can occur up to altitudes of 400 m on the ice sheet. In general the meltwater infiltrates into the underlying snow pack and refreezes, so that melting seldom represents a net loss. However, in wind-scoured 'blue ice' areas significant amounts of surface meltwater may be lost by evaporation during summer. According to Mellor (private communication) 'blue ice' areas around the Australian base at Mawson may lose as much as 50 cm water by ablation each year. Overall, however, ablation appears to be a minor item of wastage in Antarctica.

Large masses of snow are blown off the edge of the ice sheet into the sea each year. When Loewe (1956) estimated that upwards of 18×10^{12} gm (approx. 18 million tons) of snow is transported across each kilometre of the exceptionally windy Terre Adélie coast each year, it was generally felt that such a high transport of snow would not apply to the Antarctic coastline as a whole. However, Mellor and Radok (1960) have since found that drift losses along MacRobertson Land coast are at least comparable to the values obtained by Loewe in the much stormier Terre Adélie area. More measurements around the Antarctic coastline are needed but it does seem that previous estimates of the drift loss have been on the low side. Mellor believes that as much as $1-2 \times 10^{17}$ gm of snow is lost from the Antarctic Ice Sheet each year by wind drifting.

Very little is known of the magnitude and rates of melting beneath ice shelves. Direct measurements of bottom melting are almost impossible to make and there are some, for instance Debenham (1949), who believe that the reverse process of accretion of sea ice to the bottom of ice shelves may be more important. How-ever, most glaciologists are inclined to the view that bottom melting is at least effective under the thicker ice shelves. For instance Crary (1961) has deduced from the temperature profile in the deep drill hole at Little America V that up-wards of 80 cm of ice is melted off the bottom of the Ross Ice Shelf near its seaward edge each year. This agrees closely with Swithinbank's estimate of 87 cm of melting at the bottom of the ice shelf at Maudheim (Swithinbank, 1962). In 1958 a deep hole was drilled 257 m to the bottom of the Ross Ice Shelf, near Little America V (Ragle et al. 1960). No sea ice was observed in cores from the bottom of the ice shelf. Detailed microscopic examination of these cores by Gow (1963) revealed glacial ice only and all the indications are that the bottom of the shelf at Little America V is melting.

The most important single item of wastage in Antarctica is the discharge of icebergs along the edge of the ice sheet. In order to obtain reliable estimates of the quantity of ice discharged each year we need to know the rates of flow and thickness of ice at the edge of the ice sheet. Neither is constant. The inland ice ultimately reaches the sea either as a broad sheet, as ice streams and valley glaciers, or as ice shelves. Recent measurements show that the ice streams and shelves move at comparable velocities of about 400 m/yr. At the coast the edge of the grounded ice sheet moves much more slowly, at about 20 m/yr on the average. Ice shelves are about 200 m thick at their seaward edges. Ice streams are probably thicker, of the order of 300–400 m, but the undifferentiated edge of the ice sheet is much thinner, probably no more than 170 m thick on the average. Thus, the ice streams although they discharge along a mere 8% of the Antarctic coastline, nevertheless contribute much more to wastage than the much slower moving and thinner continental sheet ice that reaches the sea along 55% of the coastline.

Ice shelves, though somewhat thinner on the average than ice streams, discharge along five times the length of coastline, and are therefore the major sources of icebergs. The following values are given by Mellor (1959b), for the quantity of ice discharged annually by berging:

Ice Shelves discharging along 7500 km of coast;						48×10^{16} gm/yr
Ice Streams	„	„	1500	„	„	„	7×10^{16} gm/yr
Ice Sheet	„	„	11000	„	„	„	2×10^{16} gm/yr
				Total loss		57×10^{16} gm/yr

MASS BUDGET

Turning to the question of the mass budget of Antarctica, we need only to consider net ablation, losses by berging, and melting beneath the ice shelves in our estimate of wastage. Evaporation of snow above the firn line can be neglected since it is most probably balanced by direct crystallization of hoar-frost on the surface of the ice sheet. Since net accumulation is measured rather than precipitation we need not consider losses due to the drifting of snow off the edge of the ice sheet. Rather, the snowdrift estimate is added to the net accumulation to give a measure of the precipitation. Current estimates of the mass budget (recently reviewed by Wexler, 1961) indicate a surplus of accumulation in Antarctica. The following estimate by Mellor (1961) will give some idea of the quantities involved in the annual ice budget of Antarctica.[1]

Net accumulation	$+17 \times 10^{17}$ gm	Equiv. to 1.7×10^{12} tons of water
Calving of icebergs	-5.7×10^{17} gm	
Net ablation	-0.74×10^{17} gm	Equiv. to -7.0×10^{11} tons of water
Bottom melting	-0.48×10^{17} gm	
Accumulation excess	$+10^{18}$ gm	Equiv. to 10^{12} tons of water

From these figures it would appear that Antarctica is currently gaining about twice as much snow as it is losing. This means that we would have to more than double Mellor's estimate of wastage to achieve a balanced budget, or reduce the accumulation by half. Present indications are that Mellor's value for the accumulation is a reliable one, but it is very likely that the wastage if anything has been underestimated. For instance, it is almost impossible to measure bottom melting directly, and the value assigned to it is probably not much better than a working

[1] In his estimate of wastage Mellor used an average thickness of 140 m for ice streams which is considerably thinner than the value of 300-400 m given in the text above. Using an average thickness of 350 m for ice streams would increase Mellor's estimate of losses from this source by about 150% but this would still be far from sufficient to balance his Antarctic Ice budget.

(a)

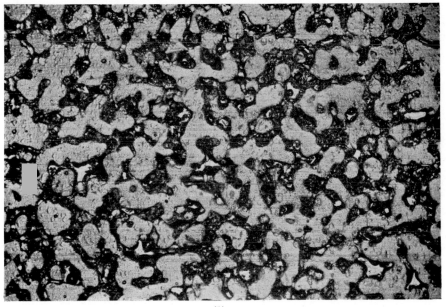

(b)

FIG. 63 THE GRAIN STRUCTURE OF SNOW AND FIRN AT THE
SOUTH POLE

Thin section photographs (a) of snow from 6 metres depth, and (b) of firn from 48 metres depth. Both magnified 9 times 'guesstimate'. Ablation can only be a minor item in the budget and it is unlikely that losses by berging could be more than double the estimate given by Mellor. Robin (1960) argues in support of a balanced budget, mainly on the basis that no lowering of sea level, corresponding to any significant increase in the ice in Antarctica, has been observed. In fact sea level around the world seems to be rising slightly (by approximately 1·1 mm per year), and this would appear flatly to contradict the idea of an increasing volume of ice in Antarctica. However, Loewe (1960) believes that there is a surplus of accumulation in Antarctica and that the observed rise of world's sea level in recent times can be explained in part at least

FIG. 64 THE FAILING ROTARY WELL DRILLING RIG ON THE DRILLING SITE AT BYRD STATION

by thermal expansion of ocean waters during the recent period of climatic warming. Obviously more reliable data on wastage are needed. Nevertheless the indications are that the Antarctic Ice Sheet is not the rapidly diminishing body of ice it was once thought to be (Odell, 1952).

Temperatures in the Ice Sheet

Snow is a poor conductor of heat. Diurnal variations of temperature seldom penetrate more than a metre below the snow surface and, as Figure 65 shows, the seasonal variations of temperature diminish very rapidly with depth. At depths of about 10 m in the ice sheet the temperature remains almost constant the whole year round. Several independent studies have shown that the temperatures at these depths are close to mean annual surface temperatures. Thus by merely drilling a 10–15 m hole and measuring the temperature at the bottom with lagged thermometers, thermohms, thermocouples or thermistors, glaciologists are able to make an accurate measurement of the mean annual temperature at any locality on the Antarctic Ice Sheet. This method is particularly suited to

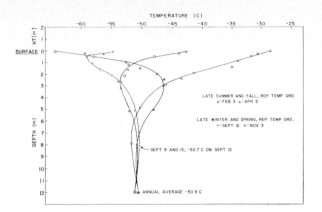

FIG. 65 ANNUAL TEMPERATURE CHANGES IN THE UPPER 12 METRES
OF SNOW AT THE SOUTH POLE
(After Giovinetto, 1960)

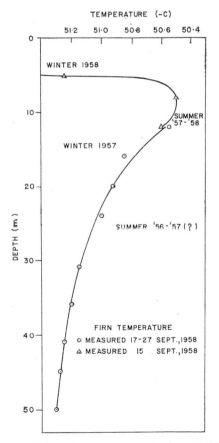

FIG. 66 ICE TEMPERATURE PROFILE TO DEPTH OF 50 METRES AT
THE SOUTH POLE
(After Giovinetto, 1960)

over-snow traverse operations, and from the large number of measurements made
during the IGY it is now possible to obtain a reasonably reliable picture of mean
annual temperature distribution over the entire surface of the Antarctic Ice Sheet.
As indicated in Figure 114 the 'cold pole' of Antarctica does not coincide with the
geographic South Pole but is displaced towards a very high part of the ice sheet
in East Antarctica, between the Pole of Inaccessibility and Vostok. The mean
annual temperature at both these locations is a very low −57° C and a world

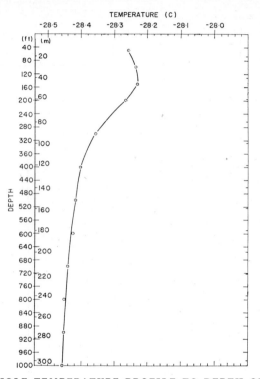

FIG. 67 BOREHOLE TEMPERATURE PROFILE TO DEPTH OF 309 METRES
AT BYRD STATION
(After Bender and Gow, 1961)

record low temperature of −88 °C (127° F below zero) was recorded at Vostok
during the winter of 1960.

Temperatures in the ice sheet are influenced by conduction of heat at the
surface, by the inflow of earth heat (geothermal flux) at the base, and by frictional
heat resulting from the flow of ice in the basal layers of the ice sheet. In the
floating ice shelves the sea supplies a constant flow of heat through the bottom.
Temperature profiles in the relatively thin ice near the edge of the ice sheet
generally exhibit positive gradients throughout, i.e. temperatures increasing
with depth. The same also applies to the floating ice shelves, at least near their
seaward edges as illustrated in Figure 49. On the inland ice sheet, however, the

temperatures are found to decrease with increasing depth (see Figs. 66 and 67 for the observed temperature profiles at South Pole and Byrd Stations). The existence of negative gradients is thought to be due to either climatic warming at the surface or to the movement of ice down slope from colder to warmer temperatures. The latter effect, first suggested by Robin (1955), has been applied by Bogoslovsky (1958) to calculate rates of movement for the ice sheet in East Antarctica. However, Mellor (1960) has deduced that improbably high rates of surface movement are required to account for the observed negative temperature profiles in East Antarctica. He concludes that climatic warming (also suggested by Robin) must also contribute to the formation of negative gradients near the surface. At some depth in the inland ice sheet temperatures must start to increase as geothermal flux and other sources of heat at the base of the ice sheet take effect. Unfortunately no holes have yet been drilled on the inland ice sheet to that depth where the overturn of temperature takes place. Wexler (1959), Jenssen and Radok (1961), and others have attempted theoretical treatments of the problem but their results merely emphasize the need for measurements to much greater depths in the ice sheet than have hitherto been obtained. In some respects the most critical part of the ice sheet is its bottom. It is, alas, the least accessible portion and until we devise the ways and means of penetrating to the bottom (very deep drilling offers the best hope here), we cannot hope to fully appreciate some of the more fundamental aspects of ice sheet behaviour, such as the mechanics of glacier flow and the erosive capacities of ice sheets.

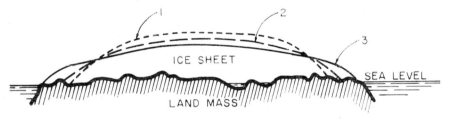

FIG. 68 IDEALIZED DIAGRAM OF THE ANTARCTIC ICE SHEET
Showing possible profiles related to unstable thickening, expansion and thinning, and renewed thickening of the ice

Movement of the Ice Sheet

Measurements of ice movement in Antarctica are extremely important since they bear directly on the problem of mass balance. This applies particularly to measurements of ice movement near the edge of the ice sheet, since it is the rate of movement in the peripheral zone that largely determines the quantity of ice discharged annually by berging.

Measurements of absolute surface movement on the inland ice sheet are greatly hindered by a lack of fixed points, e.g. nunataks, from which to survey the movement. Astronomical fixing has been attempted at a number of inland bases, but since the suspected movement is of the order of only a few metres per year

I

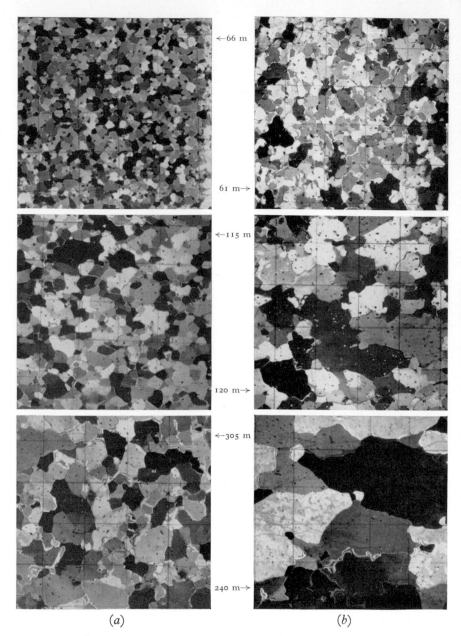

←66 m

61 m→

←115 m

120 m→

←305 m

240 m→

(a)

(b)

FIG. 69 CRYSTAL STRUCTURE OF ANTARCTIC GLACIER ICE
Thin section photographs of ice from deep drill cores from:
(a) Marie Byrd Land (Byrd Station);
(b) Ross Ice Shelf (Little America V).
Photographs taken between crossed polaroids to reveal the crystal structure.
Grid Spacing is 1 cm

several years' observations will be required before reliable estimates of the magnitude and direction of movement can be obtained.

Ice flow velocities have been measured at a number of localities along the periphery of the ice sheet. Both conventional surveying – baseline taping and theodolite survey from a fixed point such as a rock to targets placed on the glacier surface – and photogrammetric methods have been used. Following Mellor (1959a), we can conveniently describe ice movement in terms of three characteristic types of flow: 'sheet flow' which characterizes the general outward movement of the ice sheet, 'stream flow' which applies to the relatively fast-moving valley glaciers and ice streams, and 'ice shelf movement' associated with the lateral spreading of floating ice sheets. Table 5 will give some idea of the magnitude of flow measured at a number of localities on the Antarctic Ice Sheet. The results of some very recent measurements of the flow of a number of large outlet glaciers discharging into the Ross Ice Shelf are presented in Figure 70. According to Swithinbank (1963) Byrd Glacier contributes as much ice to the Ross Ice Shelf as the other six glaciers combined, including the great Beardmore Glacier. From continuity considerations alone we can calculate that it would take tens of thousands of years, if not longer, for a snow crystal deposited on the surface of the ice sheet near the Pole of Inaccessibility to reach the edge of the ice sheet in East Antarctica.

Ice, a solid substance, will with time deform even at low stresses. In a glacier this deformation is caused by the stresses set up in the ice by its own weight. This deformation results in movement, the magnitude of which is now known to depend on a number of factors. These include the shape and dimensions of the glacier, i.e., surface slope, thickness of ice and the slope and shape of the glacier bed, temperatures in the ice, especially temperature conditions at the bed and the physical and mechanical properties of the ice itself.

The ability of ice to flow in the solid state is now known to contribute significantly to glacier movement. Laboratory tests show that ice will deform even at very low stresses and that the rate of yielding (strain) increases rapidly with increasing stress. This means that ice is neither a purely viscous nor purely plastic substance but approximately combines the properties of both. This visco-plastic behaviour of ice is thought to simulate the type of flow associated with the rolling of metals. The flow law discovered by Glen (1955), that points to a simple power law relationship between stress and rate of strain, has served as a basis of many fruitful analyses of glacier behaviour (Nye, 1959b; Weertman, 1957, 1961). Ice will deform more readily at higher temperatures, and the crystal structure is also known to bear importantly on the flow rate. Laboratory tests show that single crystals of ice will deform most readily by actual slippage along the crystallographic basal plane, and by bending in such a way that differential movement is able to take place along the slip plane in a manner similar to bending a pile of papers. This process, called gliding, is also known to be effective in experimentally deformed ice composed of many crystals. Recrystallization also appears to be an essential part of the process. Since highly deformed glacier ice invariably

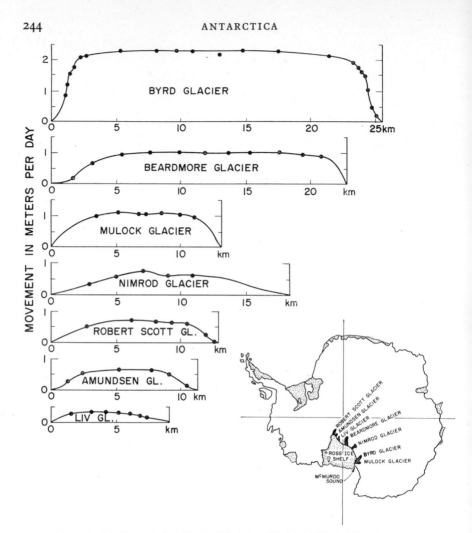

FIG. 70 RATES OF MOVEMENT OF ICE ACROSS A NUMBER OF
LARGE VALLEY GLACIERS THAT DISCHARGE INTO THE
ROSS ICE SHELF (After Swithinbank, 1963)

Note the rapid decrease in rate of flow near the sides of the largest glaciers due
to frictional resistance between ice and the valley walls.

displays strongly preferred orientation of its component crystals, it is generally
agreed that the recrystallization and 'reorientation' of individual crystals into
positions most favourable to gliding contribute significantly to glacier flow (see
Rigsby, 1960). Several other mechanisms have been proposed to account for
solid flow in glaciers, e.g. intergranular adjustments and phase changes. The
sliding of ice on its bed and the slippage along actual shear planes within the
glacier have also been postulated. All of these mechanisms operate to some extent
in the movement of ice, but their relative contributions will vary with the size and

location of the glacier. The once widely circulated view that ice is 'extruded' from beneath the glacier because of an assumed increase in the plasticity of the ice with increasing hydrostatic pressure can no longer be sustained on either experimental or theoretical grounds.

The current view is that the surface movement is produced by both sliding of the ice over its bed, and by solid flow (continuous deformation) within the glacier. Nye (1959b) proposes that the Antarctic Ice Sheet moves more or less as a block. The internal deformation is believed to be concentrated in a very thin layer at the bottom of the ice sheet, so that the outward movement of the ice sheet can be thought of as being made up of bottom sliding. Whether or not this movement takes place in discrete layers of ice near the bottom of the ice sheet, or represents an actual sliding of the ice sheet over its bed, will depend very much on temperature conditions at the base of the ice sheet. For an ice sheet at its pressure melting point it seems reasonable to assume actual sliding of the ice over the rock floor. Frictional heat may cause melting and 'lubricate' ice flow still further. If the ice sheet is frozen to the bed then actual shearing of ice layers one upon the other in the basal layer would seem necessary. It is not known whether the Antarctic Ice Sheet is at its pressure melting point or not, for this also raises the question of its erosive capacity. In the Thule area of Greenland the ice near the edge is frozen to the bed, and there appears to be no erosion of the bedrock under the 60 m layer of ice (Bader, 1961). We might reasonably expect erosion to occur under an ice sheet at its pressure melting point, but is a thick ice sheet such as exists in Antarctica capable of eroding if the bedrock is frozen?

Former Extent and Thickness of the Ice Sheet

There is ample evidence that the Antarctic Ice Sheet was once thicker and more extensive than it is at the present day (see Odell, 1952). The occurrence of erratic boulders and striated rock surfaces above the present level of the ice sheet attest to some previous greater thickness of the ice sheet. Recessional moraines, ice-free valleys, 'raised beaches' (resulting from isostatic uplift of coastal areas formerly loaded down with ice), and the occurrence of submarine moraines some distance seaward of the present edge of the ice sheet, all testify to a former expanded condition of Antarctic glaciers. An up-to-date review of the evidence of glacier variations in Antarctica is given by Mercer (1962).

Although the effects of glacier recession are most strikingly developed in coastal areas, observations during the IGY show that a thinning of the ice sheet has occurred in the interior of Antarctica as well. For instance, in the Dufek Massif, situated about 300 km inland from the Filchner Ice Shelf, extensive moraines were found approximately 100 m above the present ice surface (Aughenbaugh et al., 1958). There are other indications that the ice may have been more than 240 m thicker than it is at present. Near the Sentinel Mountains in Marie Byrd Land, Anderson (1958) recorded glacial striations on top of Fisher Nunatak, 183 m above the present level of the ice sheet, and Doumani (Cameron and Goldthwait, 1961), has observed glacial grooving as high as 450 m above the

surrounding ice on Mt Sidley. According to Péwé (1960) glaciers in the McMurdo
Sound area may have been as much as 600 m thicker than they are at present. A
minimum age of 6000 years has been suggested for the most recent advance of
ice in this area. The general lowering of the surface of the inland ice, of the order
of 300 m but up to 600 m or more in some areas, is thought by Cameron and
Goldthwait (1961) to have coincided with the retreat of the Ross Ice Shelf from
the submarine moraines.

Shrinkage in Antarctica implies both marginal retreat of the ice edge and thinning of the ice sheet. There is considerable evidence to show that both processes
have operated extensively in the past. There is very good evidence of a fairly
recent marginal retreat of the ice edge, but whether the observed thinning of the
inland ice has occurred contemporaneously or not is not so clearly established.
The decline from some former expanded condition is thought by some to have
begun as recently as 10,000 years ago. This estimate would correlate the event
with the widespread recession of glaciers in other parts of the world, especially
with the disappearance of the ice sheets in the Northern Hemisphere, such as the
Laurentide Ice Sheet of North America. However, in the absence of absolute
dating the estimate of 10,000 years for onset of marginal retreat in Antarctica
should be considered as approximate only. Notwithstanding, there are indications that the recession in Antarctica is now tapering off. Cartographic, photographic, botanical and glaciological observations over the past fifty years indicate
that the ice margins have remained stationary or have been retreating very slowly.

Recent estimates of the mass budget of Antarctica suggest that the ice sheet is
actually gaining mass at the present time. Yet direct observations show that the
edge of the ice sheet is either stationary or in slow retreat. This apparent con-
tradiction may be a matter of response. For instance even in the case of a small
valley glacier an increase of snow accumulation in the upper part of the glacier
may take some years to register as an advance at its terminus or snout. In general
the larger and colder the glacier the slower the response. The Antarctic Ice
Sheet is exceptionally large and exceptionally cold and can be expected to show a
very sluggish response to changes in accumulation; in fact it may take thousands
of years for the effects of increased accumulation in the interior to cause any
noteworthy advance of the edge of the ice sheet, which in the meantime may
have been undergoing an actual retreat. This in no way contradicts the evidence
of thinning of the ice sheet in the past, for the ice sheet may have been thinner
than is now observed. The implication here is that a large ice sheet may undergo
a considerable thickening before an expansion sets in, merely because of the
delayed response at the margin of the ice sheet. This state of affairs may well
exist in Antarctica today.

If the recent marginal retreat in Antarctica is to be attributed to climatic
amelioration, the same conditions could well cause increased evaporation (as well
as ablation) at the margin, and lead to more abundant precipitation of snow in
the interior. Only negligible melting occurs on the surface of the Antarctic Ice
Sheet. Any off-set of snow accumulation must take place by either the calving of

icebergs or by bottom melting at the edge of the ice sheet. If these sources of wastage are unable to cope with the effects of increased accumulation on the inland ice sheet, then the volume of ice must increase. For an ice sheet with stationary margins, such as appears to obtain in Antarctica today, this can only mean an increasing ice thickness.

An ice sheet cannot thicken indefinitely, but it may increase its thickness to the point where the frictional limit between the ice and the rock floor is exceeded and the ice sheet slides forward, i.e. the ice sheet thickens, becomes unstable and relaxes. There may be no immediate loss of ice, merely a marginal expansion and a compensatory thinning of the overall ice sheet. In other words, the thinning and expansion of the Antarctic Ice Sheet may well be determined by the physical properties of the ice itself and only indirectly influenced by climatic changes. This is not a new idea (for instance, see Ahlmann, 1953) and recently Weertman (1962) has presented a rather interesting discussion of the mechanical stability–instability relationships of ice-age ice sheets. The essential ideas expressed above are contained in the highly generalized diagram in Figure 68. Profile 1 represents a cross section of the ice sheet at its thickest and at the frictional limit. Profile 3 is intended to represent the ice sheet in the expanded condition. This has had the effect of overriding previously unglacierized or previously deglaciated land in the coastal areas of Antarctica. Existing ice shelves would expand and grounded shelves would probably form along a considerable part of the remainder of the Antarctic coastline. A thinning of the inland ice sheet would occur to compensate for the expansion. Profile 2 represents the condition of the ice sheet at the present day and shows the effects of both marginal recession and a rising ice sheet in accordance with current observations. As mentioned previously both the marginal retreat and apparent thickening of the inland ice can be attributed to a single cause – climatic amelioration.

Physical Properties of Snow and Ice

The Antarctic Ice Sheet is nourished and maintained by the accumulation of snow upon its surface. Glaciologists are interested not only in the broad physical features of the ice sheet but also in the physical and mechanical properties of the ice itself, and they are especially interested in the process by which snow is transformed into solid ice at depth.

Snow accumulates layer by layer on the surface of the ice sheet. Each surface layer of snow is a loosely consolidated aggregate of ice grains, whose physical properties such as density, cohesion, hardness and grain structure reflect the conditions of deposition and early post-depositional consolidation. We have already shown how the cyclical property variations of summer and winter snow layers can be used to determine annual accumulation in snow pits. Cyclical variations and layer structure (snow stratification) may persist to considerable depths below the surface but overall changes in the bulk physical properties of the snow pack will occur as the snow becomes more deeply buried.

On a dry polar ice sheet such as Antarctica the conversion of snow to ice involves both the gradual elimination of air trapped between grains of snow (densification) and changes of grain structure (recrystallization). In the first 10 m the process is essentially one which leads to an overall rounding of the grains and their rearrangement into a randomly close-packed aggregate with some intergranular bonding. Maximum packing of this type occurs at a density of approximately 0·55 gm/cm³ at a depth of about 10 m. This marks the transition between old compressed snow above and firn below (Anderson and Benson, 1962). Further densification can only take place by the deformational recrystallization of the firn grains. This is a much slower process of consolidation than occurs in the relatively simple compression of snow and the rate of densification falls off accordingly.

The structure of firn somewhat resembles a sponge. Slow recrystallization with increasing depth of burial results in gradual diminution of the interconnecting air channels until at a density of about 0·83 gm/cm³ the air spaces seal off to form isolated tubular bubbles. The firn still contains about 10% of air but it is no longer permeable—it is by definition glacier ice. Further densification can only take place by compression of the entrapped air bubbles which slowly diminish in volume and assume a spherical shape. In the deepest parts of the Antarctic Ice Sheet these air bubbles may attain pressures of between 200–300 atmospheres.

The transformation, snow→firn→ice is somewhat analogous to the process that converts a geologic sediment to a sedimentary rock, and ultimately to a metamorphic rock deep in the crust of the earth.

The time required to transform snow into glacier ice depends on both the rate at which snow accumulates at the surface and the temperature, particularly the latter. At Byrd Station it takes approximately 300 years to produce glacier ice. At Little America V only 150 years are required, but at the South Pole under the existing conditions of very low temperatures about 1000 years would be required. Figure 63 demonstrates the type of structure associated with snow and firn at the South Pole. Figure 69 shows the variations of crystal structure with depth for glacier ice at two contrasted localities. Both profiles clearly show the increase in the size of crystals with increasing depth. The much greater 'size' of crystals in the ice at Little America V can be attributed in large part to the existence of much warmer temperatures in the Ross Ice Shelf. The development of spherical air bubbles in the deeper ice at both localities can be readily observed in the thin section photographs.

Many other physical aspects of Antarctic snow and ice were investigated during the IGY. Quite apart from studies of the more basic properties such as density, permeability, porosity, crystal structure, bubble structure and geochemical properties, some researchers have conducted measurements on the visco-elastic properties of ice, ultra-sonic wave propagation, radio wave transmission through ice, seismic wave velocity in snow and ice and its variation with temperature and density, strength testing, deformation in ice and snow under a variety of stress and temperature conditions, and studies of the quantity and composition of solid particles that fall upon the surface and become entombed in the ice sheet. Space does not permit of a detailed summarizing of all the results here. Instead we might mention briefly some of the results from the American deep core drilling programme as an example of the type of glaciological research conducted during the IGY.

A modified rotary well-drilling rig (Fig. 64), with compressed air as the drilling fluid, was used successfully for drilling two deep holes in Antarctica (Patenaude

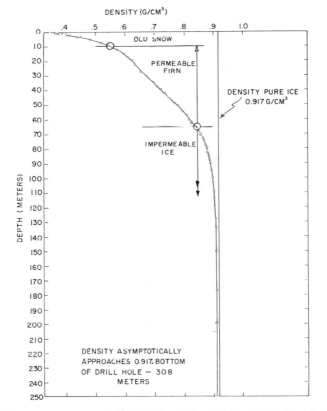

FIG. 71 DEPTH–DENSITY CURVE FOR SNOW AND ICE AT BYRD STATION
(After Bender and Gow, 1961)

et al., 1959; Ragle et al., 1960). Excellent cores were obtained to a depth of 309 m in the 2500 m thick ice at Byrd Station; and to 254 m in the Ross Ice Shelf at Little America V, that is within a metre or two of the bottom. Detailed analysis of the cores revealed an annual accumulation of approximately 15 cm of water equivalent at Byrd, and 22 cm of water at Little America V. The depth–density profile at Byrd Station is presented in Figure 71, and the approximate positions of the snow→firn and firn→ice transitions are indicated. The anomalous increase in the rate of densification below 36 m at Little America (see Fig. 48) can be attributed to the effect of deformational stresses in the ice shelf acting in addition to the overburden pressure. This deformation is also reflected in the appearance of 'strained crystals' in the ice below 60 m, and in their rapid recrystallization and reorientation to a highly preferred condition below 90 m.

At Byrd Station the average crystal size was found to increase almost linearly with depth. Figure 72*a* gives some idea of the variation of average crystal area with depth. This can be compared with the scale of changes recorded in the ice shelf at Maudheim (Fig. 72*b*). When drilled the bore holes were 15 cm in diameter. Measurements of subsequent closure in the unconfined borehole at Byrd are presented in Figure 73. After four years the bottom of the hole had closed off to less than 1 cm and the overall closure was found to conform approximately with

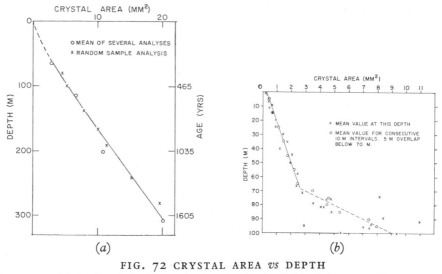

FIG. 72 CRYSTAL AREA *vs* DEPTH

(*a*) At Byrd Station;   (*b*) At Maudheim (after Schytt, 1958)

the power law of flow derived from studies of laboratory deformed ice. In the deeper parts of the hole, however, the closure has been accelerating, due most probably to the recrystallization and resultant increased plasticity of the ice in the walls of the bore hole. Identical behaviour has also been observed in ice deformed at high stresses in the laboratory. However the borehole has not inclined significantly from the vertical, indicating that very little distortion is occurring in the upper 300 m at Byrd Station, and that the surface layers are being carried along as a block by very deep-seated movement in the ice sheet. It is hoped to be able to recore this drill hole at some future date. It would be extremely interesting to compare the crystal structure of the relatively undeformed ice in the original cores with the structure of the ice deformed during bore hole closure as this would throw much needed light on the role played by recrystallization in the deformation of glacier ice.

The Antarctic Ice Sheet proves to be a source area of terrestrial and cosmic particles. These are collectively referred to as particulates, and include rock dust, volcanic ash, pollen and micrometeorites that fall upon the surface and become buried in the ice sheet. Three thin layers of volcanic ash were found in cores from near the bottom of the Ross Ice Shelf. This ash fell on the surface of the ice sheet at least 2000 years ago and very probably originated from one or more of the now inactive volcanoes located in Marie Byrd Land. Pollen particles have been found in ice cores near Scott Base and at the South Pole. Mention has already been made of the use to which the seasonal variations of particulate content can be put, in delineating annual snow layering in Antarctica (Marshall,

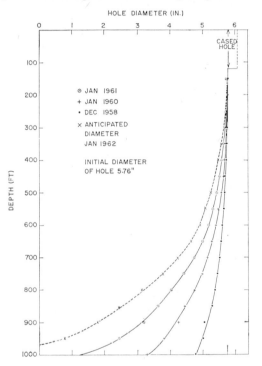

FIG. 73 CLOSURE OF THE BYRD STATION BOREHOLE
Hole drilled January 1958
(After Gow, 1961)

1962). In a recent study of micrometeorites (very small spherules of cosmic origin) from ice cores from Antarctica, Thiel and Schmidt (1961) have estimated that 184,000 × 10⁶ gm of micrometeorites are deposited upon the Earth's surface annually.

Conclusion

All existing glaciers either occupy or originate in highland areas of the Earth's surface. A highly elevated land mass of continental dimensions, centrally located over the South Pole and completely surrounded by water, would thus represent the ideal combination of conditions under which an ice sheet might be expected to form. These are precisely the conditions that exist in Antarctica today, and which have obviously proved favourable to the growth and maintenance of a very large ice sheet. These conditions have most likely prevailed for millions of years, and it seems just as likely that the ice sheet itself was established some millions of years prior to the onset of world-wide Pleistocene glaciation approximately a million years ago.

Ice sheets as large as Antarctica are known to have existed at various times throughout the Pleistocene. One of these, the Laurentide Ice Sheet of North America, is thought to have flourished as recently as 20,000 years ago. Its subsequent disappearance along with other large ice sheets in the Northern Hemisphere, with the exception of Greenland, has been attributed to recent climatic warming. These ice sheets were characterized by very active regimens and would appear to have been delicately adjusted to climatic changes. The fact that the Antarctic Ice Sheet does not seem to have been grossly inconvenienced by the recent rise of global air temperatures can most probably be attributed to its internal or 'glacially induced' climate, which effectively insulates Antarctica from those fluctuations of climate that caused such drastic waxing and waning of glaciers elsewhere during the last million years. Even at the present day the Antarctic Ice Sheet is much colder than is necessary to maintain it, and it would require a very drastic warming of the climate over Antarctica to cause any appreciable melting of the surface of the ice sheet. In contrast to the Pleistocene ice sheets of the Northern Hemisphere, the Antarctic Ice Sheet possesses a very sluggish regime. It is a particularly thrifty body and its vast size is largely a function of its thrift.

In a nutshell, we might look upon Antarctica as an example of glacially controlled climate rather than as a climatically controlled glacier. The Antarctic land mass is a prisoner of its ice sheet and the ice sheet has become a victim of its glacially induced climate. Catastrophic melting or even starvation seems most unlikely under the present conditions, and we can reasonably expect the Antarctic Ice Sheet to continue to endure as long as the present relationships of land and sea and the polar location of Antarctica persist.

TABLE 3

ANNUAL SNOW ACCUMULATION AT SELECTED ANTARCTIC LOCATIONS

Location	Annual Accumulation (cm water)
South Pole (Amundsen–Scott Station)	7
Byrd Station	15
Dronning Maud Land (Maudheim Station)	37
Dronning Maud Land (Continental Slopes)	25
Dronning Maud Land (300 km inland)	$12\frac{1}{2}$
Ellsworth Station	23
Komsomolskaya Station	20
Little America V Station	21
Norway Station	43
Roi Baudouin	38
South Ice	10
Sovetskaya Station	$7\frac{1}{2}$
Terre Adélie (15–50 km inland)	20–30
Terre Adélie (300 km inland)	10
Victoria Land Plateau	15
Wilkes Land (80 km inland)	13

TABLE 4

ANNUAL MEANS OF WIND SPEED AND TEMPERATURE AT SOME ANTARCTIC STATIONS

Location	Mean Annual Temperature °C	Mean Annual Wind Speed (metres/sec)
Cape Denison	—	22
Hallett	15	10
Mawson	—11	12
Mirnyy	—9	13
Scott Base	—20	6
Shackleton	—26	—
Wilkes	—9	6
Ellsworth	—24	7
Little America V	—24	7
Maudheim	—17	9
Amundsen–Scott (South Pole)	—51	7
Byrd	—28	9
Komsomolskaya	—54	5
Pionerskaya	—39	12
Pole of Inaccessibility	—57	4 (estimated)
South Ice	—31	—
Charcot	—38	11
Vostok	—57	5

TABLE 5

SOME MEASUREMENTS OF GLACIER FLOW IN ANTARCTICA
(SURFACE MOVEMENT)

Location	Type of Flow	Flow Rate (metres/year)
Western Dronning Maud Land (within 6 kilometres of nunatak)	Sheet Flow	1–15
Terre Adélie coast	,, ,,	30
MacRobertson Land coast	,, ,,	20
Jelbart Glacier (west tongue)	Ice Stream	100
Jelbart Glacier (east tongue)	,, ,,	300
Taylor Glacier	,, ,,	100
Robert Scott Glacier	,, ,,	500
Mirnyy	,, ,,	200
Vanderford Glacier, Wilkes Land	,, ,,	700
Beardmore Glacier	,, ,,	300
Byrd Glacier	,, ,,	760
Mulock Glacier	,, ,,	320
Skelton Glacier, Victoria Land	,, ,,	100
Maudheim Is-shelf, Dronning Maud Land	Shelf Flow	300
Ross Ice Shelf, Ross Dependency	,, ,,	300–500
Amery Ice Shelf	,, ,,	400

Bibliography

ANDERSON, V. H. 1958: Byrd Station Glaciological Data, *Ohio State University Research Foundation, Report 825–1, Part II.*

ANDERSON, D. L., and BENSON, C. S. 1962: Densification of Snow. Endicott House Conference on Applied Glaciology, Massachusetts Institute of Technology.

AHLMANN, H. W. 1953: Glacier Variations and Climatic Fluctuations. The American Geographical Society. Series 3, of Bowman Memorial Lectures.

AUGHENBAUGH, N., NEUBURG, H., and WALKER, P. 1958: Ellsworth Station Glaciological and Geological Data, 1957–58. *Ohio State University Research Foundation, Report 825–1, Part I.*

BADER, H. 1953: Sorge's Law of Densification of Snow on High Polar Glaciers, *US Army Snow Ice and Permafrost Research Establishment, Research Paper 2.*

BADER, H. 1961: The Greenland Ice Sheet, *Cold Regions Science and Engineering 1–B2. US Army Cold Regions Research and Engineering Laboratory.*

BAUER, A. 1961: Nouvelle Estimation du Volume de la Glace de L'Indlandsis Antarctique. IUGG Symposium on Antarctic Glaciology, Helsinki, 1960. *Int. Assn Sci. Hydrol. Publ.* **55.**

BENDER, J. A., and GOW, A. J. 1961: Deep Drilling in Antarctica. IUGG Symposium on Antarctic Glaciology, Helsinki, 1960. *Int. Assn Sci. Hydrol. Publ.* **55.**

BOGOSLOVSKI, V. N. 1958: The Temperature Conditions (Regime) and Movement of the Antarctic Glacial Shield. Symposium of Chamonix 1958. Physics of the Movement of Ice, *IUGG, Int. Assn Sci. Hydrol. Publ.* **47.**

CAMERON, R. L., *et al.* 1959: Wilkes Station Glaciological Data, 1957–58, *Ohio State University Research Foundation, Report 825–1, Part III.*

CAMERON, R. L., and GOLDTHWAIT, R. P. 1961: The US-IGY Contribution to Antarctic Glaciology. IUGG Symposium on Antarctic Glaciology, Helsinki, 1960. *Int. Assn Sci. Hydrol. Publ.* **55.**

CRARY, A. P. 1961: Glaciological Studies at Little America Station, Antarctica, 1957–58. *IGY Glaciological Report* **5,** American Geographical Society, New York.

DEBENHAM, F. 1948: The Problem of the Great Ross Barrier, *Geogr. J.* **112:** 196–218.

DOLGUSHIN, L. D. 1961: Zones of Snow Accumulation in Eastern Antarctica, IUGG Symposium on Antarctic Glaciology, Helsinki, 1960, *Int. Assn Sci. Hydrol. Publ.* **55.**

DONN, W. L., FARRAND, W. R., and EWING, M. 1962: Pleistocene Ice Volumes and Sea Level Lowering, *J. Geol.* **70:** 206–14.

EPSTEIN, S. and SHARP, R. P. 1959: Oxygen Isotope Studies, *Trans. Amer. Geophys. Un.* **40:** 81–4.

FLINT, R. F. 1957: *Glacial and Pleistocene Geology,* John Wiley & Sons, New York.

GIOVINETTO, M. B. 1960: Glaciology Report for 1958, South Pole Station, *Ohio State University Research Foundation, Report 825–2 Part IV.*

GLEN, J. W. 1955: The Creep of Polycrystalline Ice, *Proc. Roy. Soc.* **A228:** 519–538.

GOULD, L. M. 1940: The Glaciers of Antarctica, *Proc. Amer. Phil. Soc.* **82:** 835–76.

GOULD, L. M. 1957: Antarctic Prospect, *Geogr. Rev.* **47:** 1–28.

GOW, A. J. 1961: Drill Hole Measurements and Snow Studies at Byrd Station Antarctica, *US Army Cold Regions Research and Engineering Laboratory, Technical Report* **78.**

GOW, A. J. 1963: *The Inner Structure of the Ross Ice Shelf at Little America V, Antarctica, as revealed by Deep Core Drilling.* International Union of Geodesy and Geophysics, Association of Scientific Hydrology, Berkeley, August 1963, 272–84.

HOINKES, H. C. 1962: The Settling of Firn at Little America III, Antarctica 1940–58, *J. Glaciol.* **4:** 111–20.

JENSSEN, D., and RADOK, U. 1961: Transient Temperature Distributions in Ice Caps and Ice Shelves. IUGG Symposium on Antarctic Glaciology, Helsinki, 1960. *Int. Assn Sci. Hydrol. Publ.* **55.**

KLEBELSBERG, R. V. 1948: *Handbuch der Gletscherkunde und Glazialgeologie.* 2 vols.

KOSACK, H. P. c. 1955: *Die Antarktis,* Keyserche Verlagsbuchhandlung, Heidelberg.

KOTLYAKOV, V. M. 1961: The Intensity of Nourishment of the Antarctic Ice Sheet. IUGG Symposium on Antarctic Glaciology, Helsinki, 1960, *Int. Assn Sci. Hydrol. Publ.* **55.**

LOEWE, F. 1956: *Études de Glaciologie en Terre Adélie 1951–2,* Expeditions Polaires Françaises, Hermann et Cie, Paris.

LOEWE, F. 1960: Notes Concerning the Mass Budget of the Antarctic Inland Ice. *In Symposium on Antarctic Meteorology,* Melbourne, 1959, Pergamon Press, London.

LORIUS, C. 1961: Teneur en Deuterium de Précipitation dans l'Antarctique. IUGG Symposium on Antarctic Glaciology, Helsinki, 1960, *Int. Assn Sci. Hydrol. Publ.* **55.**

MARSHALL, E. W. 1962: The Stratigraphic Distribution of Particulate Matter in the Firn at Byrd Station, Antarctica. *Geophys. Monograph* **7**: 185–96, Amer. Geophys. Un.

MAWSON, D. 1915: *Home of the Blizzard,* William Heinemann, London.

MELLOR, M. 1958: Australian Glaciological Contributions in Antarctica; Preliminary Report, *J. Glaciol.* **3**: 279–85.

MELLOR, M. 1959a: Ice Flow in Antarctica, *J. Glaciol.* **3**: 377–85.

MELLOR, M. 1959b: Mass Balance Studies in Antarctica. *J. Glaciol.* **3**: 522–33.

MELLOR, M. 1960: Temperature Gradients in the Antarctic Ice Sheet. *J. Glaciol.* **3**: 773–82.

MELLOR, M. 1961: The Antarctic Ice Sheet. *Cold Regions Science and Engineering I–B1. US Army Cold Regions Research and Engineering Laboratory.*

MELLOR, M., and RADOK, U. 1960: Some Properties of Drifting Snow. *In Symposium on Antarctic Meteorology,* Melbourne, 1959, Pergamon Press, London.

MELLOR, M., and MCKINNON, G. 1960: The Amery Ice Shelf and its Hinterland, *Polar Record* **10**: 30–4.

MERCER, J. H. 1962: Glacier Variations in the Antarctic, *Glaciological Notes* **11**: 5–29, IGY World Data Centre A.

NOVIKOV, V. 1960: The Study of Antarctica is Continuing, *Priroda* **8**: 43–52.

NYE, J. F. 1959a: Surface Topography of the Antarctic Ice Sheet, *Nature* **184**: 786–7.

NYE, J. F. 1959b: The Motion of Ice Sheets and Glaciers, *J. Glaciol.* **3**: 493–507.

ODELL, N. E. 1952: Antarctic Glaciers and Glaciology. *In:* Simpson, F. A., ed., *The Antarctic Today,* pp. 25–55. Reed and N.Z. Antarctic Society, Wellington.

PATENAUDE, R. W., MARSHALL, E. W. and GOW, A. J. 1959: Deep Core Drilling in Ice, Byrd Station, Antarctica, *US Army Snow Ice and Permafrost Research Establishment, Technical Report* **60.**

PÉWÉ, T. L. 1960: Multiple Glaciation in the McMurdo Sound Region, Antarctica, *Ohio State University Research Foundation, Report 825-2, Part IX.*

RAGLE, R. H., HANSEN, B. L., GOW, A. J. and PATENAUDE, R. W. 1960: Deep Core Drilling in the Ross Ice Shelf, Little America V, Antarctica, *US Army Snow Ice and Permafrost Research Establishment, Technical Report* **70.**

RIGSBY, G. P. 1960: Crystal Orientation in Glacier and in Experimentally Deformed Ice, *J. Glaciol.* **3:** 589–606.

ROBIN, G. de Q. 1955: Ice Movement and Temperature Distribution in Glaciers and Ice Sheets, *J. Glaciol.* **2:** 523–32.

ROBIN, G. de Q. 1958: Seismic Shooting and Related Investigations, *Norwegian–British–Swedish Ant. Exp. 1949–52, Sci. Results, V,* Norsk Polarinstitutt, Oslo.

ROBIN, G. de Q. 1960: Progress Report on the Antarctic Ice Sheet, *Polar Record* **10:** 3–10.

RUBIN, M. J. 1962: The Antarctic and the Weather, *Scientific American,* Sept. 1962, 84–94.

SCHYTT, V. 1957: Glaciology II, *Norwegian–British–Swedish Ant. Exp. 1949–52, Sci. Results, IV,* Norsk Polarinstitutt, Oslo.

SHARP, R. P. 1956: Objectives of Antarctic Glaciological Research. *In* Antartica in the International Geophysical Year, *Amer. Geophys. Un. Geophys. Monogr.* **1:** 27–35.

STUART, A. W. and HEINE, A. J. 1961: Glaciological Work of the 1959–60 US Victoria Land Traverse, *J. Glaciol.* **3:** 997–1002.

SWITHINBANK, C. 1957–59: Glaciology I, *Norwegian–British–Swedish Ant. Exp. 1949–52, Sci. Results, III,* A and B (1957), C (1958), D and E (1959), Norsk Polarinstitutt, Oslo.

SWITHINBANK, C. 1962: *Maudheim Revisited: The Morphology and Regime of the Ice-Shelf, 1950–60, Årbok, 1960:* 28–31. Norsk Polarinstitutt, Oslo.

SWITHINBANK, C. W. M. 1963: Ice Movement of Valley Glaciers Flowing into the Ross Ice Shelf, Antarctica. *Science* **141**(3580): 523–24.

THIEL, E., *et al.* 1959: Ice Thickness and Bottom Topography of the Filchner Ice Shelf and along the Ellsworth–Byrd Traverse Route. *IGY Bulletin 30,* US Nat. Acad. Sci.

THIEL, E. and SCHMIDT, R. A. 1961: Spherules from the Antarctic Ice Cap, *J. Geophys. Res.* **66:** 307–10.

VIALOV, S. S. 1958: Regularities of Glacial Shields Movement and the Theory of Plastic Flow. Symposium of Chamonix, 1958. Physics of the Movement of Ice, *IUGG, Int. Assn Sci. Hydrol. Publ.* **47.**

WADE, F. A. 1937: Glaciological Studies in King Edward VII Land and Northwestern Marie Byrd Land, *Geogr. Rev.* **27:** 584–97.

WEERTMAN, J. 1957: On the Sliding of Glaciers, *J. Glaciol.* **3:** 33–8.

WEERTMAN, J. 1961: Equilibrium Profile of Ice Caps, *J. Glaciol.* **3:** 953–64.

WEERTMAN, J. 1961: Stability of Ice-Age Ice Sheets, *J. Geophys. Res.* **66:** 3783–92.

WEERTMAN, J. 1962: Stability of Ice-Age Ice Caps. *US Army Cold Regions Research and Engineering Laboratory, Research Report 97.*

WEIHAUPT, J. G. 1961: Geophysical Studies in Victoria Land, Antarctica, *Univ. Wis. Geophys. and Polar Res. Centre, Research Report 1.*

WEXLER, H. 1959: Geothermal Heat and Glacial Growth. *J. Glaciol.* **3:** 420–5.

WEXLER, H. 1961: Ice Budgets for Antarctica and Changes in Sea Level, *J. Glaciol.* **3:** 867–72.

WEXLER, H. and RUBIN, M. 1961: Antarctic Meteorology. *In:* Science in Antarctica, Part II, *US Nat. Acad. Sci., Nat. Res. Council Publ.* **878.**

WOOLLARD, G. P. 1958: Preliminary Report on the Thickness of Ice in Antarctica, *IGY Bulletin 13, US Nat. Acad. Sci.*

WRIGHT, C. S. and PRIESTLEY, R. E. 1922: Glaciology, *British (Terra Nova) Ant. Exp. 1910–13,* London.

CHAPTER TEN

The Land Beneath the Ice

CHARLES R. BENTLEY, *University of Wisconsin*

Introduction

As recently as 1950 there had been no measurements of ice thickness in the interior of the Antarctic Continent. The only seismic soundings had been made in 1934 by Poulter (1950) on the floating shelf ice in the vicinity of the Bay of Whales and on the northern tip of Roosevelt Island. Although valuable in pioneering seismic techniques in Antarctica, this work had provided no insight into the depth of the vast interior ice sheet. As a result there were only guesses of the average ice thickness, ranging from 600 to 1600 m, and the level of the rock surface beneath the ice was correspondingly uncertain. The protrusion of mountains through the ice in a number of places in West Antarctica lent the impression of thinness of glacial cover in this area, whereas it was widely believed that a high rock plateau of gentle relief underlay the mantle of ice in East Antarctica.

The first detailed seismic soundings of the interior ice cap were made by Robin of the Norwegian–British–Swedish Antarctic Expedition on a traverse in 1951–2 (Robin, 1958). Seismic reflection and refraction measurements were carried out along a 650 km track through the mountains onto the central plateau of Dronning Maud Land. Here the base of the ice averages only a few hundred metres above sea level. This discovery, together with the demonstration by the Expéditions Polaires Françaises in 1949–52 that the rock surface in the central parts of Greenland lies near sea level, led to a considerable increase in the estimate of the average thickness of the Antarctic Ice Sheet (Sharp, 1956). Until the IGY expeditions to the continent, however, such estimates were largely based upon scientific intuition and guesswork.

Seismic soundings connected with the IGY were begun in April, 1956 by the First Continental Expedition of the USSR (Nudelman, 1959). This marked the start of the explosive increase in the investigation of the Antarctic interior, made possible by the large-scale, concerted effort of the IGY and by continued national support and international cooperation among the participating countries. Seismic soundings have now been made along more than 25,000 km of traverse route and at twenty-three aircraft landings by groups from Australia, Belgium, the British Commonwealth, France, Japan, the USA and the USSR. In addition, measurements of ice surface elevation have been made on 30,000 km of flight

lines along which barometric and radar altimetry were combined, as well as on
several over-snow journeys which did not include seismic soundings. The work
is still proceeding, and we may hope that within the next five years it will be
possible to draw contour maps of glacial and subglacial topography for the whole
continent.

Figure 74 shows the traverse and flight routes along which the data used to
construct the succeeding maps and sections were collected. The author believes

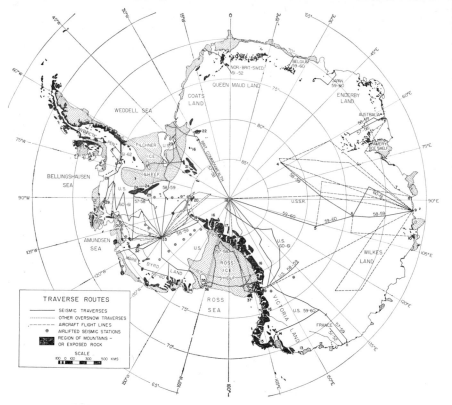

FIG. 74 TRAVERSE AND FLIGHT ROUTES TO 1962
See key (p. 274) for geographical features

this figure shows the sites of all seismic measurements of ice thickness in the
Antarctic interior, but it does not include all other over-snow traverses or all
flights. Tracks which were limited to the coastal regions, and those from which
data either were not available or have been superseded by more accurate information have not been included. A tabulation of the various traverses and the types
of measurements made on each is given by Bentley (1962).

FIELD METHODS

Before discussing the discoveries resulting from the recent expeditions, it is
worthwhile to describe briefly the geophysical techniques of exploration which

were employed. These techniques have become possible only with the advent of modern mechanized transport and the consequent vast increase in the weight of material which can be carried into the remote regions of the continent.

The basic method of ice thickness determination is seismic reflection sounding. This, in essence, is simply the measurement of the echo time of an explosion-generated sound wave which has travelled through the ice to its base and has been reflected from the underlying rock surface. The chief problem in the use of this method in the Antarctic arises on the high, cold plateaus. A prolonged disturbance, connected with conditions in the layers of firn near the surface and produced by the detonation of the explosive charge, interferes with the observation of the returning echo from the bottom of the ice. This interference has prevented reliable results being obtained from many places in East Antartica, and has been responsible for the divergence of ice thickness values reported at the South Pole. At present the only method helpful in overcoming this problem is the use of shot holes 30 m or more deep, but even this technique is not always successful. In lower areas of the continent where the problem is much less serious the seismic reflection results are usually excellent.

Measurement of the Earth's gravity field provides a valuable supplement to seismic reflection observations. Since the value of the acceleration of gravity at any point depends upon the distribution of density in the subjacent material, the large density contrast between ice and rock makes the value of gravity particularly sensitive to changes in the level of the rock surface. Furthermore, a gravity reading can be completed in a few minutes, as compared with an hour or more for a seismic reflection shot. However, gravity values also depend upon density variations within the Earth, and cannot alone yield accurate determinations of ice thickness. The normal procedure has been to use gravity observations to interpolate between the more widely spaced, more accurate, but more time-consuming seismic measurements.

Additional information about the nature of the land beneath the ice is obtained in two ways. Measurements of magnetic field strength are quickly and easily made. These provide clues to the magnetic susceptibility of the buried rock from which some conclusions concerning its composition can be drawn. Unfortunately, instrumental difficulties and lack of sufficient control have largely prevented proper evaluation of traverse magnetic data. Potentially valuable results from recent aeromagnetic surveys are not yet available.

Much more expensive of time and material, but more precise in results, is the seismic refraction technique. This method involves the detonation of explosive charges at distances varying up to 20 km or more from the detecting instruments. From the velocities of travel of seismic waves in the subglacial rock layers information on the rock types is gained. In order to produce satisfactory energy at the greater distances, charges of 100 kg or more are required. It is obvious that logistical limitations preclude the completion of very many refraction profiles.

Of prime importance in the exploration of the Antarctic interior is the determination of the ice surface elevation. This has almost always been accomplished on ground traverses by the use of altimeters (one levelling traverse between Mirnyy and Komsomolskaya has been completed by the USSR). In many cases two or more altimeters separated by several kilometres have been read to eliminate in large part the effects of atmospheric pressure variations. Ice surface elevations along aircraft flight lines are determined by taking the difference between the height of the plane, as determined by its barometric altimeter, and its height above the surface as measured by a radar altimeter. Any method of altimetry will be affected by horizontal pressure gradients in the atmosphere; various methods of correcting for such gradients have been employed. (For a tabulation giving the elevation methods used on individual traverses see Bentley, 1962.)

Subglacial Topography

The results to date of the measurements of rock surface elevations are summarized in Figure 75. Details of the rock topography must be viewed with caution because traverse tracks are too widely separated to permit positive interpolation of minor features. In some places variations along a traverse route are shown diagrammatically by short segments of contours perpendicular to the track; these do not indicate the true trend of the rock topography. The rock levels under the traverses of the Commonwealth Trans-Antarctic Expedition 1957–8 (Pratt, 1960b) and the USSR 1958–9 from Komsomolskaya to the Pole of Inaccessibility (Sorokhtin, et al., 1960) were apparently erroneously calculated from seismograms badly disturbed by interfering surface 'noise'. They are shown in Figure 75 as recomputed by Woollard (1962) on the basis of the gravity data. (Woollard specifically disclaims greater reliability for his profile from Komsomolskaya to the Pole of Inaccessibility than for the original of Sorokhtin, et al., but the present author believes that Woollard's analysis is more likely to approach the true topography.)

In considering the present level of the subglacial rock surface we must keep in mind that the continent has been depressed by the overlying load of ice. From our knowledge of isostasy elsewhere in the world it could scarcely be otherwise, and indeed the gravity observations indicate that isostatic compensation is substantially complete. (The measurements are not accurate enough to determine any slight imbalance which might result from a growing or shrinking ice cap.) This means that if the ice were to melt most of the land would rise by an amount between 25 and 30% of the ice thickness. The percentage rise would be less in those areas which would remain below sea level and thus retain part of the present load in the form of a covering sea; there would obviously be no direct effect in regions presently covered by floating ice. Although the rate of rise would only be of the order of centimetres per year, we may still take the fully recovered elevation as the best estimate of the level of the rock existing prior to glacierization. The estimated location of the shoreline existing before the growth of the ice cap, where it is appreciably removed from the present boundary of the

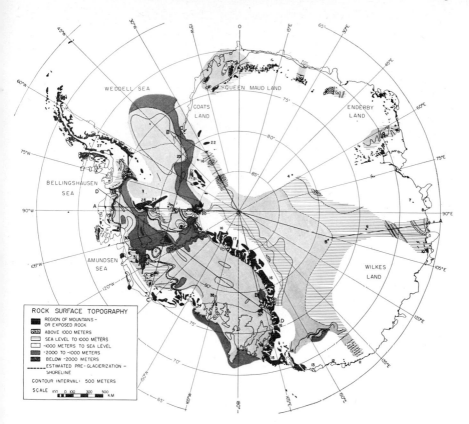

FIG. 75 ROCK SURFACE ELEVATIONS
See key (p. 274) for geographical features

grounded ice, is shown in Figure 75 by a heavy dashed line. This we may call the 'adjusted shore line'; we may correspondingly refer to elevations relative to 'adjusted sea level'.

EAST ANTARCTICA

The subglacial floor of East Antarctica is nearly everywhere above adjusted sea level; the only exception of appreciable size is a basin in the northern part of Victoria Land. The extent of this basin is not known, but it cannot reach as far west as the French traverse route, since nowhere along this track is the rock below adjusted sea level, nor does it extend as far east as the newly discovered Arctic Institute Range (Weihaupt, 1960). Although rock exposures are known along a large part of the Oates and George V Coasts, there may be interposed subglacial channels connecting to the sea to the north, and the possibility exists that the coast comprises several islands submerged by the ice.

For 2000 km, from the Admiralty and the Arctic Institute Ranges to the Queen

Maud Range, the vast Trans-Antarctic Mountains stretch in an unbroken line. They extend laterally far under the East Antarctic ice cap, having a width of from 200 to 400 km if we arbitrarily take the 500 m contour as their boundary. The mountains are thus decidedly asymmetric in topographic profile (Fig. 76); the elevation decline from the highest mountain peaks is much more gradual under the ice cap than on the side facing the Ross Sea and the Ross Ice Shelf.

The region south of the Queen Maud Range and the Horlick Mountains is still unknown, but investigations soon to be undertaken should show whether a gap in the continuity of the Trans-Antarctic Mountains exists. East of the Thiel Mountains there is a definite gap. This has been shown by gravity measurements along the US traverse from Byrd Station to the South Pole in 1960–1 (Dowling, personal communication) which, although not accompanied by seismic

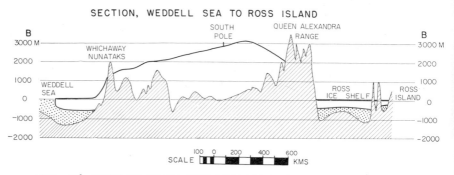

FIG. 76 SECTION FROM THE WEDDELL SEA TO THE ROSS SEA
VIA THE POLE

This section crosses the Trans-Antarctic Mountains twice; the width of the range is somewhat exaggerated, especially at the Weddell Sea end, because the profile is not drawn normal to the mountains (cf. Figs. 75 or 80). Note the asymmetry of the ice cap surface, also the trenches under both ice shelves

results, were tied to soundings at the crossing with the US 1958–9 traverse route and at the Pole. The rock floor dips to more than 1000 m below sea level near the Thiel Mountains, and remains below sea level for some 150 km to the south. Still farther south the rock again attains an elevation greater than 500 m before dropping to sea level at the South Pole (Fig. 77).

Farther to the east, beyond another unexplored region, the Commonwealth Trans-Antarctic Expedition traverse passed over high rock surface of considerable relief from the Shackleton Range as far south as Lat. 86° S (Pratt, 1960b). Between here and the relatively flat plain which exists in the vicinity of the South Pole is a valley about 100 km across cutting more than 500 m below sea level (or approximately to adjusted sea level) (Fig. 76). Unfortunately, we cannot at the present time trace the trend of this valley, or determine whether it may represent another break in the mountain chain. At any rate, we may say that the continuity of the Trans-Antarctic Mountains is broken in at least one place between the Horlick Mountains and the Shackleton Range.

A great central plain, bounded on the east by the Trans-Antarctic Mountains, reaching about 73° S in Victoria Land and south of Mirnyy, bordered between longitudes 90° E and 60° E by an apparent extension beneath the ice of the Prince Charles Mountains, and stretching an unknown distance toward Dronning Maud Land, exists under the East Antarctic ice sheet. (Note that the position of the sea level contour has little significance within this plain.) It measures some $2\frac{1}{2}$ million square kilometres in area, is relatively flat (Fig. 77), and has an elevation ranging from several hundred metres below sea level to several hundred metres above, or from a few hundred to a thousand metres above adjusted sea level. The highest portion is in west-central East Antarctica where the isostatic depression of the continent under the load of 3600 m of ice should be of the order of 1000 m. Since the present rock surface is higher, despite a greater overlying load of ice, in the central regions of the continent than nearer the Trans-Antarctic Mountains, we may conclude with some confidence that the

SECTION, BELLINGSHAUSEN SEA TO MIRNY

FIG. 77 SECTION FROM THE BELLINGSHAUSEN SEA THROUGH THE POLE TO MIRNYY

Note the striking contrast between two parts of the continent. The level plain beneath the high ice dome of East Antarctica is wider than the whole of West Antarctica. The ruggedness of the latter region is exaggerated by this profile since it runs right along the narrow mountainous spine from the Sentinel Range to the Thiel Mountains

pre-glacierization plateau surface sloped downward toward the east. The most nearly comparable physiographic feature elsewhere in the world is the high plateau of southern Africa which is perhaps twice as great in area and has about twice the average adjusted elevation.

Very little can definitely be said about the apparent subglacial extension of the Prince Charles Mountains because of the ambiguity in the seismic sounding results between Komsomolskaya and the Pole of Inaccessibility. However, the increased ruggedness of the relief (up to 1000 m in 50 km) as indicated by gravity alone is enough to suggest a mountainous region, whatever the true average rock level may be. Furthermore a crevassed zone in the ice surface has been seen near $77\frac{1}{2}°$ S, 67° E (Voronov, 1959) suggesting a high subglacial relief in this area, about halfway between the most southerly nunataks of the Prince Charles Mountains and the traverse route. The observed mountains associated with the deep embayment of the Amery Ice Shelf and the vast, recently discovered Lambert Glacier stretch inland 800 km from the coast; the likely subglacial extension of this range would increase its total length to 1500 km.

The results of the Australian traverses (Goodspeed and Jesson, 1959) suggest that westward from the Prince Charles Mountains into Enderby Land the subglacial rock elevation decreases fairly rapidly to sea level or below.

Along the Kronprinsesse Märtha Kyst the regions above and below sea level have been delimited according to the estimate by Robin (1958) on the assumption, following Nye, that the slope of the ice surface can be used to estimate ice thickness. As shown, most of the coastal areas between mountain ranges are below sea level, the 'true' coastline lying two or three hundred kilometres south of the edge of the grounded ice.

Between 200 and 400 km south of Mirnyy there is a steep-sided uplift with an elevation between 500 and 1000 m, bordered on the south by a 150-km wide depression in which a depth of 1100 m below sea level (300–400 m below adjusted sea level) is attained (Fig. 77). This uplift and depression are believed to be fault-block structures (Sorokhtin, et al., 1959). On the basis of magnetic data the apparent horst has been extended north-east to the Queen Mary Coast in the vicinity of the Bunger Hills (Glebovsky, 1959a). Magnetic data also indicate a subglacial ridge connecting Mt Brown with Gaussberg on the coast near Long. 90° E (Glebovsky, 1959b).

Along the French IGY traverse route south of the Adélie Coast the ice cap bed remains at about sea level, with a section of moderately rugged relief (up to 1000 m in 20 km) between 150 and 350 km from the coast (Imbert, 1959). The lowest point is about 600 m below sea level, and the highest about 450 m above. These results are not in good accord with those of Imbert (1953) 100 km to the east. His two measurements made 80 and 290 km from the coast showed rock levels about 1000 and 1500 m above sea level, respectively. The latter value, in view of the more recent results and Imbert's reservations about its reliability, is probably in error. The former is supported by seismic refraction results and suggests the extension beneath the ice of the low mountains farther to the east, the nearest of which is only 80 km distant.

In the vicinity of 71° S, 140° E, there is a region where the relative gravity anomaly reaches −150 milligals (Weihaupt, 1961), which if resulting entirely from rock topography, would correspond to a depression 2 km deep. Unfortunately, seismic data do not give an indisputable determination of ice thickness here, although they strongly suggest that it could not reach the required value of nearly 4000 m. Regardless of the rock level, a great volume of material with a density less than that of the normal crustal rocks is required to explain the large negative anomaly. An intriguing explanation has been offered by Schmidt (1962) who suggests that a huge crater may exist beneath the ice as the result of the impact of a gigantic meteorite. In this case a large part of the gravity anomaly would be the result of a great volume of crushed rock filling the crater. Before the possible significance of this anomaly had been realized, Barnes (1961) had already postulated a meteorite impact somewhere in Wilkes Land as an explanation for the existence of certain tektites in Southern Australia and their absence elsewhere.

WEST ANTARCTICA

The subglacial topography of West Antarctica contrasts strikingly with that of East Antarctica. This had long been assumed, but the IGY and subsequent explorations have brought to light the surprising fact that a major portion of this part of the continent exhibits a rock surface well below adjusted sea level (Bentley et al., 1960). A great subglacial basin (Byrd Basin) runs from the Ross Sea beneath the Ross Ice Shelf, eastward through central West Antarctica, opens into the eastern Amundsen Sea, continues north-eastward nearly to the Bellingshausen Sea and perhaps into its eastern part, and then bends to the south-east to an apparent junction with the Weddell Sea via the embayment of the Filchner Ice Shelf.

The discovery of the vast extent of the Filchner Ice Shelf carved another large section from the supposed land mass of West Antarctica. A 1957–8 traverse party found the shelf to reach far into the interior south-west of the Weddell Sea (Neuberg et al., 1959). Subsequently, US Geological Survey photogrammetric data from the east side of the Sentinel Range indicated that the ice surface there is only slightly above sea level, and 1961–2 traverse results disclosed an ice surface elevation of only 300–400 m as far north as 75° 15′ S at Long. 77° 10′ W (Behrendt and Parks, 1962). With its boundaries estimated from these data, the Filchner Ice Shelf becomes nearly as large as the Ross Ice Shelf.

These two great embayments from west and east nearly meet along the 90° W meridian. A structural connection between the Ross and Weddell Seas had been suggested as long ago as 1914 by Taylor, and the idea of a subglacial trough cutting across this neck of the continent has found much favour. It is now known, however, that a series of nunataks, 100 to 160 km apart, stretches from the Ellsworth Mountains south to the Thiel Mountains (Fig. 77). Seismic soundings between these nunataks show the rock surface to be slightly above adjusted sea level in most cases, although at the most southerly station (84·7° S, 87·5° W) a rock depth of over 1600 m below sea level was found (Thiel, 1961). This deep valley is limited by mountains on either side to a maximum width of 50 km and little resembles the postulated Ross-Weddell *Senkungsfeld*. There is, moreover, no indication of even a narrow trough farther to the west, although such a feature could exist south of the 1958–9 traverse route. It seems more likely that the valley is a fjord connecting to the trough under the Filchner Ice Shelf, or it may be a physiographic expression of a boundary separating the folded 'Antarctandean' mountains from the block-faulted Thiel Mountains to the south. In any case, there clearly is no broad, direct connection between the Ross and Weddell Seas. The structural significance of the rather tortuous junction which does exist north of the Sentinel Range will not be known until more geological and topographic data are available.

Now let us consider the West Antarctic subglacial topography in greater detail. Two major features appear in the Filcher Ice Shelf–Weddell Sea region (Behrendt, 1962). A vast bank extends from the central part of the ice shelf

far out into the sea. Almost the entire bank is less than 300 m in depth. Berkner
Island is formed on a small portion of this bank where decreasing water depth
and increasing ice thickness combine to produce a region of grounded ice
(Fig. 78). In contrast to the bank is the trough on its eastern and southern sides

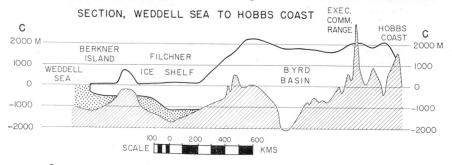

FIG. 78 SECTION ACROSS WEST ANTARCTICA FROM THE WEDDELL SEA
TO THE PACIFIC COAST

Although this section crosses both the central isthmus and Marie Byrd Land
at about the widest points, the small proportion of true land along this path is
evident. The large indentation of the Filchner Ice is particularly noticeable

(Figs. 76 and 78). This trough is at least 1000 km in length, possibly continuing
under the grounded ice as far as the Thiel Mountains. The water depth throughout its length under the shelf is greater than 1000 m, reaching a maximum value
near 82° S, 60° W of more than 1700 m.

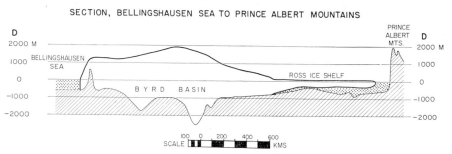

FIG. 79 SECTION ALONG THE CENTRE OF THE BYRD BASIN FROM
THE BELLINGSHAUSEN SEA TO THE ROSS SEA

The narrow, isolated ridge just south of the Bellingshausen Sea, the only
portion of this profile above adjusted sea level, is remarkable. The surprising
depth of the rock floor in the central parts of Byrd Basin, much deeper than the
continental shelves beneath the surrounding seas, is clearly illustrated

The floor of the Byrd Basin shows considerable topographic variation (Fig. 79).
A fairly smooth regular surface exists under the Ross Ice Shelf, due at least in
part to blanketing by morainal material (Crary *et al.*, 1962). Eastward from the
shelf to about Long. 130° W is a region where no observations have been made.
North and south of Byrd Station the rock surface relief is considerable, with

variations of hundreds of metres in a few tens of kilometres common, and with the relief becoming increasingly rugged toward the mountains of Marie Byrd Land and the Horlick Mountains (Bentley and Ostenso, 1961). Farther to the north-east, along the central part of the basin, the rock floor becomes quite smooth, particularly in the deepest parts. Topographic irregularities naturally become more pronounced toward the Ellsworth Mountains.

The basin reaches the Bellingshausen Sea, if at all, only through a narrow passageway on the George Bryan Coast. About 100 km inland along the Eights Coast the rock rises above sea level forming a ridge parallel with the coast. East of the George Bryan Coast at the base of Graham Land mountainous topography is again observed, with many peaks protruding through the ice. South-west of these mountains, the edge of the basin is marked by a precipitous drop of the rock elevation to below −1500 m.

Several other deeps more than 1500 m below sea level exist within the West Antarctic lowland area. The shape of the one between Byrd Station and the Horlick Mountains is quite uncertain, and it may not exist as a continuous feature at all. Both the lowest rock elevation (−2560 m) and the greatest ice thickness 4335 m) known in Antarctica are found around 80° S, 110° W. Farther to the north another deep stretches across Byrd Basin from a narrow trench between the Crary and Toney Mountains to a valley in the rugged subglacial terrain west of the Sentinel Range. This valley may continue to the south-east beneath the Nimitz Glacier and connect with the sea under the Filchner Ice Shelf.

Several isolated regions with elevations above −500 m are shown within Byrd Basin. In only one of these, at 78·5° S, 116° W, does the rock rise much above this level. The others are so close to adjusted sea level that it is impossible to judge whether they would be islands or shoals after melting of the ice and isostatic adjustment. In contrast, most of Marie Byrd Land between Edward VII Peninsula and the Walgreen Coast exhibits a rock surface above adjusted sea level, and it is likely that prior to glacierization Marie Byrd Land comprised only one or two large islands rather than an archipelago (Chang, 1962).

Under the Ross Ice Shelf the water deepens toward the mountains on the west and south (Crary et al., 1962). This is shown in Figure 75 only in the westernmost part of the shelf where the bottom depth exceeds 1000 m, but a somewhat shallower depression actually extends along the mountain front (Fig. 76). Another basin reaching over 900 m in depth lies along 80° S just to the west of the eastern border of the shelf. A few areas shallower than −500 m are shown under the shelf, as well as several in the Ross Sea north of the shelf (contours taken from the 1962 American Geographical Society map of Antarctica). There appears to be no important difference in topography of the sea floor under the shelf and under the adjacent open sea.

Ice Surface Topography

Although the chief purpose of this chapter is to discuss the form of the Antarctic Continent buried beneath the ice, we will describe briefly the morphology of the ice surface (Figure 80), particularly as it is affected by the subglacial relief. The topography of the major part of East Antarctica is fairly simple (Bugayev and Tolstikov, 1960). An irregular elliptical dome, with a maximum elevation slightly over 4000 m, is centred slightly to the east of the Pole of Inaccessibility. The shape of this high central dome is largely independent of rock topography with one major exception, the 700-km indentation of the Amery Ice Shelf–Lambert Glacier region. Here, apparently, a great gash in the rock floor, serving as the

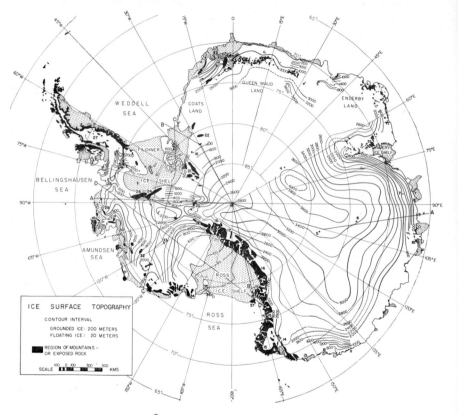

FIG. 80 ICE SURFACE ELEVATIONS
See key (p. 274) for geographical features

framework for this mammoth glacier–ice shelf system, has permitted ice flow rapid enough to maintain equilibrium with the drainage from some million square kilometres of the interior, and thus to prevent the region from being overwhelmed by the ice cap.

The modification of the simple dome by the Amery–Lambert drainage basin has resulted in a spur on the eastern side of the basin which is well shown by the 3600 m contour line. Katabatic winds caused by this divide account for the prevailing west and east winds found at stations on its opposite flanks. This feature is remarkably similar to Lamb's predicted barrier 3600 to 4600 m high around 80° S, 80° E running parallel to the 140° E meridian (Lamb, 1948).

Farther to the east a large nose is well shown by the 3000 m contour, marking the eastern edge of a broad and gentle valley between longitudes 100° E and 125° E. Between the eastern side of this nose and the Trans-Antarctic Mountains, extending from the northern coast nearly to the South Pole, is a vast area from which there may be down-slope drainage of cold air toward the Adélie, George V, and Oates Coasts. Whether the high winds measured by Australian and French expeditions on the Adélie Coast can be entirely explained in this way is debatable (Loewe and Lamb, 1956), but there seems little doubt that the surface topography has an important effect.

A large interior region in Dronning Maud Land is still unexplored. It is the only extensive section of Antarctica not yet seen by man. Surface elevations have been measured in the coastal regions, particularly along the Kronprinsesse Märtha Kyst which is mapped in detail (Swithinbank, 1959). To the east, ice surface elevations as high as 4300 m are often, but erroneously, shown on Antarctic maps. They originally appeared on a chart of preliminary and un-corrected results of the German Antarctic Expedition of 1938–9, but were not given on the final map which appeared in 1942 (Gruber, 1942). The latter map included downward adjustments of hundreds of metres in the mountain heights presented in the preliminary version. Similar errors would be expected for the ice surface elevations (Kosack, 1951); furthermore, an elevation of 2714 + 56 m was measured by a ground party of the Norwegian–British–Swedish Expedition (Robin 1958) only 50 km from a location at which the preliminary map gave 4300 m. Clearly, the extreme surface heights are invalid; values nearer to 3600 m as found by the Belgians near 74° S, 25° W (Van Autenboer and Derom, personal communication) might be expected. In any case, a high plateau un-doubtedly exists throughout most of the unknown area, whatever the nature of the subglacial land.

The effect of the barricade formed by the Trans-Antarctic Mountains is apparent in the ice divide, noticed by both Amundsen and Scott, between the mountains and the South Pole. Obstruction to the free flow of ice into the Ross Ice Shelf has resulted in a decidedly asymmetric drainage pattern with major flow towards the Weddell Sea (Fig. 76). Between the Thiel Mountains and the Pensacola Range there is a conspicuous valley in the ice surface which appears to be a reflection of the deep subglacial valley directly beneath it. This suggests the existence of an ice stream draining ice from a considerable portion of the polar plateau into the Filchner Ice Shelf (Behrendt et al., 1962).

In West Antarctica the ice topography is strongly controlled, in general out-line, by the shape of the underlying bed. In the mountainous area of Marie Byrd Land and south of the Ellsworth Mountains are two high regions forming the horns of a saddle-shaped configuration (Bentley and Ostenso, 1961). The flanks of the saddle reflect the unobstructed flow of ice into the Ross Ice Shelf and the Amundsen Sea. The effect of the ridge near the Eights Coast is shown by the ice surface maximum just to the south, indicating little drainage into the Bellingshausen Sea. Most of the ice north of the Ellsworth Mountains flows into either the Amundsen Sea or the Filchner Ice Shelf. The combined evidence of ice and rock surface topography suggests that the present ice sheet originated as separate ice caps in Marie Byrd Land, in Graham Land, and between the Ellsworth and Thiel Mountains. These caps then converged across the intervening seas, probably being joined initially by floating ice shelves which grew thick enough to become grounded and produce the present single ice sheet.

Under an ice shelf a small change in bottom level can have an exaggerated effect on the surface topography. If the ice grounds on a shoal, which may be only a few tens of metres shallower than the surrounding sea floor, the flow of the ice is impeded, snow accumulation on the surface is not carried away in the normal way by floating ice, and consequently an ice dome several hundred metres high develops. Berkner and Roosevelt Islands are prime examples of this phenomenon; geophysical measurements have not disclosed rock above sea level under either (Behrendt, 1962; Hochstein, personal communication).

Antarctic Crustal Structure

Evidence as to the crustal structure of the continent has come from four main sources: the geological nature of the rock outcrops which are, unfortunately, very sparsely distributed; seismic refraction profiles which give an idea of the nature of the upper crustal layers in regions buried by the ice; measurements of gravity and elevation both of which, by methods that are not entirely independent, give estimates of crustal thickness; and analysis of seismic surface wave dispersion which provides a measure of the average crustal thickness over a whole section of the continent. The direct geological evidence is discussed by Warren in the next chapter; results of the other types of observations will be briefly summarized here.

Seismic refraction profiles at a distance from mountain ranges and long enough to penetrate several kilometres into the subglacial crust appear to have been made only in West Antarctica (Bentley and Ostenso, 1961; Chang, 1962), on the Ross Ice Shelf (Crary, 1961), and in Victoria Land (Crary and van der Hoeven, 1961). These profiles all show wave velocities in the upper crust between 5·8 and 6·4 km/sec; after allowance is made for experimental errors these are within the range for normal granitic crustal material. The differences between the velocities from the different areas are not statistically significant. However, there is a considerable difference in the section above the granitic basement. On the eastern edge of the deep trench 150 km east of Byrd Station this section comprises about 1·5 km of rock of wave velocity 5·3 km/sec, a section very similar, although lower lying, to that in the foothills of the Sentinel Mountains. Near the Toney Mountains, at Byrd Station, and under the Ross Ice Shelf, on the other hand, a velocity of only 4·2 to 4·6 km/sec is found. The thickness of this material ranges from 3 km in the mountains to 0·5 km under the shelf. This comparison provides evidence that the marked physiographic depression in central West Antarctica divides a volcanic province in Marie Byrd Land, from a metasedimentary province in the Sentinel Mountains and region to the south-west, a conclusion supported by magnetic data. On the Victoria Land Plateau at 78° S, 135° E, where the rock surface is slightly below sea level, there is no indication of lower velocity material overlying the crustal rocks. The large sedimentary section (largely the Beacon formation) found in the Trans-Antarctic Mountains is absent.

Bouguer gravity anomalies and surface elevation data may be used to estimate crustal thickness by means of empirical curves constructed by Woollard (1959). This method was applied to West Antarctica by Bentley et al. (1960) and extended by Woollard (1962) to all parts of the continent from which data were available. Woollard concludes, 'Despite the paucity of data, there is a distinct difference in depth to the base of the crust and crustal thickness pattern beneath West and East Antarctica. Whereas East Antarctica appears to be a broad shield defined by the −40 km contour, West Antarctica is made up of several small crustal blocks having a depth to the Mohorovicic Discontinuity varying from 29 km to 36 km below sea level'. The mean crustal thickness beneath West Antarctica is about 32 km and beneath East Antarctica about 42 km.

Demenitskaya (1960) has deduced crustal thickness for the continent on the basis of elevations of ice and rock alone. Her apparent assumption of local isostatic compensation, combined with a smaller assumed crust-mantle density contrast, results in a much wider variation of crustal thickness (17 to 65 km) than that estimated by Woollard.

Woollard's conclusions regarding crustal thickness agree in general with the results of earthquake surface wave dispersion analyses. Two such studies have been made. Using principally seismograms from Scott Base and Hallett Station, Evison et al. (1960) deduced average crustal thicknesses of 35 km and 25 km for East and West Antarctica respectively, and their range of error is implied as ±5 km. Kovach and Press (1961), using the same data but a more complicated crustal model, obtained thicknesses of 40 and 30 km, and believe their results to be accurate within ±12%. Thus the two investigations produce results which are not greatly different (see also Bentley and Ostenso, 1962); furthermore, both predict a crustal thickness under West Antarctica 10 km thinner than that under East Antarctica, a difference in excellent agreement with that obtained from the gravity studies.

K

KEY TO GEOGRAPHICAL FEATURES, FIGURES 74, 75, 80

1. Kronprinsesse Martha Kyst
2. Prince Charles Mountains
3. Lambert Glacier
4. Pole of Inaccessibility
5. Vostok
6. Komsomolskaya
7. Mt Brown
8. Gaussberg
9. Mirnyy
10. Bunger Hills
11. Adélie Coast
12. George V Coast
13. Oates Coast
14. Arctic Institute Range
15. Admiralty Range
16. Trans-Antarctic Mountains
17. Queen Maud Range
18. Pole (Amundsen–Scott) Station
19. Horlick Mountains
20. Thiel Mountains
21. Pensacola Range
22. Shackleton Range
23. Berkner Island
24. Nimitz Glacier
25. Heritage Range
25 & 26. Ellsworth Mountains
26. Sentinel Mountains
27. Graham Land
28. George Bryan Coast
29. Eights Coast
30. Walgreen Coast
31. Toney Mountains
32. Crary Mountains
33. Byrd Station
34. Edward VII Peninsula
35. Roosevelt Island
36. Bay of Whales
37. Ross Island

Bibliography

BAGE, R. 1942: The Southern Sledge Journey, *Austral. Ant. Exp. 1911–14 Sci. Repts. Ser. A* **1**: 199–220.

BARNES, V. E. 1961: Tektites. *Sci. American* **205**: 58–65.

BECKER, B. 1958: South Pole Land above Sea Level. *Proc. US Naval Inst.* **84**: 141–3.

BEHRENDT, J. C. 1962: Geophysical and Glaciological Studies in the Filchner Ice Shelf Area of Antarctica, *J. Geophys. Res.* **67**: 221–34.

BEHRENDT, J. C. and PARKS, P. E. 1962: The Antarctic Peninsula Traverse, *Science* **137**: 601.

BEHRENDT, J. C., LAUDON, T. S. and WOLD, R. J. 1962: Results of a Geophysical and Geological Traverse from Mt Murphy to the Hudson Mts, Antarctica, *J. Geophys. Res.* **67**: 3973–80.

BEHRENDT, J. C., WOLD, R. J. and DOWLING, R. L. 1962: Ice Surface Elevation of Central Marie Byrd Land, *J. Glaciol.* **4**: 121–3.

BENTLEY, C. R. 1962: Glacial and Subglacial Topography of Antarctica, *Geophys. Monogr.* **7**: 11–25, Amer. Geophys. Un.

BENTLEY, C. R., CRARY, A. P., OSTENSO, N. A., and THIEL, E. C. 1960: Structure of West Antarctica, *Science* **131**: 131–6.

BENTLEY, C. R., and OSTENSO, N. A. 1961: Glacial and Subglacial Topography of West Antarctica, *J. Glaciol.* **3**: 882–911.

BUGAEV, V. A., and TOLSTIKOV, E. I. 1960: Osnovnye Cherty Relefa Vostochnoy Antarktidy, *Inf. Byull. Sov. Ant. Eksp.* **16**: 11–15.

CENTRE NATIONAL de RECHERCHES POLAIRES de BELGIQUE 1960: Expédition Antarctique Belge 1959, Rapport Succinct au SCAR.

CHANG, F. K. 1962: Structure of Northwest Marie Byrd Land, Antarctica, *Univ. Wis. Geophys. & Polar Res. Centre, Res. Rept* **2**.

COOK, J. C. 1958: Preliminary Airlifted Geophysical Explorations in Antarctica. *IGY Glaciological Rept.* **1**: American Geographical Society, New York.

CRARY, A. P. 1961: Marine Sediment Thickness in the Eastern Ross Sea Area, Antarctica. *Bull. Geol. Soc. Amer.* **72**: 787–90.

CRARY, A. P. 1959: Oversnow Traverses from IGY Little America Station. *Trans. Amer. Geophys. Un.* **40**: 311–5.

CRARY, A. P. and VAN DER HOEVEN, F. G. 1961: Sub-ice Topography of Antarctica, Long. 160° W to 130° E. IUGG Symposium on Antarctic Glaciology, Helsinki, 1960, *Int. Assn Sci. Hydrol. Publ.* **55**.

CRARY, A. P. and ROBINSON, E. S. 1962: Preliminary Results of the McMurdo to Pole Traverse, *Science* **135**: 291–5.

CRARY, A. P., ROBINSON, E. S., BENNETT, H. F., and BOYD, W. W., Jr. 1962: Ross Ice Shelf Studies, *IGY Glaciological Rept* **6**, American Geographical Society, New York.

DEMENITSKAYA, R. M. 1960: Glavnye Cherty Stroeniye Zemnoy Kory v Antarktike, *Inf. Byull. Sov. Ant. Eksp.* **23**: 10–14.

DEN HARTOG, S. L. 1961: Gravity Profiles of the 1958–59 Victoria Land Traverse, Antarctica, M.A. Thesis, Dept. Geol., Montana School of Mines, Butte.

EVISON, F. F., INGHAM, C. E., ORR, R. H. and LE FORT, J. H. 1960: Thickness of the Earth's Crust in Antarctica and the Surrounding Oceans, *Geophys. Journ.* **3**: 289–306.

V. GRUBER, O. 1942: Das Wohlthat-Massiv im Kartenbild; in Ritscher, A., *Wissenschaftliche und Fliegerische Ergebnisse der Deutschen Antarktischen Expedition 1*, Leipzig.

GLEBOVSKIY, YU. S. 1959: Podlednyy Khrebet v. Rayone Stantsii Pionerskoy. *Inf. Byull. Sov. Ant. Eksp.* **7**: 5–9.

GLEBOVSKIY, YU. S. 1959: Podlednyy Khrebet Braun-Gauss, *Inf. Byull. Sov. Ant. Eksp.* **10**: 13–17.

GOODSPEED, M. J. and JESSON, E. E. 1959: Australian Ice Thickness Measurements in Antarctica by Seismic and Gravity Methods 1957–59, *Comm. of Austral. Dept Nat'l Devel., Bur. Min. Res., Geol. & Geophys. Records* **128**.

IMBERT, B. 1953: Sondages Seismiques en Terre Adélie; Rapp. Sci. Exp. Pol. Françaises S.III, 2, *Ann. de Geophys.* **9**: 85–92.

IMBERT, B. 1959: Determination de l'Epaisseur de Glace en Terre Adélie, *C.R. Acad. Sci.* **248**: 576–9.

ISHIDA, T. 1961: Preliminary Report of Seismic Soundings along the Route to the Yamato Mts., *Antarctic Record* **13**: 8–9.

KAPITSA, A. P. 1960: Novye Dannye o Moshchnosti Lednikovogo Pokrova Tsentral'nyts Rayonov Antarktidy, *Inf. Byull. Sov. Ant. Eksp.* **19**: 10–14.

KONDRAT'EV, O. K., LOPATIN, S. S. and MANILOV, S. A. 1960: Metodika i Nekotorye Predvaritelnye Rezul'taty Seysmoglytsiologicheskits Issledovaniy i Antarktide, *Sov. Ant. Eksp., Vtoraya Kont. Eksp.* **10:** 37–95.

KOSACK, H. P. 1951: Eine Neue Karte von Antarktika. *Petermanns Mitt.* **2:** 73–80.

KOVACH, R. L., and PRESS, F. 1961: Surface Wave Dispersion and Crustal Structure in Antarctica and the Surrounding Oceans. *Ann. Geofis.* **14:** 211–24.

LAMB, H. H. 1948: Topography and Weather in the Antarctic. *Geogr. J.* **114:** 48–66.

LAZAREV, C. E. and SHUMSKIY, P. A. 1960: Predvaritel'nye Rezul'taty Gravimetricheskikh Opredeleniy Tolshchy Lednikovogo Pokrova. *Sov. Ant. Eksp. Vtoraya Kont. Eksp.* **10:** 96–100.

LOEWE, F. and LAMB, H. H. 1956: Meteorology and Antarctic Discoveries. *Geogr. J.* **122:** 535–6.

MATHER, K. B. and GOODSPEED, M. J. 1959: Australian Antarctic Ice Thickness Measurements and Sastrugi Observations, MacRobertson Land, 1957–58, *Polar Record* **9:** 436–45.

NEUBERG, H., THIEL, E. C., WALKER, P., BEHRENDT, J. C., and AUGHENBAUGH, N. 1959: The Filchner Ice Shelf, *Ann. Assoc. Amer. Geogr.* **49:** 110–19.

NUDEL'MAN, A. V. 1959: *Sovetskie Expeditsii v Antarktiku 1955–59*, Izdatel'strovo Akadamii Nauk SSSR, Moskva.

POULTER, T. C. 1950: *Geophysical Studies in the Antarctic*, Stanford Res. Inst., Palo Alto, Calif.

PRATT, J. G. D. 1960: A Gravity Traverse of Antarctica, *Trans-Ant. Exp. Sci. Rept* **2:** Trans-Ant. Exp. Committee, London.

PRATT, J. G. D. 1960: Seismic Soundings across Antarctica, *Trans.-Ant. Exp. Sci. Rept* **3,** Trans-Ant. Exp. Committee, London.

ROBIN, G. de Q. 1958: Seismic Shooting and Related Investigations, *Norwegian–British–Swedish Ant. Exp. 1949–52. Sci. Results V, Glaciology III*, Norsk Polarinstitutt, Oslo.

ROUILLON, G. 1960: Anomalies de la Pesanteur et Profil de la Calotte Glaçaire Antarctique en Terre Adélie, *C.R. Acad. Sci.* **251:** 762–4.

SCHMIDT, R. A. 1962: Australites and Antarctica, *Science* **138:** 443–4.

SHARP, R. P. 1956: Objectives of Antarctic Glaciological Research; In 'Antarctica in the International Geophysical Year', *Geophys. Monograph* **1:** 27–35, Amer. Geophys. Un.

SOROKHTIN, O. G., KONDRAT'EV, O. K., and AVSYUK, Yu. N. 1960: Metodika i Osnovnye Resul'taty Seysmicheskikh i Gravimetricheskikh Issledovaniy Stroeniya Vostochnoy Antarktidy, *Izv. Akad. Nauk. SSSR Ser. Geofiz,* 1960: 396–401.

SWITHINBANK, C. 1959: The Morphology of the Inland Ice Sheet and Nunatak Areas of Western Dronning Maud Land, *Norwegian–British–Swedish Ant. Exp. 1949–52. Sci. Results III, Glaciology I D*, Norsk Polarinstitutt, Oslo.

TAYLOR, T. G. 1914: Physiography and Glacial Geology of East Antarctica, *Geogr. J.* **14:** 365–82.

THIEL, E. C. 1961: Antarctica, One Continent or Two? *Polar Record* **10:** 335–48.

THIEL, E. C., BEHRENDT, J. C., BRADLEY, E. A., and TURCOTTE, F. T. 1959: Ice Thickness and Bottom Topography of the Filchner Ice Shelf and along the Ellsworth–Byrd Traverse Route. *Trans. Amer. Geophys. Un.* **40:** 423–6.

VORONOV, P. S. 1959: Geologicheskoe Znachenie Otkrytiya novykh got k Yugu Ot Gornoy Tsepi Printsa Charl'za v. Vostochnoy Antarktide. *Inf. Byull. Sov. Ant. Eksp.* **5:** 15–17.

WEIHAUPT, J. G. 1960: Reconnaissance of a Newly Discovered Area of Mountains in Antarctica, *J. Geol.* **68:** 669–73.

WEIHAUPT, J. G. 1961: Geophysical Studies in Victoria Land, Antarctica, *Univ. Wis. Geophys. & Polar Res. Center, Res. Rept 1.*

WOOLLARD, G. P. 1959: Crustal Structure from Gravity and Seismic Measurements, *J. Geophys. Res.* **64:** 1521–44.

WOOLLARD, G. P. 1962: Crustal Structure in Antarctica. *Geophys. Monogr.* **7:** 53–73, Amer. Geophys. Un.

CHAPTER ELEVEN

Geology of Antarctica

GUYON WARREN, *New Zealand Geological Survey*

Introduction

Since 1956 Antarctica has been subject to such an invasion by geologists that during this period more outcrops on the continent have been examined, more rocks and fossils collected, and more geologists made personally familiar with at least some of the aspects of Antarctic geology, than in the previous 183 years since James Cook first crossed the Antarctic Circle.

Because of the scientific activity of the past few years, largely initiated in co-operation with 1957–8 International Geophysical Year investigations, the state of geological research in Antarctica has improved quite suddenly from near-total ignorance in all but a few areas, to a stage at least as far advanced as the less populated and accessible areas of Asia, Africa, and South America. New plans for continuing and indeed expanding programmes in geology and crustal geophysics have been made by several nations. Thus there is justification for hoping that few if any of the larger mountain ranges in the 14,000,000 km^2 of Antarctica will remain unexamined by 1970, at least at the reconnaissance level, and that a substantial body of information will by then be available on all the more fundamental problems of the structure, stratigraphy and geological history of the continent.

BRIEF HISTORY OF GEOLOGICAL EXPLORATION

Between 1819 and 1843, many vessels on commercial and exploratory expeditions journeyed far into the Southern Ocean, working particularly around the Graham Land peninsula and the islands of the Scotia Arc. But it was not until 1895 that the first landing was made on the mainland of Antarctica, and six years later the major expeditions of Scott and Nordenskjöld pioneered organized scientific exploration of the continent. Their work initiated a period of great activity in which ten substantial scientific expeditions, all including one or more geologists, worked in the Ross Sea area, in Graham Land, and near the South Magnetic Pole. This activity was brought to an abrupt end by the onset in 1914 of World War I, and no further significant geological exploration was carried out until Byrd's 1928–30 expedition mapped a large area in the Queen Maud Range south of his base 'Little America' on the Ross Ice Shelf. In the following years, a British Commonwealth party led by Mawson examined much of the coast south of Australia; Byrd returned to Little America and from there mapped areas in Marie Byrd Land; a British expedition carried out an extensive scientific programme in Graham Land; and sledge parties of the 1939–41 US Antarctic Service mapped further large areas in Graham Land and Marie Byrd Land.

A new phase in the geological exploration of Antarctica began in 1943 with the establishment in Britain of the Falkland Islands Dependencies Survey (now the British Antarctic Survey), the first permanent governmental agency for scientific research in the Antarctic, and FIDS bases in Graham Land have been occupied continuously since then. Soon after World War II, two United States Navy task forces mapped large parts of the coastline of East Antarctica, making geological observations where possible, and in 1950 an official French expedition, the first of a continuing programme, set up its base in Terre Adélie. During that year also, the first international expedition to the continent, the Norwegian–British–Swedish Antarctic Expedition, arrived in Dronning Maud Land, and based at 'Maudheim', a station built on shelf-ice east of the Weddell Sea, successfully carried out a two-year geological and geophysical programme that in essentials provided the blueprint on which many subsequent scientific expeditions of comparable scope were planned.

The most recent and most productive chapter had its beginnings at an international meeting in Rome in October 1954 at which five nations agreed to establish International Geophysical Year bases in Antarctica. This group eventually grew to ten nations who between them had a total of nearly forty scientific stations operating in Antarctica by or before the summer of 1956–7. The majority of these stations have been maintained continuously since then. Although the 1957–8 IGY programme did not include geology as such, research in the related fields of glaciology and crustal geophysics called for extensive field traverses, and geologists travelled with these parties in nearly every instance. Geological field parties also operated independently from most IGY stations, and, as well, from various satellite stations, ships and temporary camps. Since the IGY, geological programmes have in general been accelerated and few areas now remain unexplored.

SURFACE MORPHOLOGY

Including its continental shelf, Antarctica is a roughly circular land mass about 4500 km in diameter, its coastal outline broken by the narrow curving peninsula of Graham Land, and by two deep embayments, the Ross and Weddell Seas. East Antarctica (that part of the continent, chiefly in latitudes east of Greenwich, that lies south and west of the Ross Sea and south and east of the Weddell Sea) is a high ice plateau making up about three-quarters of the total area of Antarctica. Unlike the simple dome-like surface of the Greenland ice sheet, that of East Antarctica is deeply embayed south of the Indian Ocean by the huge Lambert Glacier, whose drainage system extends well over 1000 km inland towards the Weddell Sea. The pattern of ice flow outward is also greatly affected by an immense mountain range, the Trans-Antarctic Mountains, that borders the ice sheet along its Ross Sea–Weddell Sea edge. This range stretches for 2200 km from near Cape Adare in Victoria Land, through the Queen Maud Range to the Horlick and Thiel Mountains, with summit heights of 3000 to 4000 m. The thresholds of the narrow outlet glaciers that flow through this mountain chain are seldom below 2000 m above sea level in the Ross Sea area, and the range as a consequence presents an almost complete barrier to the movement of ice outward from the continental ice sheet along this sector.

Only two other major mountain systems project through the East Antarctic ice cap – that near the Dronning Maud Land coast that stretches intermittently in an arc from near the Weddell Sea coast to the neighbourhood of Lützow-Holmbukta, and the ranges, still largely unexplored, that flank the Lambert Glacier. In most other places, the ice sheet extends to sea level, unbroken except for local nunataks near the coast, but in some localities small areas of low-lying ice-scoured rock are exposed at the coast because of the local characteristics of the ice drainage pattern and the accumulation-ablation balance.

The surface form of the ice sheet is also influenced by the sub-ice morphology to a degree dependent on both the amount of relief in the buried rock surface and the depth of overlying ice. It is also necessarily dependent on the pattern of snow precipitation and later reworking by wind. The interaction of these various factors is discussed in the preceding chapters.

SUBGLACIAL TOPOGRAPHY

The many geophysical traverses carried out during and since the IGY have now delimited the shape of the rock surface beneath the ice cap with considerable detail in West Antarctica, and in broad outline over much of East Antarctica. The subglacial topography is described and illustrated elsewhere in this volume, and it is sufficient here to mention only the features of most geological significance.

1. Much of the central area of West Antarctica is occupied by a deep basin (the Byrd Basin) with depths as much as 2500 m below sea level. Shallow channels connect this basin with the Bellingshausen, Amundsen, and Ross Seas; these are sufficiently deep to remain below sea level after deglaciation of the continent and subsequent isostatic compensation, and would thus isolate the high-standing areas of coastal Marie Byrd Land and Thurston Island as islands.

2. No sub-sea level trough of geologically significant width or depth joins the Ross and Weddell Seas. A deep channel, probably of tectonic origin, has been recognized, however, in several places immediately east of the mountains bordering the western side of the Ross Ice Shelf, and a long and narrow sub-sea level channel runs south-west from the eastern part of the Weddell Sea towards the Ross-Weddell divide, north of the Thiel Mountains. Recent geophysical investigation suggests, however, that the trench on the Weddell Sea side may be of glacial origin, excavated at a time of more intense glaciation by an active north-east flowing ice stream (Behrendt, 1962).

3. The East Antarctic continental mass is typified on a large scale by a simple structure of broad basins and swells. For the most part the rock surface is at an altitude of zero to 2000 m, rising to dome-like elevations of 3000 to 4000 m in the 0° to 90° E quadrant. There are, however, several long shallow depressions (much the largest lying immediately west of, and parallel to, the Ross Sea section of the Trans-Antarctic Mountains) in which the rock surface is slightly below present sea level, but not sufficiently so to remain submerged after isostatic uplift following deglaciation of the continent.

CONTINENTAL SHELF

It has long been known that the continental shelf surrounding Antarctica is in general at a much greater depth (commonly 400 to 500 m) than the 100 to 150 m typical of other continents. That this difference results from the depression of the continental mass by its 2000 m thick ice load was suggested early in the century by Nordenskjöld, and is at first glance the obvious explanation. Gravity information from coastal stations and off-shore islands has confirmed, however, earlier doubts as to the validity of this explanation. It is now established that at least over most of East Antarctica, including coastal localities, there is no significant departure from the theoretical value of gravity (e.g. Ushakov, 1960) whereas large negative Bouger anomalies should be present in coastal areas (of the order 100 km square or more) where the ice load is small or nil, if these areas are in fact part of a depressed slab. It is clear, considering its present, near-equilibrium isostatic state, that most of the central part of the continental mass is depressed by its ice load; it seems to be equally clear, considering *their* equilibrium isostatic state, that the unloaded coastal areas, and presumably their offshore shelves, are not depressed.

Stratigraphy

Since the earliest days of geological investigation in the Antarctic, the two-fold division of the area into 'continental shield' and 'fold mountain' provinces has to a large degree dominated thought on the geology of the continent. Although the differences in geology between Graham Land and Victoria Land, for example, are both real and important, it is easy to over-emphasize this aspect at the expense of reaching an integrated understanding of the geological and paleogeographical history of the continent as a whole. Emphasis of a two-fold division tends also to suggest, unjustifiably, that all regions within the continent may be placed easily in one or other of two master categories of tectonic environment. Such is not the case, nor indeed is there reason to suppose that with increasing knowledge, for which there is ample scope, will a simple two-fold division be found adequate.

With this in view, the stratigraphy of the continent is described first in chronological order of the major rock units, as a basis for later discussion of geological history and structure.

1. Precambrian Complex

INTRODUCTION

Metasediments, migmatites and intrusive rocks known or presumed to be of Precambrian age are widespread throughout Antarctica (Fig. 81), and, so far as they can be considered a stratigraphic unit, form the basement over the entire area within the continental margin. In common with the Precambrian rocks in most other continental shields, the basement complex of Antarctica comprises an almost limitless variety of rock types, and these have been subject to metamorphism of an equally great variation in type, degree and age.

Although the great majority of outcrops that have been examined in East Antarctica are of Precambrian rocks, and plutonic and metamorphic rocks that may

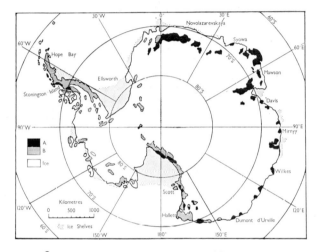

FIG. 81 DISTRIBUTION OF PRECAMBRIAN ROCKS
A. Areas within which Precambrian rocks are known or inferred to occur;
B. Areas in which no Precambrian rocks are known

be Precambrian are known in many West Antarctic localities, the proportion of the continental basement as a whole that is not buried below younger rocks or ice is extremely low – it certainly cannot exceed 1% – and outcrops are small and discontinuous. For these reasons, the production of an integrated geological history of the Precambrian, a slow and difficult task in any continent, is unusually difficult in Antarctica, and far from completion. Indeed, because of the vast areas completely lacking exposed rock, many major uncertainties will always remain.

In East Antarctica, where Precambrian rocks are greatly better exposed and known than elsewhere in the continent, the rocks consist principally of sequences of schist and paragneiss, often of geosynclinal thickness, that have been migmatized to varying degrees, and in which are developed large intrusive bodies of varied composition and usually unknown relationship. In many areas, these crystalline masses were originally developed, or were subsequently metamorphosed, under conditions of high temperature and pressure, forming rocks of granulite facies, and nearby metasediments appear as schists and gneisses of similar metamorphic grade. Subsequent retrogressive metamorphism to rocks of almandine–amphibolite facies has occurred in many places. High-grade amphibolites (chiefly hornblende–plagioclase schists and gneisses) and pyroxene and hornblende granulites occurring in association with these rocks are presumed to be metamorphosed equivalents of ancient basic volcanics or intrusives.

Small areas of relatively unaltered but very ancient sedimentary and plutonic rocks still remain, however, in this predominantly metamorphic Precambrian complex, and the unmetamorphosed state of a rock is not in itself any guarantee of its Paleozoic or younger age.

Outside the East Antarctic shield, very little is known of the detailed stratigraphy of the Precambrian. No radio-isotope determinations giving a Precambrian age are known to the writer from rocks outside the shield, but there is little doubt that this reflects the virtual lack, up to the present, of determinations from these areas rather than the absence from them of Precambrian rocks.

The ever-increasing list of radio-isotope absolute ages from East Antarctica will gradually provide a framework on which the geological history of the complex may be based. At present, however, the great majority of such ages are from K^{40}/A^{40} determinations, and these can only give *minimum* ages for the potassium–mineral formation unless it is known (and few areas in Antarctica would qualify in this respect) that the rock has not subsequently been heated to a temperature greater than about $150°$ C (Kulp, 1961). A similar limitation applies to Rb^{87}/Sr^{87} determinations on biotite. Present information from both stratigraphic and radio-isotope age sources is still insufficient to enable firm conclusions to be reached on the details of Precambrian sedimentary and tectonic history, other than to suggest that orogenic and intrusive phases were frequent and widespread during the last 1000 million years of the Precambrian. No support is given in the available age data for hypotheses suggesting a small number of well-defined, continent-wide cycles of tectonic activity alternating with quiescence; indeed the data, if taken at face value, tend to oppose such a view.

DISTRIBUTION AND PETROGRAPHY

Dronning Maud Land $(5°$ W to $16°$ $E)$

The western parts of these ranges were examined by the Norwegian–British–Swedish expedition of 1949–52 (Roots, 1953). The oldest rocks are chiefly acidic to intermediate banded gneisses, a medium-grained quartz–microcline–sodic plagioclase–biotite rock being typical, but garnetiferous and amphibole-rich gneisses are also widespread. In places there are pods and lenses of partly mobilized gneiss, grading into poorly foliated migmatite. Pegmatites formed by replacement of the gneisses and amphibolites are found in nearly every outcrop.

The central Dronning Maud ranges consist predominantly of schist and gneiss of granulite facies. The great majority have been highly migmatized, but retrograde metamorphism to lower-grade schist, partly a cataclastic effect, has occurred in some places. Ancient basic and ultrabasic rocks are widely developed, evidently having been intruded before metamorphism into the original sediments, and subsequently partially altered to crystalline schists. In many places partial mobilization of the migmatite has resulted in the injection of granite, aplite, and pegmatite veins (Ravich et al., 1961).

In the eastern part of the ranges, similar granulite facies metamorphics predominate, but there is a much wider occurrence of calc-silicate marble and diopside rocks. Migmatization is relatively slight and of local development, but cataclastic deformation is intense and widespread (Ravich, 1959).

Although there is no doubt that the gneissic rocks throughout the area are of Precambrian age, no radio-isotope confirmation of this is yet available, all existing K^{40}/A^{40} age determinations from the area (Ravich and Krylov, 1960) evidently reflecting the widespread effects of the intrusion of a sub-alkaline granitoid complex (p. 294) in the early Paleozoic.

Sör Rondane Mountains (22° to 28° E)

These consist largely of a gneissic complex in which migmatization is widespread. Biotite and amphibole gneisses predominate, together with massifs of dioritic gneiss, and in one area the rock is interspersed with layers of pure crystalline limestone and calc-silicate gneiss (Picciotto, 1960). A series of Rb^{87}/Sr^{87} determinations on biotites from rocks in this complex (Deutsch et al., 1961) all give ages, as in the Dronning Maud ranges, similar to those from early Paleozoic granitic intrusives that crop out in nearby nunataks.

Lützow-Holmbukta area (38° to 40° E)

The metamorphic complex in the area near the Japanese station Syowa consists of hornblende-pyroxene dioritic gneiss comparable with some of the charnockites of the coastal hills of Enderby and Adélie Lands, and widely distributed quartzo-feldspathic gneiss. In this area also, evidence as to the age of formation of the Precambrian rocks has been obliterated, at least in the biotites, by later metamorphism (Nicolaysen et al., 1961).

Enderby Land to Vestfold Hills (45° to 80° E)

The basement complex of Enderby Land and the Mawson area contains rocks ranging from relatively low-grade metasediments (hornfels, quartzite), through a variety of partially mobilized banded or granular paragneisses and orthogneisses. into migmatite, granitic gneiss, and bodies of charnockitic granite (Crohn, 1959). The granitic gneisses contain abundant bands and lenses of ferromagnesian minerals (pyroxenes, garnet, magnetite), and quartz veins and pegmatites are common. This area also experienced an early Paleozoic metamorphic episode contemporaneous with the intrusion of charnockitic granites, but rocks as old as 627 million years[1] have also been reported (Starik *et al.*, 1960).

Further east, in the Vestfold Hills, basic ortho- and clino-pyroxene plagio-clase gneisses and schists predominate, regionally metamorphosed to granulite facies (Ravich, 1960a). Measurements on rocks from this area have given a series of radio-isotope ages that range between 1104 and 1482 million years, and two determinations give a figure of about 1790 million years for an arkosic sandstone (Starik *et al.*, 1959, 1960; Voronov and Krylov, 1961). These latter are, to the writer's knowledge, the greatest ages yet determined from Antarctic rocks.

Wilkes Land (Gaussberg, 89° E, to Rennick Glacier, 162° E)

Six main areas of Precambrian rocks have been investigated in this sector: (1) the area near Mirnyy station (Voronov and Klenova, 1957); (2) the Bunger Hills, and nearby localities (Ravich, 1957; Ravich and Solov'ev, 1957); (3) the Windmill Islands and the Grierson Hills, near Wilkes Station (Robertson, 1959; Ravich, 1960b); (4) isolated coastal outcrops (Henry Bay, Al'bov Rocks, Porpoise Bay) in the sector 120° to 130° E (Klimov and Solov'ev, 1958); (5) Terre Adélie (Stillwell, 1918; Heurtebize, 1952); and (6) outcrops (Wilson Group) on the George V and Oates Coasts (Klimov and Solov'ev, 1958; Klimov, 1960).

The field relationships of the various Precambrian rock units in these areas, combined with radio-isotope age data (Starik *et al.*, 1959, 1960) together suggest that the original rocks were geosynclinal sediments with associated basic lavas and dikes, that have subsequently been regionally metamorphosed to granulite facies plagioclase-pyroxene and hornblende gneiss and amphibolite. They have been partially migmatized in many cases, and the vein material of the migmatites commonly gives radio-isotope ages in the range 940 to 1230 million years, but rocks as old as 1540 million years have been found (Bellair and Delbos, 1962). In the Bunger Hills and Vestfold Hills areas, however, later migmatization, 670 to 780 million years ago, may also be recognizable, and is thought to be contemporaneous with the emplacement at that time of charnockitic norite and diorite (Ravich and Kuno, 1961). In some areas, particularly near Mirnyy Station and in the Bunger Hills, early Paleozoic metamorphism again caused widespread mobilization and injection of granitic material.

Trans-Antarctic Mountains[2]

In the Rennick–Beardmore sector of the Trans-Antarctic Mountains, the oldest rocks, consisting of high-grade gneiss, schist and marble, very probably of Precambrian age, make up a relatively small proportion of the total exposure, and

---

[1] Picciotto and Coppez (1962) have recently reviewed Antarctic radio-isotope dates and have recalculated all to standard decay constants. Wherever possible, the recalculated age given by them is quoted in this chapter.

[2] Problems of stratigraphic nomenclature and correlation in the Trans-Antarctic Mountains have recently been discussed, more fully than is possible here, by Grindley and Warren (1963).

no firm correlation with other Precambrian rocks of East Antarctica is yet possible. It is convenient to defer the description of these rocks until the next section (below), where their relationship to the early Paleozoic Ross Supergroup metasediments, with which they are very commonly associated, is discussed.

South of the Beardmore area, Schetelig (1915) has described high grade gneiss and amphibolite from Mt Betty, at the foot of the Axel Heiberg Glacier, and similar rocks occur in the foothills of the Queen Maud Range at least as far south-east as the Leverett Glacier (Gould, 1935). They are likely to be of Precambrian age.

No undoubtedly Precambrian rocks have been reported from the Horlick or Pensacola Mountains, but a porphyritic hypersthene quartz monzonite in the Thiel Mountains (Ford and Aaron, 1962) in places has charnockitic affinities, with cordierite locally conspicuous. The rock is intruded by biotite granite, but has not been metamorphosed since the Precambrian (Ford *et al.*, 1963). High-grade gneiss and schist in the Shackleton Range on the south-east side of the Filchner Ice Shelf is also likely to be of Precambrian age.

West Antarctica

Mapping has to date revealed few formations in West Antarctica that can confidently be regarded as Precambrian, but the isolation and small area of exposure of many of the outcrops visited make the stratigraphy particularly difficult to determine, and very few radio-isotope age determinations are yet available. Gneisses have been described from various localities in Marie Byrd Land, but they are not closely similar to those of any other area, and their age remains unknown.

A granulitic plagioclase-pyroxene rock, thought to be a mafic charnockite, has recently been found in the Bellingshausen Sea area (Drake, 1962). It is intruded by the immense quartz–diorite batholith that crops out over much of Thurston Island, and may prove to be the correlative of some of the Precambrian granulite facies gneisses of East Antarctica.

In Graham Land, the 'Basement Complex' consists of intensely foliated orthogneiss, paragneiss, schist, and amphibolite, found on the Fallières Coast in the south-west, and as erratics from unknown sources on the east coast (Adie, 1954). Although very likely to be Precambrian, the only direct evidence as to the age of the complex is that it was eroded to a sub-mature relief before the Jurassic, and is greatly more deformed and metamorphosed than rocks of probable early Paleozoic age.

2. Ross Supergroup – Late Precambrian and Cambrian

INTRODUCTION

Thick folded sequences of mildly metamorphosed greywacke, argillite, impure limestone and conglomerate are widely developed in the basement rocks throughout the Ross Sea section of the Trans-Antarctic Mountains and in a number of other localities (Fig. 82). The limestone in several places contains the sponge-like

Cambrian fossil *Archaeocyathus*, or closely allied genera, and it is likely that many or all of the greywacke-limestone sequences throughout the area were laid down as semi-continuous deposits during Cambrian and possibly late Precambrian times. Most of these rocks subsequently underwent mild regional metamorphism, and were steeply folded and in most places locally thermally metamorphosed during the Ross Orogeny (Gunn and Warren, 1962) probably of Ordovician age.

As well as these relatively unmetamorphosed sequences, schist and marble of considerably higher grade are also widespread throughout the Trans-Antarctic

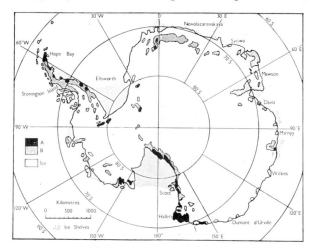

FIG. 82 DISTRIBUTION OF LATE PRECAMBRIAN AND PALEOZOIC
FOLDED METASEDIMENTS

A. Areas within which late Precambrian and Paleozoic metasediments are known or inferred to occur;

B. Areas in which no such rocks are known

Mountains and the name 'Ross System', suggested by Harrington (1958), appears to have been intended to include all these basement sedimentary and metamorphic rocks.

Geological surveys carried out since 1958, now including most areas between the Rennick Glacier in the north and the Queen Maud Range in the south, have made it appear likely that two quite distinct units are present in the basement rocks of the region – (1) an upper greywacke-limestone-conglomerate unit, at least in part of Cambrian age, and in few places more than mildly altered by regional metamorphism, and (2) a lower unit, including rocks of rather similar original lithology, but now of markedly higher metamorphic grade. Nowhere has gradation between the two units been clearly established, and they are likely to be separated by a substantial time interval. Both units have in places undergone early Paleozoic thermal metamorphism.

It is now suggested that this division be recognized by abandoning the name

'Ross System'[1]; by applying the name Ross Supergroup, with local formation names wherever appropriate, to the upper (Cambrian ?) unit; and by using, for the present, local formation names for the high-grade Precambrian metasediments of the lower unit. The establishment of larger stratigraphic groupings in the Precambrian, not only in this area but throughout the continent, must await a better understanding of the regional stratigraphy of these rocks.

DISTRIBUTION AND PETROGRAPHY

Table 6 sets out the principal rock units of the Ross Supergroup in the Trans-Antarctic Mountains, and the relation of these units to older metasediments in the area.

1. Steeply dipping mildly metamorphosed greywacke and argillite (the Robertson Bay Series of Rastall and Priestley, 1921) are exposed along the shores of Robertson Bay, immediately west of Cape Adare, and similar rocks are now known to extend as far as the Rennick Glacier, 300 km to the west (Solov'ev, 1960a). Further west, relatively mildly metamorphosed quartz-biotite and sericite schist and phyllite, marble and calcareous slate crop out in the western sector of the Oates Coast. These relatively mildly metamorphosed rocks, described as the Berg Series by Klimov and Solov'ev (1958), may be slightly older than the Robertson Bay Group which contains fragments identical in lithology to material from the Berg rocks (Solov'ev, 1960a). The Berg Group is provisionally included in the Ross Supergroup.

The greywacke and argillite of the Tucker Glacier area (Moubray Group of Harrington, 1958) are closely similar to the rocks at Robertson Bay, 100 km to the north, and it is likely that investigation of the intervening area will establish continuity between the two localities. If this is so, the name Robertson Bay Group is appropriate for all the low-grade metasediments in the basement of northern Victoria Land, east of the Rennick Glacier.

Rocks described by Smith and Priestley (1921) as graphitic mica schists are common as boulders on the Priestley Glacier moraine in Terra Nova Bay. They have undergone thermal metamorphism, but are much less intensely altered than most metamorphic rocks in the area, and may represent a local equivalent of the Berg Group.

Gneissic granite, biotite paragneiss, marble and various highly metamorphosed impure quartzites ('granulites') also occur in Terra Nova Bay, but most of the available information (Smith and Priestley, 1921) is from erratic material. There is little doubt, however, that these rocks are of Precambrian age.

2. In the McMurdo Sound area, Gunn and Warren (1962) have shown that the oldest metasediments are (a) mildly metamorphosed greywacke and hornfels (Teall Greywacke) and limestone (Anthill Limestone) to the south, and (b) marble with schist and gneiss of high metamorphic grade (Koettlitz Marble) to the north. These rocks were all referred to the Skelton Group.

[1] The use of 'System' in this way conflicts, in any case, with all stratigraphic codes with which the writer is familiar.

TABLE 6

STRATIGRAPHIC UNITS IN THE ROSS SUPERGROUP AND OLDER METASEDIMENTS OF THE ROSS SEA SECTOR OF THE TRANS-ANTARCTIC MOUNTAINS

	Oates Coast and Northern Victoria Land	McMurdo Sound Area	Byrd Glacier– Beardmore Glacier	Beardmore Glacier– Shackleton Glacier
Ross Supergroup [Cambrian and Late Precambrian]	Greywacke, argillite, dolomitic slate (Robertson Bay Group); schist, phyllite, marble (Berg Group).	Greywacke, argillite, hornfels, limestone (Skelton Group) in Skelton Glacier; schist, marble, quartzite (Koettlitz Group) in Koettlitz Glacier (formerly part of 'Koettlitz Marble').	Greywacke, argillite, hornfels (Beardmore Group); conglomerate, quartzite, limestone (Byrd Group).	Greywacke, hornfels, schist, rare limestone (Beardmore Group).

Inferred Regional Unconformity

	Oates Coast and Northern Victoria Land	McMurdo Sound Area	Byrd Glacier– Beardmore Glacier	Beardmore Glacier– Shackleton Glacier
Wilson, Nimrod and unnamed Groups [Precambrian]	Schist, paragneiss (Wilson Group).	Marble, granofels, schist (formerly part of 'Koettlitz Marble').	Scapolite marble, amphibolite schist, quartzite (Nimrod Group).	High grade schist and gneiss (Nimrod Group).

It now seems likely, however, that the Koettlitz Marble may include rocks of widely different ages and metamorphic histories. Besides the schist and lime-stone[1] of the Koettlitz Glacier area, which are very probably correlatives of the (? Cambrian) Teall and Anthillformations a short distance to the south-west, the Koettlitz Marble as originally defined includes, in areas to the north, completely recrystallized marble, coarse-grained biotite schist and granofels, and paragneiss, all of almandine amphibolite facies. Gradation between the lowest and highest grade metasediments has not been established, and it is likely that some at least of the high grade metamorphic rocks had already been folded and appreciably metamorphosed before the deposition of the Koettlitz Glacier sequence. On this basis the name Koettlitz Marble is abandoned. The rocks to which the name was applied are now referred (a) to the Teall Greywacke, Anthill Limestone, or one or more new subdivisions of the Ross Supergroup, whichever course or courses seem appropriate after examination and comparison of the Skelton Glacier and Koettlitz Glacier sequences[2], and (b) to one or more unnamed Pre-cambrian formations, for those rocks that predate the Ross sediments.

Details of the petrography of the Teall Greywacke and Anthill Limestone have been given by Gunn and Warren (1962). The former is a steeply dipping and complexly folded greywacke/argillite sequence, at least 2000 m thick, that has been in part thermally altered to hornblende and biotite hornfels. The Anthill Limestone, of which several masses crop out nearby in the Skelton Glacier area, is closely similar in structure and metamorphic grade, but no contacts between the two have yet been seen. In all places so far investigated, small glaciers flowing into the Skelton separate the two formations, and their relation remains unknown.

The Anthill Limestone consists of at least 3000 m of well-bedded impure limestone, mostly pale grey or greenish in colour, with variable amounts of black or grey calcareous argillite and siltstone. This is in places hornfelsic, and the limestone is for the most part quite coarsely crystalline. No organic remains have been found in either the greywacke or the limestone.

The Ross Supergroup and older metasediments in the McMurdo Sound area are associated in the basement complex with a wide variety of granitic rocks. Three main groupings have been recognized in these, differentiated largely on the basis of degree of deformation (Gunn and Warren, 1962).

(a) Intimately associated with the high-grade metasediments are coarse-grained dioritic and granodioritic rocks with well developed gneissic structure. These rocks are complexly folded and now of almandine amphibolite facies. In some areas, fine-grained margins at the contact with marble or high-grade schist give direct evidence of the intrusive origin of the gneiss, but in the main contacts are obscure, and the relative ages of the various gneissic masses are unknown.

---

[1] The outlines of what may be archaeocyathid fossils have recently been found in lime-stone from this area (Blank et al., 1963).

[2] An apparently conformable sequence including limestone with archeocyathine remains has recently been described by Blank et al. (1963). These rocks have been included as the Koettlitz Group in the Ross Supergroup by Grindley and Warren (1963).

There is little doubt that most are Precambrian, and should be excluded from the Granite Harbour Intrusive Complex (p. 294) to which they were referred by Gunn and Warren (1962), unless it becomes established that the rocks they invade are in fact metamorphosed Ross Supergroup sediments.

(b) Outcrops of a granodioritic batholith, virtually continuous over wide areas, can be correlated petrologically from Terra Nova Bay to the McMurdo Sound area, and all are referred to a single formation, the Larsen Granodiorite. The rock is intruded into, and contains numerous inclusions of, the gneiss, schist and limestone mentioned above, but is itself weakly gneissic in most places. Its age and relation to the Ross Supergroup are not yet certain, but if the Cambrian/ Ordovician radio-isotope age of gneiss from Gneiss Point (Goldich et al., 1958) dates the intrusion of the Larsen Granodiorite, it remains part of the Granite Harbour Intrusives. It is the 'grey biotite granite' of the early writers.

(c) All these rocks are intruded by undeformed granitic masses of a wide range of composition and probably of early Paleozoic age. They are described in the next section (p. 293).

3. Near 81° S, in the area south of the Byrd Glacier, a thick siliceous algal limestone, petrographically identical to archaeocyathine limestone further south, appears to underlie greywacke/argillite and roundstone conglomerate formations each of the order of 1000 m thick (D. N. B. Skinner, personal communication). The entire sequence is overlain unconformably by Beacon sediments, appears to be in fault contact with high-grade (?Precambrian) metasomatized scapolite marble and corrugated schist, and can confidently be correlated with other Ross Supergroup units.

4. Similar sequences have recently been mapped in the Nimrod-Beardmore region by Gunn and Walcott (1962), Laird (1963) and Grindley (1963). Near the Nimrod Glacier, folded thermally metamorphosed greywacke and argillite (Goldie Formation of Gunn and Walcott) is overlain by Cambrian archaeocyathine limestone (Laird and Waterhouse, 1962) and greywacke, limestone and conglomerate of the same or similar lithology and structure have been mapped in many places throughout the Queen Alexandra and Queen Elizabeth Ranges to the Beardmore Glacier. Marble and schist comprising the Miller Formation of Gunn and Walcott were included by them, with the Goldie Formation, as part of the local (Beardmore) group of the Ross 'System'. However, these rocks are of greatly higher metamorphic grade, and unless gradation between the two formations is established, the Miller Formation, like its counterparts to the north, should be excluded from the Ross Supergroup.

The Nimrod Group has recently been proposed by Grindley et al. (1963) to include the Miller Formation and other high-grade Precambrian metamorphic rocks in the Nimrod–Beardmore–Axel Heiberg region.

5. Folded quartzites and argillites, in places hornfelsic, have been reported from the Thiel Mountains, east of the Horlicks (Ford and Aaron, 1962). Possible organic features have been found in the rocks, and correlation with Ross Supergroup sediments elsewhere seems likely.

A thick sequence of steeply dipping greywacke-type metasediments makes up most of the southern group of the Pensacola Mountains (A. B. Ford, personal communication). The rocks compare lithologically with the Thiel metasediments, and may also form part of the Ross Supergroup.

6. Low-grade metasediments older than Beacon Group sandstone have been reported from the Shackleton Range, south-east of the Filchner Ice Shelf (P. J. Stephenson, personal communication). Archaeocyathine limestone, although not yet known in place, has been found as erratic boulders in the Whichaway Nunataks a short distance to the south, and establishes the presence locally of Cambrian rocks.

7. In the western part of the Dronning Maud ranges, east of the Weddell Sea, green and grey slate, quartzite and chloritic phyllite and low-grade schist crop out in three isolated localities (Roots, 1953). The age of these rocks is unknown, and their provisional inclusion in the Ross Supergroup must at present be based merely on their broad lithological similarity to other rocks of the group.

8. On the same basis, thick low-grade metasedimentary sequences in the north-western part of Marie Byrd Land (Wade, 1945; Warner, 1945) have been tentatively correlated with the northern Victoria Land rocks, 1200 km distant across the Ross Sea (Edsel Ford and Rockefeller Groups of Harrington, 1958). Confirmation of this correlation must await more detailed investigation of the stratigraphy and structure in both areas.

9. Relatively low-grade metasediments have been reported from a number of isolated nunataks lying in a line running south-west from the Ellsworth Mountains, and from some parts of the Ellsworth Mountains themselves. Present information is altogether insufficient to make possible a useful opinion as to the age of these rocks, but some at least may eventually prove to be correlatives of the Ross sediments of Victoria Land.

It is appropriate to mention here that late Precambrian or early Cambrian algal and psilophytic spores have been recovered from erratic boulders in the Vestfold Hills (78° E), at Farr Bay (94° E), and near Mt Sandow (100° E) (Korotkevich and Timofeev, 1959). They occur in reddish sediments and in green slates and phyllites, all similar to rocks cropping out in Mt Sandow.

3. Early Paleozoic Granitic Complex

INTRODUCTION

Radio-isotope age determinations so far available from the basement complex show a marked grouping in the 400 to 540 million year range within their total spread of at least 1500 million years. Rocks of this age (principally the late Cambrian and Ordovician of Kulp's 1961 scale) are now known in almost every region for which absolute age measurements have been recorded, and much of the continent clearly experienced a period of major plutonic activity during this time.

The early Paleozoic age determinations come from granitic rocks of a wide range of composition and structure – granite in the strict sense, granodiorite,

diorite, pegmatite, aplite, and granitic gneiss. Besides these, various schists, paragneisses and charnockitic granites have also yielded early Paleozoic radio-isotope ages. Most are closely associated with intrusive granitic masses, and the ages they now give are clearly due to metamorphism contemporaneous with, and locally doubtless accentuated by, the intrusion of granitic material.

A great many intrusive masses have already been described from the complex, and although several related groups may well be present, correlation between the rocks in separate areas at present relies largely on age determinations and broad petrological similarities, with all their inherent uncertainties. Within restricted areas, such as Ainsworth Bay (Klimov, 1960) and the McMurdo Sound district (Gunn and Warren, 1962), study of the detailed petrological and field relationships has made it possible to establish local intrusive sequences and to correlate with some certainty discrete but comagmatic plutons.

The name Granite Harbour Intrusive Complex was proposed by Gunn and Warren (1962) to include all intrusives into Ross Supergroup sediments in the McMurdo Sound district that are older than the formation of the pre-Beacon peneplain. Correlation of rocks from areas such as the Horlick Mountains, where no Ross sediments are known, with this unit may be possible where close petrological similarity to rocks of the Granite Harbour Intrusive Complex can be shown, and where other evidence of broad age equivalence is available.

DISTRIBUTION AND PETROGRAPHY

Western Dronning Maud Land

Although much of the crystalline complex that constitutes the principal unit throughout the region is likely to be of Precambrian age (Ravich, 1959), all radio-isotope ages known to the writer from this area are in the range 375 to 465 million years. In the central sector, a complex of 'subalkaline granitoids' (Ravich et al., 1961), predominantly of granosyenite but including syenite, gabbroic rocks and smaller masses of granite and granodiorite, is intruded into migmatized Precambrian gneiss and schist. The granitoids are largely undeformed, and were presumably emplaced at the time indicated by their radio-isotope age. Further east, a large intrusive body of porphyritic hornblende granite (Ravich, 1959) may be of similar age. Throughout much of the eastern sector, however, no intrusive bodies clearly younger than the main body of ancient gneisses have been described, and the Ordovician radio-isotope ages that have been obtained may merely indicate deep-seated metamorphism and metasomatism on a regional scale at this time.

Sör Rondane Mountains

Twelve Rb^{87}/Sr^{87} ages on biotites from a wide variety of stratigraphic units in the Sör Rondane Mountains all fall within the range 430 to 490 million years (Deutsch et al., 1961), clearly dating the last major metamorphic episode in the area. The youngest rocks known are intrusive bodies of coarse-grained red granite and diorite (Picciotto, 1960), and may have been emplaced at this time.

Lützow-Holmbukta

Nicolaysen *et al.* (1961) and Saito *et al.* (1961) have recorded ages of 470 to 500 million years from pegmatites and a charnockitic gneiss near the Japanese station in Lützow-Holmbukta. No undeformed granitic intrusives have been described.

Mawson Station Area

Near Mawson station, large bodies of partially mobilised and reinjected charnockitic granite, with associated pegmatite and aplite, cut all other basement rocks (Crohn, 1959). Whole-rock K^{40}/A^{40} determinations from the area have given ages of 516 million years for the charnockite and 476 million years for an included schistose xenolith (Starik *et al.*, 1960).

Mirnyy Station to Bunger Hills

Ages between 400 and 470 million years have been obtained from granite, charnockite and schist near Mirnyy Station (Ravich, 1958; Starik *et al.*, 1959, 1961). Further east, in the Bunger Hills and nearby areas, migmatite, gneiss, and pegmatitic granites give ages ranging from 630 million years (late Precambrian) through to 440 million years, possibly suggesting an earlier start to the metamorphism in this area than elsewhere in the continent. A single determination of 318 million years from a granite porphyry on David Island (Starik *et al.*, 1961) compares with similar ages from the Oates Coast (see below).

No granitic material emplaced or mobilized since the Precambrian has yet been recognized along the scattered coastal outcrops between the Bunger Hills and Ainsworth Bay, 2000 km to the east.

George V and Oates Coasts

Between Ainsworth Bay and Cape North, low-grade schist, phyllite, and marble (Berg Group) and weakly migmatized Precambrian biotite gneiss (Wilson Group) are associated with a number of geographically isolated and petrographically distinct granites, some of which are porphyroblastic (Klimov and Solov'ev, 1958; Klimov, 1960). All these rocks give radio-isotope ages of 410 to 515 million years, with the exception of two determinations (313 and 318 million years, Carboniferous on Kulp's 1961 scale) from biotite hornblende granites near the Rennick Glacier (Starik *et al.*, 1959).

Trans-Antarctic Mountains

Little is yet known of the granitic rocks of Victoria Land north of the Mawson Glacier. Granodiorite bosses intrude the Robertson Bay Group (? Cambrian) in the Tucker Glacier area (Harrington, 1958), and intrusive granitic masses of several generations, with associated pegmatitic and aplitic dikes and veins, were found during brief surveys in Terra Nova Bay (Smith, 1924).

The McMurdo Sound granites are now known in more detail, and radio-isotope age determinations (Goldich, Nier and Washburn, 1958; Angino, Turner and Zeller, 1962) have confirmed that the last major episode of metamorphism and granite emplacement in the area took place during the early Paleozoic.

A wide variety of undeformed 'granites' intrude all the older basement rocks, including the weakly gneissic Larsen Granodiorite described earlier (p. 292). Most widely distributed, but found chiefly as isolated plutons 25 km or less in length, is the Irizar Granite (Gunn and Warren, 1962). This is the 'pink granite' of the early reports, and is characterized in the field by its coarse pink or red potash feldspars. Hornblende is always present in small amount.

Two granodiorite batholiths of rather variable composition crop out in the Mawson and Skelton Glaciers, and a number of small intrusive bodies of undeformed hornblende diorite have been mapped.

Most of these intrusions are geographically isolated, and their relationship is still largely unknown. All, however, predate the Kukri Peneplain, which was developed in this area not later than the lower Devonian (and is probably older); many or all are younger than the Ross Supergroup (? Cambrian) metasediments. Emplacement during or near the Ordovician is therefore indicated on stratigraphic grounds, in agreement with the radio-isotope age data.

Microgranitic and microdioritic dikes are widespread. Some are plainly related to nearby plutonic bodies, but others, particularly some of the more basic lamprophyres, may be early differentiation or contamination products of the much younger dolerite intrusions.

Undeformed granites intruding Ross sediments have also been reported from the ranges to the south. Porphyritic microcline biotite granite plutons and small stocks of gabbro invade greywacke and archaeocyathine limestone north of the Nimrod Glacier (Laird, 1963); and in the country south of the Nimrod, Gunn and Walcott (1962) have recorded a number of biotite–muscovite–microcline granite plutons, thought to derive from a single batholith (Hope Granite). Closely similar granite also intrudes greywacke and phyllite in the Queen Alexandra Range, north-west of the Beardmore Glacier (Grindley, 1963).

Granite at Mt Betty, near the mouth of the Axel Heiberg Glacier in the Queen Maud Range (Schetelig, 1915) is petrographically and chemically similar to the Hope Granite.

Little is known of the granitic intrusives in the southern parts of the Queen Maud Range, but further east, in the Horlick Mountains, Long (1959) has shown that a porphyritic biotite granodiorite underlies the Beacon Group sediments. A similar rock also crops out in a small nunatak to the north-east, between the Thiel and Ellsworth Mountains, south-west of the Filchner Ice Shelf (Treves, 1959).

In the Thiel Mountains themselves two biotite granite bodies, one of them porphyritic, intrude the predominant quartz monzonite porphyry and in places produce contact effects in (? Ross Supergroup) argillites (Ford and Aaron, 1962).

Marie Byrd Land

A large stock-like body of granodiorite intrudes metasediments, possibly of early

Paleozoic age, in the Edsel Ford Ranges, east of Sulzberger Bay (Warner, 1945), and can be compared with a structurally and petrographically similar alkaline granite batholith intruding schist and phyllite in the Rockefeller Mountains to the west (Wade, 1945).

Thurston Island

The predominant rock throughout the island is a quartz diorite of batholithic proportions (Drake, 1962). Its age is not known, but it intrudes, and contains inclusions of, high-grade metamorphic rocks, and is overlain by young basalts.

Graham Land

Coarse-grained white and pink granites intrude the 'Basement Complex' in several localities in south-west Graham Land, and have been tentatively referred to the early Paleozoic (Adie, 1954). They are also found as erratics on the eastern coast, and may once have been of considerable extent.

Isolated outcrops of sheared tuffaceous andesitic flows, breccias and agglomerates, together with apparently unrelated propylitized andesitic lavas, are also assigned to the early Paleozoic, xenoliths of similar composition having been found in the pink granite mentioned above.

4. Paleozoic and Mesozoic Continental Sediments – Beacon Group

INTRODUCTION

Flat-lying continental or near-shore sediments unconformably overlie metamorphic and igneous rocks of early Paleozoic or Precambrian age throughout the Trans-Antarctic Mountains and in other localities in East Antarctica. All show similarities of lithology and structure, and together form a stratigraphic unit of the greatest significance in the elucidation of the geological history and paleogeography of the continent.

NOMENCLATURE AND DEFINITION

Horizontal sedimentary rocks were first examined in place by Ferrar in the McMurdo Sound district in 1903, and he gave them the name Beacon Sandstone Formation (1907). The word Beacon had subsequently been applied in a variety of ways to lithologically and structurally similar sequences throughout the Trans-Antarctic Mountains, and the formal name Beacon System was suggested by Harrington (1958). Later writers (e.g. Gunn and Walcott, 1962; Allen, 1962; Gunn and Warren, 1962; Grindley, 1963) have all preferred the usage Beacon Group, however, and its use is extended here to include all similar sequences in East Antarctica.

The base of the Beacon Group is defined by an erosional surface of great extent, called the Kukri Peneplain (Gunn and Warren, 1962) in the Trans-Antarctic Mountains, that is cut on deformed metamorphic and plutonic rocks and their intrusives. Throughout the area between the Horlick Mountains and the Mawson Glacier, the time of formation of the peneplain can be fixed within rather narrow limits in that the surface is cut across granitic rocks almost certainly of Ordovician age, and is overlain by sediments not younger than Devonian. In northern Victoria Land, however, where Beacon rocks are thin or absent and as yet undated, the upper age limit is fixed only by the presence of overlying lavas of probable Jurassic age.

The upper limit to the Beacon Group or its correlatives cannot yet be easily defined. The youngest rocks actually examined by Ferrar in 1903 were probably *Glossopteris*-bearing (Permian) sandstones near the head of the Taylor Glacier, but no reason exists for excluding from the Beacon Group the conformable and lithologically similar Triassic rocks in the same area. Horizontal continental sediments contain Jurassic fossils to the north, and sediments of typical Beacon lithology are interbedded with Jurassic lavas in the area west of Wood Bay (H. S. Gair, personal communication). West of McMurdo Sound, lavas of the same formation are interbedded with glacial sediments. No younger rocks are known in these areas apart from late Tertiary or Quaternary volcanics.

On this basis, all known pre-Cretaceous sedimentary rocks above the Kukri Peneplain, excluding those predominantly of volcanic origin, or lenses within lavas, are here included in the Beacon Group; the question of the future inclusion of other rocks that may be discovered must be decided by consideration of their structural and lithological relationship to known Beacon sequences.

DISTRIBUTION

Rocks of the Beacon Group are now known in all areas of the Trans-Antarctic Mountains with the exception of the Admiralty Mountains in northern Victoria Land, the Thiel Mountains, and the northern parts of the Pensacola Mountains. They have also been recorded in western Dronning Maud Land, in hills flanking the Lambert Glacier (68° E), and in nunataks on the George V Coast. This distribution (Fig. 83) suggests that continental and estuarine sediments of the Beacon Group may once have formed a semi-continuous fringe near the margin of the East Antarctic continental mass, surrounding central eroding source areas.

No Beacon rocks are known outside East Antarctica, but on geophysical evidence they may underlie the veneer of predominantly glacial sediments beneath the Ross Sea and Ross Ice Shelf (Crary, 1961).

LITHOLOGY

Well stratified pale yellow or buff sandstone is the predominant lithology in most Beacon Group sequences. In the McMurdo Sound area quartz arenite is typical, with lesser amounts of impure feldspathic sandstone, but elsewhere silty arkosic sandstone predominates. Cross-bedding is very common.

Siltstone is present in all sections as thin and impersistent bands within sandstone, and commonly also as formations of wide extent and considerable thickness. In most sections there is an upward increase in the proportion of siltstone. Most of the siltstones and many of the sandstones contain carbonaceous material;

seams of coal, usually with a high ash content, are present in most areas, and in some sections total 10 m or more.

Conglomerates, pebbly bands, grits, and thin limestones or calcareous sandstones occur as minor constituents in many areas.

Sediments of glacial origin have been recognized in several localities, at least two glacial epochs of widely different age being represented.

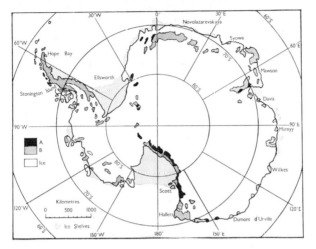

FIG. 83 DISTRIBUTION OF BEACON GROUP

A. Areas within which Beacon Group sediments are known or inferred to occur;

B. Areas in which no Beacon Group rocks are known

THICKNESS

The greatest thickness of Beacon Group sediments now exposed in any continuous section probably does not exceed 1500 m, but in many localities it may once have been of the order of twice this amount. According to Schopf (1962), the rank of Permian coals in the Horlick–Beardmore area suggests that it was developed under a static load greater than 7300 m; no support for a figure approaching this order of thickness is found in the available stratigraphic evidence.

SEQUENCE AND AGE

Beacon successions have been described in detail only from the McMurdo Sound district (particularly by Allen (1962), Gunn and Warren (1962), and Webb (1963)), the Queen Alexandra Range (Grindley, 1963), and the Horlick Mountains (Long, 1962); representative columns of these and several other localities have been given by Grindley.

Marked changes laterally in both facies and thickness are common in predominantly continental deposits, and are certainly so in the Beacon rocks. Correlation is further complicated by the presence of local unconformities (particularly those below the glacial beds) and disconformities. Relatively few disconformities have been recognized in the field (by leached surfaces, for example), but the existence of many others must be inferred from paleontologic and stratigraphic evidence.

In a highly generalized form, the sequence in the Beacon Group is as follows:

1. The basal beds, directly overlying the peneplaned surface of the igneous and metamorphic rocks of the basement complex, are of widely variable age and lithology. Their total age range varies from almost certainly pre-Devonian in parts of the McMurdo Sound district to very probably Mesozoic on the George V Coast. Lithologically, the lowest beds in the Horlick Mountains are fossiliferous shallow-water marine sandstone and siltstone; elsewhere the lowest sediments are unfossiliferous, and range from coarse breccia and roundstone conglomerate to pebbly quartz arenite, grit, or alternating arkose/siltstone sequences.

2. Throughout the 900 km of the Trans-Antarctic Mountains between the Mawson and Beardmore glaciers, the thin basal beds are succeeded by a thick, uniform, pale yellow quartz (or less commonly arkosic) arenite. In the north, this is in places at least 1000 m thick, and contains in the upper part one or more bands of reddish or greenish siltstone with a Middle or Upper Devonian freshwater fish fauna (Woodward, 1921; Gunn and Warren, 1962) and a sparse Lower or Middle Devonian flora (Plumstead, 1962). Structures believed to be of organic (possibly marine) origin are common throughout the lower beds (Vialov, 1962), but none are diagnostic as to age. If, as seems likely, a slow rate of accumulation can be assumed, it is probable that the arenite ranges down into the Silurian.

In the Horlick Mountains, up to 50 m of marine Lower Devonian sediments rest on basement rocks, and are themselves overlain with parallel unconformity by glacial beds.

3. In the Queen Alexandra Range, arenite is succeeded by about 300 m of fluvioglacial and glacial sandstone, shale and tillite, grading upwards into dark carbonaceous shale, and similar rocks, about 400 m thick, have been described from the Horlick Mountains. In both areas, the glacial beds and shales are unfossiliferous but underlie sandstones containing *Glossopteris*, and on analogy with similar sequences in other southern continents, a Carboniferous age has been suggested (Long, 1962; Grindley, 1963).

Glacial sediments are quite unknown beneath *Glossopteris*-bearing sandstones in any other Beacon sequence; whether this absence is due to facies differences, to a temporary hiatus in deposition, or to subsequent erosion of glacial sediments, remains a matter of conjecture.

4. Conformably overlying the dark shales in the two areas mentioned above are beds of arkosic sandstone and siltstone containing, at several levels, plant remains of the distinctive *Glossopteris* flora. Beds predominantly of the same lithology and containing *Glossopteris* are now known from the Theron Mountains (29° W; Plumstead, 1962); the Horlick Mountains (Schopf, 1962); Mt Weaver, Queen Maud Mountains (Darrah, 1941); in several places between the

Beardmore and Nimrod Glaciers (Grindley, 1963; Gunn and Walcott, 1962); and various localities in the McMurdo Sound district (Gunn and Warren, 1962; Plumstead, 1962). The paleobotanical evidence is not sufficient to indicate a precise time equivalence for these various collections, but ages close to Lower Permian are likely.

Carbonaceous arkosic grit and sandstone crop out at the Amery locality (Lambert Glacier, 68° E), and contain coal with a rich Permian pollen and spore flora (Crohn, 1959). About 50 m of sediment are exposed, but a total thickness of at least 300 m is likely.

In the upper Beardmore district, the formation containing *Glossopteris* is about 700 m thick, although determinable plant material is present in a few horizons only (Grindley, 1963). No equivalent thickness has been measured in other localities.

5. Carbonaceous arkosic sandstones and siltstones containing leaves of Triassic age occur in the area south-east of the upper Beardmore Glacier (Grindley, 1963), and on and near Mt Fleming on the north side of the upper Taylor Glacier in the McMurdo Sound district (Gunn and Warren, 1962; Plumstead, 1962). Pollens and spores of Upper Permian or more probably Triassic age have been identified in the Beacon sequence from Horn Bluff, George V Coast (Solov'ev, 1960b). At Carapace Nunatak, 80 km to the north of Mt Fleming, a Jurassic flora with associated conchostracans, ostracods and spores occurs in micaceous sandstones, siltstones and associated chemical sediments. In all these localities, the exposures of Beacon sediments are relatively thin, and nowhere have *Glossopteris* and younger fossils yet been found in a continuous sequence.

6. At Allan Nunatak, on the western edge of the Victoria Land mountains west of McMurdo Sound, tough yellow-brown tillite (Mawson Tillite), at least 500 m thick, overlies the channelled and ice-disturbed surface of *Glossopteris*-bearing sandstone and quartz arenite (Gunn and Warren, 1962). Near the base the coarse material consists almost entirely of lumps of the underlying Beacon and basement rocks, but in the higher levels dense black basalt pebbles and boulders predominate. The basalt is without doubt the effusive equivalent of the Jurassic Ferrar Dolerite sills (Gunn and Warren, 1962), and at Carapace Nunatak, 15 km to the south, basalt flows, in places with pillow structure, are interbedded with tillite. The contact between tillite and the nearby fossiliferous Jurassic sediments is not exposed, but the latter are horizontal and at a slightly lower altitude.

Small areas of glacial sediments also crop out in localities to the north and south of those mentioned, extending over a total distance of 100 km.

A number of relatively large areas of Beacon rocks, particularly those in western Dronning Maud Land, and a host of isolated outcrops in all areas, have yet to have diagnostic fossils recognized in them. In most cases, no other reliable means of determining stratigraphic position within the group is yet available, and it is not possible to relate these rocks to the generalized sequence described above.

PALEONTOLOGY

Detailed descriptions of the fossil collections from a number of horizons and localities in the Beacon Group are now available, but much remains to be done, and work to this end is known to be in progress in many places. Because of this, and because of the inherent difficulty of presenting useful summaries of paleontological data, it is thought appropriate here merely to list the more important papers on Beacon Group paleontology, and to refer the interested reader directly to these.

Animal Fossils

Devonian freshwater fish remains from the McMurdo Sound district are fully described by Woodward (1921). Brief determinations of new material are given in Gunn and Warren (1962).

No description of the Devonian marine fauna from the Horlick Mountains has yet been published, but an outline of the types of fossils present is given by Doumani and Long (1962).

Various obscure trails and borings from Beacon rocks, probably of pre-Permian age, have been described by Vialov (1962).

Conchostraca and ostracods from the Jurassic horizon at Carapace Nunatak, upper Mackay Glacier, are being studied in England.

Plant Fossils

Seward (1914) published the first comprehensive description of the various plant collections made by the early British expeditions. Discussion of his results, with particular reference to his identification of a gymnospermous wood and a pollen grain, is found in papers by Walton (1923), Edwards (1928), Seward (1933) and Cranwell (1959).

Darrah (1936) briefly described a supposed Jurassic flora from the Queen Maud Mountains, but later (1941) redescribed and illustrated the collection, showing it to be considerably older.

Permian spore and pollen determinations from the Lambert Glacier area are listed in Crohn (1959).

Fossiliferous rocks were collected in 1957–8 in a number of Beacon localities near McMurdo Sound, and in the Theron Mountains and Whichaway Nunataks, by geologists of the Trans-Antarctic Expedition. Plumstead (1962) has given a comprehensive account of the fossil floras in these collections.

Schopf (1962) has described in detail the microflora, wood, leaves and seeds found in the *Glossopteris*-bearing sediments of the Horlick Mountains.

ORIGIN AND DEPOSITIONAL ENVIRONMENT

The principal source rocks from which most of the Beacon sediments derive are undoubtedly the Precambrian and early Paleozoic granites and gneisses of the basement complex of East Antarctica. There is little evidence, however, as to the location of these eroding source areas within the continent, although as a first approximation one may assume that the more highly feldspathic sediments were deposited closer to their source than were their low-feldspar equivalents.

Marine fossils occur at the base of the section in the Horlick Mountains (Long, 1962) and fossil 'problematica' that may be of marine origin have been described by Vialov (1962) from arenites in the McMurdo Sound region. The majority of the Beacon Group sediments are continental deposits, however, as evidenced by the wide development of fluviatile and aeolian cross-bedding, by the presence of coal and highly micaceous sandstones at many horizons, of mudcracks (Allen, 1962) and freshwater faunas (fish, conchostracans), and, in particular by the absence of marine fossils throughout great thicknesses and over wide areas. The typical depositional environment seems to have been a wide fringing plain of dunes, lakes and estuaries; the higher proportion of fine material in the younger rocks may be due in part to the establishment of a substantial flora in the late Paleozoic, and a consequent reduction in the effectiveness of silt-removing processes.

Glacial conditions in the late Paleozoic, and again in the Jurassic, resulted in the formation locally of lodgement tills and fluvioglacial deposits. These are known at present only in the Trans-Antarctic Mountains, between the Horlick Mountains and McMurdo Sound.

STRUCTURE

Bedding in the Beacon Group is everywhere close to horizontal, and dips as great as 10° are unknown except where an intrusive dolerite wedge has caused local tilting. In general, however, the dolerite sills, although having abrupt discontinuities at vertical joints, are of remarkably constant thickness between these joints. The vertical dislocation consequent on sill intrusion, although very common, thus leaves the beds above and below essentially parallel.

There is no evidence for the 'domical' structure suggested by Hamilton (1960) for the Beacon rocks in the McMurdo Sound area, where dips of 5° or less to the south or west prevail except for small areas of dolerite-induced tilting; nor has any evidence of broad anticlinal structure been described from any other part of the Trans-Antarctic Mountains.

Block faulting of uncertain age (certainly post-Jurassic, probably late Tertiary or Quaternary) has played a major role in determining the present altitude and attitude of the larger structural units in the Trans-Antarctic and Dronning Maud Mountains, but in many places it is difficult to distinguish between these dislocations and those accompanying the earlier intrusive episodes.

5. Paleozoic Geosynclinal Sediments – Trinity Peninsula Group

Metasedimentary sequences dominated by altered greywacke and dark grey siltstone crop out in a number of localities in Graham Land, and constitute the Trinity Peninsula 'Series' of Adie (1957). No diagnostic fossils are yet known, but worm casts and tracks and doubtful fish scales have been recorded from the type rocks at Hope Bay, and carbonaceous material is common throughout. Such determinable plant material as is available suggests a late Paleozoic age; correlation of the group with lithologically similar sequences in South Georgia and the South Orkneys has been suggested, and if this proves correct, a Carboniferous age appears most likely (Adie, 1957).

The rocks are best known in the Trinity Peninsula – Tabarin Peninsula area at the northern tip of Graham Land, where they make up the majority of the exposed rocks. Outcrops also occur in many places along the east coast of Graham Land for 1500 km to the south, and rocks that may form part of the group are known in scattered localities on the west coast. Although greywacke and argillaceous sediments predominate, conglomerate, arkose, quartzite, and rare impure limestone are also present in the total thickness of more than 600 m. The rocks were severely contorted and sheared by pre-Jurassic cataclastic metamorphism, and were subsequently thermally metamorphosed to widely varying degrees in the thermal aureoles of Andean intrusive bodies of early Tertiary age.

A preliminary account of the geology of the Ellsworth Mountains 700 km to the south-west of southern Graham Land has recently been given by Anderson *et al.* (1962). The rocks consist of a thick sequence of slightly metamorphosed clastic sediments in which quartzite, argillite and conglomerate predominate. They are of unknown age, but may be partially equivalent to the rocks of the Trinity Peninsula Group.

6. Jurassic Basic Igneous Rocks – Ferrar Group

Thick horizontal sills of dolerite, their dark colour in striking contrast to the pale Beacon sediments in which they are commonly emplaced, are prominent features of almost all the higher ranges throughout the length of the Trans-Antarctic Mountains. The sills and their associated dikes have been examined and described since the earliest expeditions; only during the last few years has it been discovered that thick sequences of their extrusive equivalents are also present in several areas.

NOMENCLATURE

The name Ferrar Dolerite is well established for the intrusive rocks, which, at the time of the name's proposal (Harrington, 1958), were the only rocks known to have been developed during this magmatic episode. Grindley (1963) proposed the name Kirkpatrick Basalt for the thick extrusives recently found in the Queen Alexandra Range, and it is here adopted for all lavas and pyroclastic rocks associated with Ferrar Dolerite.

Clastic sediments continued to accumulate for some time after the first extrusion of lava, and in places there is interfingering of basalt with Beacon Group sediments. Lenses of sediment enclosed within lava, and sediments consisting predominantly of tuffaceous and pyroclastic material genetically related to the lavas, can conveniently be included, however, with the Kirkpatrick Basalt.

These two formations, the Ferrar Dolerite and the Kirkpatrick Basalt, together constitute the Ferrar Group.

DISTRIBUTION

In the Trans-Antarctic Mountains, sills and dikes of Ferrar Dolerite are found wherever Beacon Group sediments are present, and also as sheets in or on the basement rocks in many of the surrounding areas from which Beacon rocks are now absent.

The sills occur as horizontal sheets of great extent and up to 450 m thickness. The basement-Beacon contact (Kukri Peneplain) has been invaded in almost all areas, and one or uncommonly two subhorizontal sheets have in most places been injected, transgressive to the structure, within the basement rocks. Above the peneplain sill, Beacon Group sediments and sills of Ferrar Dolerite are commonly of the same order of total thickness.

Basaltic and doleritic dikes up to a few metres wide are numerous, but are seldom continuous over long distances, especially within the Beacon Group. Bosses, laccoliths, and wide, dike-like masses have been described by Gunn and Warren (1962) from the McMurdo Sound area, and by Grindley (1963) from the Queen Alexandra Range.

Lavas, tuffs and pyroclastics, closely related on stratigraphic and petrologic evidence to the dolerite, are now known in several parts of the Trans-Antarctic Mountains. These volcanic sequences, which consist predominantly of a succession of lava sheets, are at least 1500 m thick in the inland mountains west of Terra Nova Bay (H. S. Gair and J. F. Ricker, personal communication) and at least 1200 m thick in the upper Beardmore Glacier region (Grindley, 1963; V. R. McGregor, personal communication), but only thin sequences, including silty sandstone and tuffaceous sediments, remain in the McMurdo Sound region (Gunn and Warren, 1962).

In the northern Pensacola Mountains, bordering the Filchner Ice Shelf, the Dufek Massif consists of a horizontally banded basic lopolith about 40 km long. Although mentioned here with the basic intrusives of the Ferrar Group, there is no substantial evidence as to its age, and it may well have been emplaced in the Precambrian. The possibility that it is younger is suggested primarily by its gently tilted but apparently unfolded structure, unlike any pre-Ordovician rocks yet described from the Trans-Antarctic Mountains, and by the absence of any basic rocks other than thin dikes elsewhere in the Precambrian complex of East Antarctica. On the other hand, pegmatitic and felsitic dikes cutting the basic mass, though possibly emplaced as late-stage differentiates soon after the intrusion of the main body, may represent the local equivalents of the early Paleozoic granitic intrusives that occur throughout East Antarctica; if such is the case, the Dufek igneous mass is plainly of early Paleozoic or greater age.

A description of the mass has been given by Aughenbaugh (1958), and a preliminary account of its petrography and mineralogy by Walker (1958). Many similarities are evident to the banded Bushveld lopolith, Transvaal, and particularly to the Stillwater complex of Montana.

In western Dronning Maud Land, basic sills and dikes intrude flat-lying

L

Beacon-type sedimentary rocks; in one area of isolated nunataks, intermediate to basic flows overlie and are in part interbedded with rocks believed to be part of the same sedimentary assemblage (Roots, 1953). Little detailed information is yet available, but some at least of these basic igneous rocks are likely to be the local equivalents of the Ferrar Group.

Basic dikes intrude the Precambrian basement in many of the coastal areas of the remainder of East Antarctica, but in the absence of radio-isotope age determinations indicating an age equivalence to the Ferrar Group, no firm basis for their correlation with rocks of the Trans-Antarctic Mountains is available. In the Lambert Glacier area, however, dolerite dikes, the youngest intrusives, show particularly close petrological similarities to the Ferrar Dolerite. Unfortunately no contact with the Permian Beacon rocks in the area has been seen, but correlation with the Victoria Land dolerites is supported by Crohn (1959).

PETROGRAPHY

Detailed petrographic descriptions of the Ferrar Dolerite have been given by many authors, of whom may be mentioned Benson (1916), Mawson (1916) and Browne (1923), and more recently Solov'ev (1960b), Gunn and Warren (1962) and Gunn (1962).

The sills were emplaced from tholeiitic basaltic magmas, evidently of rather uniform bulk composition. Early (possibly in part pre-intrusive) differentiation by crystallization and gravitational settling of orthopyroxene has resulted in the development of rocks of widely variable mineralogy and chemistry, ranging from cumulates with as much as 70% hypersthene to granophyres and pegmatoid rocks containing up to 30% quartz and few mafic minerals.

Between these extremes, the 'normal' dolerite approximates to 40% pyroxene (augite, pigeonite, hypersthene), 45% plagioclase (typically An_{60-75}, but widely variable), and 12% quartz-feldspar micropegmatite, with biotite, hornblende and iron ores as accessories.

Gunn and Warren (1962) briefly described the thin flows and tuffaceous rocks within and above tillite in the inland nunataks west of McMurdo Sound, where many of the lavas exhibit well-developed pillow structure. Little has yet been published on the detailed petrography of any of the thick sections of extrusive rocks. A preliminary account by Grindley (1963) shows that the thicker flows are typically rather coarse-grained and strongly differentiated, although the late-stage felsic differentiates that are common in the dolerite seem to be absent. In general the upper margins of the flows are vesicular, and quartz, calcite, and particularly zeolite amygdales and geodes are very common, as near McMurdo Sound.

The basalts of the Ferrar Group, like the dolerites, show wide variability in their chemistry, but all rocks of the group form part of a single differentiation series parallel to, but distinct from, the tholeiitic flood basalts and basic intrusives of other southern continents (Gunn, 1962). Their chemistry is quite unlike that of the much younger olivine- and alkali-rich McMurdo Volcanics.

The sedimentary bands and lenses within the Ferrar Group are poorly known. Near McMurdo Sound they consist of thin zeolitized tuffaceous sandstones and siltstones; bands principally of quartz sandstone, without obvious tuffaceous or volcanic material, predominate in the upper Rennick Glacier to the north, and should probably be included in the Beacon Group. No petrographic details are known of the sediments associated with the Kirkpatrick Basalt in its type area.

AGE

West of McMurdo Sound, Ferrar Group basalt conformably overlies Beacon Group sediments containing lower Jurassic plants and freshwater crustaceans (Gunn and Warren, 1962). In one locality recently examined, a flow also under-lies, apparently with a sedimentary contact, what is likely to be the same fossili-ferous horizon (D. N. B. Skinner, personal communication). This stratigraphic evidence suggesting an age close to early Jurassic for at least part of the volcanism in the McMurdo Sound area is complemented by absolute age determinations of 191, 175 and 169 million years for dolerites from localities on the Oates Coast (Starik et al., 1959; Starik et al., 1961), and 162 million years from a dolerite sill in Victoria Valley, McMurdo Sound area (Evernden and Richards, 1962). These all fall within the range late Triassic to mid-Jurassic on Kulp's (1961) scale.

The inception of volcanism in the McMurdo Sound area is also recorded in the Mawson Tillite (Beacon Group; see above), which is devoid of volcanic rocks at the base, but contains abundant Ferrar Group basalt pebbles in the higher levels.

No direct evidence for the age of the youngest rocks developed during this period of volcanism is available, but it is assumed that the duration of the period was relatively short, and it is highly unlikely that any of the Ferrar rocks are as young as Cretaceous (i.e. less than 135 million years on Kulp's (1961) scale).

7. Late Mesozoic Rocks

In East Antarctica, no rocks younger than the early Jurassic Beacon sediments and the Ferrar Group volcanics that are partly interbedded with them, yet older than the late Tertiary or Quaternary volcanics, are known in place, al-though pebbles of late Cretaceous or Tertiary mudstone have been found in moraines near McMurdo Sound (Cranwell et al., 1960). In Graham Land, however, post-Triassic rocks predominate, and the late Mesozoic members of the succession may be conveniently described together. Unfortunately, although much has been published on the paleontology of these rocks, nothing is yet available giving an integrated account of their distribution, lithology or structure.

Freshwater or marine sediments of Jurassic age overlie the eroded surface of the Trinity Peninsula Group, or the igneous and metamorphic rocks of the Basement Complex, in several places. In the north, dark lacustrine shale and mudstone contain an abundant middle Jurassic flora (Hallé, 1913), together with freshwater gastropods, fish and beetles (Adie, 1962). In the south-west, on Alexander Island and the mainland to the east, a marine sequence including limestone, grit and shale contains transported remains of Jurassic plants, and a rich late Jurassic marine fauna with molluscs, brachiopods, annelids (Cox, 1953) and ammonites (Howarth, 1958). This sequence continues without significant interruption into the early Cretaceous, although the ammonites appear to be confined to two well-marked horizons, Lower Kimeridgian (Upper Jurassic), and Aptian (Lower Cretaceous).

While Jurassic and early Cretaceous sedimentation continued in the south, volcanic activity had begun in the northern parts of Graham Land with the eruption of andesitic and rhyolitic flows, agglomerates and tuffs. In the north, these overlie the Jurassic plant beds of Hope Bay; in north-west Graham Land and near Marguerite Bay they rest directly on the eroded Paleozoic rocks; and on Alexander Island the volcanism is recorded by the incoming of tuffaceous material in the marine sediments.

No middle Cretaceous rocks are known in Graham Land, but richly fossiliferous late Cretaceous marine sequences of sandstone, greensand and minor conglomerate crop out on Snow Hill, Seymour and James Ross Islands near the north end of the Graham Land peninsula. The paleontology of these rocks has been described in some detail, particularly by Wilckens (1910), Spath (1953), Howarth (1958) and Ball (1960), and indicates a Campanian age.

8. Andean Intrusive Suite (Late Cretaceous)

Intrusive bodies of variable but related composition constitute the most widespread and structurally the most important rock unit of Graham Land. These rocks, ranging from basic gabbro to alkali granite, were emplaced probably in late Cretaceous or early Tertiary times as batholiths and boss-like intrusive masses, and have been fully described by Adie (1955). It will be sufficient here to outline their major characteristics.

DISTRIBUTION

The intrusives occur throughout Graham Land, but are of unknown extent to the south. It is possible that some of the granitic intrusives of the Eights Coast region and the alkaline granite and granodiorite of Marie Byrd Land (Wade, 1945; Warner, 1945) may be genetically related to those of Graham Land, but until more petrological and radio-isotope age information is available, any suggestion of a relationship between the rocks in the two areas is speculative. On the other hand, close mineralogical, chemical and age similarities between the Graham Land intrusives and those of western Patagonia and the South American Andes are well established.

PETROGRAPHY

The rocks form a normal calc-alkali series, evidently derived from a common magmatic source by crystallization-differentiation processes. The most common rock type is quartz diorite, with andesine the predominant feldspar, quartz and orthoclase in minor amounts, and biotite the principle ferromagnesian. Xenoliths are common in the diorites, fragments of schist from the Basement Complex being most common in the south. In other areas, xenoliths are often of the local country rock and include Jurassic volcanic rocks in a gabbro near Marguerite Bay.

Relatively small intrusive masses of biotite granite, coarse grained granodiorite, and gabbro accompany the quartz diorite. The gabbros are thought to be early basic accumulates of the parent magma.

AGE

Very little direct evidence is available to date the period of intrusion of these rocks. They intrude and contain inclusions of the late Jurassic volcanics, but are nowhere seen in contact with any of the Cretaceous sediments. A late Cretaceous or early Tertiary age was suggested by Adie (1955) on analogy with the closely similar Patagonian intrusives, and two Cretaceous potassium–argon ages have recently been determined on a granite and a granodiorite from Trinity Peninsula (Halpern, 1962).

9. Tertiary Sediments

On and near Seymour Island in north-east Graham Land, the late Cretaceous sediments are unconformably overlain by estuarine or freshwater conglomerate and sandstone with a rich early or middle Tertiary flora (Dusen, 1908). These beds are overlain by calcareous sand, conglomerate and a thin band of greensand which together contain a rich and varied flora and marine fauna including a wide variety of marine invertebrates and cetacean and penguin remains. The paleontology of the Seymour Island and Cockburn Island Tertiaries was described in the detailed reports of the 1901–3 Swedish Expedition; this and more recent evidence suggests that these restricted but important beds are principally of Oligocene or early Miocene age.

Pebbles of calcareous mudstone containing Upper Cretaceous to Oligocene pollen and hystrichosphaerid grains and poorly preserved Foraminifera occur in moraines on White Island and Minna Bluff, near McMurdo Sound (Cranwell *et al.*, 1960). No outcrops of similar rocks are known, but the pebbles must presumably have been carried east or north by ice from an area south-west of McMurdo Sound.

10. Late Tertiary and Quaternary Volcanics

Victoria Land, Marie Byrd Land and Graham Land all experienced a major episode of basic volcanic activity in the late Tertiary or Quaternary, and there is a young volcanic cone at Gaussberg near Mirnyy Station. Only at Mt Erebus in McMurdo Sound has volcanic activity continued into historic times, but on geomorphic evidence many other volcanic centres have been active in post-glacial times.

GAUSSBERG

Except in Victoria Land the only known rocks of post-Triassic age in East
Antarctica are the young basic lavas of Gaussberg, an isolated mountain on the
coast 170 km west of Mirnyy. The volcano was discovered by the German
expedition of 1901–3, and its geology and petrology have been described by
Philippi (1906) and Reinisch (1906). It is a relatively symmetrical volcanic dome
about 400 m high, and appears to be formed entirely of leucite basalt with augite,
olivine, biotite, iron ore and apatite, together with glassy leucite basalt tuffs.

A potassium-argon determination on basalt from Gaussberg gave an age of
about 20 million years, i.e. Miocene (Starik *et al.*, 1959).

VICTORIA LAND

Young basic volcanics make up the Balleny Islands off the north coast of Victoria
Land (Mawson, 1950; Vincent, 1950), and there are many volcanic domes, cones
and lava sheets dissected to varying degrees from Cape Adare in the north to
Minna Bluff 800 km to the south. All these are united under the name McMurdo
Volcanics (Harrington, 1958). All the offshore islands along this coast are composed entirely of McMurdo Volcanics, but no volcanics are known to occur more
than 40 km inland.

The petrography of many of the lavas and pyroclastic rocks has been described
by Smith (1954, 1959). All are alkali-rich basic volcanics forming an olivine
basalt–trachyte–phonolite–kenyte association, but very little is yet known of the
sequence or relative frequency of the members.

Many of the volcanic cones and domes have been deeply dissected during
Pleistocene ice advances, but no direct evidence is available to indicate the
time of inception of volcanism. In few places, however, has the original volcanic
form been entirely lost, and it seems likely that all the volcanics are middle
Tertiary or younger in age.

No volcanic rocks of possible late Tertiary or Quaternary age are known in
the Trans-Antarctic Mountains south of the Skelton Glacier.

MARIE BYRD LAND

Young lavas and associated pyroclastics occur throughout Marie Byrd Land,
and are the predominant rocks over most of the central part of the region. In the
west, Warner (1945) has described alkaline basalt flows and cinder cones from
the Fosdick Mountains in the Edsel Ford Ranges, but no other volcanics are
known in these ranges or in the King Edward VII Peninsula to the west.

The major features of the geology of the scattered central Marie Byrd Land
mountains have been described by Doumani and Ehlers (1962). The Executive
Committee Range, the Crary Mountains, and Toney Mountain all appear to
consist of volcanic rocks of the alkaline basalt suite, with trachyte predominant,
and basalt, trachyandesite and andesite all widely developed. In all these areas
tuffs, agglomerates, and volcanic bombs suggest that the volcanics are of local
origin, and this is confirmed by the presence of craters in some places.

North of the Executive Committee Range, Mt Petras and an unnamed escarpment consist principally of acid pyroclastics of rhyolitic to dacitic composition with rare rhyolite flows. Near the western end of the escarpment, granodiorite is overlain by olivine basalt. Local post-depositional folding has taken place.

In the Jones Mountains, south-east of Thurston Island in eastern Marie Byrd Land, basaltic volcanic rocks overlie quartz diorite (Drake, 1962), but no young volcanics have been reported from the Ellsworth Mountains to the south.

GRAHAM LAND

In north-eastern Graham Land, the last phase of volcanic activity began in the Miocene when olivine basalt lavas and pyroclastics were erupted, principally in the James Ross Island area. Intermittent volcanicity seems to have continued since that time, and lavas of undoubted Quaternary age are present in the Bransfield Strait area.

11. Quaternary Deposits

RAISED MARINE SEDIMENTS

Sands and silts containing marine shells of late Tertiary or more probably Quaternary age are known from coastal localities in a number of areas of Antarctica.

The presence of these young marine deposits at up to 600 m above existing sea level is clearly due to different factors in different places. Eustatic sea level changes, post-glacial isostatic uplift, tectonic uplift and elevation of deposits by ice-gouging, or combinations of these have each been locally important.

In the Vestfold Hills (78° E), Crespin (1960) has described assemblages of well-preserved Foraminifera and thin-shelled molluscs, particularly *Pecten* species, in unconsolidated terrace sand near sea level. The Foraminifera are thought to indicate a Recent age.

Marine sediments at up to 30 m elevation contain algae and pelecypod and gastropod shells in the Windmill Islands near Wilkes Station (Cameron *et al.*, 1959), and similar deposits have been recognized in many localities along the Victoria Land coast and on the islands near McMurdo Sound. These isolated deposits have been described in detail by Speden (1962), and grouped into two formations. The older, commonly tuffaceous, Scallop Hill Formation is characterized by the extinct pectinid *Chlamys* (*Zygochlamys*) *anderssoni*, occurs at heights of up to 600 m, and has been glaciated. An early Pleistocene interglacial age is suggested. The younger Taylor Formation is found at lower levels (in most places below 20 m), appears not to contain any extinct species, and is probably of last glacial or post-glacial age.

The 'Pecten Conglomerate' of Cockburn Island, Graham Land, has much in common with the Scallop Hill Formation of McMurdo Sound, but time equivalence of the two, although possible, is by no means certain. Late Pleistocene or

Recent marine deposits in Graham Land have been described by Andersson (1906) and Nichols (1960).

CONTINENTAL DEPOSITS

During the last main Pleistocene glacial advance, inundation of the continent by ice seems to have been complete, except for the summits of the higher ranges. As a result, the unconsolidated deposits formed during interglacial or early glacial times have largely been removed, although glaciated slopes, high-level benches, and thin lateral moraine remnants give evidence of earlier ice levels.

Post-glacial ablation till veneers the floors of all the ice-free valleys, and fluvioglacial gravels, lake silts, and screes are widespread.

Structure

Geophysical evidence on the structure of Antarctica, incorporating topographic, seismic, seismological, magnetic, and gravitational data, has recently been reviewed by several authors, including particularly Ushakov (1961), Woollard (1962) and C. R. Bentley in the present volume.

On geological evidence, a wide structural difference between East and West Antarctica has been stressed since the earliest times. The validity of this distinction remains undoubted, at least so far as it relates to differences between East Antarctica and Graham Land, but the structural relationships of the intermediate areas, particularly the Ellsworth Mountains and western Marie Byrd Land, are still by no means clear.

EAST ANTARCTICA

The structural development of East Antarctica may be simply stated. A complex of folded Precambrian and Cambrian sedimentary and igneous rocks was refolded during the early Paleozoic, accompanied by widespread metamorphism and mobilization, the emplacement of granitic masses in most areas, and orogenic uplift. Erosion and peneplanation followed in the late Ordovician and Silurian, although granite intrusion, possibly accompanied by local folding, continued into the Carboniferous in north-east Victoria Land. With this exception, East Antarctica has remained an essentially stable continental shield since the Devonian. Although dislocated by extensive block faulting, of uncertain but probably Tertiary age, the Paleozoic and Mesozoic continental Beacon sediments and overlying flood basalts retain today what are essentially their original depositional attitudes.

The question of the relationship between the East Antarctic platform and the structurally and stratigraphically similar platforms of other southern continents has been debated at very great length for many years, but no generally acceptable answer seems yet to be in sight. The geological information gathered in Antarctica during the last decade, though causing a marked revival of interest in the problem, has done little to narrow the gap between the opposed dogmas of continental stability and continental drift. The stratigraphy and structure of East

Antarctica have proved to be both sufficiently similar to, and sufficiently different from, those of the other southern continents to provide some encouragement to both hypotheses, and it is more than ever obvious that geological considerations alone cannot provide a final solution.

GRAHAM LAND

Although Graham Land and East Antarctica possibly shared a common geological history in Precambrian times (the evidence is altogether inadequate to do more than speculate on this), it is very clear that they have developed independently since the early Paleozoic. As has been shown many times, Graham Land has evolved as an extension, through the Scotia Arc, of the South American Andes, and has shared with the other parts of the Andean mobile belt repeated periods of sedimentation, folding, intrusion and volcanicity since the middle Paleozoic.

ELLSWORTH MOUNTAINS AND MARIE BYRD LAND

It is in the important areas between the two dissimilar tectonic regions of East Antarctica and Graham Land that present geological information is poorest. There is sufficient, however, to show that the stratigraphy and structure of the rocks in these areas are by no means as closely related to that of Graham Land as has frequently been assumed (e.g. by Adie's inclusion (1962) of all West Antarctica in his 'Andean Province'), and it now seems possible that a transition may exist there between East Antarctica and Graham Land.

In the Ellsworth Mountains, the information so far available (Anderson et al., 1962) indicates the presence of thick sequences of folded quartzite, argillite and conglomerate (? tillite), intruded locally by basic sills. The age of these rocks is not known, but is probably Paleozoic, and they may represent the off-shore equivalents of the continental middle and late Paleozoic sediments (Beacon Group) of the Trans-Antarctic Mountains. Although the Ellsworth rocks have been folded and metamorphosed, they have not been subject to the intense metamorphism, intrusion and volcanism that has been experienced by the Paleozoic sediments (Trinity Peninsula Group) of Graham Land, and seem to lie in a transitional zone between the stable mass of East Antarctica and the highly mobile environment of Graham Land.

The structural position of Marie Byrd Land is still obscure. The Thurston Island area consists principally of a quartz diorite batholith that may be petrologically and chronologically related to the Andean Intrusives of Graham Land, but over much of central Marie Byrd Land only young volcanic rocks are exposed. In the Edsel Ford Ranges and the King Edward VII Peninsula, metasediments of unknown age, related on slender evidence to the Robertson Bay Group of north Victoria Land by Harrington (1958), are intruded by granitic rocks with both East and West Antarctic affinities (Stewart, 1945).

Until more is known of the geology of these important regions, their inclusion with Graham Land and the South American Andes as a structural entity does not appear to be justifiable.

Economic Geology

To the extent that the presence of economically significant mineral deposits can be predicted on stratigraphic evidence, the rocks of Antarctica may be expected to contain many potentially valuable minerals. However, despite the many reconnaissance surveys that have now been undertaken throughout the continent, no mineral deposit of a quality and quantity approaching economic importance has yet been reported.

Mineral fuels (petroleum, natural gas and coal) seem to be the only natural resources with any potential large-scale use within the continent itself. No trace of petroleum or natural gas has yet been reported, but estimates of enormous coal reserves in the Beacon sediments of the Trans-Antarctic Mountains have been made from time to time. Most of the coal so far examined, however, is thin, impersistent, of high ash content, and very commonly severely baked. When mining and transport costs are also taken into account, it seems unrealistic to suppose that coal will ever be used in the Antarctic as a major alternative to imported oil or nuclear fuels.

Because of transportation difficulties within and beyond Antarctica, only minerals having a high value-to-mass ratio are ever likely to be exploitable, and this reduces the potentially useful minerals largely to the ores of the more valuable metals and to precious stones. Even with these minerals, the development costs of any mining venture are likely to be so great that only an unusually rich or extensive ore body would be capable of economic production.

The eventual discovery of rich mineral deposits comparable with those of other continents must be expected, and these will eventually form a useful reserve against the depletion of high-grade deposits in other parts of the world. In the present state of mineral economics, however, few of such deposits are likely to be capable of profitable exploitation in the isolation and harsh environment of Antarctica.

Bibliography

ADIE, R. J. 1954: The Petrology of Graham Land: I. The Basement Complex; Early Paleozoic Plutonic and Volcanic Rocks, *Sci. Rep. Falkland Islands Dependencies Survey* **11**.

ADIE, R. J. 1955: The Petrology of Graham Land: II. The Andean Granite-Gabbro Intrusive Suite, *Sci. Rep. Falkland Islands Dependencies Survey* **12**.

ADIE, R. J. 1957: The Petrology of Graham Land: III. Metamorphic Rocks of the Trinity Peninsula Series, *Sci. Rep. Falkland Islands Dependencies Survey* **20**.

ADIE, R. J. 1962: The Geology of Antarctica, *Geophys. Monogr.* **7**: 26–39, Amer. Geophys. Un.

ALLEN, A. D. 1962: Geological Investigations in Southern Victoria Land, Antarctica: Part 7 – Formations of the Beacon Group in the Victoria Valley Region, *N.Z. J. Geol. Geophys.* **5:** 278–94.

ANDERSON, J. J., BASTIEN, T. W., SCHMIDT, P. G., SPLETTSTOESSER, J. F., and CRADDOCK, J. C. 1962: Antarctica: Geology of the Ellsworth Mountains, *Science* **138:** 824–5.

ANDERSSON, J. G. 1906: On the Geology of Graham Land, *Bull. Geol. Instn Univ. Uppsala* **7:** 19–71.

ANGINO, E. E., TURNER, M. D., and ZELLER, E. J. 1962: Reconnaissance Geology of Lower Taylor Valley, Victoria Land, Antarctica, *Bull. Geol. Soc. Amer.* **73:** 1553–62.

AUGHENBAUGH, N. B. 1958: Preliminary Report on the Geology of the Dufek Massif, *Ohio State University Research Foundation, Report 825-1*, Part 1: 164–208.

BALL, H. W. 1960: Upper Cretaceous Decapoda and Serpulidae from James Ross Island, Graham Land, *Sci. Rep. Falkland Islands Dependencies Survey* **24.**

BEHRENDT, J. C. 1962: Geophysical and Glaciological Studies in the Filchner Ice Shelf Area of Antarctica, *J. Geophys. Res.* **67:** 221–34.

BELLAIR, P. and DELBOS, L. 1962: Age Absolu de la Dernière Granitisation en Terre Adélie, *C.R. Acad. Sci.* **254:** 1465–6.

BENSON, W. N. 1916: Report on the Petrology of the Dolerites collected by the British Antarctic Expedition, 1907–9. *Rep. Brit. Ant. Exp. 1907–9, Geol.* **2:** 153–60.

BLANK, H. R., COOPER, R. A., WHEELER, R. H., and WILLIS, I. A. G. 1963: Geology of the Koettlitz–Blue Glacier Region, South Victoria Land, Antarctica, *Trans. Roy. Soc. N.Z., Geol.* **2:** 79-100.

BROWNE, W. R. 1923: The Dolerites of King George Land and Adelie Land, *Sci. Rep. Australasian Ant. Exp. 1911–14, A,* **3:** 245–58.

CAMERON, R. I., LÖKEN, O. G. and MOLHOLM, J. R. 1959: Wilkes Station Glaciological Data 1957–58, *Ohio State University Research Foundation, Report 825-1*, Part III, 173 pp.

COX, L. R. 1953: Lower Cretaceous Gastropoda, Lamellibranchia, and Annelida from Alexander I Land (Falkland Islands Dependencies), *Sci. Rep. Falkland Islands Dependencies Survey* **4.**

CRANWELL, L. M. 1959: Fossil Pollen from Seymour Island, Antarctica, *Nature* **184:** 1782–5.

CRANWELL, L. M., HARRINGTON, H. J., and SPEDEN, I.G. 1960: Lower Tertiary Microfossils from McMurdo Sound, Antarctica. *Nature* **186:** 700–2.

CRARY, A. P. 1961: Marine-Sediment Thickness in the Eastern Ross Sea Area, Antarctica, *Bull. Geol. Soc. Amer.* **72:** 787–90.

CRESPIN, I. 1960: Some Recent Foraminifera from Vestfold Hills, Antarctica, *Sci. Rep. Tohoku Univ., Spec. Vol.* **4:** 19–31.

CROHN, P. W. 1959: A Contribution to the Geology and Glaciology of the Western Part of Australian Antarctic Territory, *Bur. Min. Resour. Aust. Bull.* **52.**

DARRAH, W. C. 1936: Antarctic Fossil Plants, *Science* **83:** 390–1.

DARRAH, W. C. 1941: La Paleobotanica Sudamericana, *Lilloa* **6:** 213–39.

DEUTSCH, S., PICCIOTTO, E. E., and REINHARZ, M. 1961: Age Measurements on Antarctic Rocks (Queen Maud Land), *Nature* **191:** 1286–7.

DOUMANI, G. A., and EHLERS, E. G. 1962: Petrography of Rocks from Mountains in Marie Byrd Land, West Antarctica, *Bull. Geol. Soc. Amer.* **73:** 877–82.

DOUMANI, G. A., and LONG, W. E. 1962: The Ancient Life of the Antarctic, *Scientific American* **207:** 168–84.

DRAKE, A. A., Jr. 1962: Preliminary Geologic Report on the 1961 US Expedition to Bellingshausen Sea, Antarctica, *Science* **135:** 671–2.

DUSEN, P. 1908: Über die Tertiäre flora der Seymour-Insel. *Wiss. Ergebn. Schwed. Südpol. Exp.* **3:** 1–27.

EDWARDS, W. N. 1928: The Occurrence of *Glossopteris* in the Beacon Sandstone of Ferrar Glacier, South Victoria Land, *Geol. Mag.* **65:** 323–7.

EVERNDEN, J. F., and RICHARDS, J. R. 1962: Potassium–Argon Ages in Eastern Australia, *J. Geol. Soc. Aust.* **9:** 1–49.

FERRAR, H. T. 1907: Report on the Field Geology of the Region Explored during the *Discovery* Antarctic Expedition, 1901–4, *Nat. Ant. Exp. 1901–04, Nat. Hist.* **1:** 1–100.

FORD, A. B., and AARON, J. M. 1962: Bedrock Geology of the Thiel Mountains, Antarctica, *Science* **137:** 751–2.

FORD, A. B., HUBBARD, H. A., and STERN, T. W. 1963: Lead Alpha Ages of Zircon in Quartz Monzonite Porphyry, Thiel Mountains, Antarctica – a Preliminary Report. Article 208 in *U.S. Geol. Surv. Prof. Paper 450–E:* E105–7.

GOLDICH, S. S., NIER, A. O., and WASHBURN, A. L. 1958: A40/K40 Age of Gneiss from McMurdo Sound, Antarctica, *Trans. Amer. Geophys. Un.* **39:** 956–8.

GOULD, L. M. 1935: Structure of the Queen Maud Mountains, Antarctica. *Bull. Geol. Soc. Amer.* **46:** 973–84.

GRINDLEY, G. W. 1963: The Geology of the Queen Alexandra Range, Beardmore Glacier, Ross Dependency, Antarctica; with Notes on the Correlation of Gondwana Sequences. *N.Z. J. Geol. Geophys.* **6:** 307–47.

GRINDLEY, G. W., MCGREGOR, V. R., and WALCOTT, R. I. 1963: Outline of the Geology of the Nimrod–Beardmore–Axel Heiberg Region, Ross Dependency, Antarctica, *Paper presented at SCAR Symposium on Antarctic Geology, Cape Town, September 1963.*

GRINDLEY, G. W., and WARREN, G. 1963: Stratigraphic Nomenclature and Correlation in the Western Ross Sea Region, Antarctica, *Paper presented at SCAR Symposium on Antarctic Geology, Cape Town, September 1963.*

GUNN, B. M. 1962: Differentiation in Ferrar Dolerites, Antarctica, *N.Z. J. Geol. Geophys.* **5:** 820–63.

GUNN, B. M., and WALCOTT, R. I. 1962: The Geology of the Mt Markham Region, Ross Dependency, Antarctica, *N.Z. J. Geol. Geophys.* **5:** 407–26.

GUNN, B. M., and WARREN, G. 1962: Geology of Victoria Land between the Mawson and Mulock Glaciers, Antarctica, *N.Z. Geol. Surv. Bull.* **71**, 157 pp., 2 maps; and *Trans-Antarctic Exp. 1955–58 Sci. Reps.* **11**.

HALLE, T. G. 1913: The Mesozoic Flora of Graham Land. *Wiss. Ergebn. Schwed. Südpol. Exp.* **3**: 3–124.

HALPERN, M. 1962: Potassium-Argon Dating of Plutonic Bodies in Palmer Peninsula and Southern Chile, *Science* **138**: 1261–2.

HAMILTON, W. B. 1960: New Interpretation of Antarctic Tectonics, *U.S. Geol. Surv. Prof. Paper 400-B*: 379–80.

HARRINGTON, H. J. 1958: Nomenclature of Rock Units in the Ross Sea Region, Antarctica, *Nature* **182**: 290.

HEURTEBIZE, G. 1952: Sur les Formations Géologiques de la Terre Adélie, *C.R. Acad. Sci.* **234**: 2209–11.

HOWARTH, M. K. 1958: Upper Jurassic and Cretaceous Ammonite Faunas of Alexander Land and Graham Land, *Sci. Rep. Falkland Islands Dependencies Survey* **21**.

KLIMOV, L. V. 1960: Granity Poberezh'ya Bukhty Einsuert (Bereg Korolya Georga V), *Trudy Nauchno-Issl. Inst. Geol. Arkt.* **113**: 123–46.

KLIMOV, L. V., and SOLOV'EV, D. S. 1958: Nekotorye Cherty Geologicheskogo Stroeniya Poberezh'ya Zemli Uilksa, Berega Korolya Georga V i Berega Otsa, *Dokl. Akad. Nauk SSSR* **123**: 141–4.

KOROTKEVICH, E. S., and TIMOFEEV, B. V. 1959: O Vozraste Porod Vostochnoy Antarktidy (po Dannym Sporovogo Analiza), *Inf. Byull. Sov. Ant. Eksp* **12**: 41–6.

KULP, J. L. 1961: Geologic Time Scale. *Science* **133**: 1105–14.

LAIRD, M. G. 1963: Geomorphology and Stratigraphy of the Nimrod Glacier – Beaumont Bay Region, Southern Victoria Land, Antarctica, *N.Z. J. Geol. Geophys.* **6**: 465–84.

LAIRD, M. G., and WATERHOUSE, J. B. 1962: Archaeocyathine Limestones of Antarctica, *Nature* **194**: 861.

LONG, W. E. 1959: Preliminary Report of the Geology of the Central Range of the Horlick Mountains, Antarctica, *Ohio State University Research Foundation Report 825-2, Part VII*.

LONG, W. E. 1962: Sedimentary Rocks of the Buckeye Range, Horlick Mountains, Antarctica, *Science* **136**: 319–21.

MAWSON, D. 1916: Petrology of Rock Collections from the Mainland of South Victoria Land, *Rep. Brit. Ant. Exp. 1907–9, Geol.* **2**: 201–37.

MAWSON, D. 1950: Basaltic Lavas of the Balleny Is. *Trans. Roy. Soc. South Aust.* **73**: 223–31.

NICHOLS, R. L. 1960: Geomorphology of Marguerite Bay Area, Palmer Peninsula, Antarctica, *Bull. Geol. Soc. Amer.* **71**: 1421–50.

NICOLAYSEN, L. O., BURGER, A. J., TATSUMI, T., and AHRENS, L. H. 1961: Age Measurements on Pegmatites and a Basic Charnockite Lens occurring near Lützow-Holm Bay, Antarctica, *Geochim. Cosmoch. Acta* **22**: 94–8.

PHILIPPI, E. 1906: Geologische Beschreibung des Gaussbergs, *Deutsche Südpol. Exp. 1901–03*, **2:** 47–71.

PICCIOTTO, E. E. 1960: Geological Reconnaissance of the Sör-Rondane Mountains (Queen Maud Land), *Nature* **186:** 740.

PICCIOTTO, E., and COPPEZ, A. 1962: Bibliographie des Mésures d'Âges Absolus en Antarctique, *Ann. Soc. Geol. Belg.* **85:** 263–308.

PLUMSTEAD, E. P. 1962: Fossil Floras of Antarctica, *Sci. Rep. Trans-Antarctic Exp.* **9:** 154 pp.

RASTALL, R. H., and PRIESTLEY, R. E. 1921: The Slate–Greywacke Formation of Robertson Bay, *Nat. Hist. Rep. Brit. Ant. (Terra Nova) Exp., 1910, Geol.* **1:** 121–9.

RAVICH, M. G. 1957: Gornye porody Oazisa Bangera. *Trudy Nauch. – Issl. Inst. Geol. Arkt.* **95:** 104–22.

RAVICH, M. G. 1958: Absolyutnyy Vozrast Dokembriyskikh Porod Tsentral'nogo Sektora Vostochnoy Antarktidy, *Inf. Byull. Sov. Ant. Eksp.* **1:** 31–3.

RAVICH, M. G. 1959: Kratkie Svedeniya o Geologicheskom Stroenii Vostochnoy Chasti Gor na Zemle Korolevy Mod v Vostochnoy Antarktide, *Dokl. Akad. Nauk SSSR* **128:** 152–5.

RAVICH, M. G. 1960a: Gornye Porody Oazisa Vestfoll', *Trudy Nauch. – Issl. Inst. Geol. Arkt.* **113:** 25–52.

RAVICH, M. G. 1960b: Gornye Porody Kholmov Grirson i Ostrovov Uindmill (Oazis Grirson), *Trudy Nauch. – Issl. Inst. Geol. Arkt.* **113:** 53–81.

RAVICH, M. G., and KRYLOV, A. Ya. 1960: Ob Absolyutnom Vozraste Porod Vostochnoy Chasti Gor na Zemle Korolevy Mod, *Inf. Byull. Sov. Ant. Eksp.* **20:** 15–17.

RAVICH, M. G., and KUNO, V. G. 1961: Charnokity Oazisa Bangera, *Izv. Akad. Nauk SSSR, Ser. Geol., 1961*, **11:** 64–77.

RAVICH, M. G. and SOLOV'EV, D. S. 1957: Novye Dannye o Geologicheskom Stroenii Oazisa Bangera v Vostochnoy Antarktide, *Dokl. Akad. Nauk SSSR.* **115:** 1177–90.

RAVICH, M. G., SOLOV'EV, D. S., REVNOV, B. I., and SHULYATIN, O. G. 1961: Predvaritel'nye Dannye o Geologicheskom Stroenii Tsentral'noy Chasti Gor na Zemle Korolevy Mod (Vostochnaya Antarktida), *Inf. Byull. Inst. Geol. Arkt.* **25:** 5–34.

REINISCH, R. 1906: Petrographische Beschreibung der Gaussberg–Gesteine, *Deutsche Südpol. Exp. 1901–03*, **2:** 73–87.

ROBERTSON, R. 1959: Preliminary Report on the Bedrock Geology of the Windmill Islands, *Ohio State University Research Foundation, Report 825–2.*

ROOTS, E. F. 1953: Preliminary Note on the Geology of Western Dronning Maud Land, *Norsk Geol. Tidssk.* **32:** 18–33.

SAITO, A., TATSUMI, T., and SATO, K. 1961: Absolute Age of Euxenite from Antarctica: *Antarctic Record* **12:** 31–6.

SCHETELIG, J. 1915: Report on Rock-Specimens Collected on Roald Amundsen's South Pole Expedition, *Skr. VidenskSelsk., Christ. 1. Mat.-naturv. Kl.* **4**: 1–32.

SCHOPF, J. M. 1962: A Preliminary Report on Plant Remains and Coal of the Sedimentary Section in the Central Range of the Horlick Mountains, Antarctica, *Ohio State Univ. Inst. Polar Studies Rep.* **2**.

SEWARD, A. C. 1914: Antarctic Fossil Plants, *Nat. Hist. Rep. Brit. Ant. (Terra Nova) Exp., 1910, Geol.* **1**: 1–49.

SEWARD, A. C., 1933: An Antarctic Pollen-Grain; Fact or Fancy, *New Phytologist* **32**: 311–3.

SMITH, W. C. 1924: The Plutonic and Hypabyssal Rocks of South Victoria Land, *Nat. Hist. Rep. Brit. Ant. (Terra Nova) Exp., 1910, Geol.* **1**: 167–227.

SMITH, W. C. 1954: The Volcanic Rocks of the Ross Archipelago, *Nat. Hist. Rep. Brit. Ant. (Terra Nova) Exp., 1910, Geol.* **2**: 1–107.

SMITH, W. C. 1959: The Volcanic Rocks of Cape Adare, South Victoria Land, *Nat. Hist. Rep. Brit. Ant. (Terra Nova) Exp., 1910, Geol.* **2**: 109–50.

SMITH, W. C. and PRIESTLEY, R. E. 1921: The Metamorphic Rocks of the Terra Nova Bay Region, *Nat. Hist. Rep. Brit. Ant. (Terra Nova) Exp., 1910, Geol.* **1**: 145–65.

SOLOV'EV, D. S. 1960a: Nizhnepalozoiskie Metamorficheskie Slantsy Berega Otsa, *Trudy Nauch.-Issl. Inst. Geol. Arkt.* **113**: 147–58.

SOLOV'EV, D. S. 1960b: Osadochno-Vulkanogennaya Seriya Bikon Utesa Khorn-Blaff (Bereg Korolya Georga V), *Trudy Nauch-Issl. Inst. Geol. Arkt.* **113**: 159–82.

SPATH, L. F. 1953: The Upper Cretaceous Cephalopod Fauna of Graham Land, *Sci. Rep. Falkland Islands Dependencies Survey* **3**: 60 pp.

SPEDEN, I. G. 1962: Fossiliferous Quaternary Marine Deposits in the McMurdo Sound Region, Antarctica, *N.Z. J. Geol. Geophys.* **5**: 746–77.

STARIK, I. Ye., KRYLOV, A. Ya., RAVICH, M. G., and SILIN, Yu. I. 1961: The Absolute Ages of East Antarctic Rocks, *Ann. New York Acad. Sci.* **91**: 576–582.

STARIK, I. Ye., RAVICH, M. G., KRYLOV, A. Ya, and SILIN, Yu. I. 1959: Ob Absolyutnom Vozraste Porod Vostochno-Antarkticheskoy Platformy, *Dokl. Akad. Nauk SSSR* **126**: 144–6.

STARIK, I. Ye., RAVICH, M. G., KRYLOV, A. Ya., SILIN, Yu. I., ATRASHENOK, L. Ya., and LOVTSYUS, A. V. 1960: Novye Dannye ob Absolyutnom Vozraste Porod Vostochnoy Antarktidy, *Dokl. Akad. Nauk SSSR* **134**: 1421–3.

STEWART, D., Jr. 1945: The Petrography of Some Intrusive Rocks from King Edward VII and Marie Byrd Lands, Antarctica, *Proc. Amer. Phil. Soc.* **89**: 148–51.

STILLWELL, F. L. 1918: The Metamorphic Rocks of Adelie Land; Section 1, *Sci. Rep. Australasian Ant. Exp. 1911–14, A*, **3**: 1–230.

TREVES, S. 1959: Description of Specimens from a Nunatak in the Ross-Weddell 'Graben'. *Ohio State University Research Foundation, Report 825–2*.

USHAKOV, S. A. 1961: Rezul'taty Geofizicheskikh Issledovaniy Stroeniya

Zemnoy Kory v Antarktide, pp. 38–52 in *Antarktika: Dokl. Komissii, 1960.* Akad. Nauk SSSR.

VIALOV, O. S. 1962: Problematica of the Beacon Sandstone at Beacon Height West, Antarctica, *N.Z. J. Geol. Geophys.* **5:** 718–32.

VINCENT, P. 1950: Expedition Antarctique, Compagne devant la Terre Adélie (1948–1949): Géologie, *Exp. Pol. Françaises, Publ. Prélim.* **9:** 26–32.

VORONOV, P. S., and KLENOVA, M. V. 1957; Predvaritel'nye Dannye o Geologicheskom Stroenii Rayona Sovetskoy Yuzhno-Polyarnoy Observatorii Mirnyy, *Dokl. Akad. Nauk SSSR* **115:** 1153–6.

VORONOV, P. S., and KRYLOV, A. Ya. 1961: Vozraste Drevneyshikh Porod Antarktiki, *Inf. Byull. Sov. Ant. Eksp.* **28:** 11–15.

WADE, F. A. 1945: The Geology of the Rockefeller Mountains, King Edward VII Land, Antarctica, *Proc. Amer. Phil. Soc.* **89:** 67–77.

WALKER, P. T. 1958: Study of some Rocks and Minerals from the Dufek Massif, Antarctica, *USNC-IGY Ant. Glaciol. Data, Rep.* **825–1:** 209–32, Ohio State Univ.

WALTON, J. 1923: On Rhexoxylon, Bancroft – a Triassic Genus of Plants exhibiting a Liane-Type of Vascular Organization, *Phil. Trans. Roy. Soc. Lond.* **B212:** 79–109.

WARNER, L. A. 1945: Structure and Petrography of the Southern Edsel Ford Ranges, Antarctica, *Proc. Amer. Phil. Soc.* **89:** 78–122.

WEBB, P. N. 1963: Geological Investigations in Southern Victoria Land, Antarctica. Part 4 – Beacon Group of the Wright Valley and Taylor Glacier Region, *N.Z. J. Geol. Geophys.* **6:** 361–87.

WILCKENS, O. 1910: Die Anneliden, Bivalven und Gastropoden der Antarktischen Kreideformation, *Wiss. Ergebn. Schwed. Südpol. Exp.* **3,** Pt. 12.

WOODWARD, A. S. 1921: Fish-Remains from the Upper Old Red Sandstone of Granite Harbour, Antarctica, *Nat. Hist. Rep. Brit. Ant. (Terra Nova), Exp., 1910, Geol.* **1:** 51–62.

WOOLLARD, G. P. 1962: Crustal Structure in Antarctica, *Geophys. Monogr.* **7:** 53–73. Amer. Geophys. Union.

CHAPTER TWELVE

The Oases in the Ice

R. H. CLARK, *Victoria University of Wellington*

Introduction

Exposed rock is not plentiful in Antarctica. Almost all the land is covered by the great ice cap; only towards the margins of the continent where this thins do mountains project above the ice. As the coast is approached, more and more of these rocky mountain summits – nunataks – appear, finally merging into more or less continuous valley walls, between which outlet glaciers flow seaward.

In some parts of Antartica, this general picture is modified. Between the nunataks and the coast, lofty ice-free walls rise above glaciated valleys—but the glaciers which once flowed through these valleys and eroded them have largely disappeared and no large masses of ice remain.

These are the Antarctic 'Oases'. They are of especial scientific interest because in contrast with the rest of the continent they display extensive outcrops of bedrock. They provide 'windows' through which the geology of the continental margins can be glimpsed. In them, post-glacial processes have begun. Soils have started to form (McCraw, 1960); lichens, mosses and algae exist; certain lakes act as natural heat reservoirs. Frost-patterned ground may be studied in detail, and many other features of scientific and general interest are present.

The largest oasis yet encountered in East Antarctica is in the mountains of south Victoria Land. It includes the so called 'dry valleys', one of which, the Taylor, was first observed by scientists of Scott's expeditions. The oasis lies opposite Ross Island, across McMurdo Sound, and in recent years has been the subject of considerable study by New Zealand and American scientists. Eight successive expeditions from the Victoria University of Wellington have published considerable data on this region, and it is now one of the best-known parts of Antarctica. It is referred to here as McMurdo Oasis.

A smaller ice-free area, Bunger Oasis in Wilkes Land, has been studied mainly by scientists of the USSR. Other oases are known in Graham Land, and elsewhere on the continent (see Lebedev, 1959, pp. 78–83). In this chapter, only the McMurdo Oasis will be described in some detail; it is of special interest in view of its large extent and its southerly situation.

The main part of McMurdo Oasis lies between the Debenham and Cotton Glaciers to the north and the Ferrar Glacier to the south, extending from Lat. 77° 10′ S to Lat. 77° 45′ S. Its western boundary is the inland ice margin

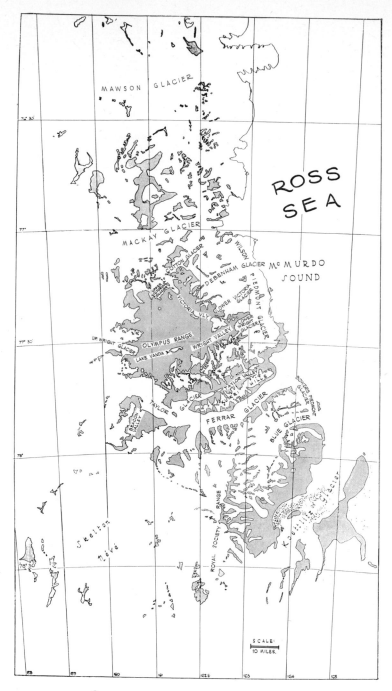

FIG. 84 LOCALITY MAP OF MCMURDO OASIS

(Long. 160° 20′ E). and its eastern the edge of the Wilson Piedmont Glacier (Long. 163°E). It includes the lower Taylor Dry Valley, the Wright Valley, the Victoria Valley, and a number of smaller valleys, mostly ice-free (Fig. 85). The total area is approximately 2500 km². A further ice-free region, of about 1200 km², lies north-west of the Koettlitz Glacier, some 50 km south-east of the main part of the Oasis, and a much smaller area extends to the north, across the Mackay Glacier east of the Convoy Range. Altogether, the McMurdo Oasis affords nearly continuous rock exposures from the Mawson Glacier to the Koettlitz, a distance of 150 km.

FIG. 85 NORTHERN PART OF MCMURDO OASIS
View from above western end of Wright Valley looking north east over peaks of the Olympic Range to the Upper Victoria Valley system

(*US Navy photograph*)

Relief in the oasis is considerable, the tops of the valley walls rising over a thousand metres above the floors, which are open and relatively flat. The valleys mainly trend from west-south-west to east-north-east, normal to the coast, except for the upper reach of Victoria Valley which trends about northwest-wards.

Geology of McMurdo Oasis

The geology of McMurdo Oasis has been described as 'layer cake geology' [1] because of the prominence of flat lying upper formations of contrasting lithology. The lowest and oldest rocks, forming the basement, are complex metamorphics and granites; capping these are thick light coloured shales and sandstones,

---

[1] By R. H. Wheeler.

intruded – as filling in the layer cake – by massive sheets of black dolerite (Fig. 86).

The basement rocks, gneisses, marbles, schists and metagreywackes, intruded by masses of granite, are well exposed in the lower levels of the McMurdo Oasis, along the Koettlitz margin, in the lower Taylor, the lower Wright and Victoria Valleys. They show complex structures; recent work in the Koettlitz area by Blank *et al.* (1963) suggests that the structure contains overturned folds and thrust faults.

The rocks are old; some are lower Paleozoic and some still older. Most were deposited as sediments in an ancient sea. These sediments were compressed, folded, hardened. Limestones were altered to marbles, and sandstones to quartzites and schists. Some were converted to granite-gneiss, and more granite was injected as liquid magma into the complex. Dikes, of varying compositions, but with lamprophyres predominating, were intruded as swarms into the mass.

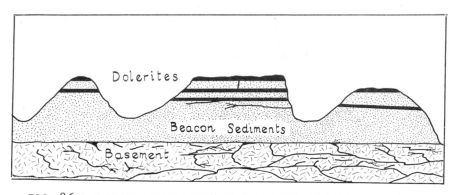

FIG. 86 DIAGRAMMATIC SECTION OF ROCKS OF MCMURDO OASIS

Then occurred a prolonged period of erosion, during which the basement rocks were worn away to a lowland area of little relief. The end result was an extensive plateau very like those of the continental shields of Africa, Australia and other large land masses.

The Beacon sediments, which form the bulk of the Royal Society Range, and most of the mountains in the west of the Oasis, are sandstones, siltstones and shales. They contain coal seams, often thin; rare fossils include plants and fish remains. These rocks range in age from Devonian or earlier to possible Jurassic (Gunn and Warren, 1962) – a period extending from about 400 million to about 200 million years ago. The sediments are continental in character, and were deposited on the older crystalline basement under terrestrial conditions, some possibly in lakes, and others in inland basins similar to those of Nevada and eastern California.

Into these sediments, some considerable time after their deposition, were injected the great sills and sheets of dolerite magma which soldified to form the hard, black, jointed rock so prominent in the Oasis. Some of the dolerite sheets approach 300 m in thickness, and, being reasonably resistant to the form of erosion prevalent in Antarctica, they form the summits of some of the more notable peaks in the western part of the Oasis. A sample of dolerite from McMurdo Oasis has been shown by Evernden and Richards (1962) to be about 165 million years old.

The coal and plant remains in the Beacon rocks show that at times the climate was appreciably warmer than now; calcareous rocks in the basement indicate even older warm periods in the history of the continent. However, the Mawson tillite above the Beacon (Gunn and Warren, 1962) and the tillites further south near the base of the Beacon rocks (Grindley, 1963) are clear evidence of former glacial periods.

Rocks of the Oasis younger than the dolerites include a few examples of Quaternary McMurdo volcanics, exemplified by a small basalt volcano in the Taylor Valley and a series of small cones and scoria along the margin of the Koettlitz Glacier. In addition, extensive Quaternary moraines are formed on the valley floors and sides.

The dry climate and frequent winds have caused certain desert features – ventifacts, mushroom rocks and sand dunes (Fig. 87) to develop.

Climate

The present-day summer climate in McMurdo Oasis is, by Antarctic standards, fairly mild. Average summer temperatures are a little higher than at Scott Base, where the mean day temperature for the months of December and January (years 1957–8) was $-4.8°$ C, with an extreme maximum figure of $+4°$ C. The highest temperature recorded in the Oasis by a University of Wellington expedition was $+12.2°$ C. This was, however, exceptional and summer temperatures in the Oasis are close to freezing point, within the range $-4°$ C to $0°$ C, with not infrequent thaws. Precipitation is very low.

Two factors combine to ameliorate temperature conditions. Westerly winds blowing down into the Oasis from the high Antarctic plateau produce a compressional effect with consequent heating of the air stream in the valleys. In addition, exposed rock has a much lower albedo than snow or ice, and so the Oasis absorbs more solar radiation. Thus the valleys are relatively warm because they are ice-free; this is an effect rather than a cause of deglaciation.

Biology

The temperatures in the Oasis are too low for higher plants, and lichens, algae and mosses are the only relatively common living things. An occasional skua gull may be seen; but of more interest are the mummified carcasses of Crabeater and Weddell Seals which are quite common in McMurdo Oasis. These have been found throughout the valleys at elevations up to 700 m, and at distances of as much as 60 km from the sea. Some are very fresh; others have been highly abraded by sand-laden winds. Radio-carbon dates so far obtained give ages for some of the carcasses up to 2600 years – though it must be remembered that due to upwelling of bottom waters in the Ross Sea, 'old' carbon remains in circulation for a long time, and present-day fish can give a C^{14} age of 1200 years. Consequently C^{14} dates of samples from fish-eating animals in this region must be regarded with caution.

The presence of seal remains at such distances from the sea and at relatively high elevations is not easy to explain. Presumably the seals crossed the Wilson Piedmont Glacier, descended into the Wright or Victoria Valleys, and then proceeded up-valley as long as they were able. Various speculations have been

FIG. 87 BARCHAN TYPE SAND DUNES IN VICTORIA VALLEY
Moraine covers the valley floor. The hill in the background is of basement granite intruded by dykes. To the left is the snout of the Packard Glacier
(*Photo. Victoria University of Wellington Antarctic Expedition,* 1)

advanced to account for this apparently suicidal migration. Suggestions that the carcasses are those of anti-social individuals who turned their backs on their fellows – and the coast – have been made. It is considered more likely, however, that the seals simply got lost. Presumably some individuals found their way up the surface of the Wilson Piedmont Glacier, wandered over it, and descended the inland face in error, then took the line of least resistance in their search for the sea by proceeding up-valley – away from it.

Occasional Adelie Penguin remains in the Oasis show that some penguins too wandered far from their normal habitat and their food sources, to die in the dry valleys.

Solar Heated Lakes

In the summer of 1960–1, an American party drilled through the ice cover on Lake Vanda, in the Wright Valley, and on Lake Bonney in the Taylor Valley. A rather surprising discovery was made (Armitage and House, 1960). There is permanent ice about 4 m thick over Lake Vanda, which is 70 m deep. The bottom waters were found to be warm and strongly saline, the maximum temperature at the bottom being about 26° C (77° F). A temperature of 8° C was recorded in Lake Bonney, though not at the lake bottom.

During the next summer, 1961–2, both lakes were investigated further by an American party from the University of Kansas, under the direction of E. E. Angino. Lake Vanda was studied by two New Zealand scientists, A. T. Wilson and H. W. Wellman (1963).

The ice cover of Lake Vanda consists of long vertical crystals, apparently extending from top to bottom of the 4 m thick sheet. The average width of each crystal is about 5 cm. Summer temperature of the ice is at melting point; puddles of meltwater form and refreeze, and the ice itself contains some water.

Below the ice, the upper lake water increases in temperature from 0° C to 4° C and contains little salts. Further down, at 18 m, a zone is reached where the temperature is higher (8° C), and the water slightly saline. This zone extends down to 40 m, and forms a convection cell. In it are red algae.

The deeper water is appreciably hotter, temperature reaching a maximum of 26° C at the lake bottom. Here the salinity is marked; the dissolved salts are almost entirely chlorides, mainly of calcium, with some sodium and a little potassium and magnesium. The concentration of total chloride near the bottom is of the order of 80,000 parts per million.

An explanation of the retention of hot water at the lake bottom is readily forthcoming, for the salinity of the bottom waters produces a sufficiently high density to prevent the convection which would otherwise result in movement of the hot bottom waters to higher lake levels.

There are a number of possible explanations of the cause of the high temperature of the bottom waters, but two stands out as clearly worthy of serious consideration. These are, first, heat from geothermal sources and secondly, solar heating. The temperature of the lake at any given depth is remarkably constant, to within a fraction of a degree. This is strong evidence against a geothermal source such as a hot spring. Heat flow measurements show a reversal of the geothermal gradient at the lake bottom; the rock beneath the lake is colder than the bottom waters. This further reduces the likelihood of geothermal heat being the cause of the warm water.

Measurement made by heat recording instruments sited below the ice cover of Lake Vanda show that solar heat is penetrating the ice and entering the lake water. The long vertical ice crystals probably act as light pipes, facilitating transmission of sunlight down into the lake, where some of it reaches and warms the lake bottom.

When due allowance has been made for absorption in the passage down, and for heat loss outwards from the lake bottom, the heat energy measured as entering the lake was found to be sufficient to account for the hot bottom waters. Thus it is the opinion of Wilson and Wellman that Lake Vanda is a solar heat trap, which is storing the Sun's energy in its saline bottom waters.

There are other features associated with Lake Vanda which are of considerable interest. The dissolved salts in the lake may have been derived from the sea and

FIG. 88

Upper Wright Glacier flowing over a barrier formed by dolerite sills intruding Beacon sediments. The Ice Sheet may be seen in the background

(*US Navy photograph*)

contributed to the lake by the stream – the Onyx – which flows into Lake Vanda. It is considered that the total salt in the lake could have been contributed in about 50,000 years (A. T. Wilson, personal communication). Although this figure cannot be regarded as other than highly approximate, it probably gives a minimum age of the salt in the lake, and consequently the order of the age of the deglaciation which produced the Oasis.

It should be pointed out, however, that this assumes that the salts within the lake were contributed to it since deglaciation of the Wright Valley. In the opinion of the present writer, it is not certain that such an assumption is justified. In the event of extension of the Wright Glacier down valley, it appears possible that at least some salt might remain within the hollow occupied by the lake during a period of glacial advance.

Comparison of rates of diffusion of the dissolved salts with the present salinity gradient suggests that about 1000 years ago the lake temporarily was 70 m lower than at present (Wilson, 1964a), and since then has been steadily rising. C^{14} date of algal remains from a high terrace indicates that the lake was about 50 m higher than at present some 3000 years ago. (A. T. Wilson and H. W. Wellman, personal communication.)

Origin of McMurdo Oasis

At present the cause of the deglaciation which produced the Oasis is uncertain. The possibility of high geothermal gradient has been considered and rejected, but it should be pointed out that the largest oasis in East Antarctica adjoins the largest group of volcanoes of which at least one is currently active. The present writer is not yet fully convinced that this proximity is merely coincidence; however, no link has been found.

Local meteorological conditions have been considered. That the valleys of the oasis are warmer than the 'white' valleys of neighbouring regions has already been discussed; this is effect, not cause of deglaciation.

A current view is that decrease in height of plateau ice has been of major importance in the deglaciation of the Oasis. The upper reaches of the valleys are stepped; the stepping is partly controlled by the numerous thick dolerite sills which intrude the Beacon Sandstone. Dolerite is a hard but well-jointed rock, and under less extreme climatic conditions would be readily eroded by glacial action. But glacial erosion is largely accomplished by the process of 'glacial plucking', which depends on local thawing, percolation of meltwater into joints, refreezing and consequent 'plucking' as the glacier flows. Under Antarctic conditions, it appears unlikely that significant melting could occur at the base of high ice such as the Upper Wright Glacier, and consequently hard dolerite, even though jointed, has formed an effective barrier.

Lowering of plateau ice level to the west of the Oasis has, on this hypothesis, resulted in the shutting off of ice flowage through the Oasis by the obstructions caused by the dolerite sills (Fig. 88). Stagnant ice in the valleys was slowly lost by sublimation, leaving only vestigial glaciers in the upper parts of the valleys, and tongues from the Wilson Piedmont Glacier moving up the lower extremities. This hypothesis is set out in more detail by McKelvey and Webb (1961). From the work of Wilson it appears likely that the flow of the through glaciers ceased about 50,000 years ago. The present Upper Wright Glacier may indicate the start of a new phase of flow.

These observations of Wilson have led to a new theory for the origin of ice ages (Wilson, 1964b). If the last major glacial retreat in the McMurdo Oasis occurred about 50,000 years ago, then this area was not extensively glaciated during that last glaciation which affected areas outside Antarctica.

Wilson considers that the Antarctic ice sheet is growing. When its thickness is appreciably greater than at present it becomes unstable. The pressure melting point of ice at its base is reached and some of the mass slides into the sea, resulting in great shelf development. The shelf, extending out to about 50° S Latitude, appreciably increases the Earth's albedo, and a glacial period ensues.

As cold ice from the central plateau approaches the base of the ice sheet, outwards flow slows. The unnourished ice shelf breaks up, the Earth's albedo is lowered and the glacial period is succeeded by an interglacial.

According to Wilson's theory, the Pleistocene ice age occurred because in late Tertiary times the Antarctic Ice Sheet achieved a fairly symmetrical position with respect to the South Pole. Sufficiently large ice sheet and shelf development then occurred to initiate cyclic world glaciation.

Bibliography

ARMITAGE, K. B., and HOUSE, H. B. 1962: A Limnological Reconnaissance in the Area of McMurdo Sound, Antarctica, *Limnology and Oceanography* **7:** 36–41.

BLANK, H. R., COOPER, R. C., WHEELER, R. H., and WILLIS, I. A. G. 1963: Geology of the Koettlitz—Blue Glacier Region, South Victoria Land, Region, Antarctica, *Trans. Roy. Soc. N.Z. Geol.* **2:** 79–100.

EVERNDEN, J. F., and RICHARDS, J. R. 1962: Potassium Argon Ages in Eastern Australia, *J. Geol. Soc. Austr.* **9:** 1–49.

GRINDLEY, G. W. 1963: The Geology of the Queen Alexandra Range, Beardmore Glacier Ross Dependency, Antarctica; with Notes on the Correlation of Gondwana Sequences, *N.Z. J. Geol. Geophys.* **6:** 307–47.

GUNN, B. M., and WARREN, G. 1962: Geology of Victoria Land between the Mawson and Mulock Glaciers, Antarctica, *New Zealand Geological Survey Bull.*, n.s., **71.**

LEBEDEV, V. 1959: *Antarctica*, Foreign Languages Publishing House, Moscow.

MCCRAW, J. D. 1960: Soils of the Ross Dependency, Antarctica, *Proc. N.Z. Soc. Soil Science* **4:** 30–5.

MCKELVEY, B. C., and WEBB, P. N. 1961: Geological Reconnaissance in Victoria Land, Antarctica, *Nature* **189:** 545–7.

WILSON, A. T., and WELLMAN, H. W. 1962: Lake Vanda, an Antarctic Lake, a Solar Energy Trap, *Nature* **196:** 1171–3.

WILSON, A. T. 1964a: Evidence from Chemical Diffusion of a Climatic Change in the McMurdo Dry Valleys 1200 Years Ago. *Nature* **201:** 176–7.

WILSON, A. T. 1964b: Origin of Ice Ages: An Ice Shelf Theory for Pleistocene Glaciation. *Nature* **201:** 147–9.

CHAPTER THIRTEEN

The Flora of Antarctica

GEORGE A. LLANO, *National Science Foundation, Washington, D.C.*

> We cannot expect a rich vegetation in an ice-box.
> LYNGE AND SCHOLANDER (1932)

Introduction

The Botany of the Antarctic Voyage of 1839–43 by Joseph D. Hooker, surgeon and naturalist to Captain Ross's Antarctic Expedition in the *Erebus* and *Terror*, remained for over 50 years the sole reference to the terrestrial Antarctic flora. This first list of plant names was quite brief but it established from the very beginning of botanical discovery that which 100 years of further search has failed to disprove: that the terrestrial vegetation of Antarctica is preponderantly cryptogamous. Hooker's 18 named plants consisted of nine lichens, five mosses and four algae. It failed to include flowering plants, and this fact, perhaps more than any subsequent description of the seventh continent, served to fix in the public mind the complete bleakness and inhospitality of the Antarctic landscape.

Since Hooker's time, a number of contributions have appeared which have increased our knowledge of the existence and distribution of Antarctic plants. The presence of flowering plants has been established but the bulk of botanical research has dealt with the larger terrestrial cryptogams, the fungi, freshwater algae, hepatics, mosses and lichens. Interest in Antarctic bacteriology, according to Sieburth (1961), began with Gazert's (1901) proposed programme of work on marine bacteria and organic matter planned for the German South Polar Expedition of 1901–3. Contributions to the bacterial flora of soils, air, snow and waters, as well as to the microflora of penguin rookeries and the normal and pathogenic microflora of Antarctic animals reveal a substantial interest by bacteriologists of the next two decades in Antarctic microbiology. Present trends in research, largely as a result of increased activity in Antarctica since 1957–8, point to a renascence in bacteriological investigations encompassing all habitats. The early emphasis on plant collections continues for the support of systematic and distributional studies, but these studies are accompanied by increasing inquiry into the ecological and physiological conditions of growth under Antarctic climatological conditions.

General Microbiology of Antarctica

The investigations of the early twentieth century expeditions to the south polar regions established that the Antarctic environment is not devoid of microorganisms. Ekelöf (1908) of the Swedish South Polar Expedition of 1901–3 conducted studies on Snow Hill Island and, according to Sieburth, was the first bacteriologist to carry out an ecological study in the Antarctic on a seasonal basis. Ekelöf found that bacteria were present in soils to a depth of 20 cm and reported that the bacterial soil count was ten times greater in summer than in winter. In addition, he described the cultural characteristics for twenty-nine different bacillary, coccal, spiral and filamentous forms.

Of equal historical interest are the floristic studies of bacteria by Pirie (1912) in the South Orkneys, by Charcot (1906) along the western coast of Graham Land, and by McLean (1919) at Commonwealth Bay in George V Land. Following a lapse of twenty years in Antarctic bacteriological studies, Darling and Siple (1941) reported a qualitative study of bacteria in samples of ice, snow and sediments. Sieburth (1958) notes that these early studies showed that, despite the sparseness of the viable microflora of the air surrounding the continent, micro-organisms in detectable numbers survive to contaminate snow and glacier ice.

The flora of the upper Antarctic air in the vicinity of the mountains west of McMurdo Sound have been studied at various levels up to 6000 m. Meyer (1962) reports no microbes above 3000 m; below this altitude two species of bacteria (chromogenic, non-spore-forming rods) were isolated. In general, it was found that the numbers and kinds of micro-organisms are few in the Antarctic air and that they correlate quite well with the organisms isolated from Antarctic soils. The microbial content of the air, as in soils, drops markedly during the austral winter.

Samples of exposed soils from de-glaciated valleys, moraines, nunataks and mountain ranges assayed for microbial populations reveal the presence of bacteria, actinomycetes, yeasts, moulds and algae in varying quantities. Meyer states that some soils yield almost no organisms while others give several hundred thousand per gram. Where lichens and mosses are absent, bacteria and actino-mycetes comprise about 40% of the isolates. The dominant soil bacteria are the pigmented cocci; spore-forming rods are rare and motile gram-negative pigmented rods of the flavobacterium group are scarce. Some of the yeasts and bacteria are obligate psychophiles; a few are strict anaerobes. No thermophiles were encountered.

Boyd and Boyd (1963a) observed occasional changes in microbial numbers of soil microorganisms of Ross Island, and like Meyer (1962) report that micro-organisms could not be detected in some soils. Bacterial species common to tem-perate regions were isolated from a number of different samples. Thermophilic bacteria were present in some of the soils, and a significant portion of the bacterial population was capable of growth at 2° C. In a comparison of Arctic and Antarctic soil bacteria, Boyd (1962) found that bacteria and microorganisms were generally lower in the Antarctic. He adds, however, that thermophilic bacteria were, in many instances, the predominant type.

The studies of Flint and Stout (1961) on the microflora of soil samples from McMurdo Sound revealed more chromogenic bacteria than are normal to

temperate soils; spore-forming bacteria were rare but there was a large proportion of gram-positive cocci. Attempts to isolate aerobic nitrogen-fixing bacteria
were unsuccessful. However, Boyd (1963a), also working in the McMurdo Sound
region, demonstrated two important steps in the vital nitrogen cycle, involving
nitrate reduction and ammonification. Barghoorn and Nichols (1961) studied the
black lacustrine and marine sediments in a deep saline pond in the upper portion
of Wright Dry Valley and found that the black colour is due to the presence of
iron sulphide, precipitated by sulphate-reducing bacteria, *Desulfovibrio desulfuri-
cans* in the presence of decaying organic matter of algal (blue-green) origin. The
viability of sulphate-reducing bacteria in the sediments was demonstrated in the
laboratory by culturing in anaerobic liquid media. According to the authors,
sulphate-reducing bacteria are quite probably widely distributed in Antarctica.
The nitrogen fixing bacteria, *Azotobacter chroococcum* and *A. indicus* were reported isolated from corings of lake sediments from the Windmill Islands, Wilkes
Station, by Boyd and Boyd (1962).

Investigations of another small pond in the south fork of the Wright Valley,
which remained unfrozen during ambient temperatures of $-24°$ C, revealed a
salinity of 380,000 parts per million. Diatoms were observed but no zooplankton.
Meyer recorded three species of bacteria (*Bacillus megaterium*, *Corynebacterium*
sp., *Micrococcus* sp.) and one heterobasidiomycetus fungus (*Sporidiobolus* sp.).
Repeated air sampling in the area showed no organisms present. Bacteriological
analyses of airborne samples from the South American–Antarctic sector, however,
revealed negative gram bacilli, occasional micrococcus and dipteromorphous
bacilli, a high percentage being psychrophilous (Margni and Corte, 1962).

Except for contaminating bacteria from ships, personnel and supplies, the only
major source of bacteria in the Antarctic is from animal excrement. 'Volcanic
soils on hills, inaccessible to penguins but adjacent to penguin rookeries at
Deception Island, were found to contain bacterial types and populations similar
to the faecal material in the rookeries' (Sieburth, 1961).

Samples obtained of faeces from Scott's camp at Cape Evans and Shackleton's
camp at Cape Royds, both on Ross Island, provided an opportunity to investigate
microbial survival under natural conditions. From the Cape Evans material, a
number of cocci, pigmented rods and non-pigmented rods and a single *Rhodotorula* (pink yeast) were isolated. The isolates from the Cape Royds samples were
'predominantly non-pigmented rods, both gram-positive and negative; a few
cocci were also encountered. Five different moulds were also isolated, and a single
Rhodotorula' (Meyer, 1963). None of the material yielded *Escherichia coli* and
other enteric bacteria were of low incidence. The author concludes that the
survival of microbiota expected to be present only as a minor component indicates
that these have retained sufficient viability so as to comprise the major component
of the population. Boyd and Boyd (1963b) sampled the soils of Ross Island and
nearby mainland for coliform bacteria. None was found in penguin colonies or in
soil recently contaminated by human sewage; in a sample of pony manure left
from an earlier expedition, the results were also negative with one exception

where *Escherichia coli* were present. Studies with two freshly isolated human strains of *E. coli* and the isolate from pony manure showed that the death rate was extremely rapid although the animal strain was more resistant. Research into the survival of sewage bacteria (*E. coli*) in zero-centigrade sea water (Anonymous, 1963a) for the development of sanitary systems in polar regions confirms previous studies which showed that low temperatures, as encountered in polar areas, favour survival of bacteria in sea water. Numbers of bacteria in sewage discharged into polar waters are reduced largely through dilution, sedimentation and the presence of antagonistic organisms.

Yeasts are relatively scarce biological components of Antarctic air but are found with more frequency in Antarctic soils. In some cases, moulds and yeasts comprise 60% of the total isolates. These include the non-pigmented mycelial *Trichosporon* and non-mycelial *Rhodotorula* types. Earlier DiMenna (1960) succeeded in obtaining cultures of the yeast *Candida scottii* from McMurdo Sound soil samples. Meyer, Morrow and Wyss (1962) analysed for viability a 50-year-old yeast found in an intact bottle of baker's yeast at Scott's 1911 camp. Five successive layers were sampled. The uppermost proved negative. The second sample produced several colonies of *Rhodotorula*. From the following successive layers were isolated *Saccharomyces cerevisiae* Hansen, *Rhodotorula pallida* Lodder, the moulds *Absidia corymbifera* Lichtheim, *Rhizopus arrhizus* Fisher, and the bacteria, *Bacillus* sp., *Pseudomonas* sp., and members of the Micrococcaceae.

The dominant air micro-organisms are the spores of the moulds *Penicillium* and *Aspergillus*. According to Meyer, *Alternaria* and *Hormodendrum* occur with less frequency than in comparable temperate climate samplings. Corte and Daglio (1963) isolated 169 colonies of airborne spores collected near Bahía Esperanza, Ellsworth Station and on the Danco Coast during the summer of 1960–1. Eight microfungus genera were identified: *Penicillium*, *Aspergillus*, *Mucor*, *Cladosporium*, *Curvalaria*, *Helminthosporium*, *Phycomyces*, and *Micelliae sterilia* of which only the first three were known from the Antarctic Continent and the rest, together with their species, are for the first time recorded from the south polar environment (Corte and Daglio, 1963). A recently published list of Antarctic microfungi by Corte and Daglio (1964) reports that 107 species have been isolated from soil, air, snow and mosses. The majority correspond to sterile mycelia; *Penicillium janthinellum* is the most frequent. Most of the fungi are cosmopolitan and of wide geographical distribution. In general, the mycological flora is represented by a few genera of many species.

Flint and Stout (1960) remarked on the scarcity of soil actinomycetes in the McMurdo Sound soils and they succeeded in isolating only a *Streptomyces* from one site. Meyer found both the soft actinomycetes (*Nocardia*) and dry actinomycetes (*Streptomyces*). 'Eighty-five per cent of the mould isolates are encompassed in twelve genera: *Aspergillus*, *Penicillium*, *Scopulariopsis*, *Fusarium*, *Alternaria*, *Hormodendrum*, *Cladosporium*, *Pullularia*, *Helminthosporium*, *Curvularia*, *Chaetomium*, and *Phoma*. More than 50% of the mould isolates are *Aspergillus*, *Penicillium*, or *Hormodendrum*. In soils associated with moss,

Chaetomium and *Phoma* are more prominent. The dry actinomycetes are rare in such soils.' Tubaki (1961) reported the isolation of algicolous fungus, *Blodgettia borneti* from frozen soil samples obtained near the Japanese Antarctic Expedition base at East and West Ongul Islands, Prince Olav Coast. From 92 probes into five soil samples from the South Orkney and South Shetland Islands and the tip of Graham Land, Harder and Persil (1962) extracted three lower phycomycetes: *Rhizophydium utriculare*, *R. sphaerotheca*, and *Hyphochytrium* cf. *catenoides*. These are soil phycomycetes of world-wide distribution.

Antarctic Phanerogams

The only flowering plants known to occur on the Antarctic Continent are members of the Gramineae and Caryophyllaceae families. The distribution of phanerogams is restricted to Graham Land and its offshore islands, the South Shetlands and the South Orkney Islands. On the Peninsula, no phanerogams have been reported from the east coast or islands in the Weddell Sea; their distribution along the west coast of Graham Land extends to the southern part of Adelaide Island, Marguerite Bay.

The grass *Deschampsia antarctica* Desv., first described by Hooker in 1837, after a specimen collected by Dr James Eights of Albany, New York, on the South Shetland Islands during a voyage of 1829–30, was the first flowering plant reported from the Antarctic. The species was seen by Hooker on Cape Horn, the Falklands and on Kerguelen; it is known only from the Southern Hemisphere, and extends from high Andean valleys on the 34th parallel south to Tierra del Fuego, South Georgia, and to Latitude 68° 50′ W on Graham Land. The species was rediscovered in 1898 by Racovitza of the Belgian Antarctic Expedition at Cape van Beneden. Skottsberg (1954) saw it growing there in 1902: 'Under special circumstances *Deschampsia* will form patches large enough to allow us to speak of a *Deschampsia* association, either more or less pure, with a bottom layer of bryophytes and lichens. It was observed with flowers everywhere.' Parodi (1949) refers to Hooker's species as *Deschampsia elegantulo* Steud.; the new combination, according to Skottsberg, is unnecessary and may be avoided by citing the species as *Deschampsia antarctica* Desv. Parodi (1949) also reports *D. parvula* (Hook. fil.) Desv., as another grass species closely resembling *D. antarctica* Desv., and also found in Antarctica. According to Skottsberg (1954), *D. parvula* Steud. is a separate species and does not occur in the Antarctic.

The pink, *Colobanthus crassifolius* (D'Urv.) Hook. fil., while rarer than *Deschampsia*, is found in the same localities in Graham Land. As in the case of *Deschampsia antarctica*, Hooker also failed to encounter *Colobanthus crassifolius* during his Antarctic voyage.

Further search has revealed another phanerogam: a single specimen of *Poa annua* L. found by Frödin in Whaler's Bay, Deception Island, in 1953. Skottsberg records: 'As far as I know this is the first record of a weed in the Antarctic.'

'*Colobanthus*,' observes Skottsberg (1954), 'is an old Antarctic genus and *Deschampsia* is well represented in the South. We have reason to believe that *C.*

crassifolius and *D. antarctica* belonged to the Preglacial flora but we have no right to assume that they were able to survive the glacial epoch. It seems safer to regard them as Postglacial immigrants, the only vascular plants that managed to cross the wide Drake Strait and establish themselves successfully in high southern latitudes.' Seed-bearing plants are, so far, known only from Graham Land; it is quite likely that the species in question will not be reported from elsewhere on the continent, and that their present distribution was established before the arrival of the sealers and whalers. There is no question but that the Earth's seventh continent is, to all practical purposes, uniquely devoid of a flowering vegetation. However, Antarctica has not always been a land without vegetation. As a result of his Antarctic experience in 1839–43, Joseph Hooker was of the opinion that the Antarctic Continent had at one time been well vegetated. Skottsberg's contribution to Antarctic botany began in 1901 while on the Swedish Antarctic Expedition, when the first fossil remains of temperate-type vegetation were recovered from Seymour Island, thus vindicating Hooker's views. Plant fossils have now been studied from six sites in West Antarctica, all in Graham Land and its associated islands, with a time range of from Middle Jurassic to Lower Tertiary. Forty-one sites are known from East Antarctica, principally in the Trans-Antarctic Mountains and mostly of Permo-Carboniferous age (Plumstead, 1963). *Nothofagus* and conifers are associated with the fossil flora of West Antarctica; *Glossopteris, Arberiella, Samaropsis* fossil vegetation is characteristic of the ancient flora of East Antarctica.

Skottsberg contributed 69 papers and books on Antarctic botany in the period 1902–1960; much of his interest was directed toward systematics and distribution of the more numerous and varied floras of the Subantarctic islands. Greene and Greene (1963) define all land south of 60° S, but including the South Sandwich Islands and Bouvetøya, within the Antarctic zone; South Georgia, Prince Edward Islands, Crozet and Kerguelen Islands, and Heard and Macquarie Islands are considered in the Subantarctic zone. The vascular and cryptogamous floras of the latter group are characterized by a high degree of endemism. Greene and Greene have prepared check lists of native floras for both zones with a list of synonyms and a special section on sources of materials for each island in order to clarify discrepancies in the various accounts of these floras. Moore (1964) proposes the need to apply the methods and concepts of modern taxonomy to solve the problems posed by the disjunct floras circling Antarctica before further successful progress can be made in understanding the evolution and distribution of the southern circumpolar vascular vegetation.

The Cryptogamous Flora

The first fungus known from the Antarctic was recorded by the Belgian Antarctic Expedition on the grass *Deschampsia antarctica*. This fungus is *Sclerotium antarcticum* Bomm. et Rous (1905), and its distribution is dependent on the presence of the grass which is restricted to Graham Land. Other fungi have been reported on some of the Subantarctic islands close to Antarctica. Martinez (1951) recorded three species of Agarics from Deception Island and, more recently, Singer (1957) has described another, *Omphalina antarctica*. The occurrence of *Galactina adae* (Stadler) Boudir [*Peziza domiciliana*] on wood suggests that this fungus was brought onto the island on lumber imported from Argentina. Singer in 1964 on the basis of a systematical ecological investigation of Antarctic basidiomycetes reports a total of five species and one variety of the genera *Omphalina* and *Galerina*; two of them are known only from Antarctica and in his opinion belong to the aboriginal mycological flora of the continent.

The fresh-water diatom vegetations of the Kronprins Olav Kyst have been studied by Fukushima (1962a, b) who reports on samples collected from brackish and fresh water ponds in the Kasumi Rock and Shin-nan Rock ice-free areas. Thirty algae samples, predominantly blue-green, were collected in the Kasumi Rock area. He found the diatom flora of the fresh water ponds different from that of the brackish ones. The principal species of the fresh and brackish ponds were, respectively, *Navicula muticopsis* and *Navicula cryptocephala*. Thirty-four of 46 species reported have been identified. The Shin-nan Rock area has four ponds with a sparse population. Of the 34 species reported, four are endemic. Individuals of four pelagic species are common in a pond nearest the sea as well as in the adjacent sea.

Wille's (1928) review of the freshwater algae listed in Antarctic expeditionary publications numbered, according to Drouet (1961), some 160 taxa, 'chiefly of Myxophyceae and the smaller Chlorophyceae'. The freshwater diatoms reported from the Antarctic region number about sixty taxa (Carlson, 1913; Fritsch, 1917). Drouet's (1962) revision of Antarctic Oscillatoriaceae (blue-green algae) includes some fifty species reported in the literature on the Antarctic flora. Of these, about twenty, along with numerous subspecific taxa, have been described as new; but according to Drouet, most of these are referrable to the three most common terrestrial species of the Continent; i.e. *Microcoleus vaginatus* (Vauch.) Gom., *M. chthonoplastes* (Mert.) Zanard, and *Plectonema Nostocorum* Born, or to other widely distributed species found in Antarctica.

Field studies carried out since 1957 have enlarged our knowledge of the terrestrial algae of Antarctica. Flint's and Stout's (1960) work on the microbiology of the McMurdo Sound region reports on ten genera of terrestrial algae; these include *Chlamydomonas, Chlorella, Chlorococcum, Stichococcus, Nostoc, Hantzschia, Bumilleriopsis, Radiosphaera, Heterothrix, Heterococcus*. Of this list, the last four genera, according to the authors have not been reported previously from the continent. Algae from terrestrial and fresh water habitats in Antarctica were examined by Holm-Hansen (1963) for ability to fix atmospheric nitrogen; *Nostoc commune* was the only species capable of growing in nitrogen-free medium and nitrogen fixation by this species was verified by assimilation of N^{15}.

In commenting on problems in the taxonomy and geographic distribution of Antarctic marine algae Papenfuss (1964) states:

> Many Antarctic marine algae have a geographical range which extends into

M

the Subantarctic. It seems advisable, therefore, as far as the algae are concerned, to regard the Antarctic and Subantarctic as forming a single biogeographic province. A total of some 400 species, representative of more than 150 genera, have been reported from the following localities: Palmer Peninsula (Graham Land), Enderby Land, Commonwealth Bay (George V Land), the Terre Adélie coast, Victoria Land, Fuegia, Falkland Islands, South Georgia, South Orkneys, South Shetlands, Prince Edward Islands, Îles Crozet, Îles Kerguelen, Heard Island, Macquarie Island, Auckland Islands, and Campbell Island.

Large gaps exist in our knowledge of the morphology and taxonomy of Antarctic algae, and, at present, little can be concluded about the identity and distribution of many of the forms. A fairly large number has been referred to species erected on material from other parts of the world, including the Northern Hemisphere. These identifications require confirmation. More than thirty genera have been established on material from Antarctica. Several of these genera, including some of the largest of Antarctic algae, cannot be assigned to known families (or orders), nor are they sufficiently understood to justify the creation of new families.

A systematic list and bibliography of Antarctic and sub-Antarctic benthic marine algae, including synonyms, has been published in the *Antarctic Research Series* by Papenfuss (1964). He includes only four Chlorophycophyta, Xanthophyceae, Phaeophycophyta, and Rhodophycophyta. Neushul (1963) pioneered in the use of scuba for the underwater study of marine algae. He collected three endemic brown algae, *Ascoseira*, *Cystosphaera* and *Phyllogigas*, describing for the first time the reproductive bodies of the latter genus.

Skottsberg (1964) compiled a list of Antarctic algae, excluding species of the Cyanophyceae and freshwater species, which indicates that the total number of Antarctic marine algae species is 96. Of this total, 39·6% or 38 are reported endemic, including six species known only from South Georgia. Twenty-one are cited as circumpolar and another 18 have a reported distribution in temperate seas of both hemispheres.

Only four species of Hepaticae have been described from Antarctica; all are apparently restricted to the northernmost tip of Graham Land and the off-lying islands.

Mosses are more numerous and more widely distributed. Steere (1961) lists some seventy species although he adds that several may turn out to be synonymous with other species, thereby reducing this number. 'Whereas one finds many species and genera endemic to Arctic regions and widely distributed therein, the Antarctic mosses and liverworts show a low percentage of endemic species and a surprisingly large percentage of species with a broad, almost cosmopolitan distribution, especially in the Northern Hemisphere' (Du Rietz, 1940).

Greene, when reviewing problems and progress in Antarctic bryology at the Antarctic Biological Symposium, Paris (1964) noted, in part:

Although the presence of bryophytes in the Scotia Arc–Graham Land Sector has been known since the visit of Eights over 130 years ago, knowledge of the taxonomy and distribution of this group of plants in Antarctic regions is still very defective. No assessment is available of the total flora from the Sub-antarctic zone and such a list for the Antarctic zone has only recently been published. The taxonomic status of many of the reported species is in doubt, either due to the inadequacy of existing description or to the suspicion that many of the 'new species' ought to be treated as synonyms of existing taxa.

Field work in South Georgia has added many species and genera to the island's flora, e.g. *Sphagnum fimbriatum*. Revision work on the genus *Tortula* has resulted, amongst other changes, in the reduction of *T. rubra* to the status of a synonym of *T. robusta* and the addition of *T. serrata* to the South Georgian check list.

Although the fruiting of mosses has been reported as rare in the area, pro-visional results from a study of the reproductive behaviour of *Polytrichum strictum* suggest that this moss is capable of completing its life cycle on South Georgia.

Field survey elsewhere in the Scotia Arc–Graham Land sector has revealed the presence of a considerably richer bryophyte flora than previously suspected and material has been obtained of many genera and species not previously re-ported from the Antarctic zone.

Lichens comprise the bulk of the terrestrial vegetation and although absent from much of the available ice-free surfaces, they are still the most abundant and the most widely distributed element of the Antarctic flora. In a land without blossoms, lichens provide a modicum of colour. The question of how many species make up the Antarctic lichen flora has long been a matter of general interest. Llano's (1956) estimate of about 400 taxa, based on the numbers re-ported in the literature, does not exclude the probability of duplication through synonymy. There is no doubt that the great profusion of forms and the necessity for critical study makes any enumeration of the Antarctic lichen flora highly arbitrary. It is quite certain, however, that the lichens of the Antarctic are less representative in families and genera and far less numerous in species than the lichen vegetation of the Arctic. It is also quite evident that, of the three life-forms characteristic of lichens, the crustaceous is predominant; and that the foliose and fructicose forms are in the minority. However, published reports on the lichens reveal various philosophies in classification which have led to serious confusion in the systematics of Antarctic lichens and have given rise to numerous questions in nomenclature. This is one reason why even at this late date there is still uncertainty as to the actual number of plants ascribed to the region. Ant-arctic lichenology, in brief, has inherited a number of problems of taxonomic significance which necessitates the restudy of earlier specimens if there is to be a better understanding of the lichen vegetation of the continent, or of its relation-ship to the vegetation of both the Southern and Northern Hemispheres.

Geographical Distribution

Vegetation in the form of lichens or mosses has been reported from almost all ice-free land accessible from the sea; and it is quite apparent that the pattern of plant distribution in Antarctica is circumpolar. It is also quite probable that this pattern represents the manner by which plants first became established; the coasts were first exposed, and from the periphery plants succeeded in invading favourable sites in the interior. As indicated earlier, the vascular flora represented by the genera *Deschampsia* and *Colobanthus* is restricted to a narrow zone along the western coast of Graham Land; there is little doubt that seed plants appeared on the continent much later than the cryptogams and that they most probably invaded the continent from South America, unless they represent relics of the pre-Quaternary Period.

Jules Cardot's (1908) study of the collections of the Swedish South Polar Expedition, which also includes reference to earlier materials, is still the only comprehensive review of the bryophytes of Antarctica. Cardot lists 47% of the then known species as indigenous to the Antarctic Continent; the remaining 53%, including species found on some Subantarctic islands, are for the most part described as cosmopolitan. He concludes that the Antarctic bryological flora is more Boreal than Magellanic. Bartram (1938) described five mosses collected on nunataks by the second Byrd Antarctic Expedition. He states: 'It is not without significance that these mosses, in a broad way, are closely allied to some of the most cosmopolitan specific types . . .', adding: ' . . . where did these mosses come from? Introduction through the agency of birds or by means of air currents is possible but hardly probable. A more likely theory is that these are representative of a few extremely hardy, vigorous remnants of a former climax vegetation that have managed to maintain a hold on life in the face of increasingly rigorous conditions of almost unbelievable severity.' Horikawa and Ando (1961) in a report on the mosses of Ongul Islands list four species. Two of these (*Ceratodon purpureus* (Hedw.) Brid., and *Bryum argenteum* Hedw.) have a world-wide distribution; one (*Bryum inconnexum* Cardot) was first recorded by Cardot from Graham Land but may have a more extended range in Marie Byrd Land, McMurdo Sound, and Queen Mary Land. The fourth species (*Bryum ongulense* Horikawa et Ando) is described as new. Clifford (1957) records *Bryum antarcticum* Hook. f. et Wils. from Mawson and Terre Adélie noting that it also occurs in Marie Byrd Land (Bartram 1938), Victoria Land (Cardot 1907), Kaiser Wilhelm II Land (Brotherus 1906) and in several localities in Graham Land. Cardot early observed that it was quite probable that the circumpolar Antarctic moss flora is very uniform. Recent records appear to bear out this statement.

The Antarctic lichen flora is more numerous in species and is more wide-spread than the mosses; at many sites, it is the only vegetation. Agreement on the geographical relationships of this group is, however, sharply divided. The first opinion was expressed by Taylor (Hooker and Taylor, 1844) who stated: ' . . . we find in the list of Antarctic lichens, a great number common to our

Northern Hemisphere.' Vainio (1904), who reported on the Belgian collections, and Darbishire (1912) who examined the Swedish materials, found that over half of the species brought back by these expeditions from Graham Land are common to Arctic regions. Lamb's (1948) critical study of the Antarctic Pyrenocarp lichens he collected in Graham Land lists about one-half of the species as cosmopolitan. Hue (1915) reported that 81% of the species described from the material collected by Charcot's expeditions to Graham Land were endemic. Dodge and Baker (1938) described 94% of the second Byrd Antarctic Expedition lichens as new to science.

Dodge (1964) describes the Kerguelen Islands' lichen flora as completely endemic with no close relationship with that of Antarctica. The Macquarie Island flora, according to Dodge, shows a close relation to the alpine flora of the South Island of New Zealand, the Aucklands, and Campbell Island. The flora of Tierra del Fuego is considered to have some relations to the flora of the Graham Land portion of the Antarctic Peninsula via the South Shetlands.

The solution to questions on the geographical distribution of the Antarctic lichen flora lies in lichen systematics, and primarily on the re-assessment of type material, the re-evaluation of past collections, and the study of new collections which are now sufficiently representative of the Antarctic vegetation to permit a better insight into the problem of endemism. The reviews of the genus *Neuropogon* by Lamb (1939, 1948a) and of the Antarctic Pyrenocarp lichens (Lamb, 1948) have served to clarify the situation with respect to these lichen groups. In the case of *Neuropogon*, Lamb has established that it is predominantly Antarctic and Subantarctic in distribution and of southern origin; that with the exception of one species, *Neuropogon sulphureus*, long considered a bi-polar species, the genus is restricted to the Southern Hemisphere. Llano's (1950) monograph of the Umbilicariaceae indicates a greater uniformity of the Antarctic species of this cosmopolitan lichen family than is indicated in the literature. One species, *Omphalodiscus decussatus* extends throughout the continent, both along the coast and on nunataks, often in dense colonies, and frequently to the exclusion of all other vegetation.

Floristic Regions

The insularity of Antarctica is one reason for the paucity of species in the flora as a whole. The availability of ice-free land suitable for the establishment of vegetation is severely restricted and it is estimated that this may not exceed 10,400 km^2 in a continental area of 14,000,000 km^2. Brown (1906) stressed the unfavourable factors for plant growth, particularly 'the short and inadequate summers' and 'in this want of a season of growth'. Skottsberg (1905) suggested that the strong Antarctic winds constituted another unfavourable factor. Siple (1938) considered that the effect of wind-driven snow 'must have a strong bearing upon the distribution problem of the plants.' Perkins (1945) observed that: 'the greatest single factor limiting the number and type of plants and their distribution in the Antarctic is that of available water'.

It has been apparent from the earliest explorations that the vegetation of Graham Land is more profuse, and richer in species than elsewhere on the continent. It is characterized by a greater abundance of mosses and lichens; it is also a unique locality for two Subantarctic groups of plants, the vascular genera *Deschampsia* and *Colobanthus* and five liverwort species (Steere, 1961). Bryant (1945) found on Lagotellerie Island (67° 56′ S, 67° 24′ W): 'A surprising little valley . . . behind a rocky ridge, and immediately named Shangri-La Valley because here, . . . one could find grassy slopes and spongy banks of moss.' This biologically favourable condition extends as a narrow zone along the western coast of the peninsula and includes the offshore islands, from approximately 62° to 68° S. The area is one of higher summer temperatures and more fluid precipitation and meltwater than is recorded elsewhere on the continent.

Antarctica, in brief, consists of two major botanical regions, the peninsula region and the rest of the continent. On the continent, a further distinction is apparent in that mosses, in general, and some lichens are more frequently encountered along the coast than inland. This coastal distribution forms an interesting geographical and ecological grouping which may be identified as the oceanic element in contrast to those species found inland on nunataks and snow-free mountain slopes, comprising the continental element.

The climate of the Antarctic coastline in contrast to that of Graham Land is extremely dry; many areas may be considered physiological deserts. The climate of the McMurdo Sound region is rigorous and characterized by low temperatures and very light precipitation, all in the form of snow. The mean annual air temperature on Ross Island is approximately $-17°$ C. In the peak of summer, November to January, when the average daily hours of bright sunshine are greatest, air temperature has been known to rise two to three degrees above 0° C. The lichen flora on Ross Island occurs only in the area around McMurdo Station and consists entirely of minute crustaceous lichen species spread thinly along frost cracks over the ground or in niches and crevices in the rock. The two pre-requisites which appear to favour plant growth at McMurdo are basic to all habitats in Antarctica. These are the dark-coloured substrate with a relatively high ground temperature; and a meltwater source from surrounding ice fields or light snow flurries during the austral summer.

Across from Ross Island in the lee of the dominating Royal Society Range lies the largest contiguous region of bare land in Antarctica. The area is 15–25 km wide and at least 150 km long; it consists of alternating eastward winding ridges and valleys, with an average relief of 1000 to 2000 m and a total relief of 4000 m. Taylor Dry Valley (Llano 1962) which lies in the rain-shadow of the Royal Society Range proved to be without vegetation at levels below 1000 m. Along this altitude, infrequent snow flurries provide a source of meltwater during the austral summer, and in this zone, crustaceous lichens and the foliaceous *Umbilicaria* were found growing on dolerite and granite ledges.

The Bunger Hills and Vestfold Hills 'oases' of the Knox Coast comprise other large areas which are notably ice-free in the summer months and have little or no vegetation. According to Kirchak (1958), katabatic winds and frontal cyclones together sweep the ice surface and oases free of snow in winter. A relatively warm microclimate forms in the oases in the summer. The 'oases', according to Dolgushin (1958), possess a dry desert climate; the average monthly relative humidity for the summer in the Bunger Hills is 40–45%, at times falling to 15%.

There are, however, many other localities along the Antarctic coast which have a well developed vegetation. The summit and slopes of the headland at Cape Hallett, for example, proved unexpectedly rich in mosses and lichens. Lichens predominate not only on the summit but on the unstable debris of the steep slopes down to about 100 m above the upper limits of the large penguin rookery which covers almost all of Seabee Hook. The lichen flora here has a luxuriousness out of all proportion to its surroundings. This is particularly true of the vegetation on the summit but it is equally apparent on the loose talus of the steep, 500 m slope. An obvious factor in the development of the vegetation at this locality is the 70,000 penguin rookery at the base of the headland and its 1200 years' accumulation of guano. This is raised by air currents as a fine powder and serves to fertilize the face of the slope and the summit. No lichens were found on the fifty-five acres of the rookery proper.

Wilkes Station on the Antarctic Circle is an area with a varied and profuse cryptogamic vegetation (Llano 1958). Mosses are in the minority and occur in small pockets of sandy soil. The crustaceous lichens predominate, covering rock ledges and boulders in great profusion from the sea shore inland to the edge of the ice. Foliaceous and fructicose lichen forms are represented, respectively, by the families Umbilicariaceae and Usneaceae, often in dense mats to the exclusion of the crustaceous forms. The extent and richness of the lichen flora in this area clearly indicate a long period of establishment, but plant growth is undoubtedly favoured by the downward drainage of meltwater from upper snow fields, and the availability of nitrate products from the surrounding nesting areas of penguins and oceanic birds.

Ecology

The ecological succession of plant life in a de-glaciated area begins with the appearance of algae. This is the present stage of the foreland of the Wilson Piedmont Glacier, Victoria Land, and Cape Evans and Cape Royds, Ross Island. Soil micro-organisms appear next, and eventually mosses and/or lichens. Some lichens grow on mosses and destroy them. The only organisms which feed on lichens to any appreciable extent are the Collembola and mites; and since these arthropods do not serve as food for other organisms, the cycle represents a simple and primitive food chain.

The success of lichens in becoming established on newly exposed land is more a function of their resistance to severe drought than to extreme low temperatures. In either situation, lichens persist in a dormant state (Scholander, 1953) for long periods, and this is essentially their means for survival under Antarctic conditions. Siple (1938) recorded a black bulb reading on rocks of 48·9° C, and noted that plant growth on nunataks must be adapted to unfavourable temperature changes. Rock temperatures in the Horlick Mountains were found to vary from −15° C to 27·8° C within a three-hour span. Thus, while the plants are in the polar zone, their circum-ambient world is that layer of warm air immediately above the ground. For the period during which the Sun shines, the plant is immersed in a micro-climate not much different from a warm summer's day under temperate conditions.

Success in colonization is dependent on growth; and lichen metabolism, no less than that of other plants, requires some fluids and nutrients. The variation of the lichen vegetation even over a small area is remarkably striking and serves to illustrate the dependence of the vegetation on snow cover whose melt provides the principal and often the only source of moisture.

The response to ammoniacal decomposition products is equally evident in the amount of vegetation. Siple (1938) observed that mountain peaks which harbour bird rookeries are also the richest in plant cover, and that the difference in the quantity of vegetation is astounding. Lichen associations are notable for their nitrophilous communities. This is a common phenomenon around penguin rookeries and skua nesting areas; at Cape Hallett and Wilkes Station the pattern of the lichen vegetation extends from the outer boundary of the rookeries in broadly definable bands according to the decreasing nitrate content of the habitat.

The question whether lichen vegetation precedes the nesting of birds on nunataks or follows their appearance is pertinent to ecological succession. The occurrence of lichens in the absence of bird life in the Taylor Dry Valley has been noted. A similar condition was also observed on the Haupt Nunatak near Wilkes Station. Here the rocks protrude through the ice cover as a low ridge. Moisture is derived from the melting of ice and snow crystals blown onto the dark, sun-warmed rocks. Vegetation is well established, but largely on the lee side of the ridge as well as on rocks partially below the ice where melt-back leaves each rock in a hollow. The rocks thus encased in a 'greenhouse' of translucent snow, and appropriately lighted and moistened by trickles of moisture from melting, powdered snow, are completely protected from wind.

Goldman (1964) reports that the flora and fauna of Antarctic fresh waters are subject to severe climatic restrictions. Productivity in the littoral melt zone of the dry valley lakes in Victoria Land was appreciably higher than that recorded beneath the ice. The limited phytoplankton population under almost 4 m of ice in these lakes is adapted to low light intensity. Evidence of nitrogen deficiency was found in the littoral zone of Lake Vanda. Algal growth at Cape Evans was severely inhibited by high light intensity during the middle of the Antarctic summer. Samples of phytoplankton which were protected from 80% of the incident light by neutral density filters had higher rates of carbon fixation than did samples which were less shaded. The skua population contributed appreciable quantities of organic nitrogen and salts to one lake. The abundance of the birds and a measurable change in the salt concentration associated with their activity is believed to influence the melting and primary productivity of the lake.

Skuas spend much of their time swimming and bathing in fresh water melt ponds and this, plus their wide ranging habits, is, undoubtedly, a strong factor in the dispersion of algae throughout the periphery of the Antarctic Continent.

Investigation of melt water pools and ponds from 39° E to 49° E by Megura (1962) revealed some algae on the bottom in water heated by solar radiation from 1°–14° C; air temperature is reported at below 5° C. Nutrient salts were very scant; traces of PO_3, NO_2 and NH_3 were detected. SiO_2 and dissolved oxygen were present in minute quantities.

Murray (1963) lists 30 lichens and four moss species and varieties from Cape Hallett. Rudolph (1963) carried out a vegetational analysis of a plot 400 by 93 feet which he describes as having a relatively abundant plant cover, covering about 15·4% of the area. Of this, 12·8% is algae, 2·4% mosses, and 0·2% lichens. The plants include *Prasiola crispa*, *Bryum argentium*, *Xanthoria mawsoni*, *Parmelia coreyi*, *Caloplaca antarctica*, and *Buellia frigida*. The distribution of these types is dependent on the availability of water in their microhabitats. Moisture content of the plants may reach over 1000% of dry weight in summer, air temperatures up to 42°F, and as high as 68° F at $\frac{1}{4}$ inch above the moss cover. Occasional rock surface temperatures of 90° F were measured.

Holdgate (1964) states that in the 'outer Antarctic zone' on Signy Island, South Orkneys, plant growth is less dependent on incident radiation. He reports a fairly rich flora of bryophytes and two species of flowering plants. The vegetation is distributed in accordance with exposure, ground moisture, insolation and soil stability. The two flowering plants are concentrated in wet lowland 'radiation traps.' The moss mats capacity to absorb radiation is related to the structure of the mat and its large air space. Holdgate's observations in the South Sandwich group leads him to suggest that ecological rather than distributional difficulties underlie the barrenness of many Antarctic regions.

The Antarctic vegetation is characterized as one of pioneer associations, and includes a number of habitats which, while not entirely unique to the Antarctic environment, serve to identify various ecological situations. In general, the distribution of lichens throughout Antarctica is dependent on irrigation by meltwater. Their disposition over rocks and the ground outlines the pattern of drainage, and wherever there is sufficient moisture, lichens may be found. Lamb (1948) observed that in the Antarctic amphibious lichens may be in contact with water for only short periods of time during the growing period. The marine amphibious Pyrenocarps occupy two habitats which Lamb identifies as the salt spray and the inter-tidal zones. *Verrucaria serpuloides* M. Lamb, is unique in that it tolerates constant submersion in sea water. This lichen occurs at the same level as encrusting algae, forming a submarine association just below the lowest ebb tide. The moss, *Bryum korotkevicziae* Sav.-Ljub. et Z. Smirn., forms a similar submarine association with algae (Savicz-Ljubitskaja, 1959) to depths of 33–36 m in the fresh waters of Lake Figurnoye, of the Bunger and Vestfold Hills.

While the edge of the permanent land ice marks the limit of vegetation, many lichens and mosses are highly tolerant to prolonged snow cover and are found in areas where snowdrifts persist until quite late in the season. These are adjusted to a very short growing period and in some years may possibly remain covered throughout a growing season. Snow banks in the lee of high boulders are also important in the establishment of lichen colonies on the apex of these boulders which cannot possibly be irrigated by other meltwater sources.

Luxuriant lichen vegetation is found beneath scree, under loose rubble over flat ground and, in one area, below a thin layer of marble chips. Indeed, the vegetation around McMurdo Station is found largely growing in miniature caves under the talus on slopes or in the innumerable frost cracks over the ground where blown snow provides the primary meltwater source. The degree of light available to the plant varies from very little to subdued and, in some cases, the site is quite dark.

The occurrence of cryoplankton in the interior has not been reported despite the many observers who have participated in field and traverse activities. It is apparently a phenomenon of coastal areas and here of limited occurrence. Llano (1962) observed red and green snow algae only in the vicinity of Wilkes Station during a period of thaw in late January 1958. The colouration was vivid and occurred only in a saddle where the snow was highly saturated with water; the area was adjacent to bare ground from which soil particles, guano dust, penguin feathers, etc., had been blown onto the snow. The cryoplankton, according to Dr Francis Drouet, Philadelphia Academy of Sciences, included the algae, *Protococcus nivalis* (Bauer.) Ag., and *Ancyclonema nordenskiöldi* Buggr, diatoms, and undetermined fungi. Corte (1962) reports that of 18 species of algae recovered from semi-frozen lakes in the Hope Bay area, five are typical components of the snow cryoplankton. The latter species had not been described previously from this area of Antarctica.

Biliography

ANONYMOUS. 1963: Papers on Antarctic and Sub-Antarctic Botany by Dr C. J. F. Skottsberg, *Polar Rec.* **11**(74): 605–8.

ANONYMOUS. 1963a: *Survival of Sewage Bacteria in Zero-Centigrade Sea Waters*, US Naval Civil Eng. Lab., Port Hueneme, Cal., Tech. Rept. R. 256.

BARGHOORN, E. S. and NICHOLS, R. L. 1961: Sulfate-reducing Bacteria and Pyritic Sediments in Antarctica. *Science* **13**: 190.

BARTRAM, E. B. 1938: Second Byrd Antarctic Expedition-Botany. III. Mosses. *Ann. Missouri Bot. Gdn.* **25**: 719–24.

BOMMER, E., and ROUSSEAU, E. 1905: *Champignons*. Results Voyage S.Y. *Belgica*, 1897–99, *Rapp. scientifiques, Bot. Anvers.*

BOYD, WILLIAM L., and JOSEPHINE W. BOYD, 1962: Presence of *Azotobacter* Species in Polar Regions, *J. Bacteriol.* **83**(2): 429–30.

BOYD, WILLIAM L. 1962: Comparison of Soil Bacteria and their Metabolic Activities in Arctic and Antarctic Regions, *Polar Rec.* **11**(72): 319.

BOYD, WILLIAM L., and JOSEPHINE W. BOYD, 1963a: Soil Microorganisms of the McMurdo Sound Area, Antarctica, *Appl. Microbiol.* 11(2): 116–21.

BOYD, WILLIAM L., and JOSEPHINE W. BOYD, 1963b: Viability of Coliform Bacteria in Antarctic Soil, *J. Bacteriol.* 85(5): 1121–3.

BROTHERUS, V. F. 1906: Deutsche Südpolar-Exped. 1903–5. 8, Botany.

BROWN, R. N. RUDMORE, 1906: Antarctic Botany: its Present State and Future Problems, *Scot. Geogr. Mag.* 22: 473–84.

BRYANT, H. M. 1945: Biology at East Base, Palmer Peninsula, Antarctica. *In:* Reports on Scientific Results of the US Antarctic Service Expedition, 1939–41, *Proc. Amer. Phil. Soc.* 89(1): 256–69.

CALMAN, W. T. 1937: James Eights, a Pioneer Antarctic Naturalist, *Proc. Linn. Soc. Lond.* 4: 171–84.

CARDOT, J. 1907: National Antarctic Expedition 1901–4. Nat. His. 3 Musci.

CARDOT, J. 1908: La flore bryologique des terres Magellaniques, de la Georgie du Sud et de l'Antarctide, *Wiss. Ergeb. Schwed. Südpolar-Exped. 1901–3* 4(8): 1–298.

CARLSON, G. W. F. 1913: Süsswasseralgen aus der Antarctis, Südgeorgien und der Falkland Inseln, *Wiss. Ergeb. Schwed. Südpolar-Exped. 1901–3* 4(14): 1–94.

CHARCOT, J. B. 1906: Bacteriologie. *In: Le Français du Pole Sud*, Paris, 463.

CLIFFORD, H. T. 1957: New Records for Antarctic Mosses, *Australian Journ. Sci.* 20(4): 115.

CORTE, ALFREDO. 1962: Fresh-Water Algae in Semifrozen Lakes of Hope Bay, Antarctic Peninsula, *Contrib. Inst. Antartico. Argentino* 69.

CORTE, ALFREDO, and DAGLIO, C. A. N. 1963: Micromycetes Isolated in the Antarctic, *Contrib. Inst. Antartico Argentino* 74.

CORTE, ALFREDO, and DAGLIO, C. A. N. 1964: A Mycological Study of the Antarctic Air, *Biol. Antarctique, Premier Symp. SCAR*, Hermann, Paris, 115–20.

DARBISHIRE, O. V. 1912: The Lichens of the Swedish Antarctic Expedition, *Wiss. Ergeb. Schwed. Südpolar-Exped. 1901–3* 4(11): 1–74.

DARLING, C. A., and SIPLE, P. A. 1941: Bacteria of Antarctica, *J. Bact.* 42: 83.

DESVAUX, E. 1853: *In:* C. Gay, *Flor. Chil.* 6: 338, 339.

DI MENNA, M. E. 1960: Yeasts from Antarctica. *J. Gen. Microbiol.* 23: 295–300.

DODGE, C. W., and BAKER, G. E. 1938: Second Byrd Antarctic Expedition. Botany II. Lichens and Lichen Parasites. *Ann. Missouri Bot. Gdn.* 25: 515–718.

DODGE, C. W. 1964: Ecology and Geographic Distribution of Antarctic Lichens, *Biol. Antarctique. Premier Symp. SCAR*, Hermann, Paris, 165–71.

DOLGUSHIN, L. D. 1958: Geographical Observations in the Antarctic. *Izvestiya Akademii Nauk SSSR, Seriya Geograficheskaya* 1: 28–47.

DROUET, F. 1961: A brief Review of the Freshwater Algae of Antarctica. *In: Science in Antarctica* 1: 10–12. US Nat. Acad. Sciences Publication 739.

DROUET, F. 1962: The Oscillatoriaceae and their Distribution in Antarctica, *Polar Rec.* 11(72): 320–1.

DU RIETZ, G. E. 1940: Problems of Bipolar Plant Distribution, *Acta Phytogeogr. Suec.* 13: 215–82.

EKELÖF, E. 1908: Bakteriologische Studien während der Schwedischen Süd-polar-Expedition, *Wiss. Ergeb. Schwed. Südpolar-Exped.* 1901–03 7(7): 1–120, Stockholm.

FLINT, E. A., and STOUT, J. D. 1960: Microbiology of Some Soils from Ant-arctica. *Nature* **188**: 767–8.

FRITSCH, F. E. 1912: National Antarctic Expedition, Natural History, 6: *Fresh-water Algae*, London.

FUKUSHIMA, H. 1962a: Diatoms from the Shin-nan Rock Ice-Free Area, Prince Olav Coast, the Antarctic Continent, *Antarctic Rec.* (Tokyo) **14**: 80–91.

FUKUSHIMA, H. 1962b: Notes on Diatom Vegetation of the Kasumi Rock Ice-Free Area, Prince Olav Coast, Antarctica, *Antarctic Rec.* (Tokyo) **15**: 39–52.

GAZERT, H. 1901: The Bacteriological Work of the German South Polar Ex-pedition, *Scot. Geogr. Mag.* (Edinburgh) **17**: 470–3.

GOLDMAN, C. R. 1964: Primary Productivity Studies in Antarctic Lakes, *Biol. Antarctique, Premier Symp. SCAR*, Hermann, Paris, 291–99.

GREENE, S. W., and GREENE, D. M. 1963: Check List of the Sub-Antarctic and Antarctic Vascular Flora, *Polar Rec.* **11**(73): 411–18.

GREENE, STANLEY W. 1964: Problems and Progress in Antarctic Bryology, *Biol. Antarctique, Premier Symp. SCAR*, Hermann, Paris, 173–9.

HALE, D., and MURRAY, J. 1958: Summary of Biological Observations on the Byrd Traverse, 1957–58. Section: Botany, pp. 1–3. Symposium on Antarctic Research, Feb. 18–22. DSIR, Wellington, N.Z.

HARDER, RICHARD, and PERSIEL, I. 1962: The occurrence of Lower Soil Phycomycetes in the Antarctic, *Archiv für Microbiol.* **41**(1): 44–50.

HOLDGATE, M. W. 1964: Terrestrial Ecology in the Maritime Antarctic, *Biol. Antarctique, Premier Symp. SCAR*, Hermann, Paris, 181–94.

HOLM-HANSEN, OSMUND. 1963: Algae: Nitrogen Fixation by Antarctic Species. *Science* **139**(3539): 1059–60.

HOOKER, J. D., and TAYLOR, T. 1844: Lichenes Antarctici. *Jour. Bot. Lond.* **3**: 634–58.

HOOKER, J. D. 1847: *The Botany of the Antarctic Voyage of HMS Discovery Ships* Erebus *and* Terror *in the years 1839–1843 under the command of Sir James Clark Ross*, Reeves Brothers, London, 1844–1860, 6 vol.

HORIKAWA, Y., and ANDO, H. 1961: Mosses of the Ongul Islands Collected during the 1957–1960 Japanese Antarctic Research Expedition, *Hikobia* **2**(3): 159–78.

HUE, A. M. 1915: Lichens. J. Charcot, Deux. Exped. Antarc. Française 1908–10, *Sciences Naturelles, Documents Scientifiques*, Paris, 1–202.

KIRCHAK, O. G. 1958: Preliminary Results of Aerometeorological Studies from 1957–8, *Soviet Ant. Exped. Information Bulletin* **1**: 37–8, Elsevier Publ. Co.

LAMB, I. M. 1939: A Review of the Genus *Neuropogon* (Nees and Flot.), Nyl. with Special Reference to the Antarctic Species, *J. Linn. Soc. Lond. Bot.* **52**(342): 199–237.

LAMB, I. M. 1948: Antarctic Pyrenocarp Lichens, *Discovery Rep.* **25**: 1–30.

LAMB, I. M. 1948a: Further Data on the Genus *Neuropogon*, *De Lilloa* **14**: 139–168.

LLANO, G. A. 1950: *A Monograph of the Family Umbilicariaceae in the Western Hemisphere, Navexos*, p. 831, Office of Naval Res., Washington, 281 pp.

LLANO, G. A. 1956: *Botanical Research Essential to a Knowledge of Antarctica*, Geophysical Monograph No. 1. Pub. **462**: 124–33, US Nat. Acad. of Sci. Washington, D.C.

LLANO, G. A. 1958: *Biological work during 1957–58 USNC–IGY Program*, Annual Meeting of the American Association for the Advancement of Science, December 29, Washington, D.C., 2 pp.

LLANO, G. A. 1962: The Terrestrial Life of the Antarctic, *Sci. Amer.* **207**(3): 213–30.

LYNGE, B., and SCHOLANDER, P. F. 1932: Lichens from North East Greenland, *Skr. Svalb. og Ishavet* **41**(1): 10.

MARGNI, R., and CORTE, A. 1962: Bacteriological Analyses of Some Contaminations with Exposures in the South American Antarctic Sector Air, *Polar Rec.* **11**(72): 319.

MARTINEZ, A. 1951: Un Botanico en la Antarctica Argentino, *Idia* **4**(46): 14–22.

MCLEAN, A. L. 1919: Bacteriological and other Researches. Australasian Antarc. Exped. 1911–14, *Sci. Repts. Ser. C.* **7**(4): 1–44.

MEGURA, H. 1962: Report on the Pools and some Products of Weathering around Ponds on the Coast of Antarctica, *Antarctic Rec.* (Tokyo) **14**: 44–7.

MEYER, GEORGE H. 1962: Microbiological Populations of Antarctic Air, Soil, Snow and Melt Pools, *Polar Rec.* **11**(72): 317–18.

MEYER, GEORGE H., MARIA B. MORROW, and ORVILLE, WYSS. 1962a: Viable Micro-organisms in a Fifty-Year-Old Yeast Preparation in Antarctica, *Nature* **196**(4854): 598.

MEYER, GEORGE H., MARIA B. MORROW, and ORVILLE, WYSS. 1962b: Antarctica: The Microbiology of an Unfrozen Saline Pond, *Science* **138**(3545): 1103–4.

MEYER, GEORGE H., MARIA B. MORROW, and ORVILLE, WYSS. 1963: Viable Organisms from Feces and Foodstuffs from Early Antarctic Expeditions, *J. Microbiol.* **9**(2): 163–7.

MOORE, D. M. 1964: Experimental Taxonomic Studies in Antarctic Floras, *Biol. Antarctique, Premier Symp. SCAR*, Hermann, Paris, 195–202.

MURRAY, J. 1963: Lichens from Cape Hallett Area, Antarctica, *Trans. Roy. N.Z. Botany* **2**(5): 59–72.

NEUSHUL, M. 1963: Reproductive Morphology of Antarctic Kelps, *Botanica Marina* **5**(1): 19–24.

PAPENFUSS, GEORGE F. 1963: Problems in the Taxonomy and Geographic Distribution of Antarctic Marine Algae, *Biol. Antarctique, Premier Symp. SCAR*, Hermann, Paris, 155–60.

PAPENFUSS, GEORGE F. 1964: Catalogue and Bibliography of Antarctic and

Sub-Antarctic Benthic Marine Algae, Biology of the Antarctic Seas, *Antarctic Res. Ser.* **1:** 1–76.

PARODI, LORENZO R. 1949: Las Gramineas Sudamericanas del Genero *Deschampsia*, *Darwiniana* **8:** 415–75.

PERKINS, JACK E. 1945: Biology at Little America III, The West Base of the US Antarctic Service Expedition 1939–41. *In:* Reports on Scientific Results of the US Antarctic Service Expedition, *Proc. Amer. Phil. Soc.* **89**(1): 282–4.

PIRIE, J. H. H. 1912: Notes on Antarctic Bacteriology, *Scott. Nat. Antarc. Exped. Rep. Sc. Res. of the SY Scotia (Edinburgh)* **3**(10): 137–48.

PLUMSTEAD, EDNA P. 1963: Palaeobotany of Antarctica, *Polar Rec.* **11**(75): 786.

RUDOLPH, EMANUEL D. 1963: Vegetation of Hallett Station Area, Victoria Land, Antarctica, *Ecology* **44**(3): 585–6.

SAVICZ-LJUBITSKAJA, L. I., and SMIRNOVA, Z. N. 1959: A New Species of the Germs *Bryum* Hedw. from Bunger's Oasis, *Information Bull. Soviet Antarctic Exped.* **7:** 34–9.

SCHOLANDER, P. F., FLAGG, W., HOCK, R. J. and IRVING, L. 1953: Studies on the Physiology of Frozen Plants and Animals in the Arctic, *J. Cellular Comp. Physiol.* **42**(Sup. 1): 1–56.

SIEBURTH, J. MCN. 1958: Antarctic Microbiology, *Bull. Amer. Inst. Biol. Sci.* **8:** 10–12.

SIEBURTH, J. MCN. 1961: Antarctic Animal Bacteriology. *In: Science in Antarctica*, I, 138–46. US Nat. Acad. Sciences Publ. No. 839.

SINGER, R. 1957: A Fungus Collected in the Antarctic, *Sydowia* **1:** 16–23.

SINGER, R., and CORTE, A. 1964: A study on Antarctic Basidiomycetes, *Biol. Antarctique, Premier Symp. SCAR*, Hermann, Paris, 161–3.

SIPLE, PAUL A. 1938: Botany: I. Ecology and Geographical Distribution, Second Byrd Antarc. Exped., *Ann. Missouri Bot. Gdn.* **25:** 467–514.

SKOTTSBERG, C. J. F. 1905: Some Remarks upon the Geographical Distribution of Vegetation in the Colder Southern Hemisphere, *Ymer* **25:** 402–27.

SKOTTSBERG, C. J. F. 1954: Antarctic Flowering Plants, *Bot. Tidsskrift* **51:** 330–8.

SKOTTSBERG, C. J. F. 1964: Antarctic Phycology, *Biol. Antarctique, Premier Symp. SCAR*, Hermann, Paris, 147–54.

STEERE, WILLIAM C. 1961: A Preliminary Review of the Bryophytes of Antarctica. *In: Science in Antarctica*, I, 20–33. US Nat. Acad. Sci. Publ. **839**.

STEERE, WILLIAM C. 1962: A Preliminary Review of Antarctic Bryophytes, *Polar Rec.* **11**(72): 321–3.

TUBAKI, K. 1961: On Some Fungi Isolated from the Antarctic Materials, *Biol. Results Jap. Antarctic Res. Exped.* No. 14, 9 pp.

VAINIO, E. A. 1904: *Lichens*. Results Voyage SY *Belgica*, 1897–9, *Rapp. Scientifiques Bot.* 1–46.

WILLE, N. 1902: Antarktische Algen. *In:* Mitteilungen über einige von C. E. Borchgrevink auf dem antarktischen Festlande gesammelte Pflanzen, *Nyt Mag. Naturv.* **40**(3): 209–21.

CHAPTER FOURTEEN

Terrestrial Animals[1]

J. LINSLEY GRESSITT, *Bishop Museum, Hawaii*

Introduction

The Antarctic Continent represents the most stringent conditions for life. It is the coldest, the highest, the windiest, the most isolated, and the least inhabited of all the continents. Here is the twilight of life with a delicate balance between habitable and uninhabitable areas. With much of the continent thickly covered with ice, active life cannot be maintained over the great majority of its surface. Even the areas not covered by ice are by no means hospitable. Many ice-free environments are too dry, too cold, or too windy to support life. Terrestrial life in Antarctica is very much poorer than the marine life immediately surrounding the continent, for the air temperatures fall very much lower than sea temperatures.

Insects and their relatives may prove to be the southernmost permanent terrestrial animal inhabitants, although rotifers may occur at higher latitudes. Sea water under ice shelves extends farther south than the southernmost known animal populations, but nothing is known about life under the ice at such latitudes. Skuas (*Catharactes*) have been observed farther south than present southernmost insect records, but they are only occasional stragglers far inland.

Only a few of the major groups of non-marine animals occur on the Antarctic Continent (Protozoa, Platyhelminthes, Aschelminthes, Tardigrada, Arthropoda). (Cragg, 1959; Daugherty, personal communications). There are no true terrestrial vertebrate animals present. Of mammals there are five kinds of seals, all feeding entirely on the sea. Four of them spend most of their non-feeding time on sea ice, and the Elephant Seal lives farther north, on the fringe of Antarctica, as well as on the Subantarctic islands.

There are no land birds in Antarctica. The various sea birds (penguins, skuas,

[1] I have drawn heavily on writings of P. Dalenius and O. Wilson (1958), and Madison Pryor (1962). I am very grateful to Dr Pryor for permission to draw from his thesis. I have also drawn from field notes of R. H. Leech, T. S. Leech, C. W. O'Brien, J. Sedlacek and K. A. J. Wise, to whom I am grateful. Dr H. Janetschek has kindly helped by commenting on my draft manuscript before having had time to process his field data. Dr E. C. Daugherty and L. G. Harris have kindly allowed me to use information from their unpublished reports on free-living Micrometazoa other than insects. Dr Nixon Wilson and C. J. Mitchell have helped arrange identification of mites and have identified families represented. Dr John Salmon and Mr K. A. J. Wise have sorted and identified the Collembola material. I am indebted to Phyllis Habeck for most of the drawings, partly taken from Baker *et al.*, 1958. – J.L.G.

petrels, terns, cormorants, sheath-bills) feed almost entirely in the water, although
they nest ashore. The skua is the most nearly terrestrial, as it feeds partly on eggs
or young penguins, and on corpses and other debris ashore, as well as on algae in
melt pools. Amphibians, reptiles and freshwater fish are totally lacking from Antarctica. So, probably, are terrestrial molluscs, earth-worms and other major
groups.

Among the arthropods, or jointed-legged animals, the terrestrial crustaceans,
scorpions, centipedes, millipedes and spiders are apparently totally absent. Only
tardigrades (not strictly true arthropods), mites, ticks and five orders of true
insects are present. The tardigrades are free-living. Some of the mites are strictly
free-living, and some, with the ticks, are external parasites, primarily (or entirely)
of birds, in Antarctica. Two of the insect orders present are free-living (Collem-

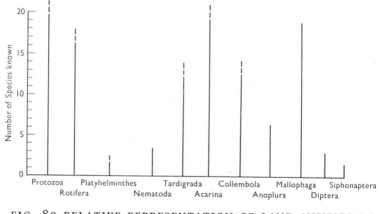

FIG. 89 RELATIVE REPRESENTATION OF LAND ANIMALS IN
ANTARCTICA

bola: springtails; Diptera: flies) and three are external parasites (Anoplura: sucking lice, on seals; Mallophaga: biting lice, on birds; Siphonaptera: fleas, on birds).

Other groups of land (and freshwater) animals present are free-living round
worms, flat worms, rotifers, and Protozoa (one-celled animals), particularly
ciliates.

The total land animal fauna of Antarctica may number little more than 150
species, although previously unknown species are still being discovered. The
approximate relative representation of species of the various groups of non-
marine animals is shown in Figure 89. The numbers for Protozoa and Rotifera
may prove to be very much greater.

Strictly speaking the Anoplura and Mallophaga (lice) and perhaps one-third of
the mites should not be considered terrestrial, as they are parasitic on birds and
mammals that are not considered terrestrial. Most of these are external parasites
in fur or feathers, or on bare skin, but some are internal parasites in nasal and
other passages, or in the alimentary canal. Additional mites are marine, and are

not included in the figures or discussion. Some of the above-mentioned are fresh-water animals. Actually, most of the lower Metazoa are semi-terrestrial, taking advantage of films of moisture in soil, mosses or lichens. Those living in water may be completely frozen for very long periods, even for more than a year, as some ponds do not thaw every summer season. Some of the mites and tardigrades frequently occur in fresh water, and springtails may float on the surfaces of ponds or streams, but except for some of the tardigrades these are not for certain the normal habitats for these particular animals.

Our knowledge of Antarctic land animals is very incomplete. No animals have been recorded from many parts of the continent. Nearly all the records are from Graham Land and Victoria Land (Murray, 1910a–d; Bryant, 1945; Gressitt and Weber, 1960; Gressitt and Pryor, 1962). In addition to very incomplete records of occurrence, little is known of the life cycles, habits and ecological relationships.

Environments

The land animal environments of Antarctica are extremely limited. Most of the known inhabited areas are near the coasts, and little if any life has been found on the few exposed far interior mountains. Nunataks near the coast, as well as ex-posed ridges, slopes or beaches, are often inhabited. Free-living populations of mites and springtails have been found from sea level to 2000 m in altitude. Roti-fers and tardigrades have been found at 3600 m. Records are known from the northern fringes of the continent south to 83° 55′ S, south of Victoria Land, near the Beardmore Glacier (Tyndale–Biscoe, 1960; Salmon, 1962).

The true land animals are mostly associated with seasonally ice-free areas (which may be snow-covered for three-quarters of the year) with certain character-istics favouring animal existence. Essential requirements are ground moisture, some protection from wind, and increase in temperature of the environment. Temperature may be raised by absorption of radiated heat from the Sun by the exposed substrate. Generally animals occur only where plants occur. Much of this is direct dependence, as some of the animals are plant feeders. On the other hand, the general environmental requirements of the animals and plants are almost identical. The tolerances of the plants seem to be a bit greater, so it is probably true that plants occur in some less favourable areas where animals (at least other than Protozoa) do not exist. Plants have been found on a number of interior nunataks where animals have not yet been found, but the matter of dis-persal and colonization is an important one, and still not sufficiently understood. The plants existing in Antarctica (lichens, algae, mosses, fungi, bacteria and in the more northern areas, especially Graham Land, also liverworts, one grass, *Deschampsia*, and one herb, *Colobanthus*) are probably more easily distributed and established than the animals. Furthermore, the plant-feeding animals cannot establish themselves without the appropriate plants preceding them, just as the predaceous animals or scavengers cannot establish themselves without their re-quired hosts or food supply being available.

A significant factor, apparently, in the existence of many of the free-living animals is the presence of birds. This association is primarily indirect, as these free-living forms do not live in the rookeries or bird nests as a rule, but more or less on the periphery, or in the general neighbourhood. Furthermore, although the greatest concentrations of birds, particularly on the more southern coasts, occur in penguin rookeries, the animals are apt to be more in association with skua nesting areas than with penguin rookeries. This has been noticed particularly on Ross Island and in the Cape Hallett area. The association seems to relate to the accumulation of debris resulting from the feeding activities of the skuas. The skuas do much of their feeding on land, and often carry the food to their rookeries or widely scattered nests, whereas the penguins feed in the sea and only regurgitate for their young in the rookeries. The debris from the activities of the skuas is apparently an important factor in soil development, which is very significant for the animal populations. With so little life in Antarctica, soil development is restricted; the soils belong to a 'cold desert system' and in general soils containing humus are very limited in occurrence. Penguin rookeries, at least of Adelie and Emperor Penguins, seem to be without free-living arthropods.

In spite of apparent dependence of insects on birds, several of the most common and widespread animals live far distant from any rookeries. This is true for mites, springtails and some of the other groups as well.

Among the favoured environments are areas with protection from the strong winds from the ice cap, and maximum exposure to the sun. These are generally slopes facing north or away from the ice cap. A fairly permanent moisture supply is required. Thus areas on slopes below snow fields, where snow-melt keeps the ground damp much of the time, are more favourable. Sea winds may help to supply moisture. Slopes that are very steep, or scree slopes where there is movement of the surface gravel are less commonly occupied. Both mites and springtails are to be found under rocks on the surface. Flat pieces of rock lying on soil or gravel are often preferred, although they may be under larger rocks or hiding in cavities in porous scoria, or in cracks in larger rocks. They may even be abundant in fine gravel or coarse sand. Trombidid mites sometimes are found under rocks in spots where no plants seem to be in evidence. They might feed on minute algae or fungi, or on the eggs of springtails where the latter are present, but often the mites and springtails seem to occur quite separately. The mites and springtails may move from feeding areas to seek micro-environments of optimum temperature and humidity when not feeding. The Sun heats the rocks on exposed surfaces and the higher humidity beneath the rocks provides a more suitable niche, which is also protected from wind. Mosses are also heated and provide a favourable environment with the warmed air and moisture retained beneath the surface of the moss mats.

There appears to be considerable movement of individuals during the seasonal cycle, and to some extent during the diurnal cycle in summer. As the snow melts off early in the season, the animals migrate to near the borders of the snow line, to benefit both from the warmth from the Sun and from the moisture from melting snow. As the snow recedes, the insects may burrow deep in soil, gravel or rock crevices, to keep in sufficiently damp environments, if they are not able to move to damp niches near the surface.

In general, mites and springtails may be found in the same environments, but often not under the same rocks. In one spot numerous mites may be found under rocks, and a short distance away springtails may be found under other similar rocks. Some kinds of mites appear more tolerant of extreme conditions, both of colder and of drier environments, than the springtails. Mites have been found in a number of places where springtails have not been taken (Dronning Maud Land; Wilkes Land; foot of Mt Discovery; Observation Hill; Mt Suess at 1750 m). The reasons for this difference, however, may be related more to the obstacles to dispersal, rather than to limitations of an ecological nature, including tolerance to the physical environment.

Animal Groups

Protozoa. Among the Protozoa (one-celled animals), the Ciliata (ciliates) occur in damp soil, among the branches or roots of mosses, particularly decayed, matted mosses, and in fresh water (Murray, 1910b). The largest are visible with a hand lens (Fig. 90 shows *Vorticella*, a well known ciliate, Murray 1910b). The soil microfauna has not been adequately investigated, but other groups of Protozoa occur also in soil. Rhizopoda (Sarcodina) occur in fresh water (Penard, 1910), as also do flagellates.

Platyhelminthes. The phylum Platyhelminthes, or flat worms, seem to number only a very few (perhaps only one) free-living species, belonging to the order Neorhabdocoela of the class Turbellaria. These are only a few millimetres or so long and live in the edges of freshwater ponds, probably feeding on decaying vegetation. This phylum is also represented by various parasitic forms living inside the bodies of seals and birds (trematodes, or flukes; cestodes, or tapeworms).

Rotifera. The Rotifera (Rotatoria), rotifers or wheel animalcules (phylum Aschelminthes) are small, non-rigid, freshwater animals barely visible to the naked eye. The largest are 1·5 mm long. They are often red or orange and *Philodina gregaria* (Fig. 91) may occur in such large numbers as to colour the water pink. That species and *Adineta grandis* are both abundant in ponds on Ross Island. A few kinds live in damp soil. Rotifers feed on organic debris and take in their food with the aid of series of cilia, or fine hair-like structures, often forming a ring, or a pair of rings, around the mouth. So far, 18 species have been recorded from Antarctica. Of these, 14 belong to the order Bdelloidida (genera: *Adineta*, 5 species; *Habrotrocha*, 3; *Macrotrachela*, 2; *Philodina*, 4 species) and four belong to the order Monogononotida (*Cephalobdella*, 1 species; *Collotheca*, 1; *Epiphanes*, 1; *Pleurotrocha*, 1 species). (See Richters, 1907, 1908; Murray, 1910c.)

Gastrotricha. The Gastrotricha (phylum Aschelminthes) resemble rotifers. They also occur in fresh water. Murray (1910b) recorded *Chaetonotus* sp. from Ross Island, but this must be quite rare.

Nematoda. The Nematoda (phylum Aschelminthes, sometimes called Nemathelminthes), or round worms, occur also in damp soil or fresh water. These

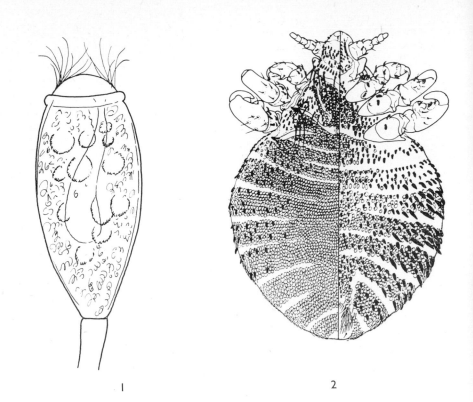

1

2

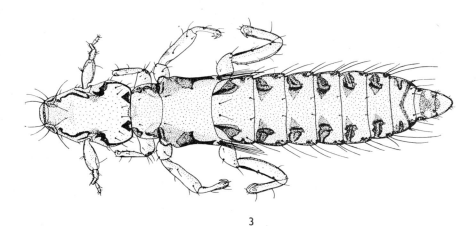

3

FIG. 90 ANTARCTIC LAND ANIMALS

1. Protozoa: Ciliata: Vorticella sp. (after J. Murray, 1910b) × 500;
2. Anoplura: seal louse, *Antarctophthirus ogmorhini* (Enderlein) × 40;
3. Mallophaga: albatross louse, *Perineus diomedeae* (Fabricius) ♂ × 40

are white, very slender and suggest tiny annelid worms. They may be a few millimetres long. They are commonly found among the roots of mosses, and are probably scavengers or plant feeders (Murray, 1910b). Parasitic round worms live in the bodies of seals and birds.

Tardigrada. The Tardigrada, or 'bear animalcules' are very small peculiar animals with hairy bodies and short spiny legs. They have been classified as arthropods (jointed-legged animals) by some, but are not true members of that phylum. They can hardly be seen with the naked eye. Tardigrades occur principally among the roots of mosses, in decayed mosses, in damp rich soil and in fresh water. They probably feed on cell-sap of living mosses, or other plants. They are sometimes found in large numbers in damp moss. *Macrobiotus* (Fig. 93) is a common type in mosses, and *Hypsibus arcticus* is an abundant fresh water species. The genus *Diphascon* has also been recorded. (See Murray, 1910d.)

Crustacea. The Crustacea are almost entirely marine. There are a few records for fresh water in Antarctica (Murray, 1910b), but these might represent marine forms blown from the sea into ponds near coasts, such as at Cape Royds.

Acarina. The Acarina (mites and ticks) may well prove to be the richest group of free-living terrestrial animals (possibly excluding Protozoa) in Antarctica. This is one of the three groups of free-living true arthropods, and probably is the most widespread group on the continent. Although important on all continents, the mites seem to be particularly tolerant of low temperatures. Of the arthropods they have been found farthest from the coast (Dronning Maud Land and Victoria Land), and among the highest in altitude (Victoria Land). They have also been found in several southern localities where other forms of animal life have not been observed. They have been found equally as far south as Collembola (83° 55′ S).

The Acarina of Antarctica belong to four suborders:

1. Mesostigmata, with at least eight families represented. Those so far recorded are mostly known from Graham Land, and include primarily free-living forms, all quite small, generally well under one millimetre in body length. The families so far identified (some not yet recorded) include Neoparasitidae (Fig. 91), Aeroseiidae, Veigaiaidae, Rhodacaridae, Cercomegistidae and Uropodidae. Some of these have been associated with penguin rookeries and some with mosses. The Parasitidae are predaceous and the Halarachnidae are nasal mites of seals.

2. Ixodides, the ticks. Two species of the genus *Ixodes* (*auritulus* and *uriae*) are recorded from penguins or other birds in Graham Land. These two species are fairly widespread on Subantarctic islands as well, but they have not been found as far south as have many of the mites. These ticks grow to quite large size, even to nearly one centimetre in length. Their eggs, laid in masses among moss near rookeries, are quite easily visible.

3. Trombidiformes. This group includes some of the most abundant free-living mites, and some of the more active types. Some of them are predaceous, presumably on eggs and young of springtails, or on other mites, or possibly on

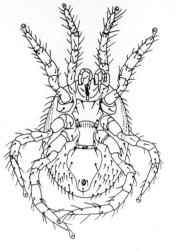

4   5   6

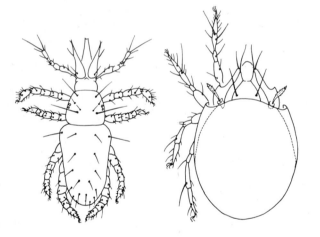

7   8   9

FIG. 91 ANTARCTIC LAND ANIMALS

4. Acarina: Neoparasitidae ♀ × 150;
5. Acarina: Rhagidiidae × 80;
6. Acarina: Erythraeidae × 100;
7. Acarina: Bdellidae ♀ × 80;
8. Acarina: Ceratozetidae × 100;
9. Rotifera: Philodina sp. × 80

rotifers, tardigrades or others. Five families are represented. The family Rhagidiidae (Fig. 91) includes *Rhagidia gerlachei* Trouessart of Graham Land. The
species in this group may be whitish, yellow or rose coloured. They are light-
sensitive and fairly fast-moving. The family Penthalodidae includes species
which are usually black with red flecks and red leg segments. They may occur in
mosses and in debris. *Stereotydeus villosus* (Trouessart) and *S. palpalis* have been
recorded from Graham Land. They are fairly fragile, long-legged, at least partly
bright red, and active. They are active at lower temperatures than oribatid mites
in the same environments. The family Eupodidae (Fig. 93) includes some of the

FIG. 92 ORIBATID MITES, Alaskozetes antarctica (MICHAEL) × 15

most abundant and southernmost species. They are generally red and black,
yellowish or greenish. A very common species has been called *Penthaleus*[1] *belli*
Trouessart. This species is often found under small loose rocks on the surface,
and it is abundant on Ross Island and in mid-Victoria Land. It might be predaceous on the eggs of springtails. Other species belong to the families Bdellidae
and Erythraeidae (Fig. 91). The southernmost record (83° 55′) appears to
represent a new species of the genus *Nanorchestes*.

   4. Sarcoptiformes, including at least five families, three of them belonging to
the suborder Oribatei. Many of these are rather flattish or roundish types, fairly

---

[1] Generic placement about to be revised. The species at McMurdo is now described as
Stereotydeus mollis Womersley and Strandtmann.

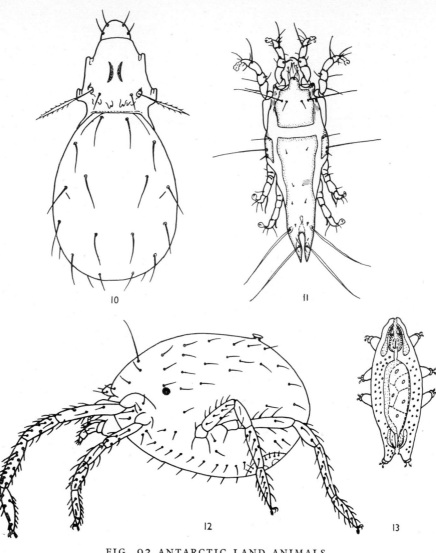

FIG. 93 ANTARCTIC LAND ANIMALS
10. Acarina: Eremaeidae × 100;
11. Acarina: Proctophyllodidae ♀ × 120;
12. Acarina: Eupodidae × 120;
13. Tardigrada: Macrobiotus sp. × 150

hard-shelled and often black. They are probably largely scavengers. The family Eremaeidae (Fig. 93) includes *Alaskozetes antarctica* (Michael), (Fig. 92), recorded from filamentous lichens, freshwater algae, mosses and rookeries in Graham Land, as well as on several Subantarctic islands; and *Pertorgunia belgicae* (Michael), with similar hosts and distribution, and reported to feed on lichens.

The family Oribatulidae includes *Maudheimia wilsoni* Dalenius, discussed in further detail below, and *Liebstadia nordenskjoeldi* (Trägårdh), found in the South Shetlands, Falklands and Tierra del Fuego. A third family of Oribatei is the Ceratozetidae (Fig. 91). In addition to the Oribatei there are two families of feather mites, Proctophyllodidae (Fig. 93) and Analgesidae. These are slender, short-legged, minute mites living between pinnae of bird feathers.

Collembola. This is one of the most primitive orders of true insects, the spring-tails. These are always wingless. The Antarctic species are mostly about one millimetre in length when full grown, and are generally black, bluish or brown, though some are white.

There are about a dozen kinds of springtails known from Antarctica. A few of them are just being named, having been collected only during the past few years. The species occurring farthest south are *Biscoia sudpolaris* Salmon (endemic genus) and *Anurophorus subpolaris* Salmon (Salmon, 1962).

Most of the genera, and several of the species, occur also on Subantarctic islands, but some species have been found only in limited areas. *Biscoia sudpolaris* has been found only at 83° 55′ S, in southern Victoria Land, and it is the only known species of the genus. The only Antarctic location of *Anurophorus* is in Victoria Land at present. *Gomphiocephalus hodgsoni* is known only from central Victoria Land and Ross Island. *Isotoma klovstadi* Carpenter is known from the Cape Hallett, Graham Land and South Shetland Islands areas. A new species of *Colonavis* has been found in Victoria Land, and a new species of *Hypogastrura* in Graham Land. Some of the more widespread species are *Friesea grisea* (Schäffer), *Tullbergia mixta* Wahlgren, *Cryptopygus antarcticus* Willem and species of *Isotoma*.

Springtails are often found in areas where lichens are abundant, and they have been found in large numbers on the undersides of loose rocks encrusted with lichens. Near Cape Barne, Ross I., and on the Danco Coast, Graham Land, as many as 100 are found on a single small rock. They are also associated with mosses. Most of the Antarctic species tend to be gregarious. Large masses of eggs (Fig. 94) have been found in protected niches under rocks. Also, frequently large masses of moulted skins are found on the underside of particular rocks. This may represent attraction to optimum moulting niches, or a gregarious moulting habit as a phase of their life-cycle.

Mallophaga. Members of this order, the biting lice, are entirely ectoparasitic. Most (in Antarctica, all) of the species live among the feathers of birds. Apparently all species of Antarctic birds are infested with biting lice, though not necessarily every individual. Some species of birds, even one individual, may have two or three species of lice. These lice are not blood-suckers, but are apparently principally scavengers, chewing upon the feathers and outer skin of the birds, and causing irritation. Their bodies are strongly flattened dorso-ventrally, and they generally remain attached to the bird feathers, even after death of the birds. The eighteen or so species recorded from Antarctica belong to two families, of two suborders. The Menoponidae include a species of *Austromenopon* on wandering albatross, and one of *Piagetiella* on cormorant. The Philopteridae includes species of *Austrogonioides* on penguins; *Saemundssonia* on skua, terns, pintado petrel and snow petrel; *Docophoroides* on giant petrel; *Pseudonirmus* on snow petrel, pintado petrel and Antarctic petrel; *Perineus* (Fig. 90) on giant petrel, albatross and terns; and a species of *Naubates* on storm petrel. These lice, being on relatively large birds, vary from about 2 to 8 mm in length. Some are very slender, but others from the tops of heads of penguins are quite broad. They vary from white through pale brown and grey to largely dark.

Anoplura. This order, the sucking lice, is also entirely ectoparasitic. Most of

FIG. 94 COLLEMBOLA (SPRINGTAILS) AND EGGS: *Cryptopygus antarcticus* × 15

the sucking lice live on mammals, and all the Antarctic species are parasites of seals. They appear to be absent from whales. As with the birds, each species of seal appears to have a species of louse associated with it. So far, apparently, only one or two Antarctic species of seal has been found to have two species of lice. Actually, records are very sparse, and more investigation on these lice on the various seals is needed.

The genus *Antarctophthirus* appears to have one species on each of the four true Antarctic species of seals (leopard, Ross, Weddell and crabeater). *Antarctophthirus ogmorhini* Enderlein (Fig. 90) has been recorded from both the leopard and crabeater seals. A species (not yet identified) was collected from Weddell seals at the edge of the Ross Ice Shelf, at the southernmost occurrence of seals. A species of *Echinophthirus* has been recorded from the leopard seal. The elephant seal is host to *Lepidophthirus macrorhini* Enderlein and the ecology of this louse was studied in detail on Macquarie Island by Murray (1958). The louse burrows part way into the seal's skin, and a protective sheath is developed, containing some air. The species of *Antarctophthirus*, however, are much broader-bodied and do not burrow into the skin past their head, although generally living in folds of skin, such as under the flippers and around the genital or anal openings. They also occur in the fur, which apparently retains enough air to supply their needs. These lice are mostly 2–4 mm long when full grown, and are brown in colour.

Diptera. This is the only normally winged higher order of insects known from

FIG. 95 MIDGE: *Belgica antarctica* JACOBS, MATING PAIR × 15

Antarctica. There are two species of midges known from the Antarctic area. One, *Belgica antarctica* Jacobs (Fig. 95) is known in Antarctica only from the west side of Graham Land, between 64° and 65° 30′ S. It is also reported from southern South America. The other species, *Parochlus steineni* Gercke (Fig. 96) is known from the South Shetland Islands, and also from South Georgia and southern South America. Both of these midges belong to the family Chironomidae. *Belgica* belongs to the subfamily Clunioninae which includes various species breeding in brackish water, although *Belgica* appears to breed largely in rock cavities filled by snow-melt, near penguin rookeries. The adults are black, wingless, and 2·5–3·0 mm in length. They are often found in company with springtails, and sometimes the latter are observed swarming over the midges and impeding their activity.

The other midge, *Parochlus steineni*, earlier known as *Tanypus* or *Podonomus steineni,* belongs to the subfamily *Podonominae.* It is sometimes fully winged, and sometimes wingless or short-winged, although the winged, flying form (Fig. 96) appears to be dominant in the South Shetlands. It is pale brown and about 5 mm long. It has been found breeding in brackish water in tidal flat areas, and in an extinct crater which accumulates snow in winter but has a tidal sea water exchange through the rocks forming the crater. The larvae live in the brackish water (which is fresher during periods of snow-melt) near the rock banks, and may feed on algae, micro-organisms, or decayed materials. The adults live on the rocks near the water, and may be caused to fly by splashing water on the rocks. The genus *Parochlus* also occurs in New Zealand. Thus trans-Antarctic dispersal, or former wide distribution are suggested.

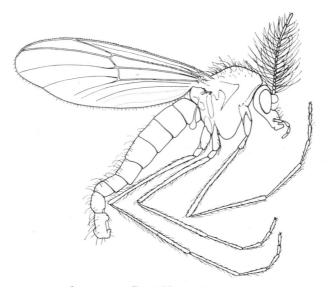

FIG. 96 MIDGE: *Parochlus steineni* (GERCKE) × 20

Siphonaptera. An apparently endemic genus and species of flea, *Glaciopsyllus antarcticus* Smit and Dunnet (1962) was recently discovered at Mawson and Davis in nests of silver-grey petrel and snow petrel (Fig. 97).

Food Chains

Little has been worked out regarding food cycles, and feeding habits of many species are unknown. The tardigrades presumably feed on mosses (or lichens or fungal masses). Springtails have been reported mainly from lichens and mosses. However, Janetschek found that microscopic fungi, almost unreported from the continent, are an important food. He states (personal communication) that Microphyta, particularly minute fungi, probably form the start of many food-chains, and are the main food of springtails in many localities, not merely those under more extreme climatic conditions where higher plants are lacking. Various groups of mites have quite different food habits. Some are parasitic in nasal cavities of birds and seals, some live in the feathers of birds and some on other parts of vertebrate hosts. Of the free-living mites, some are predaceous, some plant-feeding and some are scavengers. Many of the trombidid mites are predators, and these include most of the long-legged, more active types. The Mesostigmata are partly parasitic, partly scavengers or perhaps predators. Most of the oribatid mites are scavengers. In the freshwater pools there are some simple cycles, involving tardigrades and certain mites feeding on algae; and rotifers feeding on minute particles and micro-organisms.

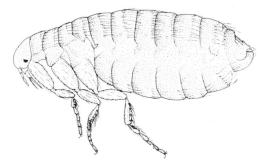

FIG. 9 7 FLEA: *Glaciopsyllus antarcticus* SMIT AND DUNNET × 25

Distribution

We are concerned with the geographical occurrence of Antarctic species because of the relevance to questions of age, history, origin and spread of the fauna, as well as to questions of tolerance to factors of the environment. A number of the species are found to have a broad occurrence in widely spaced localities. Some have been found in one or two distant parts of Antarctica, and also on one or more of the Subantarctic islands. In some cases one species may inhabit a very wide span, reaching to islands on opposite sides of the continent, or even to fringes of southern continents, including New Zealand (Dalenius and Wilson, 1958; Gressitt and Weber, 1960). In general, individual species of mites seem to be more widely distributed than those of other groups. However, some of the springtail species are known from widely separated areas, and even the two Antarctic species of flies have a wider distribution than have many flies not associated with man or domestic animals. The explanation of such distribution patterns is not clearly understood. It might indicate former extensive intervening land areas or even continental drift. However, it is more likely the result of natural dispersal, or in a few cases might represent spread by man. The land fauna of Antarctica is so limited that there is little to serve as evidence for former continental connections, or continental drift. Whether the distribution patterns of insects or other animals anywhere provide concrete evidence on the question of continental drift is disputed. Some entomologists have presented the distribution and evolution of particular insect groups as evidence of drift, and others have given opposite evidence, for the same groups, or other groups with analogous distribution patterns. Many biologists have felt that these questions are matters for geologists to decide, and that if drift in fact took place, it happened so early in the geological time scale that it would have had very little effect on the present distribution of animals.

Dispersal

The question of dispersal of the various land animals of Antarctica – all very small in size – bears on the question of the history of the Antarctic Continent and the history of its climate. If the earlier colder period on the continent was too severe for the survival of remnants of the fauna which existed there when the continent's climate was temperate, then it is likely that all or much of the present fauna has resulted from immigration in fairly recent time. This suggests transport in air currents, or by the agency of birds (Falla, 1960; Taylor, 1954).

There has been little positive evidence presented that birds carry insects from place to place, although it seems very likely that this may happen from time to time. Murray (1910c) assumed that rotifers were dispersed from one pond to another on the feet of skuas, but over greater distances by air currents. Dalenius and Wilson (1958) suggested that most mite dispersal has been affected by birds, and that winds were responsible only for local dispersal within limited areas of the continent. Indirect evidence cited was that debris of bird remains was found in the places where free-living mites live in Dronning Maud Land, showing that terns had nested in the area. These terns regularly migrate to at least Subantarctic islands, and return in summer to nest. It has also been shown that the plants of Antarctica, which are much more conspicuous than the animals, also tend to occur in areas where birds nest. Pryor (1962) pointed out that insect populations were greater near rookeries (but not within penguin rookeries). This is in part definitely correlated with food supply and soil production, for on land, bird rookeries are the main source of organic debris, which contributes to soil production, and particularly to soil enrichment, therefore providing nutriment for both plants and animals.

There is accumulating evidence to indicate that transport in air currents may be important in populating new areas. It is certainly applicable to insects and mites, and probably to most of the other groups of animals found on the continent. Trapping experiments carried on during recent years in the Pacific and in Antarctic areas (Gressitt, 1961) have shown that many insects are carried great distances across the sea in air currents. There is considerable correlation between the types of insects trapped and the representation of insects naturally established on the more isolated islands. Of course many types of insects which might be blown to Antarctica would not succeed in establishing themselves there because of the unfavourable environment. The prevailing wind directions on the continent are also not generally favourable for immigration. Winds on most parts of the continent are from the south, originating near the South Pole, and these air masses have come great distances at high altitudes from south temperate areas. Furthermore, there is a fairly regular trend of winds from the west, rotating around the continent in the seas between Antarctica and the other southern continents, where there is practically no land except for the few small Subantarctic islands, the southern tip of South America and Graham Land. Thus, insects cannot easily be blown very directly to the Antarctic Continent. Again, the habits of individual species have a great bearing on the likelihood of their becoming air-borne.

Insects have been trapped on ships in large nets flown from cables or lines from mast to deck, and in suction traps, as well as in aeroplane traps (Gressitt et al., 1960, 1961c, e). On the Antarctic Continent a young spider in good condition was trapped at Marble Point (77° S) on the Victoria Land coast near Ross Island. Several springtails were trapped at Marble Point, in Graham Land and on ships near the continent. A mite was taken 3000 m above sea level at a point half-way between New Zealand and Antarctica. Several insects were taken in similar latitudes in air nets on ships. Pryor (1962) also trapped springtails in nets at Cape Hallett.

It has been debated whether insects carried great distances in air currents would survive the adverse factors, primarily of desiccation. Gislen (1948) stated that small organisms can survive many hours in the air, and of course some types of insects are better adapted than others for withstanding desiccation. Cloudy weather is more favourable than sunny weather, from this standpoint.

Ecology of the Mite *Maudheimia wilsoni* (after Dalenius and Wilson, 1958)

This species of mite (Sarcoptiformes: Oribatei: Oribatulidae) is known for certain only from Passat and Ekberget nunataks inland in Dronning Maud Land. The two localities are 165 km apart at 150 m and 1650 m altitude, and at latitudes 71° 18′ and 72° 17′ S respectively. The mites live on slopes extending in all directions, though less often on southern slopes. They are found only where mosses are found, and where lichens are abundant. They occur mostly on the undersides of dry rocks, generally smaller and flatter ones which are more easily warmed in the sun, and more often under the bare rocks, rather than actually among the mosses or lichens. In warmer weather they disperse from under the rocks. The main factors limiting their occurrence seem to be the prevailing low temperature and the short developmental period. These factors are similar to those limiting life in the Alps, but are more stringent at high latitudes. Furthermore, the extent, nourishment content and moisture content of the soil are much more limited.

Soil temperatures exceed freezing for only about two hours a day, for only a few weeks of the year. The vegetation, particularly mosses, tends to equalize the temperature slightly. Probably winter temperatures go below −55° C. Summer temperature under the rocks may rise to +20° C for short periods.

The life-cycle of this mite is only partly known, but two seasons may be required for the complete cycle from egg to egg. Interestingly, in captivity in a snow tunnel over winter, young mites developed at temperatures constantly below freezing. They were eggs when placed in the tunnel in early winter (March) and were partly developed nymphs when taken out in early summer (November–December).

This mite is negatively phototropic. When stones were turned over, the mites moved to the other side if the temperature was high enough for activity. The warmth of the Sun caused activity, which started gradually. When activity was restored, the mites were repelled by the light, and moved to the shade. The rocks appear to offer more favourable conditions than the mosses.

Dalenius and Wilson felt that the presence of tern nests, as well as mosses and lichens, accounted for the presence of mites on the two nunataks, and not on other nunataks in the area. They concluded that birds carried the mites to the area from Subantarctic areas, but that local dispersal might have been by air currents.

Ecology of the Springtail *Isotoma klovstadi* Carpenter (after Pryor, 1962)

This species was studied by Pryor at Cape Hallett during the summer seasons 1958–9 and 1959–60. It is also known from Giekie Ridge (Cape Adare), Tierra del Fuego and Macquarie Island. Pryor found this springtail on most slopes near Hallett Station except those facing west toward the source of prevailing winds. It was at all elevations where snow-melt was available, including drainage channels, but not on flooded flats. It was abundant among mosses but scarce among lichens, and absent from rookeries. Individuals were found in dry depressions on undersides of stones. At temperatures below freezing, they were found in clusters in frost fractures of stones. Preferred niches were large flat rocks anchored on the windward side. When temperatures were high and humidity low, the springtails moved downward to cooler, damper areas, sometimes clustering in branches of moss gametophytes. They were often found with nematodes, protozoans and tardigrades, but rarely with mites. They were also found with feather boluses and egg shells.

Pryor found that these springtails move considerable distances to escape unfavourable circumstances. When temperatures are high on talus slopes, they may move into mosses where the temperature may be $11°$ C cooler. They become immobile at temperatures below freezing point. The temperature becomes lethal for this species between $-50°$ C and $-60°$ C. This species, like all Antarctic Collembola, has cutaneous respiration. It is active in the morning and afternoon when humidity is higher. During mid-day the humidity may fall to 15%, which causes the springtails to become inactive. Low humidity has the least effect on the eggs, but is most harmful to young springtails. Eggs are not viable after exposure for twenty-four hours at less than 5% relative humidity, but adults died in fifteen minutes at $5-10\%$ relative humidity. Adults were still alive after being submerged in water for five days.

The reaction to light on the part of the springtails is of minor significance according to Pryor, and much less important than reaction to temperature and humidity. He found that there was no response to light at low temperatures, although there was response to heat in darkness. He concluded that *Isotoma* is neither positively nor negatively phototrophic, and that the tendency to move to the other side of an overturned stone is reaction to temperature and humidity rather than to light.

This species overwinters in egg and adult stages. The adults are resistant to low temperatures, but may die of desiccation. The eggs, laid singly in mosses or soil, are more resistant to desiccation. The adults may aestivate in the middle of warm summer days when humidity drops.

Food consists primarily of mosses and algae, and adults may be crowded together when feeding. Spores of algae and mosses were found in digestive tracts. Sometimes they feed on dead birds. Experimentally, springtails were reared on lichens for short periods.

Climate dominates the environment, and temperature, moisture, wind and soil are critical factors. Daily temperature fluctuation may be as great in summer as seasonal fluctuation in temperate climates. The different conclusions, regarding reaction to light, by Dalenius and Wilson (for the mite) and Pryor (for the springtail) may relate partly to greater dependence on moisture in the case of the springtail.

Biocenotic Features of Antarctica

For the more southern inhabited areas of Antarctica, specifically central and southern Victoria Land, two terrestrial ecosystems may be suggested (Janetschek, personal communication): 'bryo system' and 'bare gravel system'. These may be arranged in simple form, progressing to the less favourable:

Bryo system →mosaic complex of bryo and bare gravel system →bare gravel system.

The life forms of the bryo system are similar to those of the same community on other continents. They are characterized by wide ecological tolerance. In the bare gravel community, there may be only a single species of hemiedaphic arthropod with microscopic plants as primary food. The ecological tolerance may be more restricted than in those of the bryo system, and there is more apt to be local endemism of species. The beginning of the ecological series, with the pure bryo system, probably occurs in Graham Land and on Subantarctic islands. In Victoria Land there is a microtopographically caused mosaic, with the bryo system in protected concavities of the terrain, and the bare gravel system on the more exposed rock areas.

Historically, the bare gravel system is the older one in Antarctica, and some of its inhabitants may represent the remnants of the period before maximum glaciation. After the ice cap started to retreat, elements of this system began to spread, and the bryo system was developed. Since there are many empty ecological niches in Antarctica, this process of spread is still proceeding. There is some evidence of the existence of more favourable conditions about 1000 years ago, so there has probably been much local extinction.

N

A Förna environment, intermediate between the wet and the dry, is lacking in Antarctica.

On the northern fringe of the Antarctic area proper, in the South Orkney Islands, life is richer, and a somewhat more varied fauna exists in the rich mats of mosses, lichens and other plants (Holdgate, 1964). The situation in some environments in the South Shetland Islands closely approaches that in the South Orkneys, and currently more species are recorded from the South Shetlands.

Recent Work

During the past two years reports of new species, and additional distributional and ecological information have been published in *Pacific Insects* volumes **4** to **6**. The principal results of this latest work are:

Additional species, mostly mites, and a few springtails have been discovered. Springtails have now been found south of 84° S and rotifers and mites close to 85° S; mites have been taken above 2000 m altitude in Northern Victoria Land.

Nematodes occur in algae as well as in mosses, and mites have been found close to penguin rookeries feeding on algae growing on dead penguins. Several of the trombidiform mites of Victoria Land are not predators but feed upon algae (see pp. 357, 365). *Maudheimia* feed upon arborescent lichens. The oribatid mite genus *Alaskozetes* (p. 360) has now been transferred to the Ceratozetidae.

Bibliography

BAKER, E. W., CAMIN, J. H., CUNLIFFE, F., WOOLLEY, T. A., and YUNKER, C. E. 1958: *Guide to the Families of Mites*, Inst. of Acarology, Univ. Maryland, Contr. No. 3, 242 pp.

BRYANT, H. M. 1945: Biology at East Base, Palmer Peninsula, Antarctica, *Proc. Amer. Phil. Soc.* **89:** 256–69.

CRAGG, J. B. 1959: Biological Studies in the Antarctic Regions, *New Biology* **29:** 102–21.

DALENIUS, P., and WILSON, O. 1958: On the Soil Fauna of the Antarctic and of the Subantarctic Islands: the Oribatidae (Acari), *Arkiv f. Zool. ser.* 2, **11:** 393–425.

FALLA, R. A., 1960: Oceanic Birds as Dispersal Agents, *Proc. Roy. Soc.* **B152:** 655–9.

GISLEN, T. 1948: Aerial Plankton and its Conditions of Life, *Biol. Rev.* **23:** 109–26.

GRESSITT, J. L. and WEBER, N. A. 1960: Bibliographic Introduction to Antarctic-Subantarctic Entomology, *Pacific Insects* **1:** 441–80.

GRESSITT, J. L., LEECH, R. E., and O'BRIEN, C. W. 1960: Trapping of Airborne Insects in the Antarctic Area, *Pacific Insects*, **2:** 245–50.

GRESSITT, J. L. 1961a: Problems in the Zoogeography of Pacific and Antarctic Insects, *Pacific Ins. Mon.* **2:** 1–94.

GRESSITT, J. L., and LEECH, R. E. 1961b: Insect Habitats in Antarctica, *Polar Record* **10:** 501–4.

GRESSITT, J. L., LEECH, R. E., LEECH, T. S., SEDLACEK, J., and WISE, K. A. J. 1961(c): Trapping of Air-borne Insects in the Antarctic Area (Part 2), *Pacific Insects* **3:** 559–62.

GRESSITT, J. L., and PRYOR, M. E. 1961d: Supplement to 'Bibliographic Introduction to Antarctic-Subantarctic Entomology', *Ibid.*, 563–8.

GRESSITT, J. L., SEDLACEK, J., WISE, K. A. J., and YOSHIMOTO, C. M. 1961e: A High Speed Airplane Trap for Air-borne Organisms, *Ibid.*, 549–55.

HOLDGATE, M. W. 1964: Ecology on the Antarctic Fringe. SCAR Symposium on Antarctic Biology, Paris, 1962. Hermann, Paris.

MURRAY, JAMES, 1910a: On Collecting at Cape Royds, *Rep. Sci. Invest. Brit. Ant. Exp., 1907–9*, **1:** 1–18.

MURRAY, JAMES, 1910b: On Microscopic Life at Cape Royds, *Ibid.*, 19–40.

MURRAY, JAMES, 1910c: Antarctic Rotifera, *Ibid.*, 41–65.

MURRAY, JAMES, 1910d: Tardigrada. Antarctica Tardigrada, *Ibid.*, 95–106.

MURRAY, M. D. 1958: Ecology of the louse *Lepidopthirus macrorhini* Enderlein 1904 on the Elephant Seal *Mirounga leonina* (L), *Nature* **182:** 404.

PENARD, E. 1911: Rhizopodes d'eau douce. *Rep. Sci. Invest. Brit. Ant. Exp., 1907–9*, **1:** 203–62.

PRYOR, M. E. 1962: Some Environmental Features of Hallett Station, Antarctica, with Special Reference to Soil Arthropods, *Pacific Insects* **4:** 681–728.

RICHTERS, F. 1907: Die Fauna der Moosrasen des Gaussberges und einiger südlicher Inseln, *Deutsche Südpol. Exp., 1901–3*, **9** (Zool. 1): 259–302.

RICHTERS, F. 1908: Moosbewohner. *Wiss. Ergebn. Schwed. Südpol. Exp., 1901–3*, **6** (Zool. 2).

SALMON, J. T. 1962: New Collembola from 83° S in Antarctica, *Trans. Roy. Soc. N.Z., Zool.* **2:** 147–52.

SMIT, F. G. A. M., and DUNNET, G. 1962: A new genus and species of flea from Antarctica (Siphonaptera: Ceratophyllidae), *Pacific Insects* **4:** 895–903.

TAYLOR, B. W. 1954: An Example of Long Distance Dispersal, *Ecology* **35:** 369–72.

TORRES, B. A. 1953: Sobre la Existencia del Tendipedido 'Belgica Antarctica' Jacobs en Archipirelago Melchior, *Assn Mus. Ciudad Eva Peron, Zool.* **1:** 1–22.

TORRES, B. A. 1956: Primer Hallazgo de Tendipedidos Alados en la Region Antarctica. 'Podominae', una nueva subfamilia para la citada region, *Ann. Soc. Cient. Argent.* **161:** 41–52.

TYNDALE-BISCOE, H. C. 1960: On the Occurrence of Life near the Beardmore Glacier, Antarctica, *Pacific Insects* **2:** 251–53.

PART FOUR

The South Polar Atmosphere

What is your substance, whereof are you made,
That millions of strange shadows on you tend?
SHAKESPEARE

CHAPTER FIFTEEN

Antarctic Meteorology

M. J. RUBIN AND W. S. WEYANT, *United States Weather Bureau*

Basic Factors Influencing the Antarctic Climate

Because of the astronomical relations between the Earth and the Sun, because of the distribution of land and water in the high latitudes of the Southern Hemisphere, and because of the altitude and topography of the Antarctic Continent, the climate of Antarctica is more rigorous than that of any other extensive area on Earth. Of these factors, the primary control is that of the Sun–Earth relationship, which is essentially the same at corresponding latitudes in both Northern and Southern Hemispheres; the geographic factors are basically responsible for the differences between the Antarctic and Arctic areas.

In the polar regions, the Earth's rotation, its revolution about the Sun and the inclination of its axis to the ecliptic plane result in the long polar winter night and the correspondingly long days of the polar summer. Figure 98 depicts the duration of daylight for the latitude zone from 50° S to the South Pole during the course of a year. Because of the refraction of the Sun's rays by the Earth's atmosphere, for a given location and date, the length of time the Sun is above the horizon is slightly greater than the time it is below the horizon at the same location six months later. Another lesser factor to be considered is the occurrence of perihelion in the Southern Hemisphere summer and of aphelion in the Northern Hemisphere summer, resulting in an increase of a few per cent in the solar radiation in summer at a given southern latitude over that received at the same latitude in the north on a corresponding date in its summer.

The distribution of land and water is almost completely opposite in the two hemispheres. In the north, the geographic pole is close to the centre of a large ocean area comprising the Arctic Basin. This ocean area is almost totally enclosed by the large land masses of the Northern Hemisphere. The South Pole, on the other hand, is on the central plateau of a large continental mass which nearly fills the area within the Antarctic Circle. This continent is encircled by the vast expanse of the Southern Ocean, the largest unbroken oceanic area on Earth; in winter, freezing of the ocean area outward from the Antarctic boundary greatly increases the 'effective continental area', and makes the heat source of the open water even more remote from the continent proper.

The North Pole and the surrounding polar region are at sea level, but Antarctica, with a mean elevation of about 2000 m, is the world's highest continent. This difference in elevation alone would result in the Antarctic's averaging

375

about 12°C colder than the Arctic, were all other factors equal. The high central elevation and surrounding steep slopes of the continent give rise to the strong downslope winds and frequent blizzard conditions encountered along and at the foot of these slopes.

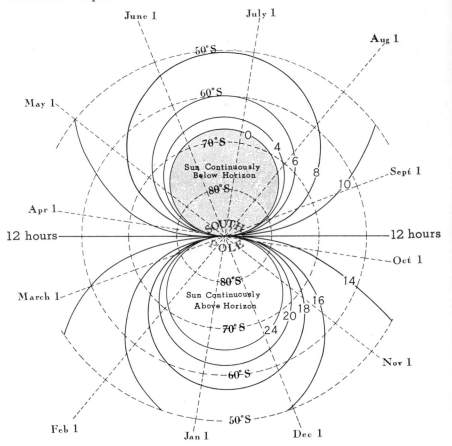

HOURS OF DAYLIGHT

FIG. 98 HOURS OF DAYLIGHT, 50° to 90° S LATITUDES
Dashed radial lines represent date, dashed concentric circles represent latitude, and solid circles indicate number of hours Sun is above horizon during a 24-hour period

Solar Radiation and the Antarctic Heat Budget

The Sun continuously radiates energy into space; this energy is largely in the visible spectrum where the Sun's effective radiation temperature is about 6000° K. In its orbit around the Sun, the Earth intercepts about 10^{-10} of this solar energy, and a large fraction of this intercepted solar radiation is reflected back to space unchanged. The remaining portion of the solar radiation reaching the Earth is the ultimate source of thermal energy for the Earth's atmosphere. The mean total radiation received per unit area normal to the Sun's rays at the top of the atmosphere is about 2 gm cal/cm² (langleys) each minute. This 'solar constant' varies by $\pm 3 \cdot 5\%$ during the course of a year because of the eccentricity of the Earth's orbit, and about $\pm 2\%$ from day to day because of fluctuations in intensity of the Sun's radiation, largely in the ultraviolet.

The important factor meteorologically is the incident solar radiation per square

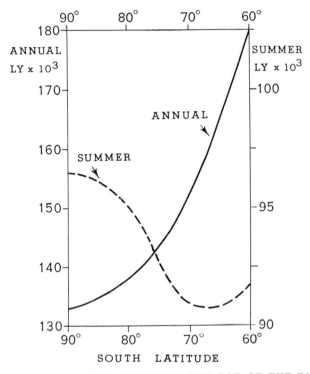

FIG. 99 SOLAR ENERGY REACHING THE TOP OF THE EARTH'S ATMOSPHERE

60° to 90° S latitudes. Solid curve represents annual total, dashed curve represents summer total

centimetre of the Earth's surface, which varies widely with latitude and with season. While the amount of solar energy reaching the top of the atmosphere annually is an inverse function of latitude, in the summer season in the Arctic and Antarctic zones the total extraterrestrial solar energy increases to a maximum at the geographic poles (Fig. 99), because of the increase of hours of sunlight with latitude. The extraterrestrial solar radiation is depleted in many ways before reaching the Earth's surface, with some being absorbed by atmospheric gases, some scattered by the atmosphere and some reflected from clouds. The

amount of solar radiation reaching the surface thus primarily depends on the
atmosphere's turbidity and the amount of cloudiness. At the South Pole, 79%
of the midsummer extraterrestrial radiation reaches the surface; at Little

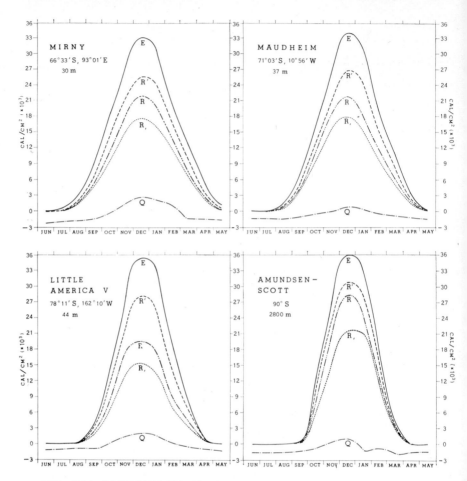

FIG. 100 COMPONENTS OF THE RADIATION BALANCE AT FOUR
ANTARCTIC STATIONS

E – extraterrestrial radiation; *R'* – amount of radiation reaching the surface
with clear skies; *R* – amount of radiation reaching the surface with average
cloudiness; *R,* – amount of radiation reflected by the snow surface; *Q* – net gain
or loss of heat by the snow surface through radiation

America, with more cloudiness, only 56% of the extraterrestrial radiation reaches
the surface. Figure 100 shows the surface radiation budget for four Antarctic
stations over the course of a year; in the figure, E represents the extraterrestrial
radiation; R' is the amount reaching the surface under cloudless conditions, and
R the amount with average cloudiness; R, represents the amount reflected by

the snow surface (R,/R is the albedo of the snow surface); Q is the net gain or loss of heat by the snow surface through radiation. Although the snow surface shows a gain of heat through radiative exchange for a short period in summer, on an annual basis the surface loses heat by radiative processes. Since the annual mean snow surface temperatures show little year-to-year variations, this heat deficit must be compensated by other mechanisms, mainly turbulent exchange of sensible and latent heat between the atmosphere and the snow surface. According to Hanson and Rubin (1962), this turbulent exchange at the South Pole amounts to 8400 cal/cm² for the dark six months and 4400 cal/cm² for the light six months of the year. This cooling of the snow surface and the lowest layers of the atmosphere through radiative heat loss results in

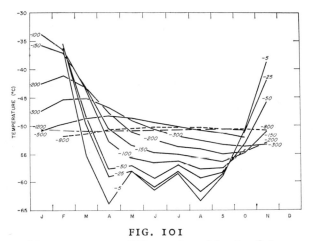

FIG. 101

Average monthly temperatures (°C) at selected levels of the upper 1200-cm layer of snow at Amundsen–Scott (South Pole) Station, January to November 1958. January and November values are each based on a single monthly observation on the 19th and 12th respectively

(After Hanson and Rubin, 1962)

the formation of a temperature inversion, i.e. an increase in air temperature with height, in the lowest portion of the atmosphere over the polar snowfields. The characteristic temperature inversion can become very pronounced; at the South Pole in mid-winter the temperature at 1 km height above the surface has been as much as 30° C higher than the surface air temperature.

Over the course of a year the Antarctic snow surface and the overlying atmosphere lose heat through the top of the atmosphere to space. If this were not balanced by a gain of heat from other sources, Antarctic temperatures would become progressively lower from year to year, which is not the case. An analysis of temperature changes (Hanson and Rubin, 1962) during a year in the upper layers of the snow surface at the South Pole shows a comparatively large range near the surface, with this range decreasing with depth and becoming nearly zero at about 10 m depth (Fig. 101). This fact rules out any appreciable heat flow upward through the ice and snow mantle to replenish radiative losses; the source of the heat necessary to achieve an annual heat balance for Antarctica must therefore be available excess heat at lower latitudes, transported to the Antarctic largely by atmospheric motions.

Upon examination of mean monthly atmospheric temperatures over the course of a year at representative Antarctic stations (Figs. 102–105), we see that, in the

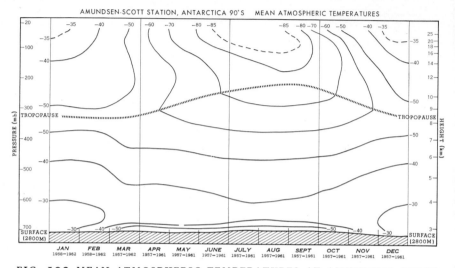

FIG. 102 MEAN ATMOSPHERIC TEMPERATURES AT AMUNDSEN–SCOTT
(SOUTH POLE) STATION

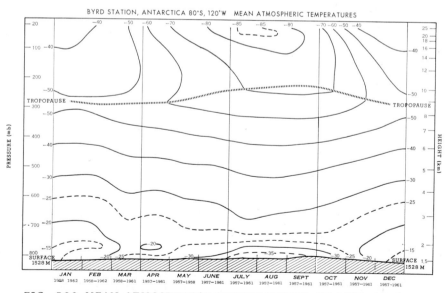

FIG. 103 MEAN ATMOSPHERIC TEMPERATURES AT BYRD STATION

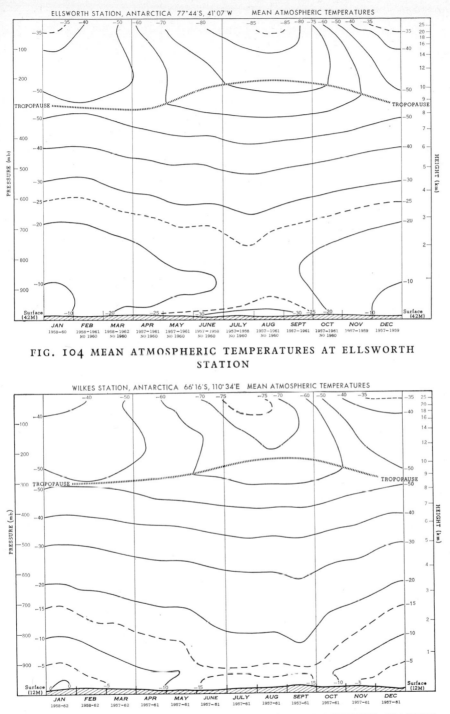

FIG. 104 MEAN ATMOSPHERIC TEMPERATURES AT ELLSWORTH STATION

FIG. 105 MEAN ATMOSPHERIC TEMPERATURES AT WILKES STATION

middle and upper troposphere, the changes in air temperature at a given level from summer to winter are comparatively small, of the order of about 10° C. Radiative losses of heat in this layer would produce a considerably greater drop in temperature (as they do in the stratosphere); the advection of heat necessary to achieve an annual balance thus appears to occur mainly in this tropospheric layer of air.

The atmosphere transports heat directly into an area by replacing cool air with warmer air; also by the transport of water vapour into an area it transports latent heat since, if the water vapour is condensed to the liquid form or transformed to the solid form, considerable heat is released to the atmosphere in this process. The net transport of latent and sensible heat southward across the Antarctic boundary appears to just balance the net annual radiative heat loss of the Antarctic atmosphere since the mean annual temperatures remain essentially the same from year to year. Calculations have been made (Rubin, 1961) of these factors in the Antarctic heat budget, and it was found that nearly 90% ($11 \cdot 5 \times 10^{21}$ gm cal) of the total advective atmospheric heat transport into Antarctica is in the form of sensible heat, with the remainder (about $1 \cdot 4 \times 10^{21}$ gm cal) in the form of latent heat. Since this amount balances the radiative heat loss, the annual heat loss by radiation to space through the top of the Antarctic atmosphere must be about $12 \cdot 9 \times 10^{21}$ gm cal.

Since the mean annual temperature of the Earth remains essentially unchanged from year to year, the planetary radiation budget must be in balance, if we neglect the very small energy sources of geothermal heat and of release of nuclear energy. Because of the Sun–Earth astronomical relationships discussed earlier, the lower latitudes have an annual surplus of radiant energy while the polar regions serve as a heat sink to dispose of this excess energy, the atmosphere (and to a lesser extent the oceans) acting as the transport media. Because of the geographic factors described previously, the south polar region is more efficient as a heat sink than its northern counterpart. Thus, in the balanced heat budget of the planet Earth, the Antarctic region is the major heat sink.

Tropospheric Circulation and Storm Tracks

The cause of the atmospheric circulation is ultimately the temperature variations produced by differential heating of the Earth's surface, although the resulting atmospheric motions are considerably modified by the nature and topography of the underlying surface. As we have seen, the Antarctic region is a heat sink; its annual radiational heat deficit would result in temperatures even lower than those observed, and a steady fall in temperature from year to year, were it not for the atmosphere's reaction to the temperature gradients produced radiationally. The atmosphere compensates for the radiational heat loss by transporting latent and sensible heat into Antarctica and by realizing potential heat through subsidence. The resulting atmospheric circulation is not a simple, steady, poleward flow of heat-laden air; because of the Earth's rotation and other geographic factors it is a complex interplay of small and large scale motions, with the net result of balancing the heat budget of Antarctica.

In the mean, the large-scale circulation tends to be zonal in high southern latitudes. In winter, westerly winds predominate in the upper and middle troposphere and the stratosphere, whirling about a cyclonic vortex usually centred over the interior Antarctic plateau. Near the surface, westerly winds also predominate in the Southern Ocean area as far south as about the 65th parallel, which is the mean position of the low pressure trough surrounding the continent (Fig. 106). Low-level easterly winds cover most of the coastal area in

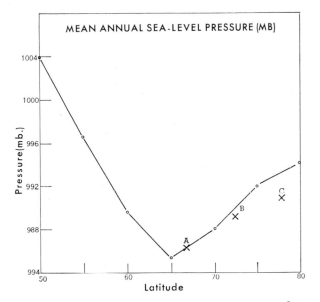

FIG. 106 MEAN ANNUAL SEA-LEVEL PRESSURE, 50° TO 80° S LATITUDES

Solid graph based on Koopmann (1953). Points *A*, *B* and *C* as follows: *A* – mean pressure, Mirnyy (66° 33′ S) and Wilkes (66° 15′ S); *B* – mean pressure, Hallett (72° 18′ S); *C* – mean pressure, Ellsworth (77° 43′ S) and McMurdo (77° 51′ S)

winter and extend inland to about 75° S in East Antarctica, and even further south over the Ross and Filchner ice shelves.

Great cyclonic storm systems, which form in the troposphere over the Southern Ocean area, move generally in curved paths from west to east off the coast of the continent, seldom penetrating the continent itself except in lower lying regions of West Antarctica. These storm systems practically never move onto the high central plateau of the Antarctic Continent, but account for most of the precipitation and heat transport along the coast and on the slopes, as well as contributing to the strong winds observed in these areas.

The variation in number, intensity and trajectory of the travelling cyclones

disrupts the climatic patterns which would be expected from radiational considerations alone, so that averages of meteorological parameters show variations
from month to month and from year to year. Over the longer periods, such as
a season or a year, much of the circulation-induced variation is averaged out, but
the same months in different years may show considerably different weather
conditions.

One example of the deviations of the observed weather from that which
radiational considerations would lead us to expect is the 'kernlose' temperature
phenomenon (Wexler, 1958), characterized by reversal of the expected drop in
temperature from month to month during the winter (Fig. 107). As the radia-

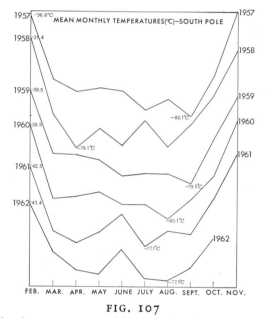

FIG. 107

Mean monthly air temperatures, March to October 1957–62, at Amundsen–
Scott (South Pole) Station, illustrating the 'kernlose' effect

tional cooling of the earlier portion of the winter season produces a strong
meridional temperature gradient, the atmosphere reacts by transporting heat
to the Antarctic Continent, which in turn results in a rise in air temperatures.
Then radiational cooling again becomes dominant, helped by the increase in
effective continental area due to the extension of sea ice around Antarctica, so
the temperature again falls until the return of the Sun in spring reverses this
temperature trend.

Over most of Antarctica, the surface wind and, in some cases, even the wind in
the layer to about 1 km is not primarily determined by the isobaric pattern as
drawn on surface weather maps, as is the case in most of the rest of the world.
The loss of heat by surface radiation produces a shallow layer of intensely cold
air over the continent's surface, and within this layer the movements of the air

are closely related to the slope of the snow and ice surface. The resulting down-slope winds, called katabatic winds, are the most important components of the surface winds observed at Antarctic stations, although they may be reinforced or weakened by the existing pressure gradients. Katabatic winds are especially strong along and at the foot of the steep slopes between the high central plateau and the coastal region, and are responsible for the high wind speeds, frequent blizzards and nearly constant wind directions observed at many stations on these slopes and along the coast. The outflow of air in the surface layer helps balance the mass inflow at higher tropospheric levels; the net heat transport into Ant-arctica in this circulation partly compensates for the atmosphere's heat losses by radiational processes. Katabatic effects lead to relatively constant wind direction even over the gentler slopes of the interior of the continent, giving rise to ripple and dune-like snow surface patterns, called sastrugi. These sastrugi in turn provide meteorologists with valuable information as to prevailing wind directions in large areas from which no long periods of wind observations are available, but in which sastrugi patterns are known from surface traverses or from aerial observations.

The Upper Atmosphere over the Antarctic

While atmospheric soundings were made by earlier expeditions (Court, 1951), it is only since the beginning of the International Geophysical Year that a systematic probing of the Earth's atmosphere has been carried out simultaneously from several widely separated Antarctic sites. Having several years of such measurements, we are able to describe the temperature distribution and the circulation of the Antarctic atmosphere and their changes with time. Examination of time cross-sections of atmospheric temperatures at Antarctic stations reveals several interesting facts about the atmospheric temperature regime. At the South Pole (Fig. 102), such a section based on mean monthly temperatures shows that the atmosphere may be conveniently divided into three parts for discussion of the temperature regime. The first of these is the atmospheric layer from the Earth's surface to a height of about one kilometre, characterized by a strong temperature inversion (i.e. temperature increasing with altitude) and a consider-able range in temperature ($>30°$ C) over the course of a year. Above this surface layer lies the free troposphere, extending to the tropopause height of 8 to 10 km and characterized by a substantial and fairly regular fall of temperature with height, with little temperature variation ($<10°$ C at a given level) from month to month during the year. The tropopause, defined as the level at which the decrease of temperature with height becomes markedly less or reverses, is the lower boundary of the stratosphere which the following paragraphs will consider in some detail.

The stratosphere extends upward from the tropopause to heights far above those regularly reached by the meteorologists' sounding balloons, but our description will be confined to the lower portion which has been regularly probed, extending to 25 to 30 km in the warmer part of the year and to 18 to

20 km in the Antarctic winter season. Referring again to our mean temperature cross sections (Figs. 102–105), we note that the general pattern of behaviour of the stratosphere is similar at all of the four representative Antarctic stations examined here, which cover a range of latitude from the geographic Pole (Amundsen–Scott Station) to the Antarctic Circle (Wilkes Station). Interesting features of this pattern include: (a) a higher tropopause in winter than in summer; (b) a weakening of the tropopause during the winter; (c) a large annual range of temperature ($>40°$ C), with a relatively regular and gradual decrease during the autumn and early winter and a more rapid warming in the spring.

The phenomenon of a higher tropopause in winter than in summer is somewhat anomalous. In most of the Earth's atmosphere, meteorologists have observed that the tropopause tends to be higher in the warmer season of the year and generally higher in tropical and subtropical regions than at higher latitudes. The troposphere, as its name implies, is the region of overturning of air and resultant vertical mixing. In the Tropics, and in the temperate zone in summer, the determining factor of tropopause height is convection resulting from heating of the lower troposphere; since the cumulus and cumulo-nimbus clouds thus formed, and their associated vertical air currents, extend to considerable heights, the mean tropopause level is determined in general by the amount and intensity of this convective activity. Thus the troposphere extends to greater heights in the Tropics than in higher latitudes, and to greater heights in the summer rather than the winter season. In the Antarctic, the snow-covered surface and the persistent temperature inversion in the lowest layers of the troposphere effectively inhibit such convective activity. However, the travelling cyclones of middle and high latitudes have vertical motions associated with them, and the seasonal variation in intensity of such vertical motions may explain the observed variations in tropopause height over the Antarctic.

The phenomenon of the 'disappearance' of the Antarctic tropopause was first noted and described by Court (1942) and explained as a radiative phenomenon by Rubin (1953). The more recently obtained observations substantiate the fact that, on many individual wintertime radiosonde observations at Antarctic stations, the tropopause cannot be found, with a temperature decrease with height extending upward to above 18 km, the average maximum height reached by such soundings in winter. Such a tropopause disappearance may persist for several days, but even in the coldest months the tropopause is re-established and may be located on the mean soundings for such months. It is true that, even when present, the tropopause is markedly weaker in winter than in summer, as may be seen by comparing the vertical temperature structure through the tropopause in the coldest and warmest months on the time cross-sections of temperature (Figs. 102–105). The exact mechanics of the interrelation of radiative cooling, convective cooling and horizontal heat exchanges which produce these temperature patterns are not known. It seems likely that the radiative cooling of the stratosphere may result in a rather uniform lapse rate of temperature in the troposphere and stratosphere during periods when tropospheric circulation is quiescent. When vigorous cyclonic activity is affecting the troposphere it produces considerable vertical exchange; the upper limit of these vertical motions is determined by the height of the level where the tropospheric temperatures resulting from adiabatic cooling are equal to or less than those reached in the lower stratosphere by radiative cooling. This level will then show an increase, or at least a much smaller decrease, of temperature with height, and fulfill our definition of a tropopause.

The large annual range of temperature observed in the lower stratosphere is a result of the prolonged radiational cooling occurring during the long sunless

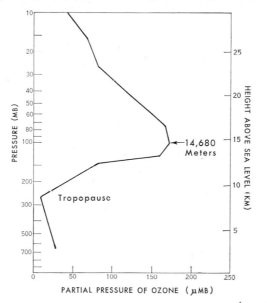

FIG. 108 OZONE SOUNDING, AMUNDSEN–SCOTT (SOUTH POLE) STATION, 0217 GMT, 27 OCTOBER 1962

period, and the rapid warming occurring after the Sun's return and the breakdown of the winter cyclonic circulation. Here the mean charts, although they illustrate considerably more rapid heating than cooling, fail to give a true indication of the suddenness of the spring warming in some years, as they smooth out such large temperature changes in the averaging process. The rapid warming which occurs during some spring seasons, as discussed below, can hardly be the direct result of absorption of solar energy by the Antarctic stratosphere, although this solar energy is the fundamental source of the observed warming.

A major agent in the direct transformation of solar energy to heat at middle stratospheric levels is ozone, which effectively absorbs ultra-violet radiation from the Sun. Atmospheric ozone is concentrated mainly at stratospheric levels; in winter the height of the ozone maximum over Antarctica is in the 15 to 20 km layer (Fig. 108), lower than found elsewhere. At the Earth's surface ozone concentrations are smaller, averaging 40 to 50 micrograms per cubic metre, but are still of interest as a tracer for atmospheric circulation. Both surface and total ozone values appear to have a maximum in the winter, when there is no Sun to produce ozone in the polar regions. It appears likely (Wexler *et al.*, 1960) that ozone is transported to Antarctica from lower latitudes, probably in the circulation associated with the great cyclonic storms of the troposphere. Surface ozone amounts may also be augmented by ozone production in static electricity discharges associated with the frequent blizzards of the Antarctic.

Figure 109a shows the annual march of temperature at the South Pole at the 50-mb level (about 18 km), which is well within the Antarctic stratosphere. The rather regular cooling from the end of summer to mid-winter is easily seen, as is the small variation in this cooling pattern from year to year. The lowest temperatures at this level are generally reached in August, with a relatively small temperature increase in September and early October. During late October and November, the major portion of the stratospheric warming occurs with a considerable variation in pattern from year to year. Figure 109b shows the warming pattern for five different years in greater detail. The most rapid and greatest warming took place over a two-week period in 1957, with a rise in temperature of about 35° C (63° F). The most gradual warming occurred in 1959, with temperatures in early November of that year more than 35° C lower than those on the corresponding 1957 dates. The other years examined fell somewhere between these two extremes, with 1961 following the 1959 pattern very closely. The rapid warmings, particularly those of 1957 and of 1960, are very difficult to explain on the basis of direct absorption of solar radiation only, and a satisfactory explanation must be sought in dynamic processes occurring in the Antarctic stratosphere. In 1957 the extreme warming was associated with the passage of a jet stream over the South Pole, and the displacement of the coldest air at 50 mb toward the Weddell Sea and the South Atlantic Ocean.

The patterns of stratospheric circulation are closely linked to the temperature distribution and its changes. The stratospheric cooling in autumn and early winter results in the formation of a strong meridional (north-south) temperature gradient between the south temperate zone stratosphere and the Antarctic. This temperature gradient in the stratosphere induces an increasing westerly circulation with height. At the time of lowest Antarctic stratospheric temperatures, stratospheric maps (Fig. 110) show development of a vast cyclonic circulation with its centre over the interior Antarctic plateau; observations have indicated that the extremely strong west winds whirling about this cold core cover a broad zone from the Antarctic periphery to latitudes 45° or 50° S. The belt of maximum westerlies within this zone is termed the polar night jet stream. As we have seen, since the temperatures in the Antarctic stratosphere in winter continue to decrease with height above the 50-mb level, the poleward meridional temperature gradient is thus preserved above that level, and the westerlies continue to increase with height. The absolute maximum speed of these westerlies is thus far beyond the range of our measurements, but it seems probable that it is well in excess of 100 m/sec (200 knots). As the spring warming occurs, the stratospheric cyclone

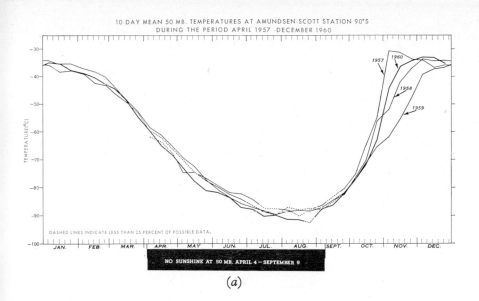

(a)

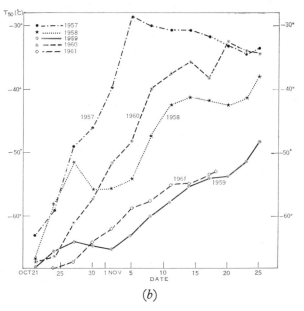

(b)

FIG. 109

(*a*) Ten-day mean 50-mb temperatures at Amundsen–Scott (South Pole) Station, 1957–60;

(*b*) Three-day mean 50-mb temperatures at Amundsen–Scott Station, 1957–61, showing mid-spring warming

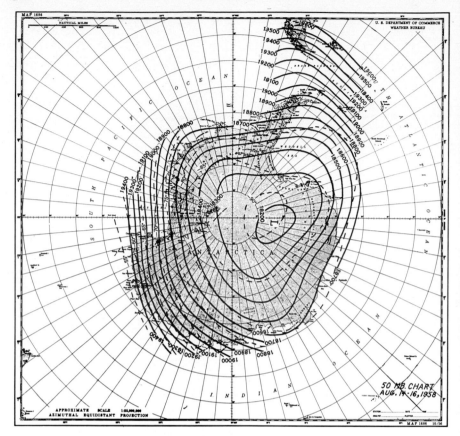

FIG. 110 50-MB CHARTS FOR ANTARCTIC REGION, SHOWING
WINTER CYCLONIC CIRCULATION
(After Ropar and Gray, 1961)

becomes weaker, and in years where this warming is greatest (such as 1957),
the circulation actually reverses as the Antarctic stratosphere air becomes very
warm, with an anticyclone becoming established over the Antarctic Continent
at stratospheric levels by late spring (Fig. 111). However, in the years with
more gradual warming such as the 1959 season, the westerlies persist through
the spring with the weakened cyclonic circulation pattern maintaining itself into
the early summer.

During the Antarctic winter of 1962 the radiosonde observations taken at
Byrd Station reached consistently higher levels than any other radiosonde
observations taken during the Antarctic winter. This series of observations
indicates that, while the decrease of temperature with height does extend well
above the 50-mb level, in every instance this temperature trend reverses itself
at some higher stratospheric level, and there is a warming with height. However,

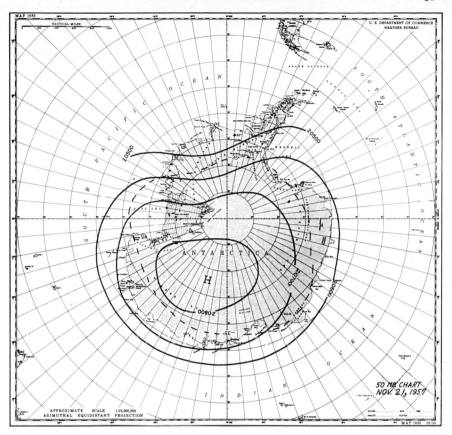

FIG. 111 50-MB CHARTS FOR ANTARCTIC REGION, SHOWING LATE
SPRING ANTICYCLONIC CIRCULATION OF 1957
(After Ropar and Gray, 1961)

this occurs at a very high level (generally at about 25 km) and must be considered too high to represent a true tropopause, since the levels directly below
this must still contain stratospheric air. Even though the temperature does, at
some higher level, begin increasing with height, this increase must become very
considerable before the actual poleward temperature gradient is reversed; thus
the increasing westerlies must extend to very great heights indeed, with the
speeds reaching very high values. Figure 112 shows the temperature pattern in
the Antarctic stratosphere over Byrd Station in August 1962, for the levels
above 100 mb (about 14 km).

In comparing the behaviour of the Antarctic stratosphere with that of the
north polar stratosphere, the following differences may be noted. The temperatures in the Antarctic stratosphere in mid-winter reach levels 5 to 10° C lower
than those of the Arctic. Over the Arctic Basin, sudden warmings can occur

during the winter season as early as late December or January, and well before
the return of the Sun to stratospheric levels. In the Antarctic, as we have noted,
the rapid warmings never occur until well after the spring equinox. Similarly,
while in general there is a north polar stratospheric cyclone and a north polar
night jet stream, the speeds reached are very likely less in the Northern Hemisphere, and the circulation pattern is not as regular and consistent through the
Arctic winter as it appears to be in the Southern Hemisphere winter. The
basic reason for this may again be, as noted earlier, the differences in land and
sea distribution in the polar regions of the two hemispheres.

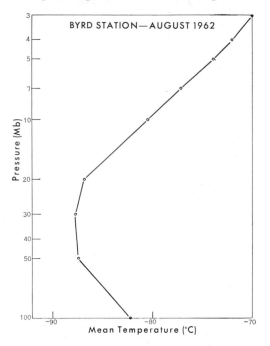

FIG. 112 MEAN TEMPERATURES, BYRD STATION, AUGUST 1962,
FOR THE ATMOSPHERE ABOVE 100 MB

Atmospheric Water Vapour, Carbon Dioxide and Radioactivity

Because of the low temperatures, the water vapour concentration in the Antarctic
atmosphere is about one order of magnitude less than that of temperate latitudes.
As elsewhere, the lowest atmospheric layers have the highest water vapour
concentrations, which are important as strong absorbers of long-wave radiation,
although small in an absolute sense. A limited series of measurements of stratospheric water vapour, taken at McMurdo Sound using balloon-borne frost-point
hygrometers, indicate very low concentrations but an increase in water vapour
from the lower to the middle stratosphere, a phenomenon which has been
observed elsewhere in the world.

The concentration of carbon dioxide at the surface has been determined both by analysis of samples and by a continuous record of the carbon dioxide concentrations at the surface. Such continuous records were obtained at Little America V during the International Geophysical Year and at the South Pole from 1959 onward. The Antarctic is particularly well-suited for representative measurements of atmospheric carbon dioxide, having neither vegetation nor industrial areas to produce local or seasonal variations in carbon dioxide content. Thus, in the summary of carbon dioxide measurements presented by Keeling (1960), the Antarctic values are free from the marked seasonal variations noted at Northern Hemisphere sites. At the South Pole, the CO_2 concentration has an annual average of about 313 (parts per million by volume), somewhat less than that observed at relatively uncontaminated sites at middle latitudes of the Northern Hemisphere and in the equatorial region, implying a CO_2 sink in the Southern Ocean area.

Atmospheric radioactivity measurements have been made at several Antarctic sites. The natural radioactivity of the air is extremely low, and because of this, radioactivity from fission products, although itself low on an absolute scale, represents a larger percentage of the total atmospheric radioactivity than elsewhere in the Southern Hemisphere. There is some evidence that fission product radioactivity has a late spring or summer maximum and a winter minimum in the Antarctic (Lockhart, 1960). Radioactive fission products injected into the stratosphere have proven valuable tracers of stratospheric motion. A series of measurements with balloon-borne gamma radiation detecting instruments is being instituted in the Antarctic to find the concentrations and vertical distribution patterns of such fission products in the Antarctic stratosphere.

Concentrations of the natural isotopes in the surface snow layers of Antarctica help in identification of the annual snow layers and thus in determination of the annual accumulation at locations on these snowfields of the continent. The O^{18}/O^{16} ratio in fallen snow is closely related to the temperature at which the atmospheric water vapour has been transformed into precipitation, so that seasonal and thus annual identification of the snow layers is possible. This technique is still subject to errors because of some annual or seasonal layers being depleted (or even entirely removed) by wind erosion.

Air–Ice–Water Interactions and the Water Mass Budgets

The ice–atmosphere–ocean interchange of mass and energy is complex, with each component acting as a transportation medium and also as an energy source or sink, related to both long-term climatic changes and to shorter period meteorological variations. Of the water mass of the Earth, the Antarctic ice cap stores about 22×10^{15} tons (Thiel, 1962), a little less than 2% of the water in the oceans of the world (about 14×10^{17} tons). The Earth's atmosphere acts as a transport medium, but is not important for water storage, holding only about 3×10^{13} tons of water. Thus water mass transfers between ocean and ice cap are slow; if the present average annual rate of precipitation over Antarctica (about 15 cm of water equivalent) were projected back in time, it would have taken over 100 centuries to accumulate the present Antarctic ice, even if no ice at all were lost from the Antarctic during that time.

With information now available, it has been possible to summarize factors entering into the Antarctic ice mass budget, and to use the results to estimate annual accumulation and precipitation over the continent, as well as latent heat transport across the Antarctic boundary (Rubin, 1962). Assuming an annual balance of the ice mass, and using the best available maximum and minimum

ACCUMULATION MAP OF ANTARCTICA

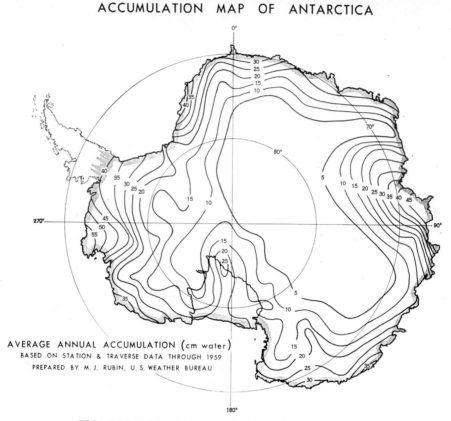

AVERAGE ANNUAL ACCUMULATION (cm water)
BASED ON STATION & TRAVERSE DATA THROUGH 1959
PREPARED BY M. J. RUBIN, U. S. WEATHER BUREAU

FIG. 113 ACCUMULATION MAP OF ANTARCTICA

estimates of mass loss through oceanic melting, ablation, calving of icebergs, etc., the computed average annual precipitation is from 10·8 to 16·6 cm (water equivalent). Using snow accumulation measurements and mapping the isopleths (Fig. 113), an average annual accumulation of 14·5 cm is obtained; the precipitation value derived from this accumulation amount is 14·6 cm per year (minimum) to 19·2 cm per year (maximum). The corresponding values of heat transport into Antarctica have been discussed previously.

The exchange of heat and water vapour between the ocean surrounding Antarctica and the overlying atmosphere is part of the broad problem of ocean–air interactions. A study of this exchange (Viebrock, 1962) indicates that an evaporation minimum occurs at or just south of the Antarctic Convergence, with the absolute minimum occurring in winter in the Southern Indian Ocean region; the wind speed, which shows a maximum approximately at the Antarctic Convergence, is apparently only a minor factor in evaporation, with the vapour pressure difference the dominant factor. The sensible heat flux also shows a minimum at the approximate mean position of the Antarctic Convergence. In the minimum zone (50–55° S) values are negative, indicating a transfer of heat from air to water; in all other zones from 45° S to the Antarctic coast (averaged around the hemisphere) the heat flow is upward.

Environmental Climate and Weather

The meteorological factors which make the Antarctic so inhospitable to life and so resistant to man's efforts to explore, describe and understand it are embodied in the various elements of surface weather, particularly the extremely low temperatures, strong winds and frequent blizzards.

Considering first the temperature, Antarctica is by far the coldest area of the Earth. The lowest temperature thus far observed, −88·3° C, occurred at Vostok, a USSR station 3420 m high at 78° 27′ S, 106° 52′ E. Before the establishment of year-round observing sites on the high interior plateau of Antarctica, the world's lowest temperatures had been observed in the Verkhoyansk–Oimekon area of north-eastern Siberia, with the observed minimum −67·7° C at Oimekon. Referring to the map of mean annual Antarctic temperatures (Fig. 114), it seems probable that the entire region within the −45° C isotherm, an area of nearly 4,000,000 km², experiences minimum temperatures as low as −73° C (about −100° F). The isotherm patterns on the map reflect the influence on temperature of elevation and of latitude, with the largest temperature gradients existing up the steep slopes surrounding the central plateau. The rate of fall of mean temperature with height on these slopes is about the same as that of rising dry air in the free atmosphere (about 10° C per kilometre).

The radiationally produced temperature inversion in the surface layer of air, mentioned earlier as characteristic of the Antarctic temperature regime is best developed in the cold season but is present to a lesser degree in summer as well. Short period variations in surface temperatures are strongly influenced by other meteorological considerations such as cloudiness and wind speed. Since high winds tend to destroy the surface inversion by vertical mixing of the air in the inversion layer, periods of strong winds and blizzards are usually accompanied by a rise in temperature. However, those exposed to outside weather under such conditions gain no benefit from the higher temperature induced, since this temperature rise is more than offset by the higher winds which increase the chill factor greatly. Cloudiness, and particularly low cloudiness, can cause remarkable temperature rises when it appears in previously clear winter skies over interior Antarctica. Besides effectively blocking the loss of heat to space from the surface and lower atmosphere, the clouds themselves act as radiators of heat to the

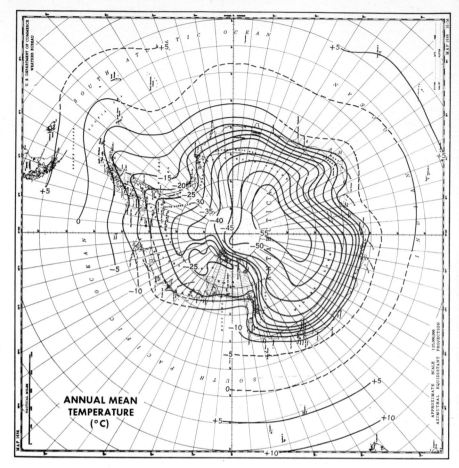

FIG. 114 MEAN ANNUAL TEMPERATURES OF ANTARCTICA

surface, since the temperature at their level is often much higher than that at the surface. For example, at the South Pole at 0245, 18 September 1957, the temperature was $-73 \cdot 3^\circ$ C ($-100 \cdot 0^\circ$ F). By 0800 of the same day an overcast moved in and snow began falling, with temperatures increasing to $-56 \cdot 2^\circ$ C ($-69 \cdot 1^\circ$ F) by noon, with a radiosonde observation at this time showing a temperature of $-30 \cdot 0^\circ$ C at 330 m above the surface.

At stations along the coast temperatures are less rigorous, with most stations not on a permanent ice shelf experiencing some above-freezing temperatures during the summer months, and with winter minima only occasionally below -40° C. Thus some specialized animal and plant life can exist in the environment found at many coastal sites, although no forms of life indigenous to the vast interior snowfields has yet been reported.

The slopes and much of the coastal area of Antarctica are regions of strong and persistent winds, largely due to the downslope or katabatic effect discussed earlier. Even at interior stations with a relatively gentle slope to the snow surface, the prevailing surface winds remain remarkably constant in direction, and seem to be determined by the slope of the terrain rather than other meteorological considerations. When surface winds reach about 10 m/sec, snow is picked up by the winds and transported through the air. With winds as high as 15 m/sec or more, such blowing snow reduces visibility to near zero, and results in the well-known Antarctic blizzard. At Byrd Station (80° S, 120° W), such 10 m/sec winds occur over two-thirds of the time and 15 m/sec winds occur about one-third of the time, giving drifting snow problems perhaps worse than at any other of the interior Antarctic stations (Morris and Peters, 1960).

The amount of cloudiness at Antarctic stations shows a seasonal variation, with minimum cloud amounts generally being observed during the winter season. Interior stations have less cloudiness than coastal areas, although local factors such as terrain, prevailing winds and nearness of the ocean affect the cloud regime considerably at any particular location. At low latitudes, over the surrounding Southern Ocean area, observations are sparse; it appears that cloudiness in this region is considerably greater than at any of the continental stations. Since sunshine amounts are the converse of cloud amounts, interior stations generally have proportionately more sunshine than stations on the coast.

Precipitation is difficult to measure directly in Antarctica, because of the high frequency of blowing snow. The map of average annual snow accumulation (Fig. 113) provides a good first approximation to the annual precipitation; this precipitation is greatest on the coast and the slopes surrounding the interior plateau, with the highest elevations of the interior receiving less than 5 cm (water equivalent) per year. The precipitation is nearly all in the form of snow, although rain and freezing rain have been observed at most stations on the immediate continental coast as well as in Graham Land.

Any description of the Antarctic environment must include mention of the striking optical phenomena frequently observed in Antarctica. Because of the refractive effect of the strong vertical temperature (and hence density) gradients which exist in the layers of air nearest the ground, mirages are common. Such effects include both superior and inferior mirages and looming of objects actually below the observer's horizon. The frequent presence of ice crystal clouds and fogs gives rise to complex halo phenomena which often include Sun pillars, tangential arcs, parhelia (mock Suns) and other circles and arcs as well as the common 22° halo (Blake, 1959).

The climatology of selected Antarctic stations is graphically depicted in Figures 115 and 116; these show the mean annual and mean monthly temperatures, cloudiness, pressure and wind speed for three stations in West Antarctica (Fig. 115) and in East Antarctica (Fig. 116), including in each instance a high interior station, a coastal station and an intermediate site. Besides the mean data, the graph shows temperature extremes, prevailing wind direction, and in some cases speed and direction of the maximum winds observed. Many of the facts

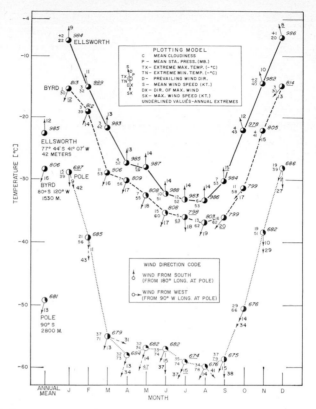

FIG. 115 GRAPH OF CLIMATOLOGICAL DATA FOR AMUNDSEN–SCOTT
(SOUTH POLE) STATION, BYRD STATION AND ELLSWORTH STATION
Data plotted as shown on station model illustrated

previously mentioned, such as the winter cloudiness minimum and the constancy of the prevailing winds, are readily apparent from these graphs. The 'kernlose' effect can also be discerned, although obscured somewhat by the averaging process.

Conclusion

The continent of Antarctica was for a long time one of the great unknown areas of the world. Meteorologically, before 1957 most of our data came from a few coastal sites, and covered periods ranging from a few months to a year or two. The climate of the high interior of the continent was unknown, and the sporadic and isolated sets of observations yielded scant knowledge of the day-to-day weather patterns of the Antarctic region.

The Antarctic meteorology which has been described here is based largely on data obtained thus far during the era ushered in by the International Geophysical Year of 1957–8; this era is marked by the establishment of permanent stations

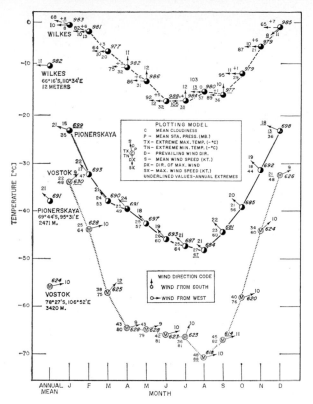

FIG. 116 GRAPH OF CLIMATOLOGICAL DATA FOR VOSTOK,
PIONERSKAYA AND WILKES STATION
Data plotted as shown on station model illustrated

on the interior plateau, including one at the geographic pole and one near the
highest elevation so far explored, and of a network of reporting stations providing
representative meteorological coverage, operating on a year-round basis and using
the latest meteorological instrumentation. A wealth of data has thus far been
obtained; this article treats only some of the phases of Antarctic meteorology
which have been described and investigated during the past few years, and such
treatment is far from exhaustive.

Even though much remains to be done with the Antarctic meteorological data
thus far obtained, we cannot help looking towards the future of meteorology in
Antarctica. New types of instrumentation and new vehicles for instruments will
increase our knowledge about the Antarctic's atmosphere, permitting a more
detailed analysis of conditions in those regions now only grossly described, and
an extension of our information upward to higher reaches of the atmosphere and
outward to the great circumpolar ocean area, now little known as compared to
the Antarctic Continent itself.

Measurements of the vertical distributions of ozone and water vapour, and changes in these quantities with time, will help fix the role of the Antarctic atmosphere as the Earth's main heat sink, and lead to better descriptions of the general circulation at all atmospheric levels. The use of meteorological rocket soundings will enable us to more than double the vertical extent for which we have data on the state of the atmosphere. Meteorological satellites, which are already at times photographing the Antarctic coastal regions, will provide pictures of cloud conditions and of the spectrum of terrestrial radiation from the entire continent several times daily. The use of constant-level balloons drifting freely over the Southern Ocean area will help fill this gap in our current meteorological knowledge. The Antarctic is still a meteorologically challenging area, about which much remains to be learned and fitted into the larger edifice of global meteorology. It remains a climatologically unique continent, far from completely known or understood, but of great importance to the accurate depiction of the behaviour of our planet's atmosphere.

Bibliography

BLAKE, J. R. 1959: Observations on Unusual Low Altitude Solar Haloes in Antarctica. Presented at *Antarctic Symposium, Buenos Aires, Argentina,* 17–25 November.

COURT, ARNOLD 1942: Tropopause Disappearance during the Antarctic Winter, *Bull. Amer. Met. Soc.,* **23:** 220–38.

COURT, ARNOLD 1951: Antarctic Atmospheric Circulation, *Compendium of Meteorology,* T. E. Malone, ed., Boston, 917–41.

HANSON, K. J. and RUBIN, M. J. 1962: Heat Exchange at the Snow-Air Interface at the South Pole, *J. Geophys. Res.* **67:** 3415–24.

KEELING, C. D. 1960: The Concentration and Isotopic Abundances of Carbon Dioxide in the Atmosphere, *Tellus* **12:** 200–3.

KOOPMANN, G. 1953: Entstehung und Verbreitung von Divergenzen in der oberflächennahen Wasser bewegung de antarktischen Gewässer, *Deutsche Hydrographische Zeitschrift, Ergänzungsheft 2,* Deutsches Hydrographishes Institut, Hamburg, Table I (p. 14).

LOCKHART, L. B., Jr. 1960: Atmospheric Radioactivity in South America and Antarctica, *NRL Report* 5526, US Naval Research Laboratory, Washington.

MORRIS, W. R. and PETERS, N. L. 1960: Inside Antarctica No. 5 – Byrd Station, *Weatherwise,* **13:** 162–5.

ROPAR, N. J. and GRAY, T. I. 1961: Description of the 50-Mb. Patterns over Antarctica in 1958, *Monthly Wea. Review* **89:** 45–52.

RUBIN, M. J. 1953: Seasonal Variations of the Antarctic Tropopause, *Journ. Met.* **10:** 127–34.

RUBIN, M. J. 1962: Atmospheric Advection and the Antarctic Heat and Water Budget. *Geophys. Monogr.* **7:** 149–59, Amer. Geophys. Union.

THIEL, E. 1962: The Amount of Ice on Planet Earth, *Ibid.*, 172–5.

VIEBROCK, H. J. 1962: The Transfer of Energy between the Ocean and the Atmosphere in the Antarctic Region, *J. Geophys. Res.* **67**: 4293–302.

WEXLER, H. 1958: The 'Kernlose' Winter in Antarctica, *Geophysics* **6**: 577–95.

WEXLER, H., MORELAND, W. B., and WEYANT, W. S. 1960: A Preliminary Report on Ozone Observations at Little America, Antarctica, *Monthly Wea. Rev.* **88**: 43–54.

(a)

35 mm roll-film camera
Ektachrome E2, f/28
several minutes' exposure

(b)

FIG. 117
PHOTOGRAPHS OF
AURORAE OBSERVED
FROM BYRD STATION
(*Photo: Howard le Vaux*)

CHAPTER SIXTEEN

The Aurora Australis

M. GADSDEN, *D.P.L. Auroral Station, Omakau, Otago, New Zealand*[1]

Introduction

From earliest times, records have been kept of displays of the aurora: the appearance of great shafts of light across the night sky is sufficiently rare in temperate latitudes to excite wonder and curiosity in an observer. Even in polar regions, where aurorae occur almost every night, the beauty of a display is enough to cause people to watch it. It is not surprising that observations of aurorae find a place in most polar expedition journals.

Auroral displays most commonly appear as contorted bands of white, green or red light stretching across the sky; most often the red colouration appears very faintly at the top of a display (Fig. 117a), although sometimes an aurora is red from top to bottom (Fig. 117b). The whole display is usually in violent motion: bands move rapidly across the sky, often appearing and disappearing within a minute or two; rays shoot up and flicker across the sky and sometimes the whole sky is filled with a light which flashes on and off every few seconds. What causes all this? How does one set about trying to understand the processes that occur?

In this chapter, the second question will be answered – although, since the answer to the first question cannot yet be given, the answer may be wrong. Because of this, there will be no attempt here to give a fair summary of all that is known about the aurora. Because the causes are not yet understood, any summary of the known facts is bound to be a list of little coherence. One cannot yet say, *this* is important, *this* is just a minor detail. Since the majority of auroral knowledge comes from observations made in the Northern Hemisphere – for geographical and ethnological reasons – any attempt at such a summary would in any case be rather outside the scope of this chapter. In what follows, therefore, reference will be made specifically to observations of the aurora australis only.

Methods of Observation

The obvious way to observe an aurora is to look at it; this is what has been done for many centuries. There are instrumental aids, however, which it would be foolish to reject and in the special conditions of Antarctic observation there may

---

[1] Now with Airglow and Aurora Section, Central Radio Propagation Laboratory, Boulder, Colorado.

well be reasons for relying solely upon instruments. Some observations made by
a visual observer can be quite satisfactorily carried out by automatic instruments.
For example, the recording of the position, brightness and colour of an aurora is
quite satisfactorily done by photography; under polar conditions, it is better done
photographically. (At a station where twenty-four hours of darkness a day are
experienced during the winter, it is a two-man job to observe the aurora continuously; with an all-sky camera and colour film, a continuous record of the aurora is
obtained with the effort of a few man-hours a week.)

The increasing use of the all-sky camera in auroral research has brought about

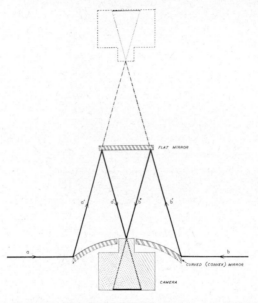

FIG. 118 DIAGRAMMATIC REPRESENTATION OF TYPICAL ALL-SKY
CAMERA SYSTEM

The paths of two light rays from the horizon are shown. The camera can be
placed in either of two positions. One position is shown in dotted outline and
when this position is used, the flat mirror is not needed. With a flat mirror in
the position shown, the camera is placed below the main curved mirror

a change in the synoptic studies of auroral displays. The camera is, basically,
very simple. It is based on the reflecting properties of a curved mirror: a mirror
similar in shape to the hub-caps of many cars. Looking into such a mirror, one
sees a reflection from 'all round' – in a room, for example, one can see reflected
all four walls and the ceiling at once. The sketch (Fig. 118) shows the paths of
two light rays coming in from opposite directions, a and b, and being reflected
by the curved, convex, mirror into the directions a′ and b′. A camera placed above
the mirror in the position shown in dotted outline would then be able to photograph all the rays such as a and b, giving an image of the whole of the hemisphere
above the plane of the convex mirror – together with the reflection of the camera

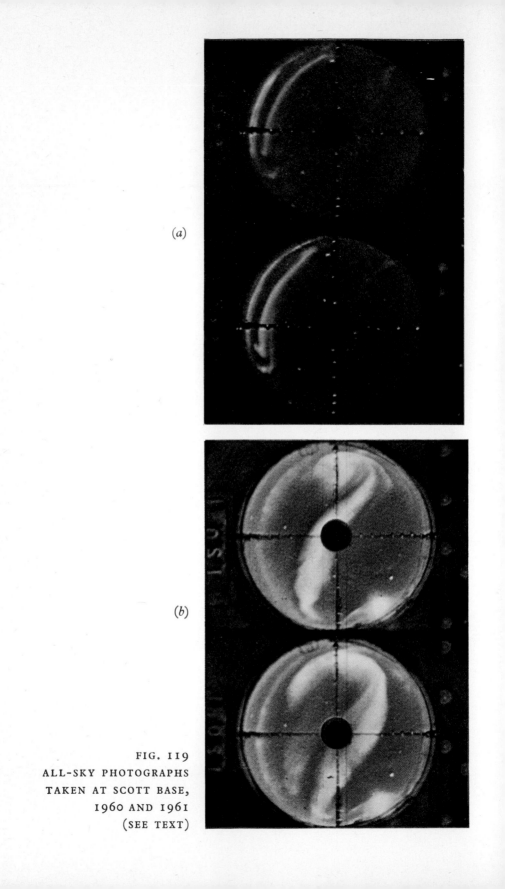

(a)

(b)

FIG. 119
ALL-SKY PHOTOGRAPHS
TAKEN AT SCOTT BASE,
1960 AND 1961
(SEE TEXT)

itself. A system such as this can be made more compact by putting a second (often flat) mirror halfway between the curved mirror and the camera: this in effect folds the system in two by reflecting the rays a', b' down along the path a'', b''. The camera can then be placed under the convex mirror, photographing the incoming light through a hole in the convex mirror. This arrangement of the camera is shown in full outline in Figure 118.

Figure 120 shows the interpretation of all-sky photographs. The edge of the circular image is the horizon; north, east, south and west are determined from the intersections of the camera arms with the horizon. The zenith, which is blocked from the photograph by the second mirror, is in the centre.

Typical photographs taken by all-sky cameras are shown in Figures 119

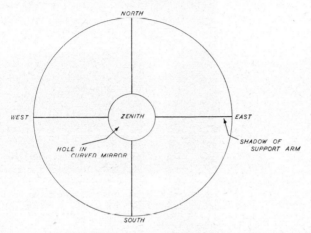

FIG. 120 INTERPRETATION OF ALL-SKY PHOTOGRAPHS

The horizon is imaged round the circumference of a circle and the zenith is at the centre of the circle. A small area of sky around the zenith is obscured, either by the camera or by the hole in the main mirror through which the camera operates

and 122: the photographs were taken at Scott Base and Hallett Station in 1960 and 1961, and are typical of polar displays. There is some unavoidable colour distortion in the photographs but the record of the main colouration is truthful. There are several points worth noting about the photographs. First, the pairs of photographs in Figure 119 are taken one minute apart, and the lower set shows how rapidly the aurora in polar regions can change in position and colour: in the interval of a minute, the aurora has moved across from one side of the zenith to the other, the red colouration stretching into the zenith in the lower picture has disappeared and one of the fainter bands has vanished. For contrast, Figure 119a shows quite a steady form of aurora photographed from Scott Base. The photographs from Hallett station, shown in Figure 122, were taken with exposures that vary from frame to frame; this is done to get some idea of the relative brightness of auroral forms observed at different times. It will be noticed from the longer exposed frames of both the pairs of pictures in Figure 122 that there is a general feeble, red glow over most of the sky: this is quite characteristic of high latitude auroral displays.

Figure 121 shows, in monochrome, two all-sky photographs obtained from Lauder, New Zealand; in the camera used, the second mirror is supported by a perspex dome which covers the instrument and so the mirror appears, in the photographs, to be unsupported. The background of stars can be seen plainly in these photographs and makes the determination of the position of the aurora quite easy. Figure 123 illustrates the value of the all-sky camera for monitoring auroral displays.

A technique of photography which has been much used in Norway is that of parallactic photography. Using this technique, an aurora is photographed simultaneously with two or more cameras spaced some kilometres apart. Because

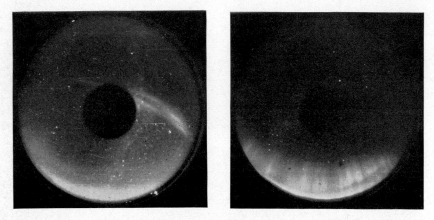

FIG. 121 ALL-SKY PHOTOGRAPHS TAKEN AT LAUDER, 1959

the aurora is not infinitely distant from the cameras, a change in position of the camera causes the aurora to change its position among the background of the stars. Careful measurement of this apparent shift relative to the stars, and triangulation based on the known positions of two cameras, gives the actual position of the aurora above the Earth's surface. The measurement and analysis necessary after obtaining the photographs are rather prolonged and the technique has not been very popular in the Southern Hemisphere; Geddes (1939) has made and reduced the most extensive set and he found the heights of the aurora australis to be very similar to the heights of the aurora borealis measured in the Northern Hemisphere. Some more photographs have been obtained and reduced by the Carter Observatory, Wellington; some photographs have been taken, but not yet reduced, on an Invercargill–Lauder baseline. The Australians have arranged for a pair of cameras to be operated at Mawson – one close to the base and one, some miles away, which is arranged to make exposures automatically, on command from the base.

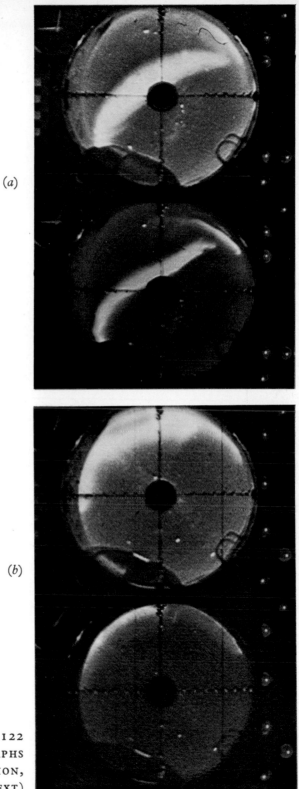

FIG. 122
ALL-SKY PHOTOGRAPHS
TAKEN AT HALLETT STATION,
1961 (SEE TEXT)

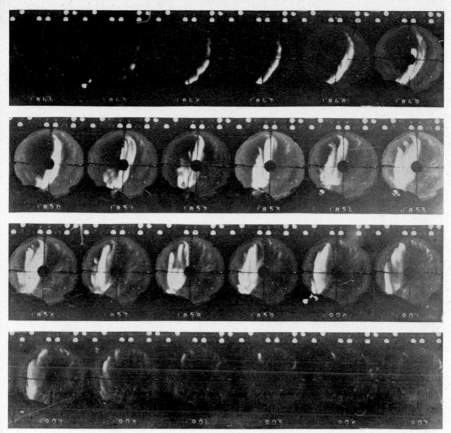

FIG. 123 ALL-SKY PHOTOGRAPHS OF AURORAL DISPLAY, HALLETT
STATION, 1844–1907 GMT 19 JULY 1958

The photographs were taken at minute intervals and show bands rising in the
east passing through the zenith (where four bands are visible at 1855), and
dying away in the west

Another instrument of great value in auroral research is the spectrograph.
This instrument is used to photograph the light of the aurora or the night sky
after the light has been sorted for colour; different colours present in the auroral
light are brought to a focus at different places on a photographic emulsion.
By measurement of the positions of the images and of the total exposure of each
image, one is able to deduce much useful information. The presence of oxygen
and nitrogen atoms and molecules and, occasionally, of hydrogen atoms in the
atmosphere at auroral heights has been established by the use of a spectrograph.
The temperature of the molecules emitting light can be measured. Some informed guesses of the processes causing the emission can be made. In the case
of the emission from hydrogen atoms, clear evidence is frequently obtained of
high speeds of movement of the atoms.

The measurement and analysis of a spectrographic photograph can take many hours of skilled work; this means that the data are obtained slowly, although this slowness of reduction has the advantage of giving a considerable volume of information. If one is prepared to lose some of this volume of information (it may be that some of it is redundant or of no immediate interest) for the sake of speed in collecting the data, then a photometer is used. In this instrument, the colour sorting is done by coloured filters or a spectroscopic arrangement working over a limited range and the light is detected, measured and recorded by photoelectric means.

A comparatively new technique for the study of the region in which aurorae occur is that of radar. It has been found that a radar with a range of some hundreds of kilometres will often show the presence of large areas of excess electrons in auroral regions at the same time as an auroral display. This technique, it was hoped, would make possible the study of auroral displays in daylight or cloudy conditions and thus add significantly to the existing knowledge of the occurrence of aurorae as a function of both time and position in the atmosphere. Unfortunately, there is a serious doubt about the identification of the echoes observed with the luminous aurora: this topic will be dealt with more fully in a later section of this chapter.

The Aurora Australis – Before 1957

In 1957 the International Geophysical Year started; this date forms a convenient date to divide a review of what is known about the aurora australis. Until the IGY, knowledge of the aurora australis depended on observations obtained at intervals of years by the various Antarctic expeditions, on the long, valuable records obtained in New Zealand by Geddes (1937, 1939a, b) and later by McQuistan, Thomsen and their colleagues at Carter Observatory (McQuistan, 1959; McQuistan and Frankpitt, 1957a, b; Thomsen, McQuistan and Frankpitt, 1956) and on the observations from Macquarie Island (Jacka, 1953, 1954).

The position of the southern auroral zone was not well known; White and Geddes (1939) had made an estimate of the zone from the comparatively meagre observational evidence at their disposal. Shortly after their work was published, Vestine and Snyder (1945) re-examined the data and, by comparison with Northern Hemisphere observations and with magnetic observations, derived an auroral zone which remained the most widely accepted estimate until the results of the IGY.

With the exception of these studies, very little analysis of the behaviour of the aurora australis had been made. The displays were, from expedition reports and from the New Zealand observations, known to be similar to the aurorae observed in the Northern Hemisphere. It was thus reasonably assumed that the southern aurorae were more or less exact counterparts of the northern aurorae. The reasons for this relative neglect are due to geographical circumstances. The northern auroral zone (Fig. 124) crosses Alaska, northern Canada, Iceland and northern Norway, all relatively accessible areas. The southern auroral

zone, on the other hand, lies entirely over ocean and the Antarctic Continent
(Fig. 125). What stations were available for auroral observation suffer severely
from cloudiness of the sky.

FIG. 124 POSITION OF THE NORTHERN AURORAL ZONE
(HATCHED RING)

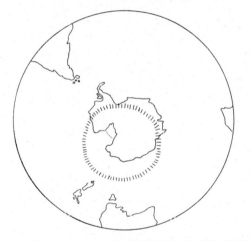

FIG. 125 POSITION OF THE SOUTHERN AURORAL ZONE
(HATCHED RING)

The IGY marked a considerable step forward in the understanding of the
behaviour of the southern aurorae. During the IGY, stations carrying out auroral
observations were established all over Antarctica. (A glance at Figure 126 will
show the high density of observatories.) The observations made from these
stations have given, and are still giving, excellent factual information about the
behaviour of the aurora australis.

Other information obtained before the IGY period relates to the simultaneous occurrence of aurorae in the two hemispheres. Little and Shrum (1950) used records collected at Carter Observatory (Wellington) and those collected at Cornell University, New York State, to show that the number of days when auroral displays were seen in both hemispheres is greater than the number of days one would expect by chance coincidence if the aurorae occurred in the two hemispheres quite independently. This conclusion is, of course, a long way from establishing that the two auroral displays are identical in form, or even that they are caused by the same agency or produced in the same way. There is no reason to suppose that different agents are involved; however, it should be remembered

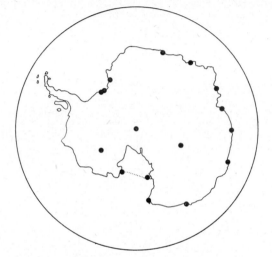

FIG. 126 MAJOR IGY AURORAL OBSERVATORIES ON THE ANTARCTIC
CONTINENT

that this evidence of simultaneity is not a demonstration that there is a common cause.

From Geddes' work (in the papers referred to above), the conclusion to be drawn is that there is no obvious difference between the aurorae in the two hemispheres.

This, then, was the situation up to the beginning of the IGY: there was some rather incomplete knowledge of the position of the zone of maximum occurrence and no evidence to suggest that the aurora australis was in any way different to its northern counterpart. What more is known now? In the following sections, a few of the results of recent investigations will be mentioned. There are many questions still to be answered and most aspects of the southern aurora are still under active investigation.

The Southern Auroral Zone – Synoptic Analysis

Many papers have been published in the last few years dealing with the observations from particular stations. These papers are so numerous that it would be pointless to list them all; taken collectively, they confirm, in general terms, that the daily and seasonal variations of the aurora australis are similar to those variations found from Northern Hemisphere observations of the aurora borealis:

1. The daily variation in frequency of auroral occurrence shows a general character varying with the location of the observing site; outside the auroral zone, the frequency is a maximum at, or near to, local geomagnetic midnight. Inside the auroral zone, the time of maximum occurrence may move away from geomagnetic midnight and, at some stations, the single maximum no longer occurs and two distinct maxima are observed.

2. The seasonal variations in frequency of occurrence are known best for stations outside the auroral zone, for the simple reason that aurorae cannot be observed in daylight and the observations made inside the zone are, therefore, limited to winter months only. For stations outside the auroral zone, there is little doubt that aurorae are most frequently observed at the equinoxes, that is, around 21 September and 21 March. It is, perhaps, worth suggesting here that, since the seasonal variation in occurrence is the same as in the Northern Hemisphere, Little and Shrum's work on the simultaneous occurrence of aurorae in the two hemispheres may be strongly affected by the identity of the seasonal variations in the two hemispheres. They present no evidence to show that, *for a given time of the year*, the number of days with aurorae observed in both hemispheres is not equal to the number of coincidences expected by chance.

Considerable interest is attached to the determination of the position of the auroral zone. The expectation was that it would prove to be in exact (magnetic) correspondence to the northern zone. Any departures from exact correspondence would be of great importance in theoretical considerations; naturally, for any theory of auroral production must not only predict the similarity of the two zones but also explain any differences.

In studying diurnal and seasonal variations in the frequency of occurrence of aurorae, observations from a single station will suffice; the labour of analysis is comparatively light and thus many analyses of these variations have been made. To determine the location of the southern auroral zone as a whole requires observations from as many stations as possible. The most recent analyses are those of Gartlein, Nack and Sprague (1959), Feldstein (1960) and Bond and Jacka (1962). Gartlein, Nack and Sprague, using relatively limited data, have derived the auroral zone marked 'A' in Figure 127. Feldstein has taken data from twenty Southern Hemisphere stations and obtained 'B' (Fig. 127) as the auroral zone; his analysis is, however, open to the objection that the data he used refer to 1957 for some stations and to 1958 for others. If the auroral zone changed its mean position between the middle of 1957 and the middle of 1958, then it is possible for the shape of the auroral zone to be incorrectly derived.

Without doubt, the best analysis of the southern auroral zone is that of Bond and Jacka. One of the troubles in synoptic studies is the problem of allowing for interference to the observations from cloud, twilight and moonlight, and from the effect of varying magnetic activity. It is difficult to know how these interferences and effects have been allowed for in any particular analysis and so when, as in an analysis of the auroral zone, one requires to compare observations from several stations it is risky to use reduced data. Bond and Jacka have overcome these difficulties by obtaining unreduced data from twenty-two stations (they did not use the data from two of these stations for reasons given in their paper). These data were then analysed in the same way, so ensuring that as far as possible the separate stations enter into the analysis in a uniform manner. The auroral zone that Bond and Jacka found gave the position of maximum occurrence in the years 1957 and 1958 as 'C' in Figure 127. A point to notice particularly about the auroral zone is that it is circular and centred on 120° E, 75° S. This point is one of the intersections of the eccentric dipole axis with the Earth's surface; the centre of the auroral zone is definitely not coincident with

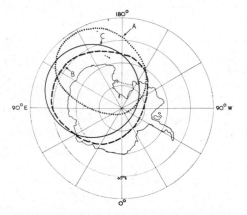

FIG. 127 THREE SOUTHERN AURORAL ZONES DERIVED FROM IGY
OBSERVATIONS
A. Gartlein, Nack and Sprague; B. Feldstein; C. Bond and Jacka

the magnetic dip pole (the point where the surface magnetic field is vertical) and the auroral zone does not lie along an isocline (the locus of a given tilt of the Earth's magnetic field from the horizontal).

Using Bond and Jacka's auroral zone, it is interesting to compare the northern and southern auroral zones. As Feldstein has pointed out, the two zones differ markedly in shape, the southern zone being quite circular and the northern zone elliptical. In a recent paper, Nikolsky (1961) suggests that this apparent difference between the two zones is due to differences in analysis of the two zones. Recent work in the Northern Hemisphere has suggested that there may be two auroral zones instead of the one simple one normally considered; Nikolsky suggests that the determined Antarctic auroral zone in reality consists of two auroral zones. It must not be forgotten, however, that determined auroral zones are somewhat of a statistical fiction. The zone is, by definition, *the line of maximum frequency of occurrence* of aurorae and is not to be thought of as the shape in which aurorae occur, or that auroral displays necessarily tend to lie along the zone. The method of analysis of the observations is, therefore, vital in interpretation of the results; for example, it is possible (but not probable) that aurorae occur along the sides of a hollow square, the orientation of the square turning with the Sun – such an auroral distribution could give a circular auroral zone.

Before leaving the question of the southern auroral zone, we should return to the simultaneity of occurrence of aurorae in the Northern and Southern Hemispheres. As mentioned earlier, some theoretical interest is attached to observations of aurorae simultaneously from two stations, one in each hemisphere: the two stations should be near one meridian of longitude (so that the local time of day is the same at a given instant at the two stations) and close to being the same distance from the appropriate auroral zone. The great difficulty in studying this problem is that of the opposite seasons; when it is winter in one hemisphere, it is summer on the other. Aurorae cannot be seen in daylight and so while one set of polar stations is obtaining full night observations, the other set of polar stations is, aurorally, non-operational. If one chooses a station at the optimum longitude in one hemisphere (i.e. the longitude on which the auroral zone is at the lowest *geographic* latitude), the other station which is appropriate for comparison between the two hemispheres will tend to be at a correspondingly high latitude. Thus the comparison will tend to be limited to the equinoxes – March and September.

Gartlein (1959) has compared observations from Ellsworth station in Antarctica with observations from the United States and southern Canada. He finds that 'it appears that the US will report an aurora on any clear night hour that Ellsworth reports one. The forms are not necessarily the same in both places, nor does the Ellsworth aurora always appear to be ahead of or behind the US. . . . An aurora will be reported from both the Northern and Southern Hemispheres if visibility conditions permit. They will not necessarily look the same'.

Orientation of Auroral Arcs

Another interesting property of polar auroral displays, common to both hemispheres, is the diurnal change in the direction of simple arc forms. Weill (1958) noticed this effect in his observations from Dumont d'Urville in 1957; he finds a regular daily swing in the direction of auroral arcs. Weill points out that this swing had been observed by Mawson from Cape Denison (1912–13) but that these observations had been overlooked since then.

On the lower latitude side of the auroral zones, arcs appear lined up approximately magnetically east–west and have little daily variation in direction; according to Feldstein (1960), the change in direction during a day can be as high as 70° near the auroral zone, but 20° only is more usual for stations at lower latitudes. Inside the auroral zone, most stations report a regular rotation of the direction of auroral arcs at a speed so that one complete rotation occurs in twenty-four hours. For example, Feldstein finds this behaviour at Vostok; Hatherton and Midwinter (1960) did not note the regular rotation at Scott Base or Hallett, but Denholm and Bond (1961), in a re-examination of the data, show that there is evidence of this rotation at Scott Base, Hallett and Wilkes, and that the rotation is similar to that reported by Weill for the Dumont d'Urville observations. The phase of the rotation at all these stations is such that the arcs tend to be aligned on the azimuth of the Sun.

The Spectrum of the Aurora Australis

Prior to the IGY period, knowledge of the auroral spectrum was confined, as far as we are aware, entirely to that obtained by Northern Hemisphere observations. The work of Norwegian, Canadian and American physicists had by 1957 produced an elegant volume of knowledge of the auroral spectrum and it was with great interest that their experiments were repeated on the aurora australis. In what follows, the various emissions observed in the auroral spectrum will be considered in groups.

THE OXYGEN ATOMIC LINES AT 5577; 6300/6364A

These lines are the most prominent emissions from an aurora and are normally the emissions responsible for its colour. Since the aurora australis is, as we have seen, similar in colour to the aurora borealis, it is not surprising that the oxygen lines are prominent in the southern spectra.

Because of their intensity (thus giving a wide choice of methods of observation) and because the oxygen lines can be observed from all latitudes and on all clear nights, a considerable number of observations and a considerable amount of analysis have given some interesting results.

It is known from Northern Hemisphere observations of the green oxygen line at 5577A that this emission comes from a restricted range of heights around the 100 or 110 km levels and there is no evidence or theoretical reason for expecting the behaviour to be different in the Southern Hemisphere. Sandford (1959) has shown, from observations made at Invercargill, that the intensity of the green oxygen emission line increases with the level of magnetic disturbance (see Fig. 128). This increase occurs in the sky both to the north and to the south of Invercargill, and is apparently the same *whether or not an auroral display is seen in the sky at the time of the observation*. The night sky, in the absence of aurora, at high or low latitudes, is not absolutely black and observations have shown that, in addition to scattered starlight, there is a strong emission component present. The spectrum of this component has some emissions in common with the auroral spectrum – notably the atomic oxygen lines – and some emissions not normally associated with aurorae, thought to be emitted from heights below the typical auroral heights.

Sandford's results therefore immediately suggest that there may not be the distinction between auroral and non-auroral conditions that is normally assumed. They also suggest that the auroral zone is not necessarily as clear cut, physically, as visual and photographic observations suggest and this means that it is necessary to examine the question of what is meant, physically, by the term 'auroral'.

Nakamura (1958) has taken the opportunities offered by the voyages of the

Japanese Antarctic Research Expedition ship *Soya* to measure the intensity of the green oxygen emission at various latitudes between 35° N and 64° S (approximately). He found that, on both the 1956/1957 and 1957/1958 voyages, there was a definite variation in intensity with latitude, with a maximum at 20° Latitude and a rise in intensity at latitudes higher than approximately 40°. He also notes a pronounced dependence of the intensity observed, both at his reference station in Japan (Maruyama) and on board the *Soya*, on the level of solar activity. He also suggests that the latitude effect on intensity is most marked for low disturbances (and thus low intensities) and that when there are disturbed conditions present, these disturbed conditions are roughly equally apparent at all latitudes.

Duncan (1960) has analyzed a long series of observations from Camden, New

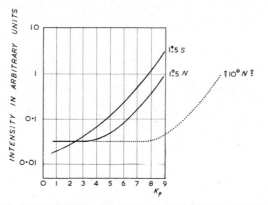

FIG. 128 THE VARIATIONS OF 5577A EMISSION WITH MAGNETIC
ACTIVITY (AFTER SANDFORD)

The dotted line indicates a possible variation for the latitude of Camden, New South Wales, to be compared with Duncan's results. It must be remembered that the magnetic activity index, K_p cannot rise above 9 and that the portion of the dotted line outside the box cannot be observed

South Wales, and finds that the intensity is independent of the level of magnetic disturbance. This is in conflict with both the Sandford and the Nakamura observations; the conflict with the Sandford observations may only be apparent, not real. One can make the suggestion that, since Camden is approximately ten degrees of latitude nearer the equator than Invercargill, Duncan's results correspond to the flat portion of the curve shown in Figure 128 for the sky to the north of Invercargill. The shift in the two curves for Invercargill (shown in full lines), corresponding to a change in latitude from $1\frac{1}{2}°$ S to $1\frac{1}{2}°$ N of Invercargill suggests that a change in latitude of 10° to the north of Invercargill might give results indicated by the dotted line in Figure 128 – in other words, wildly extrapolating. Sandford's results suggests that the Duncan results are not in conflict with the Invercargill observations. The conflict with Nakamura's observations remains.

Sandford has repeated his analysis using observations of intensity in the zenith of Scott Base (Sandford, 1961a) and finds that, at this station also, the intensity

of the green oxygen line increases with increasing magnetic activity whether or
not an aurora is present but, for these observations, the intensity is generally
higher when an aurora is present than when no aurora is observed.

Turning now to the observations of the red oxygen emission lines at 6300
and 6364A, or, since the relative intensity of these two lines is constant, considering only the 6300 line, Sandford has shown that the statistical behaviour at
Invercargill and Scott Base is very similar to that of the oxygen green line
although this must not be interpreted as indicating that the ratio of the intensities
of the green and red lines is constant. In fact the ratio varies from hour to hour
and from night to night over a range of ten to one. Northern Hemisphere
observations suggest that the red oxygen emission comes from a greater height
in the atmosphere than the green emission; the red emission height is unlikely
to be less than about 160 km, both on theoretical grounds and from observational
(rocket) results.[1] Thus the changing ratio of intensities of the red and green lines
may be due only to a change in the height of an aurora; it is not necessarily due
to a fundamental change in the type of auroral excitation. However, a change in
height is not always sufficient to explain an observed change in ratio.

Duncan's observations at Camden show that the red oxygen emission at this
latitude is sensitive to magnetic disturbance in a similar manner to Sandford's
Invercargill observations of the northern sky. In addition, Duncan and Ellis
(1959) have noted an occasional minute-to-minute correspondence between the
intensity of the red oxygen line and bursts of radio noise on 4·6 kc/s, strongly
suggesting a common origin: the connection is complicated by two observations
of 6300 emission enhancements without corresponding radio noise bursts.

Duncan (1959) has also reported an interesting observation of polarization
of the red oxygen emission from an aurora in the zenith at Camden; these
observations are interpreted by Duncan as indicating that the oxygen atoms
were excited by electrons spiralling about lines of force of the geomagnetic field.

Finally, Weill (1961) finds that the red emission observed from Dumont
d'Urville base during the IGY shows a clear statistical evidence of east–west
movements in the regions of emission.

MOLECULAR NITROGEN EMISSIONS

The spectrum of the aurora invariably contains evidence of the presence of the
main constituent of the atmosphere – nitrogen. This gas is excited in the

[1] Both the green and red oxygen lines are what are known as 'forbidden' lines; this
means that the atoms of oxygen, when excited to the states for the emission of these lines,
do not emit the radiation practically instantaneously. The atom 'hangs fire' for about
three-quarters of a second in the case of the green line and for about two minutes in the
case of the red lines. If, while the atom is 'hanging fire', it collides with another atom in the
atmosphere, the energy which can be emitted as the green or red line may be drawn off by
the other atom or used to increase the speed of movement of the oxygen atom: in either
case, the emission does not then take place. The atmosphere is sufficiently thin at 100 km
for an oxygen atom to 'hang fire' for three-quarters of a second without losing the excitation energy in this way; only in the much thinner atmosphere at heights exceeding about
150 km can a two-minute 'hang-fire' take place without a collision removing the energy.

atmosphere at auroral heights not atomically, as is oxygen, but mainly in molecular form. In general terms, atomic spectra are simple in appearance: atomic oxygen, considered in the preceding section, has only a few lines plainly observed in the region of the spectrum easily studied. Still speaking generally, the spectrum of a molecular emission appears at first sight to be very complicated; instead of a few lines, fuzzy *bands* of light are recorded by a spectrograph and several of these bands occur in regular sequence and obviously have some relation with each other.

The analysis of molecular spectra can yield, and has yielded, a great deal of information about the physical conditions in the atmosphere during an auroral display. Temperatures of the upper atmosphere have been determined and the ways in which aurorae are excited have been studied. Again, the majority of such work has been carried out in the Northern Hemisphere and will not be discussed here. Spectra of the aurora australis show very similar features to spectra of the aurora borealis.

As an example of the sort of information gained from studies of the molecular emissions, it is worth considering the investigations of Malville (1959). Malville, while wintering-over at Ellsworth Station in 1957, obtained spectra of aurorae with red lower borders. He found that the red lower border was due to increased emission in the red region of the spectrum due to molecular nitrogen and that this emission is confined to the lower portions of the aurora. From Northern Hemisphere observations he suggests that the emission arises at heights of about 70 to 90 km (approximately 20 km below normal auroral heights). He then looks for a possible excitation mechanism which will provide just enough energy to excite the observed molecular emission; an excess in energy would excite other bands which are not observed, but would be observed if there was an extra 25% of energy available. (This is the great help gained from the occurrence of many bands and energy levels in molecular spectra; the bands and energy levels are so closely spaced that one can tell just how much energy is appearing in a particular region of the atmosphere.) Malville then considers several possible reactions and concludes that his observations indicate the occurrence of bombardment of the atmosphere by protons and electrons with a particular energy.

A similar study of nitrogen emissions has been made on spectra obtained at Scott Base, taking the particular case of a band system in the blue region of the spectrum (Gadsden, 1961). The conclusions from this study were that, during July 1959, the conditions of excitation of aurorae observed from Scott Base were changing from night to night and from hour to hour; the conditions were different to those observed previously in the Northern Hemisphere (from stations at latitudes lower than that of Scott Base). The indications were that either the atmosphere was appreciably hotter over Scott Base or that a particular molecular reaction was taking place. If this molecular reaction was occurring, then the conclusion followed that the ionosphere was, during these auroral displays, much *less* dense than normal.

So far, no mention has been made of the most prominent of the nitrogen molecular bands – the so-called first negative system. These bands are very strong in auroral spectra and arise from molecular nitrogen which has been ionized. Regular photoelectric observations of this emission have been made from several Antarctic stations including, particularly, Port aux Français, Kerguelen (2000 hours of observations; Barbier and Peron, 1961) and Dumont d'Urville (Barbier and Weill, 1961). Weill (1959) has analysed data from Dumont d'Urville to determine the frequency of occurrence of aurorae for different times of day: he finds also a west–east movement of the mean position of (blue) auroral displays during the night. The observations were restricted to times when the Sun was more than $27°$ below the horizon; this means that, with the mechanical arrangement of the photometer, sunlight was incident on the atmosphere only at heights above 300 km. Weill can find no explanation of this west–east movement in the mean position of aurorae other than that sunlight is causing increased emission of the first negative bands. This effect must, therefore, mean that many aurorae (40% of the total) observed from Dumont d'Urville occur at heights above 300 km – which is quite different to the proportion observed at lower latitudes; there must also be nitrogen ions present permanently in the polar high atmosphere. The numbers of ions present at different altitudes are deduced in a later paper (Weill, 1960); he finds also that, inside the auroral zone – at geomagnetic latitudes greater than $75°$ – the numbers of nitrogen ions are only one-sixth those in the auroral zone.

Sandford (1961b, 1962) has made a study of the emission of the negative bands during periods when there is strong absorption of radio waves in polar regions, the so-called 'polar cap absorption events' (see also Chapter 17). He finds that the nitrogen bands are increased in intensity over the usual level during these events and that there is a certain amount of evidence that this enhancement does not follow the variations of the oxygen green line intensity but rather is correlated with the amount of radio absorption. For this reason, and because increased emission does not appear in twilight, he postulates that the increased emission occurs low in the atmosphere, at D-region heights, below 100 km, and is due to proton bombardment of the polar atmosphere.

Correlations of the Aurora Australis with Other Phenomena

One of the accepted techniques of geophysical research is the discovery of correlations between two or more observed phenomena. In the study of the upper atmosphere disturbances and their connection with solar phenomena, this approach has been used too widely. As a general rule, any observations of ionospheric or auroral disturbance will correlate with other observations; so interrelated are the phenomena that more valuable results come from the discovery of an absence of correlation.

This slightly paradoxical statement can be justified by considering that the discovery of a strong positive correlation does not, invariably, prove the existence of cause and effect. Usually one can interpret the correlation equally well by postulating that the correlating observations are independently correlated with another phenomenon: one cause, two effects – then the two effects will in general be mutually correlated. An example of this is given by the analysis (Evans, 1960) of the correlation between movements of aurorae and the direction of the disturbance magnetic vector. At Halley Bay he finds that the mean movement of aurorae in hourly periods is related to the departure of the horizontal magnetic vector from the quiet level to be expected in the hourly period. There is quite a significant relationship between the auroral and the magnetic observations both in amplitude and direction. Further analysis (Evans, 1961), based on records from Tromso, Norway, has shown that this apparent relationship is probably due to chance, arising from both sets of observational results having a similar dependence on the local time of observation, i.e. both sets had a similar dependence on the position of the Sun, relative to the observatory: for a given time of day, there was found to be no consistent relationship between the auroral movements and the magnetic disturbance vector.

Another example of a misleading correlation will be given in the next section.

RADAR OBSERVATIONS OF THE AURORA AUSTRALIS

Observations of echoing regions at auroral heights have been made from eight sites in the Southern Hemisphere – Lincoln and Invercargill in New Zealand, Macquarie Island in Subantarctic waters, and Halley Bay, Dumont d'Urville, Mirnyy, Vostok and Scott Base in Antarctica. Because of its geomagnetic situation, the radar at Invercargill is almost ideally sited for these observations. Shortly after the operation of the radar commenced, it was recognized (Unwin and Gadsden, 1957) that the local topography at the radar site was also, by chance, almost ideal. The following characteristics of the radar echoing regions were found from the Invercargill observations (Unwin, 1958, 1959; Gadsden, 1959a, b):

1. The echoing regions are at altitudes of 100–130 km.

2. At certain times, usually in the afternoon and evening, the echoes come from a layer which is horizontal, extended over a great area and probably less than $2\frac{1}{2}$ km thick.

3. The echoing regions are lined up with the local magnetic field so that they are most easily observed when the radar beam is incident upon them perpendicularly.

4. The echoing regions usually extend over a wide area near the auroral zone; their frequency of occurrence decreases with decreasing latitude.

5. The edges of the echoing regions appear to move out from the auroral zone during magnetic disturbances so that, for a station at relatively low latitude, the probability of observing the echoes increases as the magnetic activity increases.

6. There is a decrease in the occurrence of the echoing regions during the day, relative to night-time, which is independent of the relative decrease in magnetic activity.

7. Any apparent relationship between the occurrence of radar echoing regions

and the appearance of auroral displays arises from statistical chance: there is no statistical connection between the two phenomena at a given level of magnetic activity. For a given time of observation, there is not necessarily a correspondence in detail.

8. The echoing regions show systematic movements at speeds up to several thousands of metres per second. The speed of movement is related to the degree of magnetic disturbance observed at the surface of the Earth beneath the echoing regions. The movements are generally westerly in the early part of the night and easterly in the later part.

Later determinations of the movements of the echoing regions observed from Macquarie Island and Scott Base (Unwin and Sulzberger, private communication) having suggested a consistent pattern of movements over the polar region which is strikingly similar to the pattern of electric current flow deduced from the magnetic vector observations (see for example Vestine *et al.*, 1947). It is difficult to avoid the conclusion that radar observations are a means of studying the detailed structure of the atmospheric regions responsible for magnetic disturbances. (A radar can resolve an area only a few kilometres in diameter, in the regions of interest; in comparison, a magnetometer has discrimination only by virtue of the inverse square of the range to the disturbance, although a pair of magnetometers can give quite fine resolution under certain quite drastic assumptions.)

Seed and Ellyett (1958) have reported results from sixty-five nights of observations during the first half of 1957; their equipment was situated at the relatively low geomagnetic latitude of $47 \cdot 8°$ (some $2\frac{1}{2}°$ lower than that of Invercargill) and they observed echoes on ten of the sixty-five nights. The deduced heights of the echoing regions were all in the E-region. Seed (1958) has discussed these observations in more detail and examined possible reflection mechanisms.

Harrison and Watkins (1958) have examined the question of the simultaneity of occurrence of echoing regions in the Northern and Southern Hemispheres. They compared observations made during May–October, 1957, at Halley Bay, with observations from Jodrell Bank, England, during the same period. Echoes were observed from Halley Bay for 26% of the time and from Jodrell Bank for 2% of the time. Both sets of data show a positive correlation with the planetary magnetic disturbance and there is, therefore, a correlation between the occurrence of echoes at Jodrell Bank and at Halley Bay.

Bullough (1961) has published a very full and detailed discussion of results obtained from his radar observations at Dumont d'Urville made between May 1957 and January 1958. He finds that the aspect sensitivity of the echoing regions – that is, the quality of the regions that makes detection of the regions easiest when the radar beam is incident perpendicularly to the direction of the local magnetic field – is nowhere nearly as critical as at Jodrell Bank or Halley Bay. Bullough examines the possibility that the echoing regions are themselves modifying the local magnetic field sufficiently to restore the perpendicularity condition but concludes that any such effect, if present, would not be a sufficient effect. Indeed, in some cases he notes that this effect would be in such a direction as to make the radar beam incident on the echoing regions even further away from perpendicularity.

One of Bullough's most important results is the detection of an 'inner auroral zone' for the echoing regions. Prior to Bullough's observations, all the work with radar techniques had been carried out at observatories outside the auroral zone. It was quite plain from the Invercargill analyses that the echoing regions occurred in a 'zone', whose outer edge moved coherently towards lower latitudes at night time, and with increases in magnetic activity. It was not known whether this zone was in the form of a ring, a general cap over the polar regions or whether it was spiral in form. Bullough's observations have shown that the echoing regions tend to occur in two rings, with a marked dividing region at about 16° distance from the geomagnetic pole. Thus the echoing regions are definitely not distributed as a cap over polar regions; the evidence for or against spiral structure is not conclusive.

ASSOCIATION OF THE AURORA AUSTRALIS WITH MAGNETIC ACTIVITY

The connection between the aurora borealis and magnetic activity has been known since the early part of the eighteenth century. Stormer (1955) quotes from a paper by Hiorter published in 1747, as follows: 'But who could have imagined that there was any connection between the aurora and the magnetic [i.e. compass] needle, and that the aurorae, when passing over the zenith to the South would cause a considerable perturbation of the magnetic needle amounting to several degrees within a few minutes?' There was no reason to suppose that the aurora australis would not cause similar 'considerable perturbation' of a magnetic needle and Jacka (1953) showed that the latitudes of homogeneous auroral arcs, observed from Macquarie Island, showed a strong dependence on the level of planetary magnetic disturbance (measured by K_p). He found also that the arcs tended to move towards the equator during the first half of the night and back towards the pole during the later half of the night. Gadsden (1959) used probabilities of occurrence of aurorae observed from Invercargill and showed that this dependence on local time was probably due to the use of the planetary disturbance index and that, except for three summer months, use of the local K-index (in this case, the K-index measured at Macquarie Island) removes any dependence on local time. During December, January and February, there is a significantly higher probability of observing an aurora at a given K-index than during other months. Gadsden and Gadsden (1960) have re-analysed seven years of visual observations from Campbell Island and found that this summer maximum becomes two equinoctial (April and August) maxima for aurorae seen to the south of Campbell Island. D. W. Holmes (personal communication) has found, similarly, a maximum in the middle of winter at Hallett and minimum in the middle of winter at Scott Base. The high geographic latitudes of these two last stations make it impossible to observe aurorae between October and March, because of the long hours of twilight or daylight.

Jacka (1954) has extended his analysis of the Macquarie Island observations to include the intensity of the aurora, estimated visually on a quasi-logarithmic scale. He finds, first, that the intensity is proportional to K_p, the planetary K-index. Since K_p is a quasi-logarithmic function of the departure of magnetic field intensity from the quiet-day level, this suggests that the brightness of an aurora is a simple power function of the magnetic field variations. Secondly, he finds evidence of a dependence of auroral brightness upon local time in a roughly sinusoidal manner, with a period of eight hours and a maximum about three hours before local midnight. Jacka does not put much weight on either of these conclusions – he points out that different auroral forms should be considered separately in such an analysis. He finally derives a small and irregular, residual, seasonal variation in intensity after removal of the effect of K_p.

With the exception of Holmes's work on the seasonal variation at Scott Base, referred to above, all the previously mentioned work refers to stations outside, or under, the auroral zone. Hatherton and Midwinter (1960) have studied the probability of occurrence of aurorae over Scott Base and Hallett as a function of local K-index. The probability of occurrence over Hallett increases with increase in K-index at all K-indices; at Scott Base, however, the probability is roughly constant up to a K-index of about 4, and then increases with increasing K-index. Sandford (1961) suggests that this behaviour is due to two different aurorae occurring. One type, the normal aurorae, occurs with a probability (approximately 25%) independent of K-index and superimposed on these aurorae are general glows (which Sandford calls the 'polar-glow aurorae') whose brightness, or probability of detection, increases with K-index. He suggests that the results of Hatherton and Midwinter refer to a mixture of both types of aurorae.

Hatherton and Midwinter also make the interesting point that auroral forms are almost invariably (80% of aurorae) overhead at both Scott Base and Hallett during times of low K-indices; at higher K-indices, the aurorae tend to move away from both stations towards the equator.

Finally, the work of Bond (1960) on auroral movements and the connection with magnetic bays must be mentioned. Movements of aurorae in the east-west direction (i.e., in general, along the length of auroral forms) were observed visually, with a theodolite, at Macquarie Island in 1958. Thirty-three cases of such movement were noted, six of east-to-west motion and twenty-seven of west-to-east motion. The speeds, in five possible cases, lay in the range 200–1000 m/sec. The local times of the east–west and west–east motions (and the speeds observed) were similar to the times Unwin finds for the radar echoing regions observed from Invercargill (see above – section on radar echoing regions). Bond shows conclusively that the *west-to-east* motions are always associated with a *decrease* in the horizontal magnetic field at Macquarie Island; conversely, the *east-to-west* motions are more likely than not to be associated with an *increase* in the horizontal field. Similar behaviour was found for the slower north–south movements: an increase in the horizontal magnetic field is associated with northwards movements and vice versa. Bond concludes that the motions take place in the direction of an electric current which would produce the observed changes in the horizontal magnetic field.

It has already been mentioned that Evans (1960) has considered similar observations, made at Halley Bay with an all-sky camera. He finds a correspondence similar to that found by Bond, i.e. a correspondence between the direction of auroral movements and the disturbance in the horizontal magnetic field measured at Halley Bay. However, as mentioned at the beginning of this section, a later analysis (Evans, 1961) based on Tromso records suggests that the apparent association is due to chance in that both auroral movement and magnetic disturbance are similarly dependent on the direction of the Sun from the observing station at the time of the observance.

Interpretation of, and Future Work on the Aurora Australis

When all the relatively isolated pieces of information about the aurora australis that are now available are considered, the overall impression is that the aurorae over the polar cap region are different in appearance and behaviour to the normal auroral zone type of aurorae. This has been pointed out by Gartlein, Nack and Sprague (1959), and in all the topics considered above there is a conflict when one tries to consider aurorae over the very high latitude stations as behaving in the same manner as those over auroral zone and temperate latitude observatories. It seems very likely that the 'auroral zone' is, in fact, a boundary between two distinct regions in the upper atmosphere. Is it, perhaps, the boundary between latitudes where the Earth's magnetic field extends out into interplanetary space without returning to the opposite hemisphere, and latitudes where the magnetic field lines return quite positively to the opposite hemisphere? To study this question, interest is at present centred on the outermost limits of the Earth's atmosphere, those regions distant some 50,000 km above the Earth's surface. Axford and Hines (1961) have pointed out some interesting general effects resulting from regarding the Earth's magnetic field as being totally enclosed in a shell (so that polar lines of force are linked between the two hemispheres) and by postulating a 'wind' of charged material blowing out from the Sun. The lower atmosphere turns with the Earth; the interplanetary gas will not do this: Axford and Hines consider the formation of large convection-like cells between the two regions.

Piddington (1960) and Cole (1961) incline to development of Alfven's (1950) concepts of disturbances being set up from electrical potential fields produced by the solar 'wind' of charged material flowing past a hollow region under the control of the Earth's magnetic field. The charged material, moving in a magnetic field, acts in a dynamo-like way to produce electric fields. These electric fields then cause currents to flow in the ionosphere, causing magnetic field changes at the surface of the Earth and possibly causing emission of light – the aurora – in the ionosphere.

Hypotheses of this kind suggest that the auroral zone is the region where the ionospheric effects are greatest; the disturbances inside and outside the zone are similar in kind, differing in detail. In fact the polar cap region is regarded, often, as the region closing the ionospheric electrical circuit.

Recent observations by the space probe Pioneer Five (Coleman, Davis and Sonett, 1960) have shown that there is a general interplanetary magnetic field. This field is very weak, only about one ten-thousandth part of the magnetic field at the surface of the Earth, but it will have a profound effect on conditions in the regions of interest, at great heights above the Earth. Dungey (1961) has mentioned some of these profound effects.

So far, no mention has been made of the regions of trapped, high energy particles that occur close to the Earth. These 'Van Allen belts' owe their existence, in part, to a property of the motion of charged particles in the Earth's magnetic field. These particles travel backwards and forwards along lines of force of the magnetic field; as the lines of force dip down towards the Earth's surface, the particles circle more and more tightly about the guiding line of force, until they reach a point where their motion is reversed and the particles are reflected back up the line of force. This reflection occurs in both hemispheres and particles can thus 'bounce' between the two hemispheres; this bouncing continues indefinitely or until some perturbation of the particle motion throws the particle out of the periodic orbit. The latitudes over which most particles are reflected and, therefore, over which the trapped particles come closest to the Earth's surface are close to the auroral zones; it is tempting to regard these trapped particles as the source of auroral energy, at least for the non-polar type of aurorae. Loughnan (1961) has shown that, with reasonable assumptions, this source of energy would be very dependent on longitude, as well as latitude. This is because the Earth's magnetic field is not centred in the Earth; the field strength is higher in longitudes of the Pacific Ocean region than in the Atlantic region. The work of Bond and Jacka (1962) has shown that the southern auroral zone is remarkably circular, i.e., its latitude is independent of longitude: it is likely, therefore, that the Van Allen belts do not have a considerable importance in auroral production.

Cole (1960) has drawn attention to the possible importance of winds in the ionosphere on the production of magnetic and auroral disturbance. To quote from Cole's paper: 'A wind system . . . blows an established pattern of ionization across the magnetic field. This generates electric fields, in the region of high electric conductivity, which drive currents and cause luminosity and maintain ionization for very much longer times than would be permitted by "quiet" ionospheric conditions.' The regions of high electrical conductivity to which Cole refers are situated at heights of approximately 110 km, the height at which the lower parts of aurorae are observed to occur.

It will be obvious by now that the problem of the aurora australis is not, even by a sanguine estimate, close to solution. Can we get a broad view of the situation?

It can be said that the general outlines of auroral occurrence and behaviour in the Southern Hemisphere are now fairly clear. The position, shape and move-

ment of the auroral zone are reasonably well established although, as Bond an
Jacka have pointed out, the mean position of the auroral zone is not sufficiently
well determined to distinguish between suggested hypotheses of auroral occurrence. The separation of polar-cap aurorae from auroral zone displays is established. What remains to be discovered is the cause and method of production
of aurorae. The fruitful line of research now seems to be that of testing hypotheses. This implies that the study of auroral physics should now move away
from observational science, towards experimental science. That is to say,
observations should be less concerned with determining what is happening and
more concerned with measuring a single variable which should do one thing on
one hypothesis and another on a second hypothesis. For example, Cole predicts a
certain relationships between the movements of ionization (and aurorae) and the
movements of the neutral material, the general atmosphere, at auroral heights.
Winds at heights of 80–90 km, approximately, can be determined by radar
observation of the trails left behind meteors as they enter the Earth's atmosphere.
These heights are, in general, lower than heights of interest in Cole's hypothesis;
can another method be found that is applicable to heights somewhat above the
meteor trail heights? The only technique that has been used is the rocket trail
method – a rocket fired up into the ionosphere is caused to leave a trail of smoke
or something similar, which is then observed to determine the direction and
velocity of its drift. This technique is expensive; it is to be hoped that some
cheaper technique will be evolved.

As mentioned earlier, the temperature of the upper atmosphere can be
measured by spectroscopic techniques. This method deserves to be employed
more often than it has been so far and it is to be hoped that systematic measurements referring to different altitudes will become available soon. Heating of the
upper atmosphere is suspected to be of great importance in auroral theory;
temperature determinations would show how much relevance heating may have.

The aurora is normally regarded as an essentially polar phenomenon; the
two adjectives, 'australis' and 'borealis' reflect this attitude. Barbier, Weill and
Glaume (1961) have found what looks like a very faint auroral display to be
observable frequently from an observatory in Africa. Is it possible, therefore,
that aurorae are world-wide, in the sense that 'australis' and 'borealis' refer only
to the opposite ends of a doughnut-shaped region surrounding the Earth?

Bibliography

ALFVEN, H. 1950: *Cosmical Electrodynamics*, Clarendon Press, Oxford.

AXFORD, W. I. and HINES, C. O. 1961: A Unifying Theory of High-latitude
Geophysical Phenomena and Geomagnetic Storms, *Can. J. Phys.* **39**: 1433.

BARBIER, D. and PERON, A. 1961: Photométrie Photoelectrique de l' Aurore à
Port Aux Français (Kerguelen), *A.G.I. Participation Français, Ser. IV.
Fasc.* **1**: 12.

BARBIER, D. and WEILL, G. 1961: L'Observation des Aurores pendant l'Année et la Cooperation Geophysiques Internationales, *A.G.I. Participation Français, Ser. IV, Fasc.* 1: 2.

BARBIER, D., WEILL, G. and GLAUME, J. 1961: L'Emission de la Raie Rouge du Ciel Nocturne en Afrique, *Ann. Geophys.* 17: 305.

BOND, F. R. 1960: Motion of the Aurora and Magnetic Bays, *Austral. J. Phys.* 13: 477.

BOND, F. R. and F. JACKA, F. 1962: Distribution of Auroras in the Southern Hemisphere, *Austral. J. Phys.* (in press).

BULLOUGH, K. 1961: Radio-echo Observations of the Aurora in Terre-Adélie, *Ann. Geophys.* 17: 195.

COLE, K. D. 1960: A Dynamo Theory of the Aurora and Magnetic Disturbances, *Austral. J. Phys.* 13: 484.

COLE, K. D. 1961: On Solar Wind Generation of Polar Geomagnetic Disturbance. *Geophys. J.* 6: 103.

COLEMAN, P. J., DAVIS, L. and SONETT, C. P. 1960: Steady Component of the Inter-planetary Magnetic Field, *Phys. Rev. Letters* 5: 43.

DENHOLM, J. V. and BOND, F. R. 1961: Orientation of Polar Auroras, *Austral. J. Phys.* 14: 193.

DUNCAN, R. A. 1959: Polarization of the Red Oxygen Auroral Line, *Planet. Space Sci.* 1: 112.

DUNCAN, R. A. 1960: Photometric Observations of 5577A and 6300A Airglow during the IGY, *Austral. J. Phys.* 13: 633.

DUNCAN, R. A. and ELLIS, G. R. A. 1959: Simultaneous Occurrence of Subvisual Aurorae and Radio Noise Bursts on 4·6 Kc/s, *Nature,* 183: 1618.

DUNGEY, J. W. 1961: R.A.S. Geophysical Discussion on Upper Atmosphere Ionization and Aurorae, *Geophys. J.* 5: 183.

EVANS, S. 1960: Systematic Movements of Aurorae at Halley Bay, *Proc. Roy. Soc.,* A, 256: 234.

EVANS, S. 1961: R.A.S. Geophysical Discussion on Upper Atmosphere Ionization and Aurorae, *Geophys. J.* 5: 183.

FELDSTEIN, Y. I. 1960: Geograficheskoye Raspredeleniye Polyanikh Siyanii i Azimut' Dug, *Issl. Pol. Siyanii,* 4: 61.

GADSDEN, M. 1959a: Studies of the Upper Atmosphere from Invercargill, New Zealand. Part II – Correlation of the Radar Echoes and Magnetic Activity, *Ann. Geophys.* 15: 395.

GADSDEN, M. 1959b: Studies of the Upper Atmosphere from Invercargill, New Zealand. Part III – Radar Echoes and Visual Aurorae, *Ann. Geophys.* 15: 403.

GADSDEN, M. 1960: Studies of the Upper Atmosphere from Invercargill, New Zealand. Part V – The Frequency of Occurrence of Aurorae and its Dependence on Magnetic Activity and Temporal Functions, *Ann. Geophys.* 16: 88.

GADSDEN, M. 1961: The Relative Intensities of some Nitrogen Bands in Auroral Spectra, *J. Atmos. Terr. Phys.* **22:** 105.

GADSDEN, M. and GADSDEN, M. N. 1960: A Note on the Analysis of Seven Years' Visual Observations of the Aurora from New Zealand and Campbell Island, *Ann. Geophys.* **16:** 414.

GARTLEIN, C. W. 1959: *U.S. Visual Observations, News Letter* **23,** Cornell University.

GARTLEIN, C. W., NACK, B., and SPRAGUE, G. 1959: Aurora Observations at the South Pole, *Trans. Amer. Geophys. Union,* **40:** 288.

GEDDES, M. 1937: The Position of New Zealand Aurora, *N.Z.J. Sci. Tech.* **19:** 55.

GEDDES, M. 1939a: The Photographic Determination of the Height and Position of Aurorae observed in New Zealand during 1937, *N.Z.J. Sci. Tech.* **20:** 289.

GEDDES, M. 1939b: Some Characteristics of Auroras in New Zealand: *Terr. Magn. Atmos. Elect.* **44:** 189.

HARRISON, D. P., and WATKINS, C. D. 1958: A Comparison of Radio Echoes from the Aurora Australis and Aurora Borealis, *Nature* **182:** 43.

HATHERTON, T., and MIDWINTER, G. G. 1960: Observations of the Aurora Australis at New Zealand Antarctic Stations during IGY, *J. Geophys. Res.* **65:** 1401.

JACKA, F. 1953: The Southern Auroral Zone as defined by the Position of Homogeneous Arcs, *Austral. J. Phys.* **6:** 219.

JACKA, F. 1954: Variations of Intensity of the Aurora at Macquarie Island, *Austral. J. Phys.* **7:** 477.

LITTLE, D. E., and SHRUM, C. E. 1950: Correlation of Auroral Observations in the Northern and Southern Hemispheres, *Trans. Roy. Soc. Canada* **44:** 51.

LOUGHNAN, C. J. 1961: Longitudinal Dependence of Radiation-belt Scattering and Auroral Primary Particles, *Planet. Space Sci.* **8:** 13.

MCQUISTAN, G. W. 1959: Observations of the Aurora Australis in 1957 and 1958, *Sci. Rep.* **9,** Carter Observatory, Wellington.

MCQUISTAN, G. W., and FRANKPITT, B. L. 1957a: Observations of the Aurora Australis in 1955 and 1956, *Sci. Rep.* **6,** Carter Observatory, Wellington.

MCQUISTAN, G. W., and FRANKPITT, B. L. 1957b: Annual, Diurnal and Geomagnetic Latitude Variations of the Aurora Australis, *Sci. Rep.* **8,** Carter Observatory, Wellington.

MALVILLE, J. M. 1959: Type-B Aurora in the Antarctic, *J. Atmos. Terr. Phys.* **16:** 59.

NAKAMURA, J. 1958: Latitude Effect of Night Airglow, *Rep. Ionosph. Res. Japan* **12:** 419.

NIKOLSKY, A. P. 1961: O Prichinakh Asimmetrii v Polozhenii Zoni Polyarnikh Siyanii v Arktikye i Antarktikye, *Pol. Siyaniya i Svech. Noch. Neba,* **7:** 61.

PIDDINGTON, J. H. 1960: A Theory of Polar Geomagnetic Storms. *Geophys. J.* **3:** 314.

SANDFORD, B. P. 1959: Studies of the Upper Atmosphere from Invercargill, New Zealand. Part IV – Correlation of the Intensity of the Forbidden Oxygen Lines in the Airglow and Aurora with Magnetic Activity, *Ann. Geophys.* **15:** 445.

SANDFORD, B. P. 1961a: The Behaviour of Night-sky 6300, 5577 and 3914 A Emissions at Scott Base, Antarctica, *J. Atmos. Terr. Phys.,* **21:** 182.

SANDFORD, B. P. 1961b: Enhancement of Night-sky Molecular Nitrogen Emission in Polar Cap Absorption Events, *Nature* **190:** 245.

SANDFORD, B. P. 1962: Polar-glow Aurora in Polar Cap Absorption Events, *J. Atmos. Terr. Phys.* **24:** 155.

SEED, T. J. and ELLYETT, C. D. 1958: Low Latitude Reflections from the Aurora Australis. *Austral. J. Phys.* **11:** 41.

SEED, T. J. 1958: V.H.F. Observations of the Aurora Australis, *J. Geophys. Res.* **63:** 517.

STORMER, C. 1955: *The Polar Aurora*, Clarendon Press, Oxford.

THOMSEN, I. L., MCQUISTAN, G. W., and FRANKPITT, B. L. 1956: Observations of the Aurora Australis in 1930–1954, *Sci. Rep.* **5**, Carter Observatory, Wellington.

UNWIN, R. S. 1958: The Geometry of Auroral Ionization, *J. Geophys. Res.* **63:** 501.

UNWIN, R. S. 1959: Studies of the Upper Atmosphere from Invercargill, New Zealand. Part I – Characteristics of Auroral Radar Echoes at 55 Mc/s, *Ann. Geophys.* **15:** 377.

UNWIN, R. S., and GADSDEN, M. 1957: Determination of Auroral Height by Radar, *Nature* **180:** 1469.

VESTINE, E. H., LANGE, I., LAPORTE, L., and SCOTT, W. E. 1947: The Geomagnetic Field, Its Description and Analysis, *Carnegie Inst. Publ.* **580**, Washington, D.C.

VESTINE, E. H., and SNYDER, E. J. 1945: The Geographic Incidence of Aurora and Magnetic Disturbance, Southern Hemisphere, *Terr. Magn. Atmos. Elect.* **50:** 105.

WEILL, G. 1958: Aspects de l'Aurore Observée à la Base Dumont d'Urville en Terre Adélie, *C.R. Acad. Sci.* **246:** 2925.

WEILL, G. 1959: Aurores Polaires et Phénomènes Crepusculaires Observés en Radiation 3914A dans l'Antarctique, *C.R. Acad. Sci.* **249:** 2092.

WEILL, G. 1960: Sur la Répartition des Ions N_2 dans la Haute Atmosphere Antarctique, *Ann. Geophys.* **16:** 223.

WEILL, G. 1961: Mouvements Est-Ouest Systèmatiques de l'Aurore Polaire, *Ann. Geophys.* **17:** 147.

WHITE, F. W. G., and GEDDES, M. 1939: The Antarctic Zone of Maximum Auroral Frequency, *Terr. Magn. Atmos. Elect.* **44:** 367.

CHAPTER SEVENTEEN

The Polar Ionosphere

J. W. BEAGLEY and G. A. M. KING, *Geophysical Observatory, Christchurch, New Zealand*

PART I

THE REGULAR IONOSPHERE AND ITS VARIATIONS

Introduction

Direct evidence of the existence of the ionosphere was first obtained by Appleton and Barnett (1925). By using a frequency modulation technique they proved experimentally that a layer capable of reflecting radio waves was present in the upper atmosphere. A year later Breit and Tuve (1926) developed the pulse technique of sounding, and exploration of the ionosphere on a world-wide scale advanced rapidly from this time. A network of sounding stations strategically placed over the globe was soon supplying information necessary for the efficient maintenance of modern short wave communication.

Knowledge of the polar ionosphere was early considered essential to an understanding of communications through the auroral zones. However, prior to the International Geophysical Year experimentation in the Antarctic area was mainly an incidental study of the various scientific expeditions to high southern latitudes. These early attempts at exploring the Antarctic ionosphere have been suitably chronicled by Shapley (1956) and a brief summary of the main events follows here.

The very first radio experiment in the Antarctic seems to have been carried out in 1911–12 by Mawson of Australia who established communication from Terre Adélie to Tasmania by means of a relay station on Macquarie Island. A wave-length of 600 m was used and the experiment effectively demonstrated the existence of what is now known to be the ionospheric E region. Very little additional research work appears to have been undertaken until 1928, when Hanson of the United States of America made the first echo soundings in the Antarctic at Little America and recorded the presence of the ionosphere E and F regions during the Antarctic winter night. At the same time Berkner, also of the United States, made radio signal strength measurements. Some effects of magnetic storms were recorded at this time. Later United States expeditions, however continued ionospheric work on a small scale only.

The next advance was effected during the High Jump Expedition of 1946–7 when an automatic sweep-frequency ionosonde was operated in Antarctic waters for about two months and gave the first detailed data on diurnal variation of critical or penetration frequencies of the ionospheric layers. The ionospheric conditions recorded during magnetic storms in this observing period appeared to exhibit known temperate latitude storm characteristics of high absorption, blanketing sporadic E and depressed F2 critical frequencies. Similar observations were taken aboard the *Commandant Charcot* a French research ship in 1949–50 (Barré and Rawer, 1951) and again in 1950–1. These shipboard observations, while of limited usefulness compared with those at fixed stations, contributed to scientific knowledge at that time. However, without making major assumptions regarding the statistical significance of the sample, it is now difficult to include them in a description of the south polar regions.

A major step forward occurred in 1951 when an ionospheric sounding station was operated by France in Terre Adélie (Bougin, 1953), providing the first extended observations on the Antarctic Continent. Of value also for ionospheric studies of the southern auroral zone was the establishment of stations at Campbell Island by New Zealand in 1944, and at Macquarie Island by Australia in 1950. These latter stations of course are to the north of the auroral zone while Terre Adélie lies well to the south of the zone.

The advent of the International Geophysical Year marked the beginning of a new era in the study of the Antarctic ionosphere. The choice of 1957–8, at the maximum of sunspot activity, for intensified research was ideally suited to high latitude investigation of phenomena in the upper atmosphere. Planning on an international scale ensured a greater degree of standardization of equipment and observing techniques. In addition a geographical distribution of stations was obtained most suited to increased understanding of the structure and dynamics of the Antarctic ionosphere and to the solution of practical problems of radio communication in this area. Seventeen ionospheric stations manned by nine countries from both the Northern and Southern Hemispheres were operating within the Antarctic Circle in a remarkably short space of time. Previously it had been tacitly assumed that many problems relating to the polar ionosphere could be clarified by results from one hemisphere only. However, data flowing to World Centres from the newly established IGY Antarctic stations soon proved that the Southern Hemisphere had much to contribute to the world picture.

Studies in related disciplines, dependent on observations made in both the Northern and Southern Hemispheres, were also promoted. These included research into the propagation of low frequency radio waves from one hemisphere to the other, observations of the simultaneity of auroral displays in the two hemispheres, and investigation of the effect of the large geomagnetic anomaly of Antarctica on phenomena of the upper atmosphere. All these projects soon yielded pertinent scientific results which could not have been obtained had observations been confined to the Northern Hemisphere alone.

Principal Laws of Behaviour of the Regular Ionospheric Layers

Before details of the south polar ionosphere are discussed some general features of the ionized upper atmosphere will be described.

The ionosphere can be defined as that part of the Earth's atmosphere where ions and electrons are present in quantities sufficient to affect the propagation of radio waves. Ionized regions usually extend from about 50 km up to great heights, but may sometimes be effective below the 50 km level. No sharp boundary or atmospheric stratification marks the base of these regions but for present purposes the D region can be supposed to be below 90 km, the E region between 90 km and 160 km and the F region above 160 km.

It was once thought that there were distinct layers of electrons in the different regions, but it has since been realized, mainly as the result of rocket measurements, that the D, E and F layers are not necessarily characterized by maxima of ionization, but are sometimes differentiated only by 'ledges' where the gradients of ion density are small. It is still convenient to refer to the E and F layers although the 'peaks' of ion density may hardly show on a curve in which electron density is plotted against real height. Because there is no clear evidence for the existence of a D layer having a peak of electron density in the D region it seems best to use the latter term when discussing this part of the ionosphere.

Knowledge of the regular D region is still comparatively limited. However, the diurnal variation of absorption of radio waves indicates some control by solar light radiation in temperate latitudes. There is evidence that cosmic-rays contribute to normal D region conditions in mid-latitudes and there appears to be an extra source of ionization due probably to turbulent transport which could explain anomalous winter days. The Antarctic D region is subject to the same sources of ionization. Low absorption during the winter night due to loss of ions by attachment to molecules is replaced by higher absorption as soon as the Sun causes photo-detachment. Turbulence seems to be continuous throughout the winter months, although it cannot cause large electron transport at high latitudes when the electron source in the lower E region is small. Polar cap absorption which is a high latitude characteristic will be discussed later in the chapter as a disturbance phenomenon.

The principal agency responsible for the ionization of the upper atmosphere is considered to be ultra-violet light radiation from the Sun, and the ionizing power of this radiation at any point on the Earth's surface, depends of course on the time of day, the season of the year and the geographic latitude.

In middle and lower latitudes the diurnal and seasonal variations of electron density in the E and F layers may be tentatively explained on the basis of the simple Chapman theory (Chapman, 1931), i.e. the production of electrons in the atmosphere results from ionization of atmospheric gas by the incoming radiation as it penetrates deeper into the atmosphere. As would be expected more electrons per unit volume are produced as the density of gas becomes greater. However, radiation is absorbed in the process and below a certain height the rate at which its intensity decreases as it travels downwards is greater than the rate at which the gas density increases. Once this critical level is reached the rate of production of electrons begins to decrease as the radiation penetrates to lower altitudes. There is then a level at which the rate of production is greatest and this is determined both by the absorption of the incoming radiation and the gradient of the gas density. For an atmosphere containing many gases and with a solar spectrum spread over a wide range of wave-lengths the problem of calculating the rate of production at each level is very complex. Chapman, however, simplified the problem by supposing that the incoming radiation had a single wave-length capable of producing photo-ionization of an atmospheric constituent, in an atmosphere whose density, and therefore absorption coefficient, varied exponentially with height.

For a flat earth the following expression for the electron distribution is thus obtained:

$$N = N_0 \exp \frac{(1 - z - e^{-z} \sec \chi)}{2}$$

Where N_0 is the electron density at a reference height where $z = 0$: z is a height normalized by the scale height H, and is zero at the height of the layer maximum for $\chi = 0$ where χ is the solar zenith angle. It is assumed that the atmospheric density is proportional to $\exp(-z)$.

Near sunrise and sunset when χ is large, it is necessary to modify the simple theory by taking account of the curvature of the Earth. The term $\sec \chi$ is then replaced by a 'Chapman Function' $Ch(R, \chi)$, where $R = R_0/H + z$ and R_0 is the radius of the Earth.

Electrons are lost from the ionospheric layers by recombination processes which change with height due to variability in molecular concentrations at different levels.

In the E region where molecular concentration is high the loss rate is quadratic and as a result E layer densities rapidly decrease at sunset. It is for this reason that the regular E layer is a significant reflecting layer in daytime only.

Molecular concentration at the F1 level is still high and the quadratic loss rate ensures that this layer also occurs in the daylight hours only. Stratification of the F region is dependent on mixing of the atmospheric gases as well as on solar zenith angle, so that there is a greater seasonal variability in F1 layer behaviour than in E. The loss rate is greater in summer when the molecular concentration is high due to increased mixing of the atmosphere.

In the F2 layer where molecular concentration is low, the loss rate is linear so that ion densities do not decrease rapidly at sunset as at the lower levels. Recombination takes place throughout the night but as the time constant is long in F2, ionization persists throughout the twenty-four hours at temperate latitudes. At high latitudes an anomalous F region persists throughout the winter night and further explanations for this behaviour will be sought later in this chapter. Seasonal variability in rates of production and loss are also apparent at the

F2 level and both heating and mixing of atmospheric gases appear to be contributory. At the F2 peak of ionization there is also loss of ions due to diffusion processes and unlike E and F1 the F2 layer is not in equilibrium between production and loss. For these reasons the theory of F2 behaviour is more complex and is not yet fully developed. At present it seems that most of the apparent anomalies in F2 can be explained by production, loss, diffusion and restraint of electrons by the Earth's magnetic field. However, the lack of equilibrium in this layer also means that it can be affected by electric fields.

As well as diurnal, seasonal and latitude variations, there exist distinct variations in the ionosphere which appear to be related to the eleven-year period of solar activity. It is knowledge of this relationship, together with an understanding of the diurnal and seasonal variation, that enables predictions of usable radio frequencies to be made.

In middle latitudes, the principal laws of behaviour of the regular ionospheric layers have been well investigated, but in higher latitudes satisfactory explanations have not yet been given to all of the complex phenomena observed. This has been due in part to the small amount of data available for the high latitudes and also to the greater degree of ionospheric turbulence and instability in the polar regions. Certain aspects of the behaviour of the layers at high latitudes can be explained by the peculiar illumination conditions of the ionosphere in these regions (they are in the Earth's shadow during the winter months) and by the effect of solar corpuscular radiation guided to polar regions along the lines of force of the Earth's magnetic field. Possible effects of atmospheric circulation at high latitudes are discussed later in the chapter.

Observation of the changing behaviour patterns of the regular ionospheric layers is made difficult by the frequent appearance of a sporadic ionization occurring at E region levels. There exists at high latitudes a type of sporadic E ionization which is similar to that observed at temperate and low latitudes. It seems to be produced as the result of wind shears forming a thin layer of very dense ionization in the regular E or night-E regions. This layer can be strongly reflecting and prevents radio wave exploration of the F region above. At Hallett Station during sunspot maximum sporadic-E of this type reaches a maximum of occurrence in the local afternoon and is more apparent during the winter months.

The second type of sporadic E ionization observed at high latitudes is closely associated with auroral activity and the occurrence of night-E or enhanced normal E. This sporadic-E appears to be an oblique reflection from patches of ionization and reaches maximum frequency of occurrence at Hallett Station during sunspot maximum in the early hours of the local morning with greatest seasonal frequency in winter. Its significance as a disturbance phenomenon will be discussed in Part II of this chapter.

The Outer Ionosphere or Exosphere

Beyond the regular ionospheric layers there is an enormous region of nearly empty space named the exosphere which was the subject of a unique programme

P

of radio measurements during the IGY. In this experiment, a remarkable type of naturally occurring radio waves is used to measure the density of the ionization and other characteristics of this little known region surrounding the Earth. The signals used are called 'whistlers and VLF emissions'. They are of unusually low frequency, ranging from less than 1000 cycles to more than 30,000 cycles and can be heard with the aid of an ordinary audio amplifier connected to a large antenna. Whistlers are produced by the dispersion of energy from lightning discharges and VLF emissions appear to be generated somewhere in the ionosphere, the mechanism however still being uncertain. More generally, whistlers and VLF emissions come within the classification of atmospherics. They include warbling and chirping sounds known as chorus, risers, hooks, hiss as well as various more complicated signals.

These odd-sounding signals are interesting and useful because their paths through space are bound to the curved lines of force of the Earth's magnetic field, as a result of previously unsuspected quantities of ionization. Flux-line paths extend far into regions at present virtually inaccessible by any other means.

The exosphere is a vital link between events occurring on the Sun and following effects in the Earth's atmosphere.

The mechanism by which the solar outbursts produce their profound effects is as yet uncertain and the new knowledge of the exosphere given by studies of whistlers and VLF emissions offers intriguing possibilities in helping us to reach an understanding of the phenomena which result when solar streams penetrate the Earth's ionosphere.

The first successful observations of whistlers on the polar side of the southern auroral zone were made by Martin (1958) at Scott Base in April 1958. Certain characteristics of these phenomena suggested that they were probably middle-latitude whistlers which had been propagated somehow to polar latitudes. The same characteristics were later observed also at Byrd and Pole Stations (Martin, Helliwell and Marks, 1960).

Detailed comparisons of the spectra of whistlers recorded at Scott Base and in New Zealand and North America coupled with simultaneous fixing of the positions of the lightning flashes which generate these phenomena, have shown conculsively that middle-latitude whistlers do in fact propagate into polar regions (Allcock, 1960). In one case at Scott Base, for instance, the lightning source was located in mid-Tasman, 4400 km away.

One significant difference in the behaviour of whistlers observed in New Zealand and at Scott Base has, however, been found. In New Zealand the reception of whistlers does not appear to be affected by prevailing geomagnetic conditions; on the other hand, at Scott Base and other polar stations their reception is greatly affected, and only during magnetically quiet periods are they heard consistently (Allcock and Rodgers, 1961). This is thought to arise because the propagation path to Scott Base traverses the auroral zone where small irregularities in ionization may prevent the propagation of very low frequencies.

Two types of VLF hiss have been heard at times on a whistler receiver at

Antarctic stations (Martin, Helliwell and Marks, 1960). Firstly there is 'normal hiss', also observed in middle latitudes, usually at frequencies below six kc/s which is associated with the occurrence of dawn chorus. In addition, in polar regions, there is 'auroral hiss' which is strongly associated with the occurrence of visual aurorae at the observing site.

Exploration of the Ionosphere

A simple method of exploring the ionosphere is to send upward a series of pulses on a radio frequency which can be varied and to record the time delay between emission and reception after reflection from the ionosphere. As mentioned earlier the pulse technique of Breit and Tuve (1926) is the basis of modern automatic sweep frequency ionosondes which map out a form of electron density profile above the observing station. A succession of pulses of short duration – thirty to 100 micro-seconds – is sent vertically upwards by a transmitter at regular intervals, and a receiver measures the time delay of the echo. The time delay (t) is expressed as the 'equivalent height' (h') from which the wave would have been reflected if it had travelled all the way with free space velocity, (c) the well-known velocity of light, so that $2h' = ct$. h' is recorded as a function of the frequency (f) in an $h'(f)$ curve, usually called an ionogram. From the virtual height–frequency curve displayed on an ionogram a true height–frequency trace can be calculated using mathematical integral methods (King, 1957). The true height is necessarily lower than the virtual height because of retardation of the exploring wave within the ionospheric layers (Fig. 129).

As a result of the permanent magnetic field of the earth, an exploring radio wave incident on the ionosphere is split into two characteristic waves, with different polarizations. These are known as the ordinary and extraordinary components and usually travel independently with their own speeds. Thus each emitted pulse returns to the ground in dual form. The ordinary wave will penetrate an ionized layer at a lower frequency than the extraordinary wave and, in the interpretation of ionograms, it is usual to concern oneself almost entirely with the critical or penetration frequency of the ordinary wave only. This frequency is, under normal conditions, the peak plasma frequency of the layer which would be recorded were the Earth's magnetic field absent. The extraordinary wave on the other hand is the component affected by the magnetic field of the Earth and is separated from the ordinary wave by approximately one half the gyro-frequency which varies from about 1·0 mc/s at the equator to about 1·8 mc/s near the pole.

Under certain circumstances, more especially when propagation is directly along the lines of force of the Earth's magnetic field, there is often a third reflection level giving another extraordinary wave (Z component) which is on the low frequency side of the ordinary component and separated from it by half the gyro-frequency. The Z component is more likely to be recorded at the higher geomagnetic latitudes as this is where the magnetic lines of force tend to be vertical.

Although they differ in detail the layout and engineering of most automatic ionosondes now adhere to a fairly standard basic design. The panoramic ionosondes constructed by New Zealand are no exception. These are sweep frequency ionosphere recorders covering the range from 1·0 megacycles per second to twenty-two megacyles per second in 7·5 seconds.

Records can be programmed at selectable intervals of 30, 15, 10, 5 and 2 minutes as well as continuously. On continuous recording three records a minute are photographed on 16 mm film and the complete cycle is repeated every 20 seconds although the actual recording interval is 7·5 seconds. Because certain

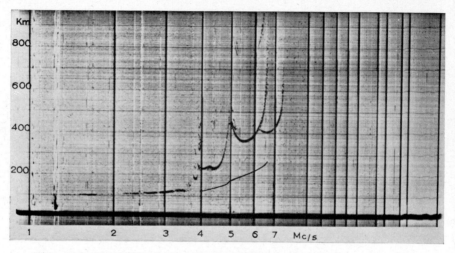

FIG. 129 CAMPBELL ISLAND DAYTIME IONOGRAM, 1205 MMT,
30 DECEMBER 1960

Showing recorded trace of virtual height *v.* frequency, and calculated true height *v.* frequency for F-region. The true height is lower than the virtual height

ionospheric parameters, viz. spread echoes, sporadic echoes and frequency minimum, which is a measure of absorption, are sensitive to the gain of the equipment, the programmer is constructed to allow certain records to be made at various gains in addition to that at normal or optimum gain.

Each record is initiated by a clock and associated switching of power supplies and camera solenoid are effected by cams on the frequency sweep potentiometer and variable oscillator drive assembly. The pulse duration is approximately 70 micro-seconds on intermittent recording. This is automatically reduced to 40 micro-seconds on continuous operation.

Interpretation of Higher Latitude Ionograms

At certain times high latitude ionograms may resemble those obtained at lower latitude stations. Usually, however, they exhibit the complicated structure that is characteristic of the ionosphere in Arctic and Antarctic regions. Apart from brief periods at the equinoxes, the ionosphere in these latitudes is either illuminated continuously by the Sun or is in almost total darkness, for periods of several months.

Conditions can be reasonably stable in the summer months, particularly at sunspot maximum, and ionograms obtained during the summer season conform more closely to an established pattern. However, this is not true for the remainder of the year when day to day observations are likely to be extremely variable even though a daily trend can still be discerned. In winter, ionograms are usually complex and interpretation may be difficult, but a representative value for the basic parameters is chosen to assist in radio-frequency prediction. Ionospheric soundings at most stations in the high latitudes are taken every quarter hour, but for the best use to be made of ionogram scalings for prediction purposes and also for many types of research, hourly data must then be scaled and summarized over a longer period – generally a month. A monthly median value to represent average conditions is usually determined for these requirements.

The weakness of the median as a representative value arises from the following causes:

1. A dearth of numerical data giving a unique description of conditions.
2. Large dispersion in the distribution of numerical values obtained.

However, the statistical significance of the median and the distribution characteristic is indicated to some extent by inclusion of median count and quartile ranges which give a measure of dispersion.

Two of the major difficulties that confront those who scale high latitude ionograms are the presence of spread echoes and the occurrence of sporadic E ionization. The rules formulated for reducing lower latitude ionograms are not always effective at high latitudes because of the different physical conditions prevailing. Frequent incidence of oblique echoes also introduces a further complexity into high latitude interpretation.

The term spread echo is applied when the ionospheric echo becomes diffuse, loses its sharply defined structure and may extend to frequencies beyond those indicative of the actual ion density of the layer. The condition is called spread-F when it occurs in F region echoes, and although spread echoes occasionally are observed in recordings of all layers, spread-F is the most frequent and troublesome manifestation. It usually occurs at night at temperate latitudes but at high latitude stations it also occurs frequently during the daylight hours. In the higher magnetic latitudes spread-F appears more frequently in winter than in summer in contrast to equatorial regions where its occurrence generally is greater in summer than winter. This general pattern however is not applicable to all parts of the world as Reber (1956) and Shimazaki (1959) have observed that spread-F is more frequent during the summer in high northern latitude stations in the Pacific area, and likewise at a corresponding number of high southern latitude stations in South America. Some of the conclusions drawn relative to this parameter, however, may be subject to doubt as spread is gain-sensitive and without standard ionosondes and standard calibration equipment for uniformity in sensitivity different stations are not strictly comparable. In the Antarctic ionosphere it is fairly conclusive that at sunspot maximum both spread echoes and oblique echoes are more prevalent during the winter months. It is also evident that their frequency of appearance increases with the degree of magnetic activity.

E region spread, which in the summer occurs mainly between midnight and 0800, with a maximum at about 0400, tends to be closely associated with E region enhancement and the presence of a sporadic type of ionization observed during auroral activity, i.e. it is a disturbance effect. Whereas E region spread echoes occurring in the early morning hours in summer do not extend in frequency much beyond the limits of the ordinary–extraordinary separation, the associated sporadic ionization, which usually consists of oblique scattered echoes, may extend to relatively high frequencies. Disturbance in the E region during the early evening hours often is not characterized by a clear E region trace or by spread, either because the E region critical frequency is low or because of a maximum of occurrence of blanketing by overhead types of sporadic ionization at this time.

E region spread is apparent on most days in summer during the early morning hours and continues through winter when E region, mainly enhanced, is present. In winter as in summer the period from midnight to 0800 is the preferential time for enhanced E region, E region spread and auroral type sporadic-E to occur.

Sample Polar Ionograms

As can be concluded from the above remarks the selection of a typical calm day ionogram at high latitudes is not an easy matter because the ionosphere is subject to short term changes due to varying atmospheric conditions and electromagnetic radiations as well as to the longer term diurnal, seasonal and sunspot cycle influences. However, although regular layer shapes can alter in a matter of seconds as a result of the short term effects they tend to return to a certain equilibrium pattern for a given time of day at a given season and at a known phase of the sunspot cycle. Sporadic layers, also influenced in formation by both atmospheric and electromagnetic conditions, are less predictable but they too have a broad diurnal and sunspot cycle behaviour. It is possible then to select an ionogram as representative of summer or winter conditions at an Antarctic station and a general prediction of its appearance can be given. The winter ionogram at sunspot maximum is characterized by an unstratified F region subject to the appearance of spread echoes and obliques at most times of the day. The summer time ionogram at sunspot maximum more nearly resembles a temperate latitude daytime pattern, has less spread, fewer obliques and often displays the third magneto-ionic component.

The reproduced ionograms compare the quiet ionosphere at Campbell Island with the quiet Antarctic ionosphere at Cape Hallett. Campbell Island has been selected as a typical temperate latitude station as the ionograms are obtained at both stations with a C4 ionosonde and are thus directly comparable. Effects of auroral activity at Campbell Island are greater than at a temperate latitude station such as Godley Head but quiet conditions at Campbell Island are fairly representative of temperate quiet conditions.

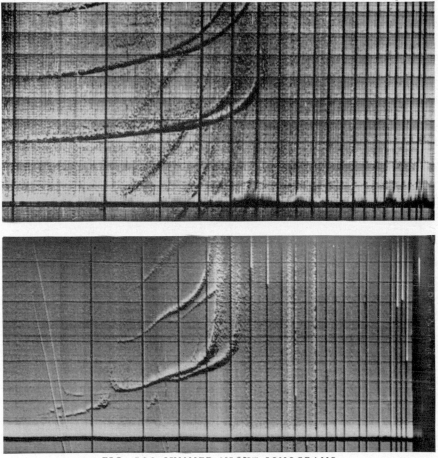

FIG. 130 SUMMER NIGHT IONOGRAMS

Upper: Campbell Island, 0100 MMT, 12 February 1960; *lower:* Cape Hallett, 2205 MMT, 2 January 1960

Figure 130 shows examples of typical temperate and high latitude summer night quiet ionograms. At Campbell Island during the summer night the Sun is below the horizon and, according to expectation, there is no regular E or F stratification present. Loss of ion density by recombination as indicated by a decrease of f_0F2 has set in in the night F region which, however, continues throughout the night as a reflecting layer. The Cape Hallett summer night ionogram is recorded near local midnight. The Sun is above the horizon for twenty-four hours at this time of the year and the E region critical frequency conforms to the cos χ law. Some tendency to stratification appears in the F region and this occurs at a much higher solar zenith angle than would be expected by analogy with temperate latitude behaviour. A feature that is charac-

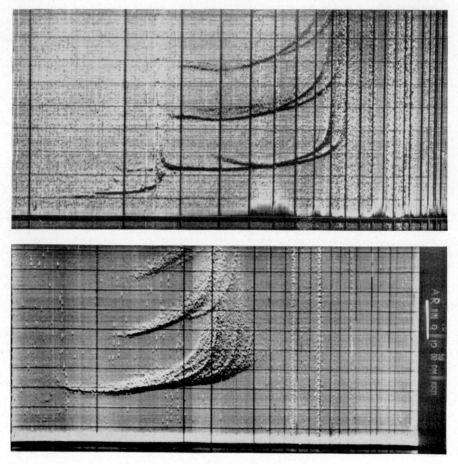

FIG. 131 WINTER DAY IONOGRAMS

Upper: Campbell Island, 1300 MMT, 22 May 1960; *lower:* Cape Hallett, 1200 MMT, 9 June 1960

teristic of high latitude ionograms – the appearance of Z echoes or the third magneto-ionic component in the E and and F regions – can be seen on the Cape Hallett ionogram.

Figure 131 compares winter days at Campbell Island and Cape Hallett. At Campbell Island the regular E region is present as would be expected from Chapman theory, and there is no F region stratification. At Cape Hallett, the regular E region is present, with the expected low critical frequency. The E region would be missing at higher latitude Antarctic stations because of the higher solar zenith angle. F region stratification also is not present and turbulence in the ionosphere is indicated by the presence of oblique and scattered F region echoes. The most remarkable feature of the Antarctic ionosphere is the

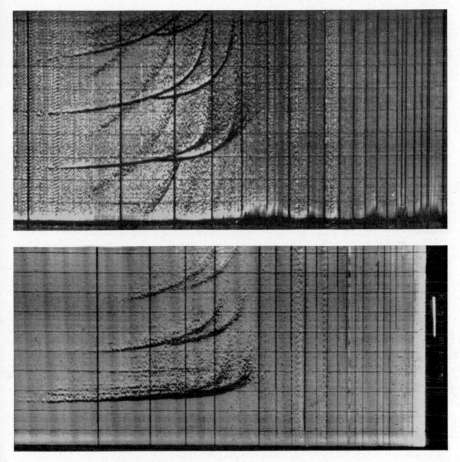

FIG. 132 WINTER NIGHT IONOGRAMS

Upper: Campbell Island, 0000 MMT, 23 May 1960; *lower:* Cape Hallett, 2240 MMT, 11 June 1960

fact that an F region of this type persists through the winter night, when there is no direct ionization by solar radiation.

Figures 132 and 133 show typical winter night time and summer day time records at Campbell Island and Cape Hallett. As is to be expected, regular E is not present at either station during the winter night, the F region has a higher critical frequency at Cape Hallett and spread echoes are present at both. Figure

132 (Campbell Island, winter night) records the presence of round cycle reflections. These high order multiples are a function of the high pulse rate of the
ionosonde and are observed more frequently during periods of low absorption.

The summer day time ionograms record the presence of the F2, F1 and E
layers. At Campbell Island, the E layer stratifies at 3·7 mc/s and a Z mode is

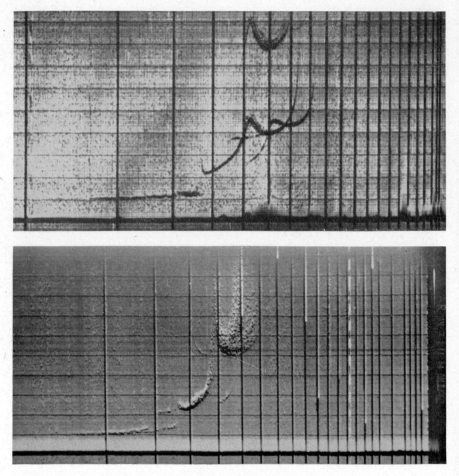

FIG. 133 SUMMER DAY IONOGRAMS

Upper: Campbell Island, 1300 MMT, 12 January 1960; *lower:* Cape Hallett,
1155 MMT, 3 January 1960

present in F2. The value of f_0F2 at Cape Hallett is less than the critical frequency for this region at a temperate latitude station. The presence of a Z
component in the E region should be noted.

Behaviour of the Regular Antarctic Ionosphere

In an attempt to deduce the behaviour of the regular Antarctic ionosphere, diurnal variations of f_0F2, f_0F1 and f_0E for December, March and June 1958, representative of summer equinox and winter conditions at sunspot maximum, have been examined at the Geophysical Observatory, Christchurch, New Zealnd.

Twelve stations, all on the polar side of the $65°$ parallel with adequate circumpolar longitude distribution, were selected. The geographic and geomagnetic coordinates of these stations are supplied in Table 7. The coordinates of the magnetic poles are given in Table 8.

The diurnal variations of the critical or penetration frequencies of the E, F1 and F2 layers of the ionosphere at the stations listed in Table 7 for summer, winter and equinox will now be considered. In passing, it should be noted that the critical frequency of a layer is directly related to the ion density by the

TABLE 7

COORDINATES OF IONOSPHERE STATIONS

| Station | Symbol | Geographic | | Mean MT | Geomagnetic | | Dip |
		Latitude	Longitude		Latitude	Longitude	
Dumont d'Urville (Terre Adélie)	TA	66° 40′ S	140° 01′ E	135° E	−75·6°	230·9°	89·5°
Cape Hallett	CH	72° 19′ S	170° 13′ E	165° E	74·7°	278·2°	84·5°
Scott Base	SB	77° 51′ S	166° 47′ E	165° E	−79·0°	294·4°	82·0°
*Wilkes Station	WS	66° 25′ S	110° 27′ E	105° E	−77·9°	178·8°	81·8°
Little America	LA	78° 11′ S	162° 10′ W	165° W	−74·1°	312·1°	80·0°
Vostok	Vo	77° 30′ S	106° 54′ E	105° E	−88·5°	150·0°	79·5°
△*Mirnyy	Mi	66° 34′ S	92° 55′ E	90° E	−77·0°	145·6°	76·5°
Pole Station	PS	90° 00′ S	00° 00′	0°	−78·5°	0·0°	75·0°
Byrd Station	BS	79° 59′ S	120° 01′ W	120° W	−70·6°	336·1°	74·5°
△*Syowa Base	SB	69° 02′ S	39° 36′ E	45° E	−69·7°	77·4°	67·0°
Ellsworth Station	El	77° 43′ S	41° 08′ W	45° W	−66·9°	14·7°	66·0°
Halley Bay	HB	75° 31′ S	26° 36′ W	30° W	−65·8°	24·3°	65·0°

△ No data for f_0F1 and f_0E for some seasons.
* Alternative months used for some seasons.

TABLE 8

COORDINATES OF THE MAGNETIC POLES

| | Geomagnetic Poles | | | | Magnetic Dip-poles | |
| | Centred Dipole | | Eccentric Dipole | | | |
	Latitude	Longitude	Latitude	Longitude	Latitude	Longitude
N	79° N	70° W	80·1° N	277·3° E	76° N	102° W
S	79° S	110° E	76·3° S	121·2° E	68° S	146° E

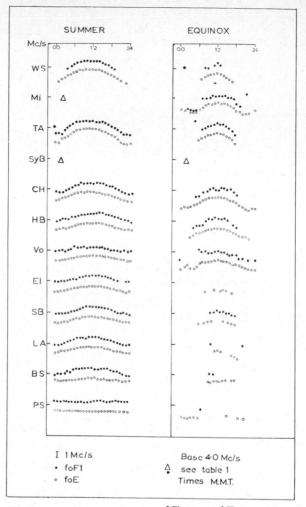

FIG. 134 DIURNAL VARIATION OF f_0E AND f_0F1 DURING SUMMER
AND EQUINOX 1958

equation $N = 1.24 \times (f_0)^2 \times 10^4$ e/cm^3 where N is the ion density and f_0 is
the critical frequency in megacycles per second.

Figure 134 illustrates what can be regarded as the normal diurnal variation of
f_0E and f_0F1 during summer and equinox at sunspot maximum. Stations are
arranged in descending order of magnetic dip. Winter has not been included as
f_0F1 is not present at this season and low frequency f_0E was not recorded at all
stations.

THE E REGION

It can be seen that the E region both during summer and equinox follows the
solar zenith angle trend closely although some stations at equinox appear to have

better observations of low frequency f_0E. The zenith angle dependence can be seen more clearly when the data are arranged according to geographic latitude of each station.

Various authors have commented on the relationship between f_0E and solar zenith angle at the different Antarctic stations. The maximum of ionization occurs during the hours near local noon and its magnitude varies with season. The greatest median values of f_0E are observed in summer gradually decreasing with the change to winter. During the polar night the normal E layers supplemented by sporadic appearances of enhanced E give place to night-E which can be observed sporadically at almost any time but appears fairly regularly in the late evening and early morning hours. Spread is characteristic of most night-E traces and the extraordinary mode is usually present due to decreased absorption during hours of darkness. It is evident then that at these latitudes E layer ionization is not entirely due to solar ultra-violet radiation.

In addition to solar ultra-violet radiation producing the normal E layer another ionization source which is not directly connected with the position of the Sun must be invoked. During the daylight hours, this ionization adds to the normal ultra-violet produced ionization, while at night it may often be intense enough to produce an E layer with critical frequency as great if not greater than that occurring during the daylight hours.

G. V. Bukin (1962) has commented on this anomalous E layer behaviour at high latitudes caused by E layer enhancement of ionization resulting from incoming corpuscular streams of radiation. Using the standard expression,

$$(f_0E)^n = (f_0E_0)^n/\mathrm{Ch}(R, \chi)$$

where $f_0E_0 - f_0E$ at sub-solar point and Ch (R, χ) is the Chapman function, he finds a latitudinal dependence in the index 'n' and considers this to be due to enhancement of ionization just mentioned. This was supported by a dependence on geomagnetic rather than geographic latitude. From his work, Bukin also concluded that night E is corpuscular in origin. The short-comings of such investigations are due to:

1. Limitations of data used. At low latitudes, difficulty in reading f_0E may be due to interference, absorption and presence of sporadic ionization while at high latitudes enhanced E region is quite frequently incorrectly interpreted as sporadic E ionization.

2. The assumption of an isothermal atmosphere.

King (1959), however, in discussing the Hallett Station E layer in 1958, has allowed for a scale height[1] gradient in the E region and his theoretical model of the atmosphere is based on the following assumptions:

1. f_0E at zero solar zenith angle is 4·0 mc/s.

2. There is equilibrium between ion formation and removal.

---

[1] Scale height = height interval in which the atmospheric pressure decreases by a factor $1/e$. It is a measure of atmospheric temperature.

3. The atmosphere has a scale height of 12 km at 100 km and 40 km at 240 km with a linear gradient between.

4. The appropriate Chapman function at each height is obtained by successive approximations (necessary because of the gradient of scale height).

5. The coefficient of electron recombination is the same at all heights.

He obtained a good approximation to the experimental values of f_0E unaffected by particle radiation when using

$$(f_0E)^4 = (f_0E_0)^4/\text{Ch } \chi$$

Extensions of King's work have enabled E region enhancement due to corpuscular radiation to be separated from normal E occurrence at Cape Hallett. Enhanced E has thus been found most likely to occur between 2200 and 1200 at all seasons. The maximum of occurrence is most pronounced from 0300 to 0600 and the incidence of enhancement appears to be greatest during the winter months.

F REGION STRATIFICATION

There is greater variability of f_0F1 than of the solar controlled f_0E, particularly in the equinoctial months, and the twenty-four hour presence of F region stratification at high solar zenith angles during the summer season does not conform with temperate latitude behaviour. Cummack (1961) has suggested that the appearance of F region stratification is dependent on geomagnetic latitude as well as solar zenith angle and this is supported by a comparison of Ellsworth and Scott Base (Fig. 134) which have approximately the same geographic latitude. Scott Base, which is at a much higher geomagnetic latitude (79·0°) than Ellsworth (66·9°), has F layer stratification for several hours of the day during March while Ellsworth has none. Additional factors relative to F region stratification will be raised in the discussion of f_0F2 variations.

THE COMPLEX BEHAVIOUR OF f_0F2

As in lower latitudes, it is the diurnal variation of f_0F2 that is most complex in the Antarctic ionosphere. Figure 135, in which stations examined are again arranged in descending order of magnetic dip, illustrates the diversity of the f_0F2 diurnal variation patterns during the summer, equinox and winter seasons. All stations supply evidence of F2 ionization during the winter night when there is little or no sunlight illuminating the atmosphere at F2 region levels. As photoionization is not adequate to account for the observed winter f_0F2, additional sources of ionization have to be invoked. Three possible sources which need to be considered are:

1. Horizontal drift of ionization into the pole.

2. Ionization formed by incoming corpuscular radiation.

3. Diffusion of ionization downward along the magnetic lines of force from the conjugate ionosphere.

Diurnal variation trends reveal two times of f_0F2 maxima which appear significant in the solution of this problem. The first occurs near local noon and is most pronounced at stations in the vicinity of the Antarctic Circle and least apparent near the pole. The second maximum occurs at approximately 0700 universal time and is suggested by the universal time trends at all stations examined. These two maxima will be discussed in greater detail.

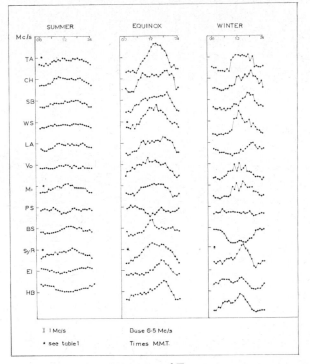

FIG. 135 DIURNAL VARIATION OF f_0F2 DURING SUMMER, EQUINOX AND WINTER, 1958

THE f_0F2 MAXIMUM NEAR NOON AND THE SEASONAL CHANGE

An abrupt decrease in noon values of f_0F2 from a winter high to a summer low was observed at both Hallett Station and Scott Base on 22 October 1958 (Fig. 136). Ionograms recorded prior to this date showed little F layer stratification but later ionograms were characterised by clearly defined stratification in the F region (Fig. 137). A quantitative analysis revealed a large increase in the recombination coefficient β at this time, which could not be explained by change in zenith angle of the Sun. Magnetic activity was minor. The change coincided with the onset of the 1958 polar stratospheric warming investigated by K. J. Hanson (1960) and it was concluded that an association might exist between the ionospheric and meteorological events. Further investigation revealed marked changes in the overall diurnal variation patterns at Hallett Station, Scott Base and Halley Bay after 22 October (Fig. 138). It seems likely that the molecular concentration in the ionosphere had been affected by changing atmospheric conditions during the polar stratospheric warming. Increase in the molecular concentration at F region levels explains the increase in β, the rate of atom ion interchange. In addition the increase in β would result in the observed ion density decreases at the F2 level and the increased F layer stratification not expected from solar zenith angle considerations alone.

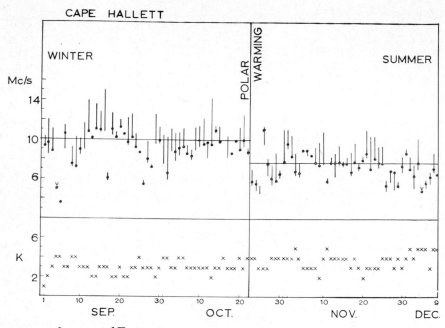

FIG. 136 NOON f_0F2 AT CAPE HALLETT BEFORE AND AFTER THE POLAR
WARMING, 22 OCTOBER, 1958

f_0F2 scalings in Mc/s; X – magnetic K index

This evidence of an atmospheric influence on f_0F2 diurnal variation immediately suggested a possible explanation of the winter Antarctic diurnal variation phenomenon. If the source of ionization was assumed to be diffusion of ions downward along the magnetic lines of force from the conjugate ionosphere, it was conceivable that changing atmospheric conditions throughout a day could affect F2 recombination rates and so produce the observed diurnal variation trends.

Wilkes (1949) describes studies of the behaviour of solar atmospheric tides which have indicated a semi-diurnal peak in the pressure wave from 0900–1000 MMT (Meridian Mean Time) for lower latitudes. This tide was found to be less effective near the pole. If it is assumed, however, that the tide is effective with diminishing intensity to the pole, that atmospheric mixing is greatest at the peak of the wave, and that recombination rates are higher in a mixed atmosphere, a minimum in the f_0F2 diurnal trend would be expected from 9–1000 MMT and a maximum at 1500–1600 MMT. It will be seen from Figure 135 that the

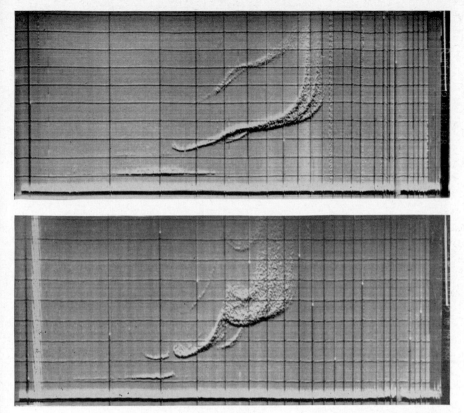

FIG. 137 NOON IONOGRAMS RECORDED AT CAPE HALLETT BEFORE
AND AFTER THE POLAR WARMING, 22 OCTOBER 1958
Upper: 1200 MMT 15 October 1958; *Lower:* 1200 MMT 27 October 1958

observed f_0F2 winter diurnal variations tend to support this argument. At some stations, however, longitude does not allow an unambiguous differentiation between the MMT and UT (Universal Time) maxima. Photo-ionization, producing a noon maximum at the lower latitude stations, creates a further obstacle to establishing the 1500 maximum with certainty.

Bellchambers, Barclay and Piggott (1962) mention that the change in f_0F2 diurnal variation pattern from winter to summer occurs very suddenly at Halley Bay, and Piggott and Shapley (1962) have commented on the same phenomenon at a number of other stations on the Antarctic Continent. However, none of these authors has associated the sudden change with the polar warming event and changing atmospheric circulation patterns. It should be remarked that at Halley Bay, although there was an immediate decrease in noon values on 22 October, the change in overall diurnal variation was not complete until 1 November. This can be explained by the fact that at onset the explosive stratospheric warming was most effective in the McMurdo and Mirnyy areas. Graham

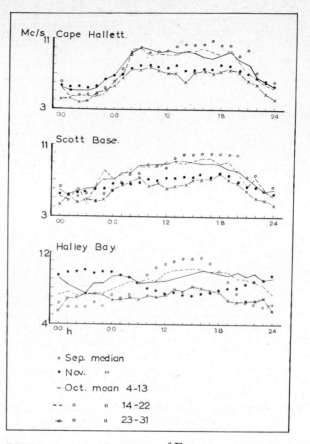

FIG. 138 DIURNAL VARIATIONS OF f_0F2 AT CAPE HALLETT, SCOTT BASE AND HALLEY BAY DURING THE POLAR WARMING PERIOD

Land, though warmed, remained somewhat cooler until the warming was completed in early November as the cold low moved off Antarctica over this sector.

An earlier seasonal change in f_0F2, less significant, and more gradual than the dramatic polar warming event, was apparent at all stations with the return of the Sun. This change was observed to occur from July to mid-September according to the latitude of the station. Increase in photo-ionization resulted in higher daytime values of f_0F2 before the polar warming became effective. When Piggott and Shapley (1962) refer to the change from winter to summer conditions at Byrd Station from 20 to 30 August it is to the return of photo-ionization at F2 levels that they draw attention. However, at Byrd Station also, there is evidence that values of f_0F2 are decreased as the result of atmospheric changes associated with the polar warming event.

THE UNIVERSAL TIME MAXIMUM OF f_0F2

The f_0F2 maximum at approximately 0700 UT at polar latitudes has been commented on by Duncan (1962) and Piggott and Shapley (1962). Stations examined for this trend at the Geophysical Observatory (Fig. 139), showed this maximum reasonably clearly in most cases. Byrd Station which appeared anomalous when plotted according to mean meridian time, appears normal when plotted on a universal time basis. The Weddell Sea stations have a clearly defined

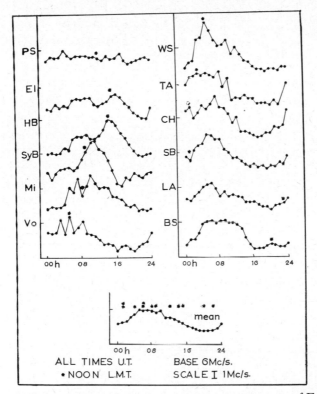

FIG. 139 UNIVERSAL TIME DIURNAL VARIATION OF f_0F2 AT ANTARCTIC STATIONS DURING WINTER, 1958

secondary UT maximum in winter and it would appear that the layer replacement phenomenon observed at Halley Bay by Bellchambers and Piggott (1958) is associated with this. Analysis of Halley Bay 1958 data seems to indicate that the secondary UT maximum is most likely to occur on magnetically disturbed days in winter. In summer the UT maximum is the main maximum and is most significant on magnetically quiet days. The change in seasonal behaviour could well be due to the modification of atmospheric influences at the time of polar warming mentioned earlier.

Duncan (1962) has found that this universal time variation is stronger in the Antarctic than the Arctic in winter and is entirely missing from the Arctic during summer. He has suggested that this is due to the separation of the geomagnetic and geographic poles. Because of this separation the daily UT time variation of the geomagnetic pole with respect to the Sun is greater in the Antarctic than in the Arctic. Duncan (1962) considers that we might expect the daily transport of the eccentric geomagnetic field through the interplanetary plasma to cause a tide in the geomagnetic field. Such a tidal oscillation could cause trapped particles to be dumped at F region levels.

In the opinion of the authors of this chapter however, a universal time effect in polar regions does not necessarily imply a geomagnetic influence alone. It has been pointed out by Wilkes (1949) that a semi-diurnal global standing wave could explain observed UT maxima of barometric pressure in the polar tropo-sphere. It is conceivable therefore that a standing wave oscillation may affect the atmosphere at ionospheric levels in polar regions also. If we again assume that molecular concentration is greatest at the peak of the pressure wave we should expect minimum values of f_0F2 from 1100–1300 UT (time of maximum of the pressure wave) and maximum values from 0500–0700 UT as the result of a standing wave oscillation. The universal time trend of the observational data lends support to this hypothesis.

Summarizing, the evidence outlined above places strong emphasis on the pos-sibility of meteorological factors influencing the diurnal variation of f_0F2 at polar latitudes. Observations of maxima near noon and 0700 UT support this conclusion. Horizontal drift of ionization towards the poles would appear to be the least likely source of winter ionization if this hypothesis holds. On the other hand diffusion of ions downward along the magnetic lines of force from the conjugate ionosphere provides an *in situ* source of ionization which could readily vary in the manner outlined above.

PART II

THE DISTURBED IONOSPHERE

Introduction

There are four distinct types of disturbance in the polar ionosphere:
1. The sudden ionospheric disturbance (SID) or solar flare effect.
2. Polar cap absorption (PCA).
3. Disturbance affecting only the F region.
4. Disturbance affecting the whole ionosphere.

As far as we know the sudden ionospheric disturbance has no properties in the polar regions which cannot equally well be studied at more temperate latitudes. Its importance for us lies in the immediate association with activity on the Sun. (Ratcliffe and Weekes, 1960.) The SID takes the form of an increase in the ionization of the D and E regions over the sunlit hemisphere at the time of a visible solar flare. It is caused by a burst of X-rays from the flare in the range of wavelengths shorter than 100 A.

The other types of disturbance also seem to be associated with activity on the Sun, but the connections are less direct. As they occur at high latitudes preferentially it is natural to attribute them to the action of electrically charged particles which are channelled towards high latitudes by the Earth's magnetic field.

Polar Cap Absorption (PCA)

Some hours after certain large solar flares, especially those associated with emission of solar radio noise in a continuous spectrum, there is strong ionospheric absorption over the polar caps which may last any time up to several days. The smaller events are readily studied on ionograms through the variations of the

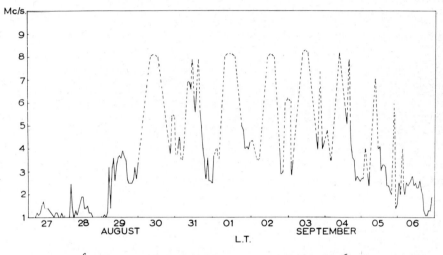

FIG. 140 f-MIN AT CAPE HALLETT, 27 AUGUST TO 6 SEPTEMBER, 1957

minimum recorded frequency, f-min, while larger events are best studied from riometer recordings of cosmic radio noise.

The absorption is steady and it shows a marked day–night effect, being stronger when the Sun shines on the atmosphere above about 60 km. Figure 140 gives an example recorded at Cape Hallett in 1957 – values of f-min from 27 August to 6 September.

The firm line on the 27th and 28th illustrates normal absorption. On the 29th absorption is well above normal. From early on the 30th there are no echoes received from the ionosphere; the dotted line gives the expected behaviour of f_0F2 from which f-min can be judged qualitatively – f-min exceeds the actual f_0F2 which is probably close to the expected value on this day. On the 31st some f-min values are recorded confirming that day time absorption is high. On the last three days of the sequence the observed values of f-min are well below the expected values of f_0F2, indicating that when no echoes are received it is because both f-min is raised and the actual f_0F2 is lower than expected; this is a result of storm-time depression of f_0F2 discussed in the next section.

The absorption is due to a layer of electrons in the D region, and from the day-night effect it can be shown that the centre of the layer is usually near 70 km (on occasion there may be electrons at heights not much above 40 km). At night-time the electrons attach themselves to neutral atmospheric molecules and thus are unable to absorb radio waves; by day visible light from the Sun detaches the electrons and the absorption rises. The change from night to day occurs at 'sunrise' at the height of the layer.

The phenomenon is restricted to high latitudes, showing strong geomagnetic control. Together with the time delay after the flare on the Sun and the height of the absorbing layer this leads to the conclusion that the electrons are produced by the impact of fast protons in the energy range 10–1000 million electron-volts (Bailey, 1959).

While a PCA is undoubtedly associated with a solar flare its persistence long after the flare has died down poses a problem. These solutions have been proposed:

1. The Sun continues to emit energetic protons after optical activity has ceased.

2. The protons are all emitted at the time of the flare, but those arriving late at the Earth have travelled a long path involving reflection from magnetic fields beyond the Earth's orbit.

3. The protons are all emitted at the time of the flare, but are trapped by tangled magnetic fields associated with a slow-moving cloud of solar gas also emitted by the flare.

4. The flare emits a slow-moving cloud of solar gas within which slow protons are accelerated to high energies by expansion of the cloud and its associated magnetic fields.

The last two explanations seem most promising. Both invoke a slow-moving cloud of ionized gas which has been a cornerstone in several theories of magnetic storms and aurorae; it is well known that flares producing large PCA events are generally followed within a day or two by major magnetic storms. Notice, though, that there is no magnetic disturbance directly connected with polar cap absorption.

From a combined study of f-min and 'scatter' echoes from a 2·3 Mc/s radar, Gregory (1963) gives reasons for believing that smaller PCA events are quite common, occurring even with small flares. For example, at Scott and Hallett he found roughly one third of all hourly observations in 1960 showed evidence of polar cap absorption.

Disturbance in the F Region Only

At middle latitudes, an ionospheric storm produces a large effect in the F region, generally reducing the electron density and breaking up the layer structure; by day, the division into F1 and F2 becomes more pronounced. In the E and D regions the effect is small except with unusually severe storms. Storm studies are therefore often based on the variations of f_0F2, the magnitude being measured by the departure of f_0F2 from its normal value.

At high latitudes, even moderate disturbances affect E and D so much that the F region cannot be observed. Minor disturbance, when F is observable, occurs every day. Clearly, the 'normal' value of f_0F2 does not represent quiet conditions, and it is not suitable as a base for measuring the magnitude of F region activity.

There are events on high latitude ionograms similar to middle latitude disturbance, but they have not been widely studied. Qualitatively we can say that the F region seems to be replaced by a new lot of ionization which has moved horizontally over the recording site. Such 'layer replacement' is going on all the time, being especially active in winter, and only the larger, more persistent, events can be called storms.

Two explanations have been offered for the middle latitude effects in the F region, and it is likely that both apply to the high latitude phenomena also.

The first explanation (Martyn, 1953) postulates a system of electric fields associated with the disturbances in the E and D regions. The mutual action of the electric fields and the Earth's magnetic field induces a 'drift' in F region ionization. The theory is complicated and we do not know how much it can account for.

The second explanation (Seaton, 1956) depends on the idea that, above a certain height near 100 km, the atomic and molecular constituents of the atmosphere are separately in equilibrium under gravity, instead of being thoroughly mixed as at lower levels. Electron recombination depends on the molecular density, and at a given height this will be altered if mixing occurs above 100 km. When a disturbance affects the E and D regions the atmosphere is heated and mixed, both above the disturbance and at considerable distances through propagation of gaseous waves. The resulting increase in recombination reduces the electron densities in the F region.

Notice that according to both explanations the F region effects are secondary phenomena.

Disturbance Affecting the Whole Ionosphere

The primary ionospheric disturbance occurs in the E and D regions. Major disturbances have their largest effect in the auroral zone and on its low latitude side, while the polar cap is especially the region of minor disturbances.

We shall look at two cases of disturbances on the polar cap which are illustrative rather than typical. The latter are often too complex for interpretation except by an experienced observer.

The first example (Fig. 141) is after midnight in winter at Cape Hallett. The regular 'morning activity' is weaker than usual so that separate E and F regions can be seen clearly. The rather spread E layer with a critical frequency near 1·7 Mc/s is not the normal E layer – it is called 'night-E' and is characteristic of disturbed conditions. The strong flat sporadic-E trace between 2 and 5 Mc/s at a height of 130 km is an oblique echo from a cloud of electrons (this is apparent from studying the sequence of records). Above it near the 200 km height mark are scattered echoes of type *a* sporadic-E – they are also oblique. The F region is not badly spread for these latitudes but one feature of the spread is interesting; above the main trace are many small weak echoes caused by forward scatter into F from irregularities at E region heights. The minimum frequency at which echoes are received, *f*-min, is the lowest recorded frequency of 1 Mc/s showing that ionospheric absorption is low – there is no D region activity.

Practically every morning this kind of disturbance carries on for many hours, although nearly always with much greater activity; the night-E layer has higher critical frequencies and is more spread, while there is often enough type *a* sporadic-E to obscure most other echoes; also the F region is usually disturbed, with low critical frequencies and much spread.

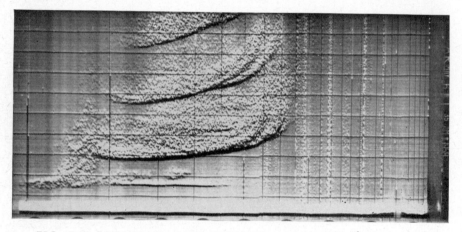

FIG. 141 IONOGRAM, CAPE HALLETT, 0135 MMT, 6 MAY 1958

On clear dark nights, aurorae can always be seen at the same time as the ionospheric disturbance is recorded.

The second example, also from Hallett but this time in the winter evening hours, has activity in both E and D regions. Figure 142 is a frequency plot showing the variations of *f*-min (dots) and the critical frequency of the night-E layer (circles). The symbol 'V' means that *f*-min is less than the lowest recorded frequency, and 'B' means that f_0E (night-E) is less than *f*-min although there is evidence, say from the appearance of the F region, that the night-E layer is present. Broadly speaking, *f*-min and f_0E have the same trend; when f_0E is high the absorption is high, and when the night-E layer is absent absorption is low. We can understand this association by considering the mechanism of ionospheric absorption.

When a radio wave passes through the ionosphere it sets the electrons in motion. They take up energy from the wave and, if not disturbed, re-radiate it. Thus the way that the wave propagates is modified but no energy is lost.

However, if the electrons are disturbed by collisions with gas molecules the energy which they have taken from the wave is transferred to the molecules and is lost; this is absorption of the radio wave. It follows that absorption is high when the densities of electrons and of gas molecules are high together – i.e. when there are many electrons in the D region.

Returning now to Figure 142, as f_0E increases the ionization in the lower part of the night-E layer increases too; and the lower part extends into the D region causing absorption. We can even estimate how far down the layer does extend by noting that ncar 80 km the atmosphere is turbulent and the layer of electrons is broken up into irregular patches. These patches can give an echo on the iono-gram not by the normal process of reflection but by 'scattering'; the echo is

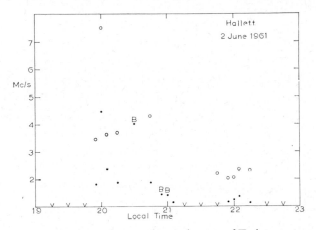

FIG. 142 VARIATIONS OF f-MIN (DOTS) AND f_0E (NIGHT-E, CIRCLES) FROM 19–23 HOURS GMT AT CAPE HALLETT, 2 JUNE 1961

very weak, and is usually seen only on records taken with especially high equip-ment sensitivity. Figure 143 is the 'high gain' record at 2001 during this dis-turbance, and the weak scattered echo is visible between $2\frac{1}{2}$ and 5 Mc/s, at a height of 80 km.

In Figure 143 the night-E layer above 5 Mc/s is obscured by type c sporadic-E developing out of it. Conditions are changing rapidly (see the high value of f_0E at 2000, one minute before) and it is interesting to try and follow some of the changes in layer structure. The type c sporadic-E at 2001 soon becomes obviously oblique, and at 2015, moving away horizontally, its range has reached almost 200 km (Fig. 144).

The final point of interest in this disturbance is the behaviour of the F region. At 1945 there are F region echoes at least to 6 Mc/s; during the active period F is obscured by E even at 4 Mc/s, while at 2130, after two 'layer replacements', there are again F echoes at 6 Mc/s. Clearly, electron densities in the F region are depressed above the active area, and the region shows horizontal movement similar to that deduced for the type c sporadic-E.

Again, on clear dark nights, aurorae can always be seen at the same time as this kind of ionospheric disturbance is recorded, but the forms are somewhat different from those accompanying the type of disturbance first considered.

From the two examples we can identify the following features of a disturbance:

1. The night-E layer is always present.
2. There are nearly always 'oblique' echoes of types of sporadic-E (some sporadic-E may be overhead).

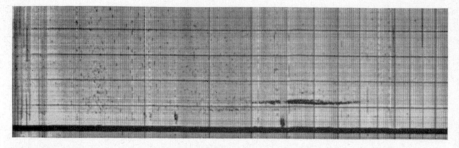

FIG. 143 HIGH GAIN IONOGRAM, CAPE HALLETT, 2001 MMT, 2 JUNE 1961

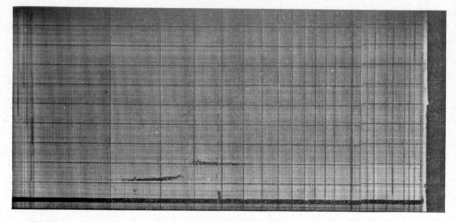

FIG. 144 IONOGRAM, CAPE HALLETT, 2015 MMT, 2 JUNE 1961

3. There is usually a depression in F region electron densities.
4. The disturbance pattern moves horizontally.
5. When observing conditions are suitable, aurorae are visible.

The differences between the examples given lie in the heights of the night-E layers and the intensities of disturbance.

From ionospheric evidence alone we cannot go much further than this. However, the association of disturbance with aurorae can be put on a more definite basis, and the auroral and ionospheric observations then complement each other.

Several workers have compared the degree of ionospheric disturbance with the light emitted by the aurora. The most satisfactory study seems to be Omholt's (1955). He compared f_0E (night-E) with the luminosity of aurorae in a particular emission band of ionized nitrogen, and found agreement with

$$I \propto f^4$$

where I is the intensity of emission, and

$$= f_0E$$

This law is what one expects if the auroral emission is due to particles subject to ordinary ionospheric recombination.

Let us extend Omholt's finding to an ionospheric record showing both night-E and the auroral sporadic-E echoes. The night-E layer corresponds to a general glow over the sky; while the sporadic-E, which is due to reflections from 'blobs' of ionization, corresponds to bright patches of light. From the ionogram we cannot determine the shapes of the 'blobs', but the bright elements of the aurora are the rays and other 'forms'. It is reasonable to identify the auroral sporadic-E with the auroral rays and 'forms'.

Many conclusions flow out of this identification, but we have space to mention only one. (See Chapter 16, 'The Aurora Australis' by M. Gadsden.)

From photographs of the aurora it is easy to get both the general horizontal movement of the disturbance and the detailed movements within the disturbance – things which we could only infer from the ionograms.

The Ionospheric Disturbance in Perspective

Just as our understanding of ionospheric disturbance was helped greatly by studying also the aurora, so geomagnetic observations add still more. Indeed, the traditional approach to theories of disturbance has been through magnetic storms and the aurora. The key fact is the delay observed on many occasions between a flare on the Sun and the onset of a magnetic storm. A delay of one to two days suggests that something is emitted from the Sun, travelling at about 1000 km/s, and its arrival at the Earth starts the disturbance. The classical theories of Chapman and Ferraro (1940), Martyn (1951) and Alfven (1950) identify it with a 'cloud' of ionized gas – protons and electrons. The theories differ in details of shape, electric fields associated with the cloud, etc.; they are ably reviewed by Chamberlain (1958).

The extension of ionospheric observations to high latitudes, the use of sounding rockets at high latitudes, the advent of satellites, and the 'fact-finding' spirit of the IGY have added enormously to the picture. Two major discoveries are polar cap absorption and the radiation belts. Several 'space probes' have already made observations on the inter-planetary medium between the Earth and the Sun. Among all this activity is a confusing number of new theories.

Even the old idea of a cloud of ionized gas has been disputed in the recent upheaval, but it has held its place while acquiring a new property – a magnetic field. As recounted earlier, the most promising explanations of PCA events require magnetic fields in the cloud, but their form is debated. They may be random fields, which trap energetic protons, or organized fields which accelerate slow protons.

As the cloud travels out from the Sun it passes through the interplanetary gas. And if the gas is dense enough it will modify the cloud. It is now agreed that the interplanetary gas is continuous with the solar corona. The corona has a high density and a very high temperature (exceeding a million degrees centigrade), so that it will expand outwards generating the 'solar wind' (Biermann, 1957). But the strength of the solar wind is still keenly disputed. Preliminary experimental data on the interplanetary gas suggest that the particle density has dropped very rapidly between the Sun and the Earth, to just a few tens per cubic centimetre and there is evidence that the medium is far from uniform, patches of gas alternating with regions of weak magnetic fields. At the moment, it seems unlikely that the interplanetary gas can effect a major change on the disturbance cloud.

When the cloud approaches the Earth it interacts with the Earth's magnetic field. Details of the interaction must be extremely complex. One gets the impression on reading the newer theories that they only scratch the surface of the problem. All the proposed mechanisms, compression of the magnetic field, hydromagnetic waves, transfer of energetic particles across the field, acceleration of particles, convection, must play a part.

Within the Earth's magnetic field lie the radiation belts. These support large fluxes of energetic electrons and protons which are depleted during severe disturbance. Most of the particles come down into the ionosphere at latitudes somewhat lower than the normal auroral zone. Until the fluxes are known more precisely we cannot say whether the radiation belts play a primary or merely a secondary part in the disturbance.

The ionospheric work considers only a small part of the overall disturbance phenomena. Its importance lies in the facts that the soundings are easy to make and that a large amount of data is already available for study. With the other ground-based observations of the aurora and geomagnetism, it serves for testing theories which are gradually being assembled by direct observation of the space between the Sun and the Earth.

Bibliography

ALFVEN, H. 1950: *Cosmical Electrodynamics*, University Press, Oxford.

ALLCOCK, G. MCK. 1960: Propagation of Whistlers to Polar Latitudes, *Nature* **188:** 732–3.

ALLCOCK, G. MCK. and RODGERS, M. F. 1961: Geomagnetic Activity and the Reception of Whistlers in Polar Regions, *J. Geophys. Res.* **66:** 3953–5.

APPLETON, E. V., and BARNETT, M. A. F. 1925: Local Reflection of Wireless Waves from the Upper Atmosphere, *Nature* **115:** 333–4.

BAILEY, D. K. 1959: Abnormal Ionization in the Lower Ionosphere Associated with Cosmic Ray Flux Enhancements, *Proc. I.R.E.* **47:** 255–66.

BARRÉ M. and RAWER K. 1951: Quelques Resultats d'Observations Iono-spheriques, Effectuées Près de la Terre Adélie, *J. Atmos. Terr. Phys.* **1:** 311–14.

BELLCHAMBERS, W. H., BARCLAY, L. W., and PIGGOTT, W. R. 1962: *Royal Society IGY Expedition, Halley Bay 1955–59,* **2,** Roy. Soc., London, Aberdeen University Press.

BELLCHAMBERS, W. H., and PIGGOTT, W. R. 1958: Ionospheric Measurements at Halley Bay, *Nature* **182:** 1596–7.

BIERMANN, L. 1957: Solar Corpuscular Radiation and the Interplanetary Gas, *Observatory* **77:** 109–10.

BOUGIN, JEAN, 1953: Notes Préliminaires du Laboratoire National de Radio-electricité, No. 172.

BREIT, G., and TUVE, M. 1926: A Test of the Existence of the Conducting Layer, *Phys. Rev.* **28:** 554–75.

BUKIN, G. V. 1962: Geograficheskoe Raspedelenie f$_o$E i Nekotorye Svoystva o Blasti E V Antarktike, *Geomagnetism i Aeronomiya* **2:** 918–24.

CHAMBERLAIN, J. 1958: Theories of the Aurora, *Advances in Geophysics,* **4:** 110–215, Academic Press, New York.

CHAPMAN, S. 1931: The Absorption and Dissociative or Ionizing Effect of Monochromatic Radiation in an Atmosphere on a Rotating Earth, *Proc. Phys. Soc. (London),* **43:** 26–45.

CHAPMAN, S., and FERRARO, V. C. A. 1940: Theory of the First Phase of a Geomagnetic Storm, *Terr. Mag. Atmos. Elect.* **45:** 245–63.

CUMMACK, C. H. 1961: Evidence of Some Geomagnetic Control on the F1-Layer, *J. Atmos. Terr. Phys.* **22:** 157–8.

DUNCAN, R. A. 1962: Universal-Time Control of the Arctic and Antarctic F Region, *J. Geophys. Res.* **67:** 1823–30.

GREGORY, J. B. 1963: Particle Influx at High Latitudes: I. Temporal and Latitude Variations; II. Solar Protons, *J. Geophys. Res.* **68:** (10).

HANSON, K. J. 1960: A Case Study of the Explosive Stratospheric Warming over the Antarctic, October 1958, *Antarctic Meteorology,* pp. 128–41. Pergamon Press, London.

KING, G. A. M. 1957: Relation between Virtual and Actual Heights in the Ionosphere. *J. Atmos. Terr. Phys.* **11:** 209–22.

KING, G. A. M. 1959: The Ionospheric E-Layer at Cape Hallett, *J. Atmos. Terr. Phys.* **16:** 186–7.

MARTIN, L. H. 1958: 'Whistlers' in the Antarctic, *Nature* **181:** 1796–7.

MARTIN, L. H., HELLIWELL, R. A., and MARKS, K. 1960: Association between Aurorae and Very Low-Frequency Hiss Observed at Byrd Station, Antarctica, *Nature,* **187:** 751–6.

MARTYN, D. F. 1951: The Theory of Magnetic Storms and Auroras, *Nature* **167:** 92–4.

MARTYN, D. F. 1953: Morphology of the Ionospheric Variations Associated with Magnetic Disturbance, I, *Proc. Roy. Soc.* **218:** 1–18.

OMHOLT, A. 1955: The Auroral E-Layer Ionization and the Auroral Luminosity, *J. Atmos. Terr. Phys.* **7**: 73–9.

PIGGOTT, W. R., and SHAPLEY, A. H. 1962: The Ionosphere over Antarctica, *Geophys. Monogr.* **7**: 111–26, Amer. Geophys. Un.

RATCLIFFE, J. A., and WEEKES, K. 1960: *Physics of the Upper Atmosphere*, Academic Press, New York.

REBER, B. 1956: World-Wide Spread-F, *J. Geophys. Res.* **61**: 157–74.

SEATON, M. J. 1956: Possible Explanation of the Drop in F Region Critical Densities Accompanying Major Ionospheric Storms, *J. Atmos. Terr. Phys.* **8**: 122–3.

SHIMAZAKI, T. 1959: A Statistical Study of World-Wide Occurrence Probability of Spread F, *J. Rad. Res. Lab.* **6**: 669–704.

WILKES, M. V. 1949: *Oscillations of the Earth's Atmosphere*, pp. 11–12, University Press, Cambridge.

CHAPTER EIGHTEEN

The Polar Geomagnetic Field
and its Fluctuations

A. L. CULLINGTON, *Magnetic Survey, Christchurch, New Zealand*

Introduction

On 17 January 1773 the Antarctic Circle was crossed for the first time by Captain James Cook. During his voyages he circumnavigated the Antarctic Continent without sighting any land, and penetrated deeply into the Antarctic when he reached Lat. 71° 10′ S in Long. 106° 54′ W on 30 January 1774. It is known that, on these excursions within the Antarctic Circle, he took measurements of the magnetic declination or variation of the compass. After Cook came the whalers and sealers, but they did not publish the results of any magnetic observations that they may have made.

Over sixty years elapsed before a determined assault was made on the Antarctic by three nations, France (Dumont d'Urville), the United States (Charles Wilkes), and Great Britain (James Clark Ross). Magnetic observations were made by each of these expeditions. Commerce across the seas was increasing and it was most important for the seafaring nations to have accurate magnetic charts showing the magnetic declination or the variation of the compass. Of these three expeditions the magnetic work of that under Ross was the most extensive as well as the most intensive.

The necessity for a magnetic survey of the south polar regions of the globe was recognized by the British Association for the Advancement of Science at the Liverpool Meeting in 1837 and communicated to the Royal Society. A joint committee from both these scientific institutions made representations to the British Government recommending 'the revival of that national support to which we are indebted for the first Chart of the Declinations, constructed by our illustrious countryman Halley in 1701, on the basis of observations collected in a voyage expressly equipped for that purpose by the British Government'. The Admiralty made available for this work the two ships *Erebus* and *Terror*, commanded respectively by Sir James Clark Ross and Captain Francis Rawdon Crozier. Both these officers were experienced in navigation through ice, and Ross in 1831 had located the North Magnetic Pole at position 70° 05′ N, 96° 46′ W. during a voyage in search of the north-west passage. The German physicist and mathematician Gauss had carried out the first mathematical analysis of the

Earth's magnetic field using the sparse data available. From this he predicted the position of the South Magnetic Pole at about 66° S, 146° E. As Ross had been the first man to find the North Magnetic Pole, it was his ambition to occupy the South Magnetic Pole as well.

Erebus and *Terror* sailed from England in September 1839 calling at Cape of Good Hope, and Hobarton in Tasmania. At both these places magnetic observatories were established for control of magnetic observations to be made during the survey. The magnetic survey was completed by Ross in April 1843 and during it he had circumnavigated the globe. Each day, with very few exceptions, both ships while at sea observed carefully the magnetic declination, magnetic dip, and magnetic force. While at Hobarton Ross learnt news of the voyages of d'Urville and Wilkes (see Fig. 24 for a comparison of their voyages). As a result of a letter from Wilkes enclosing a map of his discoveries, Ross decided to leave Hobarton by sailing south-east before striking south, so as to avoid following in the path of Wilkes. He penetrated the pack ice with his two tiny ships and came out into clear sea which now bears his name, whereupon he set his course for the magnetic pole, but on 11 January 1841 land was sighted. Ross sailed along this coast and it was not long before he realized that his hopes of sailing to the South Magnetic Pole were not to be fulfilled. The discoveries by Ross in this area are now history, but his main job was the magnetic survey of the south polar regions.

When this was completed his observations were analysed by Sabine (1868) and the first accurate magnetic charts of the Antarctic were drawn of the magnetic declination, dip and total force. Ross was not the first to carry out magnetic observations; d'Urville and Wilkes had also carried out limited observations. It is possible that Bellingshausen may have made magnetic observations before them. But Ross was the first to measure three components of the Earth's magnetic field in and around the whole of the Antarctic.

The Earth behaves like a magnet and thus has two magnetic poles. At the magnetic pole the lines of magnetic force are vertical and so there is no horizontal component to cause a compass there to lie along a particular direction. If a dip needle is used there it will stand vertical. For navigation purposes knowledge is required of the angle between the direction in which the compass needle points and the true north-south direction or true meridian. This angle is called by navigators the magnetic variation of the compass, and by scientists the magnetic declination because it is the angle through which the compass needle declines or deviates from true north.

Magnetic Charts

Edmund Halley constructed the first magnetic chart on which the values of the magnetic declination were shown by a series of curved lines, each line joining the parts which had the same value for the magnetic declination. Such lines of equal magnetic declination are called isogonals. This form of magnetic chart is still in use today and allows the navigator to deduce the true north direction from his compass reading. These isogonals must all pass through the geographical poles of the Earth because there the value of the magnetic declination depends on which meridian it is referred. Also the isogonals must pass through the two magnetic poles. This is because at these positions there is no horizontal component of the Earth's magnetic field to hold it in any particular direction. For the construction of a world chart showing magnetic declination it is necessary to know the positions of the magnetic poles. In the days of Ross it was believed that the magnetic poles were stationary, and hence the interest and importance that lay in their discovery. It is now known that the South Magnetic Pole is a considerable distance – 2000 km – from the South Geographical Pole; it is not diametrically opposite to the North Magnetic Pole and it is also known to have a diurnal movement following an elliptical path. The length of this path changes from day to day and is much longer on magnetically disturbed days than on magnetically quiet days. Thus the position of the magnetic pole covers an area rather than a point. The actual fixing of the magnetic pole area at any particular time is rendered difficult if the crustal rocks in the vicinity contain magnetic materials. In this case it becomes necessary to separate the effect of these local rocks from the general magnetic field of the Earth to determine the true position of the magnetic pole. The effect of a local deposit of magnetic material decreases inversely as the cube of the distance and at heights greater than 3000 m these anomalous effects are generally neglected. As aerial navigation is generally carried out at greater heights than this, it is the true field of the Earth that is of importance for this purpose.

Magnetic charts are drawn to show the average or normal magnetic field, i.e. the effects due to local occurrence of magnetic rocks are eliminated as far as possible. Magnetic observatories are in general established at sites where there is little or no disturbance of the Earth's magnetic field due to rocks containing ferro-magnetic materials. In the Antarctic it is extremely difficult to set up magnetic observatories in areas free from magnetic disturbance. At Scott Base, for instance, magnetic observations of H and Z in the Absolute Hut and Variometer Hut presented differences of 490 and 480 gammas in these magnetic elements respectively, in a distance of about 60 m. These differences do not determine the amount of disturbance due to the surrounding rocks. To determine this the normal field, i.e. the field that would be present if the underlying rocks were non-magnetic, would have to be measured. Some idea of the normal field may be obtained by considering the value of the field as measured on ice at sea. Hatherton (1961) reported measurements of the magnetic declination made by J. H. Miller and R. A. Carlyon on the Ross Ice Shelf. Comparison of results at the nearest station to Scott Base shows:

	Latitude	Longitude	Magnetic Declination, D
Scott Base	77° 51′ S	166° 47′ E	$156\frac{1}{2}$° E
Ross Ice Shelf	78° 00′ S	168° 39′ E	$142\frac{1}{2}$° E

The difference of 14° is probably a reasonable measure of the amount of magnetic disturbance in D due to the volcanic rocks at Scott Base.

Even when a magnetic observatory is built on ice the problem is not always solved. The magnetic observatory built at Halley Bay was on a floating ice shelf 150 m thick and below which was about 80 m of sea water. MacDowall and Blackie (1960) described how a magnetic survey revealed the presence of a moderate magnetic anomaly. The nearest land above sea level was 370 km away. It was estimated that the ice shelf with the observatory was moving at the rate of 320 m/yr across the magnetic anomaly. The observations at Halley Bay included

TABLE 9

POSITION OF SOUTH MAGNETIC POLE

Year	Location of South Magnetic Pole Latitude, S	Longitude, E	Authority
1825	76° 00′	137° 30′	Duperrey
1838	66° 00′	146° 00′	Gauss
1840	69° 30′	130° 47′	Hansteen
1840	72° 00′	136° 45′	Dumont d'Urville
1841	75° 00′	153° 45′	Ross
1840–5	73° 30′	147° 30′	Sabine
1899	72° 40′	152° 30′	Borchgrevink
1903	72° 51′	156° 25′	Chetwynd: B.N.A.E. 1901–4
1909	72° 25′	155° 16′	Shackleton: B.A.E. 1907–9
1912	71° 10′	150° 45′	Mawson: A.A.E. 1911–14
1939	70° 20′	149° 00′	Farr
1952	68° 42′	143° 00′	Mayaud
1957	69° 00′	141° 00′	Nagata
1962	67° 30′	140° 00′	Burrows and Hanley

the changes that have taken place in the Earth's field complicated by the effects due to the movement of the observatory across a magnetically disturbed area.

The principal determinations of the position of the South Magnetic Pole are shown in Table 9. The first magnetic observations on the continent were made by Bernacchi and Colbeck of Borchgrevink's *Southern Cross* (1898–1900) Expedition, and were used to fix a position for the magnetic pole. The most recent position is due to Hanley and Burrows who visited the South Magnetic Pole area in the icebreaker USS *Burton Island* in February 1962. They made magnetic observations in Commonwealth Bay at Cape Denison, Cape Hunter, and on an iceberg in the bay. A tentative fix for the position of the position of the pole from these observations is $67\frac{1}{2}°$ S, 140° E.

The magnetic total force chart for epoch 1957·5 by Nagata (1961) over the Antarctic shows that the geomagnetic field strength in this area is about 3% lower than expected from previous charts. Total magnetic field measurements between New Zealand and Antarctica made by Christoffel (1961) showed that south of Latitude 55° S the values were much lower than expected. He also showed that his measurements agreed with three isolated values obtained from extrapolated rocket flight measurements by Cahill. Bukin et al. (1960) reported that world magnetic charts in the area where Soviet stations were located in Antarctica were in error up to 10° in declination and 1–2000 gammas in magnetic force components.

Mansurov (1960) has discussed the secular variation in East Antarctica based on magnetic observations made at four stations: Oazis, Mirnyy, Pionerskaya, and Vostok. At Mirnyy the numerical value of Z, the vertical component, increased until about the middle of 1958 when it began to decrease. At Vostok the value of Z increased until the beginning of 1959 when it also began to decrease. This difference in time of about six months in the turning point of the change of Z at two stations 1400 km apart was provisionally considered to be due firstly in part to an internal cause, and secondly to what seemed to be influence of solar activity. It was also noted that H was increasing at Vostok while at Mirnyy, Oazis, and Pionerskaya the value of H was decreasing. The observations at Oazis and Pionerskaya were not carried out for so long as at Mirnyy and Vostok, so that the rates of secular change would not be as reliable as those determined for Mirnyy and Vostok.

So far the only synoptic work has been in connection with the study of the distribution of the Earth's magnetic field across Antarctica and its secular change, by Nagata (1960). According to his analysis the unexpected decrease in the geomagnetic field in Antarctica is due to a remarkably large rate of secular variation in this area. As well as this generally high rate of decrease in field, there are very strong local variations which could be attributed to a breaking out of a toroidal magnetic field system near the surface of the Earth's core beneath this area.

Rock Magnetism

When igneous rocks cool in an ambient magnetic field they acquire a permanent magnetization which is almost invariably in the direction of the ambient field. Sedimentary rocks can also acquire a permanent magnetization either by physical processes on deposition or by subsequent chemical changes. These processes are not yet fully understood, but a paleomagnetic hypothesis has been developed which postulates that, if the magnetic effects of the post-formational tectonic, physical and chemical history of the rocks can be neglected or corrected, it is possible to determine the history of the geomagnetic field throughout geological time by measuring the directions of magnetism of rocks of different ages.

Evison (1961) has contested this simple viewpoint by suggesting that the magnetic vectors of rocks are changed during plastic deformation of the rock by flow under gravity, and that such change cannot, in general, be corrected.

TABLE 10

PALEOMAGNETIC POLE POSITIONS IN ANTARCTICA

Region	Rocks	Age	Pole Position		Author
Hallett	Volcanics	Quaternary	81° S	94° E	Turnbull 1959
Ferrar Gl.	Dolerite	Mesozoic?	58° S	142° W	Turnbull 1959
Theron Mts	,,	,,	54° S	136° W	Blundell and Stephenson 1959
Wright Val.	,,	,,	51° S	132° W	Bull and Irving 1960
Ferrar Gl.	Beacon Sst.	Upper Pal-Triassic?	53° S	151° W	Turnbull 1959
Wright Val.	Basic Dykes	Paleozoic?	29° S	149° W	Bull and Irving 1960
Ongul Is.	Gneiss	Precambrian	3° S	73° E	Nagata and Shimizu 1959

In Antarctica, as well as in other continents, the directions of magnetization of rocks are being examined. Table 10 shows a list of south geomagnetic pole positions so far determined for Antarctic rocks.

The majority of measurements have been made on dolerite sills. These rocks are of particular interest because of the affinity they bear to similar rocks in Africa and Tasmania. Bull and Irving (1960) compare the pole positions of the Wright Valley dolerites with the pole positions obtained from rocks of similar age (Jurassic?) in Tasmania, Africa, India and South America (Fig. 145a). In Figure 145b they have calculated the pole positions of the magnetic vectors if the continents had been disposed on formation of the rocks according to du Toit's reconstruction of Gondwanaland. Bull and Irving infer that the smaller scatter of poles in Figure 145b lends support to the idea that the continents have drifted apart.

Diurnal Variation

Most Antarctic expeditions set up magnetic observatories at their base camps and the measurements obtained have been used to study the diurnal variation in the magnetic elements. The results of these studies were available, prior to IGY for Cape Adare, Hut Point, Cape Evans, Cape Denison, and Port Martin. As these measurements were not made simultaneously, and as they were confined to a limited sector of the Antarctic Continent, it was not possible to derive synoptic patterns of the diurnal variation in the magnetic elements across the Antarctic Continent. When the mean hourly values for the Antarctic observatories during the IGY are published, the patterns of the diurnal changes across the continent will be determined, as well as the patterns of the equivalent electric current system in the ionosphere which give rise to the observed magnetic changes during the day. Such an investigation will not be completed until it covers a full sunspot cycle. Many observatories have published hourly values for the period of the

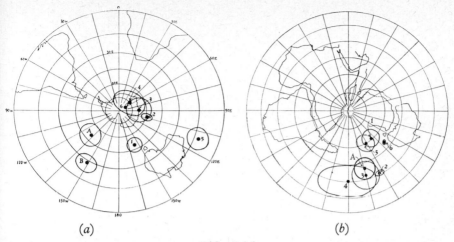

(a)   (b)

FIG. 145

a. Paleomagnetic pole positions relative to the present distribution of continents. The pole positions are numbered as follows: A. – dolerite sills of Wright Valley; B. – basic dykes of Wright Valley; 1 – Tasmanian dolerites; 2 – Karroo basalts of Rhodesia; 3 – average pole from the dolerite sills and baked contact rocks in the mines of Estcourt and Winkelhaak, South Africa; 4 – Karroo dolerites, surface samples, South Africa; 5 – Rajmahal traps of Bihar, India; 6 – Serra Geral lavas and baked Botacatu Sandstones of Uruguay. The map is a stereographic projection.

b. Pole positions relative to du Toit's reconstruction of Gondwanaland. The poles are labelled as in *a*

IGY and these include Scott Base, Little America, Wilkes Station, and Charcot. The results from the French station Charcot have been analysed and are of particular interest because this observatory is in the vicinity of the South Magnetic Pole area. Charcot is situated about 2200 m above sea level, 318 km from the coast at Lat. 69° 22·5′ S and Long. 139° 01′ E. It thus lies between the South Magnetic Pole and the South Geomagnetic Pole. The diurnal variation of the vertical magnetic field was determined for ten months from May 1957 to January 1958. The ranges in gammas of the diurnal variation for All Days, International Quiet Days, International Disturbed Days, the Quietest Days, and the Most Disturbed Days, are given for the seasons and year in Table 11.

The influence of the seasons is very clearly shown whichever type of day is considered. The difference between the Quiet and Disturbed Days would indicate that the international classification was reasonable except for summer when the range of International Quiet Days is comparable with range for International Disturbed Days. The ranges for the International Quiet and Disturbed Days are comparable with the ranges on the Quietest and the Most Disturbed Days respectively for winter months. For the equinoxes the range for International Disturbed Days corresponds roughly with ranges for the Most Disturbed Days, but this correspondence between the ranges on the Quiet Days is not so good.

TABLE II

RANGE OF DIURNAL VARIATION IN VERTICAL MAGNETIC FIELD AT CHARCOT (*Units in Gammas*)

	All Days	*Inter-national Quiet Days*	*Inter-national Disturbed Days*	*Quietest Days*	*Most Disturbed Days*
Winter	44	27	108	31	92
Equinoxes	114	127	211	91	241
Summer	188	214	255	109	303
Year	108	86	175	52	179

In summer the results are quite different for both types of day, and in particular it was found that two days which were classified as International Disturbed Days were among the Quietest Days at Charcot. The classification of International Quiet and Disturbed Days is valid for Charcot only for the winter and equinoctial months, while even for the latter the calm days may be somewhat disturbed. This may indicate the existence of zones of magnetic disturbance. Mayaud (1961) has shown that in very calm periods the most highly disturbed regions are the inner part of the southern auroral zone and the equatorial zone. Figure 146 shows the diurnal variations recorded at Hallett Station on 24 May, 4 October and 1 December 1958 which were classified as International Quiet Days.

Magnetic Activity

Magnetic disturbance on the inside of the southern auroral zone seems to have been first studied by Chree (1915, 1927) who analysed the magnetic records from the stations at Cape Evans and Cape Denison.

At Cape Evans, Chree found that the incidence of disturbance agreed closely with the incidence of disturbance recorded in temperate latitudes and that the disturbances in the Antarctic were much larger and more persistent than at any of the stations cooperating in the international scheme. He also found the twenty-seven-day period was clearly visible in the Antarctic records, being as well developed there as elsewhere. MacDowall and Blackie (1960), using local magnetic character figures for Halley Bay during period 1 May 1957 to 31 December 1958, found features of the twenty-seven-day period of recurrence of magnetic disturbance to be very similar to the features described by Chapman and Bartels.

Using K-indices Nagata (1961) compared geomagnetic activities in the Antarctic with those in the north polar region. He computed the average values of the three-hour-range geomagnetic indices, K, for eight Antarctic stations, viz.,

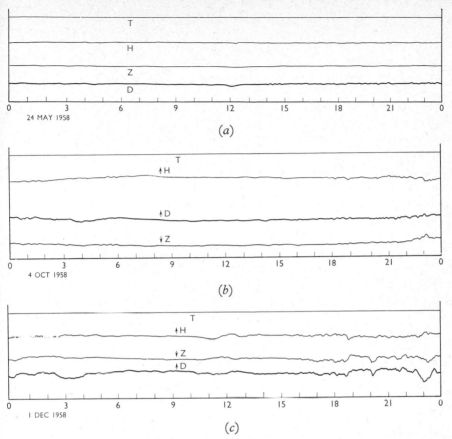

FIG. 146 DIURNAL VARIATIONS OF MAGNETIC ELEMENTS AT HALLETT
STATION ON THREE INTERNATIONAL QUIET DAYS 1958
a. 24 May;   b. 4 October;   c. 1 December

Hallett, Macquarie Island, Mawson, Mirnyy, Scott, Syowa, Wilkes, and Vostok, during 1960. These values he compared with the three-hour-range geomagnetic planetary index, Kp, which is considered to give the measure of magnetic disturbances over the whole Earth as a planet. Actually Kp index is the average of values of K at eleven Northern Hemisphere high latitude stations and at one Southern Hemisphere station, Amberley in New Zealand. For his purpose Nagata considered Kp as representing magnetic activities in the northern high latitude regions. He found by comparison of the average Antarctic K-indices with the simultaneous Kp values that the changes were almost parallel to Kp throughout a year, the correlation coefficient between the two indices during the period amounting to 0·81. He concluded that the geomagnetic activities in the south polar region are generally speaking almost parallel to those in the north polar region, magnetic disturbances taking place simultaneously in both polar regions.

He also found a definite seasonal variation in the correlation between these sets of indices. In Antarctica during southern summer when the south polar region is sunlit, the level of disturbance is higher than in the north polar region which is dark. In the southern winter the solar light conditions are reversed and the level of disturbance in the south polar region is lower than that in the north polar region which is sunlit. He also came to the conclusion that geomagnetic activities in the sunlit polar region are greater than in the dark polar region when magnetic conditions are generally quiet, while, when conditions are magnetically disturbed, the disturbances in the sunlit polar region are definitely less than in the dark polar region.

Nagata's assumption that Kp is representative of Northern Hemisphere high latitude stations may not necessarily be true. The range of Northern Hemisphere stations used in the determination of Kp lies between 60° and 30° parallels of latitude, while the range in geomagnetic latitude lies between 63° and 50°. Nagata's comparisons with Antarctic disturbances would then appear to refer to disturbances occurring on the equatorial side of the northern auroral zone.

Schlich (1960) compared the sum of the Kp indices with the sum of the K-indices determined for station Charcot for the period from April 1957 to January 1958. He found that for the months April to September the daily sums at Charcot were less than the daily sums for Kp, while for October to January the daily sums of K at Charcot were higher than the Kp daily sums. It thus appeared that the lower level chosen for $K9$ was too high in winter, was good for the equinoctial months, but was too low for the southern summer. This would be explained by the very strong seasonal variation of daytime disturbance pointed out by Mayaud (1956). This is very weak in winter and has little effect on the disturbances recorded; on the other hand during the southern summer the daytime disturbance has increased in importance such that it controls the amplitude of the magnetic disturbances. Schlich remarked that it would be impossible to define an ideal base for K-indices at Charcot that would ever agree, or only in an incomplete way, with Kp. Magnetograms from Hallett Station, and Scott Base, show very clearly the predominance of the daytime disturbance during the summer months.

In a study of the seasonal variations of magnetic activity in Canada, Whitham, Loomer and Niblet (1960) found the large seasonal variation to be a function of geomagnetic latitude. They also found that, relative to the winter level of disturbance, equinoctial activity increases more to the north and south of the main northern auroral zone than in the auroral zone itself; whereas in the Arctic summer a large increase in activity is found only inside the auroral zone. They considered the latitudinal variation of the seasonal activity to be a consequence of two effects: (a) the movement south in the Arctic winter of the daytime peak of disturbance which is widest in the north of the auroral zone and dominant inside the polar cap; (b) the movement north in the Arctic winter of the night-time peak of activity evident along the auroral zone and a little to its south

It is thus probable that the latitudinal variation of seasonal disturbance would be similar in the Antarctic, but with the directions of movement reversed.

Chree (1927) found that at both Cape Evans and Cape Denison the magnetic activity decreased from summer through equinox to winter. The diurnal distribution of magnetic disturbance at Cape Evans showed a principal maximum and minimum, and the maximum of disturbance occurred in the hour ending at 2200 GMT. At Cape Denison a principal maximum of disturbance occurred in the hour ending 0200 GMT and a quite decided secondary maximum in the hour ending at 1400 GMT.

Stagg (1935), using data from stations whose geomagnetic latitudes varied from 54.5° to 88°, showed that the diurnal variation of disturbance was controlled by local time in such a way that stations with geomagnetic latitude less than 70° have a maximum of disturbance around local midnight and a minimum around local noon, while stations with geomagnetic latitude higher than 80° have a maximum of disturbance in the forenoon with a minimum around local midnight. Stations intermediate between these two latitudes showed a diurnal distribution with two maxima and two minima; these stations were described as being in the 'transition zone' and can be regarded as having a combination of the two main types of disturbance. Nikolsky (1947), using data from a greater number of stations, recognized the disturbance during the day as spreading outside the auroral zone down to stations with geomagnetic latitude of 62°. He also considered that the time of occurrence of this daytime maximum of disturbance was controlled by universal time. Where the diurnal distribution showed two maxima and two minima, he considered that they were due to two different types of disturbance having different causes probably due to different types of solar corpuscles. Stagg and Nikolsky used observations made at different epochs and this may have contributed to the differences determined in their respective zonal boundaries. Mayaud (1956), using K-indices for a large number of stations from the Second International Polar Year, as well as data from other stations covering a longer period of time, e.g. a solar cycle, concluded that the magnetic field at the altitude of 5000 km controlled the phenomenon of disturbance much better than did the geomagnetic field by showing that the zonal boundaries were uniquely determined by the magnetic inclination at these high altitudes. He listed the properties of the daytime disturbance which he called J and night-time disturbance which he called N.

The type of disturbance J is much more rapid than the type of disturbance N.

Where disturbance J is well shown it has a degree of permanence, occurring even on magnetically calm days in winter, when N is nil or nearly absent.

Disturbance J is restricted mainly to the inside of the auroral zone which is the only region where it appears with great intensity. Disturbance N is greatest in the auroral zone and is predominant over the remainder of the Earth between the auroral zones.

Disturbance J has seasonal variation in that it increases from winter, through equinox to a maximum in summer, whereas N is most intense at the equinoxes.

The time of maximum of disturbance J inside the auroral zone is around local geomagnetic noon, whilst disturbance N has its maximum around local midnight.

By means of K-indices Lassen (1958) studied the variation of magnetic activity for the period 1944–55 at Godhavn in Greenland, geomagnetic latitude 79·8°. He found that the activity is composed of two main types J and N. The type J has its maximum in the forenoon and its variations through the day and the year follow the Sun. The daily variation of J has its maximum at local magnetic noon, while the seasonal variation has its maximum at the summer solstice. Through the solar cycle it was found that the amplitude of the daily variation in J follows the sunspot number R. He also found that the second type of activity N, which has its maximum in the evening, is most dominant in the years near sunspot minimum. Its variation through the sunspot cycle is nearly opposite in phase to sunspot number R. He concluded that the inner border of the zone of maximum N, and therefore of maximum auroral activity, is nearest to the geomagnetic pole in sunspot minimum years.

Hatherton (1961) compared the seasonal trends in diurnal variation of disturbance using K-indices at Hallett Station with Scott Base. He used the meteorological seasons and found that, though the Scott Base curves are slightly flatter than the Hallett curves, both show a similar diurnal variation of geomagnetic disturbance. Both the range of diurnal activity and the mean level of activity increased from winter through the equinoctial months to a maximum in summer. The curves showed a principal maximum and minimum, the maximum occurring around midday. Figure 146 shows the change in level of daytime magnetic disturbance from May to December at Hallett Station on International Quiet Days.

Scott Base, geomagnetic latitude 79° S, lies on the edge of Stagg's inner zone where diurnal trend shows one maximum and one minimum of disturbance. Hallett Station, geomagnetic latitude 74·7° S, lies in Stagg's transition zone where the characteristic features of diurnal variation in disturbance are a day-time maximum and a night-time maximum of disturbance. Hatherton showed that Little America V, geomagnetic latitude 74° S, has two maxima and two minima typical of Stagg's transition zone. Now Hallett and Little America have approximately the same geomagnetic latitude, but their diurnal curves of disturbance are quite dissimilar. Davies (1935) found at Little America for 1929–30 that the diurnal variation in disturbance was a single maximum type and did not conform with Stagg's idea that it was a transition zone station. The maximum occurred around 0330 hrs local time and accordingly would be night-time N disturbance. According to Hatherton it seems that the difference in latitude between Little America V and Little America I is critical or the diurnal variation of disturbance in the Little America region has changed in character during the past 30 years.

But Lassen (1958) has showed that there may be a change of pattern of diurnal disturbance with the progress of the sunspot cycle, and in particular that the daytime disturbance J follows sunspot number R. Now at Little America I in 1929, 1930, the mean values for R were 65 and 36 respectively, while at Little

America V 1957, 1958 the mean values for R were 206 and 185 respectively. This may account for the absence of a clear daytime maximum of disturbance at Little America I, even though the observations were not long past sunspot maximum year 1928 when sunspot number R was only 78. The dissimilarity of the diurnal activity curves at Hallett and Little America may mean that geomagnetic latitude is not the controlling factor for determining these zonal boundaries, but that the latter may be related to the geometry of the southern auroral zone whose centre as suggested by Hatherton (1960) lies between the South Geomagnetic and South Magnetic Poles.

This problem is made more difficult because at Charcot, geomagnetic latitude 78.3° S, the time of the daytime maximum of disturbance in 1957–8 was at 0200 GMT with the occurrence in the winter months of a small but clear nocturnal maximum at 1230 GMT. (Schlich, 1960; Larzilliere, 1960.)

The annual variation of magnetic activity at Halley Bay, geomagnetic latitude 65.5° S (MacDowall 1960) showed marked seasonal changes particularly between summer and winter. The lowest levels of activity were relatively infrequent in summer compared with winter. High activity tended to occur near the equinox with two cycles per year. The diurnal variation of activity was studied at Halley Bay by MacDowall and Blackie (1960). The particularly large change in the form of the diurnal variation of disturbance from summer to winter was attributed to a universal time component dependent on the daily and seasonal variation of the angle between the geomagnetic axis and the Sun–Earth line.

At the Soviet stations, which are all situated within the zone of maximum activity, the daily variations of the geomagnetic field have a form of a diurnal wave.

Nikolsky (1957) has made another study of magnetic disturbances in the Arctic and from this he determined the isolines of times of the simultaneous appearance of the maximum of morning magnetic disturbances. He found that the appearance of these isolines was represented by a system of spirals issuing from the Geomagnetic Pole and developing clockwise in the Northern Hemisphere. This system of spirals was then laid out by him symmetrically on a map of Antarctica, but counter-clockwise in accordance with the laws of movement of electrically charged particles around the South Geomagnetic Pole, and made to fit in the best possible way with observed times for Cape Evans, Cape Denison, and Gauss Land. The fit was by no means perfect, the differences in time being zero hours at Cape Denison, two hours for Cape Evans, and four hours for Gauss Land. The times of maximum of this daytime disturbance are gradually coming to hand and thus Nikolsky's scheme, shown in Figure 147, can be tested. Early in 1957 at Mirnyy it was found that a single well-defined maximum of disturbance took place in the interval 05–0800 GMT. On Nikolsky's diagram the 0800 GMT isoline passes through Mirnyy.

The morning maximum of disturbance at Charcot occurs around 0200 GMT, whereas according to Nikolsky the maximum should be produced about 0430 GMT. Nikolsky's system of isolines of simultaneous appearance of magnetic disturbance for Antarctica shows that the curve for 2000 GMT passes through both Scott Base and Hallett Station. The mean curves of diurnal variation of disturbance determined for both these stations by using *K*-indices show the maxima to lie in the Greenwich three-hour period 2100–2400 GMT, so that for these two Antarctic stations Nikolsky's prediction is reasonably correct. But it must not be overlooked that two out of three stations used by Nikolsky to fix the positions of the isolines lie in this area of Antarctica.

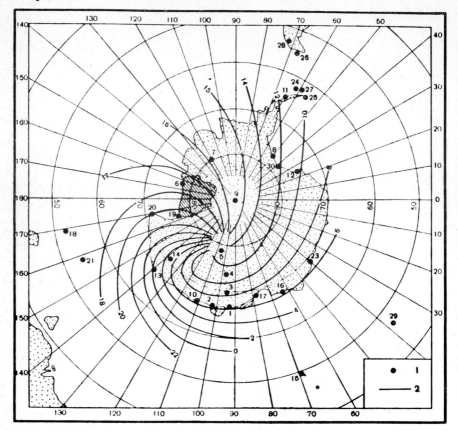

FIG. 147 ISOLINES OF MORNING MAXIMUM OF MAGNETIC
DISTURBANCE IN ANTARCTICA (UNIVERSAL TIME)
(After Nikolsky, 1957)

1. IGY stations with magnetic observations
2. Isolines of times of morning maximum of magnetic disturbance.

The results from other stations in the Antarctic will have to be studied to confirm the reality of Nikolsky's idea of spiralling disturbances.

Magnetic Storms

On some days the traces of the magnetic elements shown on the magnetograms at magnetic observatories undergo smooth and regular variations with peaks and troughs occurring at much the same time on different days. These are called Quiet Days. On other days the records show much movement or fluctuation of the traces and the smooth and regular appearance is greatly altered. These are called Disturbed Days. An office of the International Association of Geomagnetism and Aeronomy selects for each calendar month five days which appear to be the quietest and five days which appear to be the most disturbed, and these are called the International Quiet Days and the International Disturbed Days. Magnetic disturbances which occur for several hours or more are called magnetic storms, and these may be roughly classified as moderate, moderately severe, or severe. Storms in general fall into one of two classes, those in which the onset of disturbance is gradual so that it is not possible to see exactly the time of commencement, or those in which the commencement of disturbance is sudden. The study of magnetic storms with sudden commencement shows that they have world-wide effects and that they have a certain unity of pattern. Many storms occurring at different times often show broad similarities to one another in the development and distribution of their variation fields even though each may have irregularities peculiar to itself. The characteristic of these storms is the increase in the value of the horizontal component H above normal; this increase may commence suddenly, H remaining high for a few hours then decreasing rapidly to a value below normal, which is generally much more below normal than the initial increase was above normal. There is then a slow recovery to normal value of H. The recovery is at first rapid, then the rate slows down considerably. The increase is called the initial phase of the storm. The decrease to the point at which the rate of recovery begins to slow down is called the main phase. The period of slow recovery is called the last or final phase, or the post-perturbation.

One of the most important features of a magnetic storm is that through low and middle latitudes the daily mean value of H is reduced. The complete recovery to the normal value may not occur until several days after the traces have become calm. Thus the post-perturbation effects persist even during quiet days following a magnetic storm. In some months when much disturbance occurs, even the monthly value of H is depressed, compared with the adjoining months when disturbances were not so frequent.

In 1957 the month of September was notable for the occurrence of at least four severe magnetic storms and it is of interest to compare the mean monthly value of H for this month with the values for the preceding and succeeding months at observatories from the tropics to the Antarctic as shown in Table 12.

The results show that for the stations Little America, Wilkes and Scott Base which are all inside the southern auroral zone, the effects of post-perturbation in H are negligible compared with stations between the auroral zone and equator.

When magnetic storms commence suddenly they do so with remarkably world-wide simultaneity with differences of time not exceeding a minute or so. But the greatly improved precision of timing of observations of the IGY showed that the times of the sudden commencements were not simultaneous over the whole world. Gerard (1959) showed that the first impulse of the sudden commencement

TABLE 12

MEAN MONTHLY VALUES OF MAGNETIC HORIZONTAL FORCE H 1957 (*Units in Gammas*)

Observatory	Geomagnetic S Latitude	Jul	Aug	Sep	Oct	Nov	Dec
Apia	16·0°	34864	34876	34821	34875	34876	34876
Watheroo	41·8°	24842	24851	24808	24859	24856	24859
Amberley	47·7°	22108	22115	22072	22108	22094	22090
Macquarie Id	61·0°	13306	13314	13259	13321	13316	13316
Halley Bay	65·6°	20286	20288	20241	20290	20298	20304
Little America	74·0°	11188	11203	11202	11228	11230	11246
Wilkes	77·8°	9336	9340	9334	9342	9345	9362
Scott Base	79·0°	9730	9726	9733	9753	9767	9766

occurred a few seconds earlier at Scott Base than at Apia. In a study of the times of fifteen sudden commencement storms during the IGY, Williams (1960) analysed rapid run magnetograms from observatories extending from Alaska to the Antarctic. He found that the sudden commencement always occurred first in high or middle latitudes before occurring in equatorial stations several seconds later. An interesting feature was that at Little America the sudden commencements were registered first or second 85% of the time. Indeed, of the fifteen sudden commencements studied nine occurred first at Little America.

A number of sudden commencements of magnetic storms observed during the IGY was analysed by Wilson and Sugiura (1961) using rapid run magnetograms taken at six magnetic observatories including Byrd Station. They found that most of the magnetic impulses of sudden commencements were elliptically polarized except in low latitude stations where the polarization was usually linear. They also found that when the rotation of the magnetic vector at College, Alaska, was in a clockwise direction, at Byrd the direction of rotation was anti-clockwise and vice versa.

Magnetic storms shown on magnetograms from many of the Antarctic observatories do not follow the classical pattern of sudden commencement storms experienced in low and middle latitudes. The variation with storm-time is not clearly depicted, i.e. there is no definite initial phase with increase in H, followed by decrease in H, the main phase. The final phase or post-perturbation is difficult to discern. The main features of magnetic storms in the Antarctic are the greater amplitudes of fluctuations than in low or middle latitudes. The pattern of disturbance is often a succession of bay-like disturbances, called polar magnetic storms which rapidly reach their maximum of activity and disturbed conditions then die away fairly quickly so that in general the storms are relatively short-lived, rarely lasting more than about one day. Often sudden commencement storms are preceded by moderate bay disturbances that may have occurred two or three hours previously. Nagata and Fukushima (1952) analysed successive instantaneous aspects of the world-wide distribution of polar magnetic storms and concluded that they are composed of a number of elementary disturbances which take place successively with duration of from thirty minutes to two hours. Fukushima (1952) examined the variations during another magnetic storm and concluded that the disturbance field of polar magnetic storms consisted of elementary disturbances which take place intermittently or successively at some limited region along the auroral zone.

Very little work has been published on the course of storm-time changes at Antarctic stations. Chapman and Bartels (1940) discussed the storm changes in high latitudes by considering the S_D variations and the averaged storm-time variations at several Arctic stations and at Cape Evans. The averaged effect of the storm-time changes was shown by the difference between mean values of the magnetic elements on all days and on quiet days. For Cape Evans it was found that the 'all-days minus quiet days' mean difference in the (upward) vertical force was an increase of five gammas, while the 'disturbed days minus all-days' mean showed an increase of twelve gammas. Thus within the southern auroral zone disturbance increases the numerical value of the vertical force, just as in the case of the northern polar region.

For Scott Base during 1958 the difference 'disturbed days minus all-days' mean was an increase in numerical value of eight gammas.

Nagata and Kokubun (1960) examined the average behaviour of polar magnetic storms in the southern polar region using data of eighteen typical sudden commencement storms during the IGY period at three Antarctic stations, Little America, Wilkes, and Halley Bay. They used the average S_D variations where $S_D = S_d - S_q$ (or disturbed days minus quiet days).

This study has since been extended to include the data from additional observatories at Macquarie Island, Syowa, and Scott Base. The mean equivalent current system in the ionosphere that could give rise to the observed S_D magnetic variations was calculated and is shown in Figure 148(A). After comparison with the pattern of the North S_D current system (shown in Fig. 148B) determined by Nagata and Fukushima (1952) it was concluded that the South S_D current system was practically a mirror image of the North one with respect to the geomagnetic equatorial plane. Both systems show that the westward auroral zone currents are most intense about 0200 LT, and the eastward auroral zone currents reach their maximum around 1600 LT but are weaker than the former. In both current systems the polar cap currents flow along the direction approximately towards 0900 LT and the main parts of the auroral zone currents lie between 65° and 70° geomagnetic latitudes. It was found that the electric currents in the South system were much stronger than in the North system and that the ratio of the intensity of the westward auroral zone currents to that of the eastward was larger in the former than in the latter. These differences were attributed to differences in solar activity, the South system being observed at sunspot

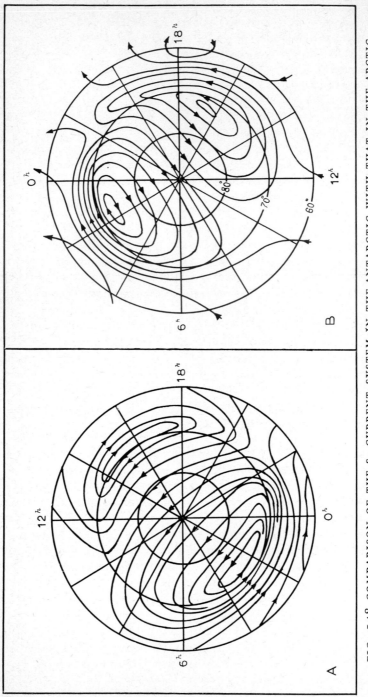

FIG. 148 COMPARISON OF THE S_D CURRENT SYSTEM IN THE ANTARCTIC WITH THAT IN THE ARCTIC

A. The mean equivalent current system for south polar magnetic storms during the IGY/IGC, 1957–59. (Electric current between adjacent stream lines is 5×10^4 amps.)

B. The mean equivalent current system for north polar magnetic storms during the Second International Polar Year, 1932–33. (Electric current between adjacent stream lines is $2 \cdot 9 \times 10^4$ amps.)

maximum while the North system applied to 1932–3 when solar activity was near a minimum. The intense westward auroral zone currents shown in the South system were attributed to the fact that polar elementary storms are much more frequent and intense on the night-time side particularly at time of sunspot maximum. From the foregoing it is concluded that the South S_D system is geomagnetically symmetrical to the North S_D system, and that corpuscular streams activate both North and South polar regions almost equally and in the same manner.

Geomagnetic Bays

The most characteristic feature of magnetic disturbance on the Antarctic magnetograms is the occurrence of bay disturbances. Magnetic storms, as mentioned previously, consist mainly of a succession of bay type disturbances. Magnetic bays also occur as isolated disturbances even when the magnetic traces are otherwise quiet. Generally it is these clear and isolated bays appearing in calm periods that are studied.

These disturbances are called bays because their magnetic traces resemble indentations of a coastline. The bays may be smooth or rugged and may last for up to an hour. They are called negative or positive bays depending on whether the horizontal component H is decreased or increased. Bays may begin with a gradual onset or they may commence suddenly. Frequently they also show Pt pulsations (see p. 483), particularly at their beginning. Sometimes they are preceded by Pt for a few minutes.

The first study of geomagnetic bays in the Antarctic was made by Chree (1909, 1921) in connection with what he termed 'special type' disturbances recorded at Hut Point in 1902–3 and at Cape Evans in 1911–12. Of eighty-two occurrences studied in 1902–3 more than half were recorded between 1900 and 2100 local mean time (LMT). In 1911–12 all this type of disturbance took place between 1700 and 2400 LMT. Of the fifty-eight cases recorded thirty-seven occurred between 1900 and 2100 LMT. Also all except six of the occurrences happened between March and September. In 1902–3 the large majority of these disturbances took place in May, June, July or August. Thus, to Chree, this phenomenon seemed to develop in winter and to occur in the evening hours. He also reported that some of these disturbances seemed to repeat themselves about the same hour on successive days.

Magnetic bays at Macquarie Island were studied during 1954 sunspot minimum by Robertson (1959). It was found that negative bays were more numerous than positive bays and had greater amplitudes and durations. Negative bays occurred around magnetic midnight whereas positive bays occurred about five hours earlier.

A daily reversal in direction of the bay producing currents is indicated, and the time at which this reversal occurs seems to vary with the seasons, being earlier in the day near the equinoxes than it is near the solstices. On many of the records it was possible to pick the transition times from inspection of the records.

During magnetically disturbed periods the ratios of H to Z bay amplitudes were observed to increase, indicating a northward movement of the bay producing currents. At the same time aurorae were seen farther north than usual. It appears that, at Macquarie Island, magnetic bays and the aurorae are closely related in both time and space.

MacDowall and Blackie (1960) reported that the type of local effect most frequently recorded at Halley Bay was baylike, and 525 were observed in the twenty months from May 1957 to December 1958. Sometimes a disturbance seemed to be repeated about the same hour on successive nights. A notable sequence of these phenomena in very similar form occurred each night from 13 to 18 January 1958. Bays occurred most frequently between 0000 and 0259 GMT and practically never between 1200 and 1459 GMT. During the most active period from 0000 to 0559 GMT field changes were almost entirely negative for H and positive for Z, and in the period before 0000 GMT the reverse field movements were most frequent showing that the disturbance current system required to produce such variations of the field at Halley Bay must reverse near 0000 GMT from an eastward flow to a stronger and more persistent westward flow. Bays were least common there during the summer season when geomagnetic activity was at a minimum compared with all other seasons of the year.

During the IGY at Hallett Station there appeared to be a definite association of umbrella type aurorae and ionospheric disturbances with certain characteristic jagged magnetic bays (Hatherton 1961). As yet no detailed study has been made concerning time of frequency of occurrence of bays at Hallett or Scott Base. But a perusal of the magnetograms from both these stations show that bays appear to occur in the evening hours and are mainly negative bays, i.e. H decreases. They may occur as early as 0300 GMT until as late as 1500 GMT and occasionally some of these bays may repeat themselves at about the same time on successive nights (see Fig. 149).

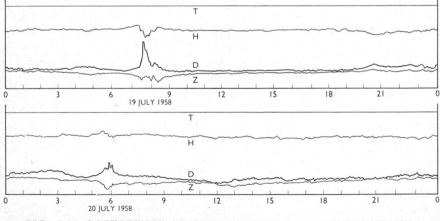

FIG. 149 OCCURRENCE OF GEOMAGNETIC BAYS ON SUCCESSIVE NIGHTS AT HALLETT STATION

Geomagnetic Pulsations

Geomagnetic pulsations are variations of the magnetic field, and have a more or less regular oscillatory form. Their periods of oscillation range between 0·1 seconds and ten minutes. These oscillations sometimes occur for an hour or more and their amplitudes may be several gammas. They occur during magnetic storms and are also associated with bay type disturbances, particularly at the beginning, but may be recorded on what would otherwise be quiet days. The characteristics of pulsations have been studied for many years by many investigators but some of the results are inconsistent and the world coverage is scanty. It has been proposed that pulsations may be caused by magnetohydrodynamic oscillations of the ionized outer atmosphere of the Earth. A study has been made by Obayashi and Jacobs (1958) of the oscillation of hydromagnetic waves induced along the geomagnetic lines of force which were treated as behaving like stretched strings. After examining records from several magnetic observatories of simultaneous geomagnetic pulsations they found that in general the period became longer and the amplitude larger with increasing geomagnetic latitude, and that occasionally, during severe magnetic disturbance, very rapid oscillations were observed in the auroral zone. They also showed that the distribution of ionic density in the outer atmosphere was in good agreement with other independent studies.

Pulsations are classified into three groups:

Pc (PULSATIONS CONTINUOUS)

These consist of a series of oscillations lasting often for many hours with periods generally between 10 and 60 seconds, and amplitudes of from 0·1 to a few gammas.

Pt (TRAINS OF PULSATIONS)

These consist of several series of oscillations, each series generally lasting only from 10 to 20 minutes and the whole phenomenon seldom lasting for more than one hour. The periods are generally longer than Pc being from about 40 seconds to a few minutes. The amplitudes may range from 0·5 to about 10 gammas.

Pg (GIANT PULSATIONS)

These consist of a series of oscillations of large amplitude, sometimes up to a few tens of gammas, and appear only in or near the auroral zones. The periods may be up to several minutes and the duration may be up to an hour.

Type Pc generally have a maximum of occurrence frequency during the morning hours. Well defined oscillations with periods less than 10 seconds have been recorded by Campbell (1959), Maple (1959), Benioff (1960) and Russian workers, notably Troitskaya. The band of frequencies for all types of pulsations described above is too wide to be fully recorded by the same instrument and special methods and techniques are being used to record pulsations in the range of periods from 0·1 to 15 seconds. Campbell (1959) reported that it was apparent that the average very low frequency natural electromagnetic spectrum has a transition from sferics to geomagnetics between 2·0 and 0·2 cycles per second.

The occurrence frequency of geomagnetic pulsations, Pc, has been analysed by Jacobs and Sinno (1960a) using data obtained during the IGY from a world-wide network of stations, and this included a limited amount of data from Byrd Station, Little America and Wilkes in the Antarctic. This analysis led them to the conclusions that the occurrence frequency of Pc's increases as the auroral zones are approached from lower latitudes, and also that the hour of diurnal maximum occurrence appears earlier at high latitude stations. Another result was that the occurrence frequency of Pc's depends not only on local time but also in part on universal time. A number of well-defined cases of Pt's and Pc's from seventeen observatories, including the three Antarctic stations mentioned above, were examined by Jacobs and Sinno. Pt's occur mainly during the night hours and often accompany a geomagnetic bay. The latitudinal distribution of amplitudes of Pt's associated with negative bays shows a very sharp maximum in the auroral zones where the peak values reach 10 gammas or more. For Pt's associated with positive bays or not accompanied by bays the distribution is much flatter, with a peak amplitude in the sub-auroral zone (about 50° geomagnetic latitude) and other subsidiary peaks in the polar and equatorial regions. The latitude trends of the amplitudes of both these types of Pt are the same as those of their associated bays and indicate that Pt's are basically closely related with bays, and that the causal mechanism of these two phenomena may be the same.

It appears that Pc's occur in at least two wave-bands, the first about 10–30 seconds and the second with periods from 30–90 seconds. Jacobs and Sinno (1960b) show that for the longer period type of Pc the amplitude increases from the equator towards the poles; these Pc's appear to have a synchronous wave form over a wide area and have amplitudes of up to 10 gammas or more in polar regions. Troitskaya *et al.* (1961) in an investigation of the characteristics of pulsations in July 1959, using earth current records, found that, in spite of great Pc activity in middle latitudes and in the Arctic, almost all Pc at Mirnyy were weak. The polar night effect found for Pc in the Antarctic and the Arctic, and the same tendency for a decrease in the number of days with Pc in winter time in middle latitudes led them to a preliminary conclusion concerning the dependence of Pc excitation on specific conditions of ionospheric stratification particularly in the F region.

At Charcot Pc's have periods generally between 15 and 35 seconds and very rarely the period might reach 45 seconds. (Schlich 1960.) Their amplitudes in the horizontal component sometimes exceed 10 gammas. They are more numerous and much clearer near local midday (about 0200 UT), and are not recorded around local midnight except during magnetic storms. There is a clear seasonal variation for Pc's which are more numerous and of greater amplitude in summer than in winter.

Pt's never appeared in a very clear way, and were too few for a systematic study.

Micropulsations, i.e. those with periods less than 10 seconds, seemed to occur at any hour and were more numerous in the months of August and September. Their periods varied between 3 and 6 seconds with amplitudes between 0·05 and 0·4 gammas. During 13 September 1957 micropulsations had a period of about 2 seconds and the amplitudes reached 1·6 gammas.

A great deal of work remains to be done on geomagnetic pulsations not only in the polar regions but also over the remainder of the Earth. During the present IQSY special efforts will be made by many nations to record pulsations and particularly micropulsations in the range 0·1 to 15 seconds. The *Argus* experiments gave rise to geomagnetic waves of small amplitude and small period and it is necessary to be able to distinguish between natural micropulsations and those that have been artificially created.

Magnetic Disturbances at Conjugate Points

It has been shown by Chree, Nagata and other workers that in general the incidence of magnetic disturbance, particularly with regard to world magnetic storms, is similar in the Antarctic and in the Northern Hemisphere. That the polar cap areas of both hemispheres have higher levels of disturbance in summer than in winter indicates that the similarity of incidence of disturbance in both hemispheres may not apply in the case of isolated or individual events of comparatively short duration. The study of whistlers and the discovery of the existence of the Van Allen radiation belts from satellite measurements during the IGY showed that the Earth's magnetic field had a very important role in controlling certain geophysical phenomena. The artificial aurora reported by Cullington (1958) and the magnetic effects described by Lawrie, Gerard and Gill (1961) generated by the explosion of nuclear devices at high latitudes above Johnston Island in August 1958, demonstrated forcibly the way the geomagnetic lines of force controlled the location of the observed phenomena. Selzer (1960) reported that rapid registrations of magnetic and telluric variations at French stations during the IGY have caused radical changes in the conceptions about propagation of hydromagnetic waves in the high atmosphere. Results from French stations showed clearly that the magnetic signals created by the high altitude (480 km above South Atlantic Ocean) nuclear explosions of the *Argus* Experiment extended in a few seconds over a large part of the Earth, including the internal part of the southern auroral zone, without, apparently, have been much directed by the magnetic lines of force of the Earth's field.

Many workers have suggested that magnetic events at places in one hemisphere may be linked with similar events in the other hemisphere via lines of force of the geomagnetic field. The problem is to establish suitable stations at each end of a line of force. Two such stations are said to be geomagnetically conjugate. Many geomagnetic events are believed to be due to charged corpuscular beams from the Sun being guided by the lines of force to impinge almost simultaneously and equally into both Antarctic and Arctic ionospheres. The full importance of this problem did not arise until the IGY and it is only recently that stations have been selected to lie at or near conjugate points. Vestine (1959) has pointed out that it may not always be feasible to calculate the true line of force owing to local distortions of the field which may so affect the motion of the plasma along the line of force that it may never reach the actual conjugate point. It may happen that similar events may occur, not at a point, but somewhere in an area around or near the conjugate point.

Nagata and Kokubun (1960) have examined the relationship between individual magnetic disturbances at geomagnetically conjugate points in the north and south polar regions. They selected Little America in Antarctica and Baker Lake in Canada to form a pair of nearly magnetically conjugate points, and adopted Churchill in Canada and Byrd Station and Halley Bay in Antarctica as reference points for Baker Lake and Little America respectively. Little America was situated at a distance of 600 km from the conjugate point to Baker Lake and about 500 km from that of Churchill. The geomagnetic latitudes of these three stations were, $-74\cdot0°$, $73\cdot7°$, and $68\cdot7°$ respectively, and for this reason Little America was considered to be practically conjugate with Baker Lake. It was found that the correspondence of individual disturbances of bay type was good in the local night-time with a correlation coefficient of $0\cdot85$. The correlation coefficient for day-time correspondence was $0\cdot51$, much poorer than the night-time figure. It was also found that the correlation between Baker Lake and Little America was much better than between Baker Lake and Churchill. This may indicate that the corpuscular beam originating in outer space tends to flow along geomagnetic lines of force towards their north and south ends on the Earth's surface.

The indications are also that the cross section of the average corpuscular beam is elongated along the geomagnetic latitude circle as compared with its breadth along the geomagnetic meridian. According to a recent study of Arctic geomagnetic and auroral data by Nagata and Kokubun (1961) the average dimensions of the activated area of a well developed polar elementary magnetic storm in night-time are, in the auroral zone, about 400 km along the geomagnetic meridian and about 2000 km, or more, along the parallel of geomagnetic latitude.

The difference in correlation between night-time and day-time disturbances may be due to the corpuscular beam in night-time having a greater cross-section than during the day-time. In addition the day-time correlation may be influenced by differences in solar radiation at the pair of conjugate points. In the case of large magnetic storms it was found that the correlation between geomagnetically conjugate points was much poorer, indicating that the relationship was being affected by changes taking place in the configuration of the magnetic field outside the ionosphere. Wescott (1961) compared magnetograms from Macquarie Island with those from nine Alaskan IGY stations, Churchill in Canada, and Cape Chelyuskin in the USSR. The magnetic variations at Macquarie Island were found to correspond remarkably well in universal time with those at several Alaskan stations, making difficult the selection of a conjugate point for Macquarie

Island. On the basis of this study an area elongated along the geomagnetic latitude could be defined as conjugate to Macquarie Island. There was good correlation between magnetic activity in the Northern and Southern Hemispheres, even small features being often reproduced in the magnetic records. This implies that the electric currents, with similar size and structure, appeared simultaneously in the ionosphere about the conjugate points located in the northern and southern auroral zones.

Earth Currents

Natural electrical currents flow in the crust of the Earth and are called earth currents. These electrical current systems are induced in the Earth by currents flowing in the ionosphere. A study of earth currents and their fluctuations reveals interesting information of events of solar origin occurring in the upper atmosphere. The general method of studying earth currents is to measure the potential differences between electrodes buried in the Earth at the ends of a well insulated line of length which varies from less than a kilometre to many kilometres. Earth currents have been measured and studied spasmodically for many decades. During the last decade a wide interest has developed in fluctuations of the geomagnetic field in the range of periods from about 10 minutes to less than a second. The amplitudes of these magnetic fluctuations are comparatively small and decrease as the period shortens. Earth current recording is a particularly suitable method for the investigation of these fluctuations. During and since the IGY earth current recordings have been made at several places on the Antarctic Continent, and particularly by the Russians at their stations at Mirnyy and Oazis. During 1961 preliminary experiments in earth current recording were carried out at Hallett Station. Difficulty was experienced in sinking the electrodes through the permafrost and so as an alternative the electrodes were placed in the sea through holes drilled in the sea ice. In the summer when the ice goes out, so do the electrodes.

The main characteristics of the earth currents at Mirnyy and Oazis have been outlined by Troitskaya (1960) who found that the amplitudes of the short period variations were quite large, being of the order of tens and hundreds of millivolts per kilometre. During magnetic storms the amplitude of activity was of the order of 800 mv/km. The amplitudes during sudden commencements and sudden impulses were between 500–2500 mv/km, while during magnetic bays the amplitudes were between 500–1000 mv/km. An interesting feature of the behaviour of the earth currents appears in the steady direction of their flow both at Mirnyy and at Oazis. The directions of flow of the earth currents determined for different characteristic types of disturbances or variations have small scatter. At Mirnyy the mean direction of current flow is N 20°–25° E, while at Oazis it is N 80°–90° E.

Using earth current records from the USSR Antarctic stations, Troitskaya (1961a) studied the pulsations of type Pc in the Arctic and the Antarctic. She found that regular pulsations Pc with periods from 20–30 seconds are typical of middle latitudes as well as polar regions. Her analysis of the pulsations Pt showed that these pulsations usually lose the form which characterizes them in middle latitudes. Other irregular pulsations (also continuous) were found to be typical of the polar regions and occurred with 50–90 second periods, together with pulsations having a shorter period, i.e., less than 15 seconds. A sharp fall in the number of hours of regular continuous pulsations recorded in winter shows the effect of the long polar night and Troitskaya considers this effect to be more noticeable in the Antarctic than in the Arctic. The world-wide occurrence of Pc is best observed during the equinoxes. The connection between the occurrence of the Pt in the middle latitudes and the disturbance in the Arctic and Antarctic is complex and variable. Diurnal variations of Pc and Pt in the polar regions are similar to their diurnal variations in middle latitudes. According to Troitskaya the seasonal maxima of the Pt and of the corresponding polar disturbances are at the equinoxes. The seasonal variation of the short-period irregular pulsations with periods less than 15 seconds has its maximum during the equinoxes also. The seasonal variation of the regular Pc has its maximum during the summer.

Troitskaya (1961b) also reported that pulsations of the beating type with periods from 1–4 seconds (called 'pearls') are sometimes observed simultaneously in the Arctic, Antarctic, and in middle latitudes. The amplitudes of the pearls in earth currents are of the order of 0·01–0·1 mv/km, while corresponding amplitudes in the magnetic fluctuation would be of the order of 0·001–0·05 gamma. The pearl type pulsations are mostly observed in the evening, during the night, and in the early morning hours.

Bibliography

BENIOFF, H. 1960: Observations of Geomagnetic Fluctuations in the Period Range 0·3 to 120 Seconds. *J. Geophys. Res.* **65**: 1413–22.

BLUNDELL, D. J. and STEPHENSON, P. J. 1959: Paleomagnetism of Some Dolerite Intrusions from the Theron Mountains and Whichaway Nunataks, Antarctica, *Nature* **184**: 1860.

BUKIN, GLOKOVA, INOSEMZEVA, MANSUROV, POPKOV, and SHPILEV, 1960: The Main Results of Investigations of Antarctic Expeditions of the USSR on the Questions of Geomagnetic Field, Ionosphere, Cosmic Rays, and Auroras. Antarctic Symposium, Buenos Aires, Nov. 1959, *I.U.G.G Monograph* **5**: 48.

BULL, C. and IRVING, E. 1960: The Paleomagnetism of Some Hypabyssal Intrusive Rocks from South Victoria Land, Antarctica, *Geophys. J.* **3**: 211–24.

CAMPBELL, W. H. 1959: Studies of Magnetic Field Micropulsations with Periods of 5 to 30 Seconds, *J. Geophys, Res.* **64**: 1819–26.

CHAPMAN, S. and BARTELS, J. 1940: *Geomagnetism*, Oxford, Clarendon Press, pp. 407–409.

CHREE, C. 1909: *Magnetic Observations, National Antarctic Expedition 1901–04*, Roy. Soc., London.

CHREE, C. 1915: Magnetic Character Figures: Antarctic and International, *Proc. Phys. Soc. London* **27**: 193–207.

CHREE, 1921: *Terrestrial Magnetism, Brit. (Terra Nova) Ant. Exp. 1910–13*, Harrison and Sons, London.

CHREE, C. 1927: Magnetic Disturbance and Aurora as Observed by the Australian Antarctic Expedition at Cape Denison in 1912 and 1913, *Proc. Phys. Soc. London* **39**: 389–407.

CHRISTOFFEL, D. A. 1961: Total Magnetic Field Measurements between New Zealand and Antarctica, *Nature* **190**: 776–8.

CULLINGTON, A. L. 1958: A Man-Made or Artificial Aurora, *Nature* **182**: 1365–6.

DAVIES, F. T. 1935: The Diurnal Variation in Magnetic and Auroral Activity at Three High Latitude Stations, *Terr. Mag. Atmos. Elect.* **40**: 173–182.

FUKUSHIMA, N. 1952: Constitution of Polar Magnetic Storms (2), *Rep. Ionos. Res. Japan* **6**: 185–93.

GERARD, V. B. 1959: The Propagation of World-Wide Sudden Commencements of Magnetic Storms, *J. Geophys. Res.* **64**: 593–6.

HATHERTON, T. 1960: Geometry of the Southern Auroral Zone and the Evidence for the Existence of an Inner Zone, *Nature* **186**: 288–90.

HATHERTON, T. 1961: New Zealand IGY Antarctic Expeditions, Scott Base and Hallett Station, *N.Z. DSIR Bull.* **140**.

JACOBS, J. A. and SINNO, K. 1960a: Occurrence Frequency of Geomagnetic Micropulsations, Pc, *J. Geophys. Res.* **65**: 107–13.

JACOBS, J. A. and SINNO, K. 1960b: World-Wide Characteristics of Geomagnetic Micropulsations, *Geophys. J.* **3**: 333–53.

LARZILLIERE, H. 1960: Étude des Observations Réalisées à la Station Charcot (Terre Adélie), Février à Décembre 1958, *Année Geophysique Internationale, Participation Française*, Ser. 3, Fasc. 1, *Magnetisme Terrestre*, Centre National de la Recherche Scientifique.

LASSEN, K. 1958: On the Variation of the Magnetic Activity at Godhavn, *L'Institut Météorologique Danois Comm. Magn. etc.* **23**.

LAWRIE, J. A., GERARD, V. B., and GILL, P. J. 1961. Magnetic Effects Resulting from the Johnston Island High Altitude Nuclear Explosions, *N.Z. J. Geol. Geophys.* **4**: 109–24.

MACDOWELL, J. 1960: Geomagnetic Observations at Halley Bay, *Proc. Roy. Soc.* **256**: 219–21.

MACDOWELL, J. and BLACKIE, A. 1960: *Royal Society I.G.Y. Antarctic Expedition, Halley Bay, Coats Lands, Falkland Islands Dependencies 1955–59*, Geomagnetism 1.

MANSUROV, S. M. 1960: Vekovye Variatsii Geomagnitnogo Polya Vostocknoy Antarktidy. Geomagnitnye Vozmushcheniya, *Sbornik Statey*, *Geomagnetizm (MGG)* **4**: 48–52, Akad. Nauk. SSSR, Moskva.

MAPLE, E. 1959: Geomagnetic Oscillations at Middle Latitudes, *J. Geophys. Res.* **64**: 1395–1409.

MAWSON, D. 1925: *Australasian Ant. Exp. 1911–14,* Sci. Rep. Ser. B.1, Terrestrial Magnetism. Government Printer, Sydney.

MAYAUD, P. N. 1956: Activité Magnétique dans les Régions Polaires. *Ann. Geophys.* **12:** 84–101.

MAYAUD, P. N. 1961: *I.A.G.A. Bull.* **121,** append. B.

NAGATA, T. 1960: *Report on Geomagnetic Secular Variation during the Period from 1955 to 1960 presented to Committee of Secular Variations and Paleomagnetism I.A.G.,* Helsinki, July–August 1960.

NAGATA, T. and FUKUSHIMA, N. 1952: Constitution of Polar Magnetic Storms, *Rep. Ionos. Res. Japan* **6:** 85–97.

NAGATA, T., and KOKUBUN, S. 1960: On the Earth Storms, 4. Polar Magnetic Storms, with Special Reference to Relation between Geomagnetic Disturbances in the Northern and Southern Auroral Zones, *Rep. Ionos. Space, Res. Japan* **14:** 273–90.

NAGATA, T., and KOKUBUN, S. 1961: *Rep. Ionos. Space Res. Japan* **15** (in press).

NAGATA, T., and SHIMIZU, Y. 1959: Natural Remanent Magnetization of Pre-Cambrian Gneiss of Ongul Islands in the Antarctic, *Nature* **184:** 1472–3.

NIKOLSKY, A. P. 1947: Dual Laws of the Course of Magnetic Disturbance and the Nature of Mean Regular Variations, *Terr. Mag. Atmos. Elect.* **52:** 147–53.

NIKOLSKY, A. P. 1957: Distribution of Magnetic Disturbances in the Antarctic, Transl. from. *Problemy Arktiki, Sbornik Statey* **2:** 241–4.

OBAYASHI, T., and JACOBS, J. A. 1958: Geomagnetic Pulsations and the Earth's Outer Atmosphere, *Geophys. J.* **1:** 53–63.

ROBERTSON, C. S. 1959: A Study of Magnetic Bays at Macquarie Island, *Dept. Nat. Dev. Bur. Min. Resources, Geol. Geophys. Australia,* Records No. 127.

SABINE, E. 1868: Contributions to Terrestrial Magnetism, II, *Phil. Trans. London,* 371–416.

SCHLICH, R. 1960: Étude des Observations Réalisées à la Station Charcot (Terre Adélie), Avril 1957 à Janvier 1958, *Année Geophysique Internationale, Participation Française,* Ser. 3, Fasc. 1, *Magnetisme Terrestre,* Centre National de la Recherche Scientifique.

SELZER, E. 1960: New Trends for Research on Rapid Magnetic Variations in Polar Regions, *I.U.G.G. Monograph* **5:** 45–6, Antarctic Symposium, Buenos Aires, Nov. 1959.

STAGG, J. M. 1935: The Diurnal Variation of Magnetic Disturbance in High Latitudes, *Proc. Roy. Soc. London,* A **149:** 298–317.

TROITSKAYA, V. A. 1960: Osnovnye Kharakteristiki Polya Zemnykh Tokov v Antarktike, *Sov. Ant. Eksp.* **9.** Nauchnye Rezultaty, 10–24.

TROITSKAYA, V. A. 1961a: Ustoych Kolebaniya i Kolebaniza Tipa Tsugov v Artike i Antarktike. Korotkoperiodicheskie Kolebaniya Elektromagnitnogo Polya Zemli, *Sbornik Statey, Geomagnetizm (MGG)* **3:** 41–61, Akad. Nauk. USSR. Moskva.

TROITSKAYA, V. A. 1961b: Kolebaniya Tipa Bieniy (Zhemchuzhiny) v Elektro-
magnitnom Pole Zemli (T = 1–4 sek), *Ibid.* **3:** 89–99.

TROITSKAYA, V. A., BOLSHAKOVA, D. V., MELNIKOVA, M. V., SERGEEVA,
K. Y., SUKHAREVA, N. N., and SCHHEPETNOV, R. V. 1961: *I.U.G.G.
Monograph* **7:** 84–93.

TURNBULL, G. 1960: Some Paleomagnetic Measurements in Antarctica.
I.U.G.G. Monograph **5:** 47, Antarctic Symposium, Buenos Aires, Nov. 1959.

VESTINE, E. H. 1959: Note on Conjugate Points of Geomagnetic Field Lines
for Some Selected Auroral and Whistler Stations of the I.G.Y., *J. Geophys.
Res.* **64:** 1411–14.

WESCOTT, E. M. 1961: Magnetic Variations at Conjugate Points, *J. Geophys.
Res.* **66:** 1789–92.

WHITHAM, K., LOOMER, E. I. and NIBLETT, E. R. 1960: The Latitudinal
Distribution of Magnetic Activity in Canada, *J. Geophys. Res.* **65:** 3961–74.

WILLIAMS, V. L. 1960: The Simultaneity of Sudden Commencements of
Magnetic Storms, *J. Geophys. Res.* **65:** 85–92.

WILSON, C. R. and SUGIURA, M. 1961: Hydromagnetic Interpretation of
Sudden Commencements of Magnetic Storms, *J. Geophys. Res.* **66:** 4097–111.

The Antarctic Treaty

The Governments of Argentina, Australia, Belgium, Chile, the French Republic, Japan, New Zealand, Norway, the Union of South Africa, the Union of Soviet Socialist Republics, the United Kingdom of Great Britain and Northern Ireland, and the United States of America,

Recognising that it is in the interest of all mankind that Antarctica shall continue forever to be used exclusively for peaceful purposes and shall not become the scene or object of international discord;

Acknowledging the substantial contributions to scientific knowledge resulting from international cooperation in scientific investigation in Antarctica;

Convinced that the establishment of a firm foundation for the continuation and development of such cooperation on the basis of freedom of scientific investigation in Antarctica as applied during the International Geophysical Year accords with the interests of science and the progress of all mankind;

Convinced also that a treaty ensuring the use of Antarctica for peaceful purposes only and the continuance of international harmony in Antarctica will further the purposes and principles embodied in the Charter of the United Nations;

Have agreed as follows:

ARTICLE I

1. Antarctica shall be used for peaceful purposes only. There shall be prohibited, *inter alia*, any measures of a military nature, such as the establishment of military bases and fortifications, the carrying out of military maneuvers, as well as the testing of any type of weapons.

2. The present Treaty shall not prevent the use of military personnel or equipment for scientific research or for any other peaceful purpose.

ARTICLE II

Freedom of scientific investigation in Antarctica and cooperation toward that end, as applied during the International Geophysical Year, shall continue, subject to the provisions of the present Treaty.

ARTICLE III

1. In order to promote international cooperation in scientific investigation in Antarctica, as provided for in Article II of the present Treaty, the Contracting Parties agree that, to the greatest extent feasible and practicable:

(*a*) Information regarding plans for scientific programs in Antarctica shall be exchanged to permit maximum economy and efficiency of operations;

(*b*) Scientific personnel shall be exchanged in Antarctica between expeditions and stations;

(*c*) Scientific observations and results from Antarctica shall be exchanged and made freely available.

2. In implementing this Article, every encouragement shall be given to the establishment of cooperative working relations with those Specialised Agencies of the United Nations and other international organisations having a scientific or technical interest in Antarctica.

ARTICLE IV

1. Nothing contained in the present Treaty shall be interpreted as:

(*a*) A renunciation by any Contracting Party of previously asserted rights of or claims to territorial sovereignty in Antarctica;

(*b*) A renunciation or diminution by any Contracting Party of any basis of claim to territorial sovereignty in Antarctica which it may have whether as a result of its activities or those of its nationals in Antarctica, or otherwise;

(*c*) Prejudicing the position of any Contracting Party as regards its recognition of any other State's right of or claim or basis of claim to territorial sovereignty in Antarctica.

2. No acts or activities taking place while the present Treaty is in force shall constitute a basis for asserting, supporting or denying a claim to territorial sovereignty in Antarctica or create any rights of sovereignty in Antarctica. No new claim, or enlargement of an existing claim, to territorial sovereignty in Antarctica shall be asserted while the present Treaty is in force.

ARTICLE V

1. Any nuclear explosions in Antarctica and the disposal there of radioactive waste material shall be prohibited.

2. In the event of the conclusion of international agreements concerning the use of nuclear energy, including nuclear explosions and the disposal of radioactive waste material, to which all of the Contracting Parties whose representatives are entitled to participate in the meetings provided for under Article IX are parties, the rules established under such agreements shall apply in Antarctica.

ARTICLE VI

The provisions of the present Treaty shall apply to the area south of 60° South Latitude, including all ice shelves, but nothing in the present Treaty shall prejudice or in any way affect the rights, or the exercise of the rights, of any State under international law with regard to the high seas within that area.

ARTICLE VII

1. In order to promote the objectives and ensure the observance of the provisions of the present Treaty, each Contracting Party whose representatives are entitled to participate in the meetings referred to in Article IX of the Treaty shall have the right to designate observers to carry out any inspection provided for by the present Article. Observers shall be nationals of the Contracting Parties which designate them. The names of observers shall be communicated to every other Contracting Party having the right to designate observers, and like notice shall be given of the termination of their appointment.

2. Each observer designated in accordance with the provisions of paragraph 1 of this Article shall have complete freedom of access at any time to any or all area of Antarctica.

3. All areas of Antarctica, including all stations, installations and equipment within those areas, and all ships and aircraft at points of discharging or embarking cargoes or personnel in Antarctica, shall be open at all times to inspection by any observers designated in accordance with paragraph 1 of this Article.

4. Aerial observation may be carried out at any time over any or all areas of Antarctica by any of the Contracting Parties having the right to designate observers.

5. Each Contracting Party shall, at the time when the present Treaty enters into force for it, inform the other Contracting Parties, and thereafter shall give them notice in advance, of

(a) All expeditions to and within Antarctica, on the part of its ships or nationals, and all expeditions to Antarctica organised in or proceeding from its territory;

(b) All stations in Antarctica occupied by its nationals; and

(c) Any Military personnel or equipment intended to be introduced by it into Antarctica subject to the conditions prescribed in paragraph 2 of Article I of the present Treaty.

ARTICLE VIII

1. In order to facilitate the exercise of their functions under the present Treaty, and without prejudice to the respective positions of the Contracting Parties relating to jurisdiction over all other persons in Antarctica, observers designated under paragraph 1 of Article VII and scientific personnel exchanged under subparagraph 1 (b) of Article III of the Treaty, and members of the staffs accompanying any such persons, shall be subject only to the jurisdiction of the Contracting Party of which they are nationals in respect of all acts or omissions occurring while they are in Antarctica for the purpose of exercising their functions.

2. Without prejudice to the provisions of paragraph 1 of this Article, and pending the adoption of measures in the pursuance of subparagraph 1 (e) of Article IX, the Contracting Parties concerned in any case of dispute with regard

to the exercise of jurisdiction in Antarctica shall immediately consult together with a view to reaching a mutually acceptable solution.

ARTICLE IX

1. Representatives of the Contracting Parties named in the preamble to the present Treaty shall meet at the City of Canberra within two months after the date of entry into force of the Treaty, and thereafter at suitable intervals and places, for the purpose of exchanging information, consulting together on matters of common interest pertaining to Antarctica, and formulating and considering, and recommending to their Governments, measures in furtherance of the principles and objectives of the Treaty, including measures regarding:

(a) Use of Antarctica for peaceful purposes only;
(b) Facilitation of scientific research in Antarctica;
(c) Facilitation of international scientific cooperation in Antarctica;
(d) Facilitation of the exercise of the rights of inspection provided for in Article VII of the Treaty;
(e) Questions relating to the exercise of jurisdiction in Antarctica;
(f) Preservation and conservation of living resources in Antarctica.

2. Each Contracting Party which has become a party to the present Treaty by accession under Article XIII shall be entitled to appoint representatives to participate in the meetings referred to in paragraph 1 of the present Article, during such time as that Contracting Party demonstrates its interest in Antarctica by conducting substantial scientific research activity there, such as the establishment of a scientific station or the dispatch of a scientific expedition.

3. Reports from the observers referred to in Article VII of the present Treaty shall be transmitted to the representatives of the Contracting Parties participating in the meetings referred to in paragraph 1 of the present Article.

4. The measures referred to in paragraph 1 of this Article shall become effective when approved by all the Contracting Parties whose representatives were entitled to participate in the meetings held to consider those measures.

5. Any or all of the rights established in the present Treaty may be exercised as from the date of entry into force of the Treaty whether or not any measures facilitating the exercise of such rights have been proposed, considered or approved as provided in this Article.

ARTICLE X

Each of the Contracting Parties undertakes to exert appropriate efforts, consistent with the Charter of the United Nations, to the end that no one engages in any activity in Antarctica contrary to the principles or purposes of the present Treaty.

ARTICLE XI

1. If any dispute arises between two or more of the Contracting Parties concerning the interpretation or application of the present Treaty, those Contracting Parties shall consult among themselves with a view to having the dispute resolved by negotiation, inquiry, mediation, conciliation, arbitration, judicial settlement or other peaceful means of their own choice.

2. Any dispute of this character not so resolved shall, with the consent, in each case, of all parties to the dispute, be referred to the International Court of Justice for settlement; but failure to reach agreement on reference to the International Court shall not absolve parties to the dispute from the responsibility of continuing to seek to resolve it by any of the various peaceful means referred to in paragraph 1 of this Article.

ARTICLE XII

1. (*a*) The present Treaty may be modified or amended at any time by unanimous agreement of the Contracting Parties whose representatives are entitled to participate in the meetings provided for under Article IX. Any such modification or amendment shall enter into force when the depositary Government has received notice from all such Contracting Parties that they have ratified it.

(*b*) Such modification or amendment shall thereafter enter into force as to any other Contracting Party when notice of ratification by it has been received by the depositary Government. Any such Contracting Party from which no notice of ratification is received within a period of two years from the date of entry into force of the modification or amendment in accordance with the provisions of subparagraph 1 (*a*) of this Article shall be deemed to have withdrawn from the present Treaty on the date of the expiration of such period.

2. (*a*) If after the expiration of thirty years from the date of entry into force of the present Treaty, any of the Contracting Parties whose representatives are entitled to participate in the meetings provided for under Article IX so requests by a communication addressed to the depositary Government, a Conference of all the Contracting Parties shall be held as soon as practicable to review the operation of the Treaty.

(*b*) Any modification or amendment to the present Treaty which is approved at such a Conference by a majority of the Contracting Parties there represented, including a majority of those whose representatives are entitled to participate in the meetings provided for under Article IX, shall be communicated by the depositary Government to all the Contracting Parties immediately after the termination of the Conference and shall enter into force in accordance with the provisions of paragraph 1 of the present Article.

(*c*) If any such modification or amendment has not entered into force in accordance with the provisions of subparagraph 1 (*a*) of this Article within a period of two years after the date of its communication to all the Contracting Parties, any Contracting Party may at any time after the expiration of that period

R

give notice to the depositary Government of its withdrawal from the present Treaty; and such withdrawal shall take effect two years after the receipt of the notice by the depositary Government.

ARTICLE XIII

1. The present Treaty shall be subject to ratification by the signatory States. It shall be open for accession by any State which is a Member of the United Nations, or by any other State which may be invited to accede to the Treaty with the consent of all the Contracting Parties whose representatives are entitled to participate in the meetings provided for under Article IX of the Treaty.

2. Ratification of or accession to the present Treaty shall be effected by each State in accordance with its constitutional processes.

3. Instruments of ratification and instruments of accession shall be deposited with the Government of the United States of America, hereby designated as the depositary Government.

4. The depositary Government shall inform all signatory and acceding States of the date of each deposit of an instrument of ratification or accession, and the date of entry into force of the Treaty and of any modification or amendment thereto.

5. Upon the deposit of instruments of ratification by all the signatory States, the present Treaty shall enter into force for those States and for States which have deposited instruments of accession. Thereafter the Treaty shall enter into force for any acceding State upon the deposit of its instrument of accession.

6. The present Treaty shall be registered by the depositary Government pursuant to Article 102 of the Charter of the United Nations.

ARTICLE XIV

The present Treaty, done in the English, French, Russian, and Spanish languages, each version being equally authentic, shall be deposited in the archives of the Government of the United States of America, which shall transmit duly certified copies thereof to the Governments of the signatory and acceding States.

In witness whereof, the undersigned Plenipotentiaries, duly authorised, have signed the present Treaty.

Done at Washington this first day of December, one thousand nine hundred and fifty-nine.

(Here follow the signatures.)

National Stations in Antarctica Since 1957

Stations and Countries	Geog. Coordinates		1957	'58	Years Maintained '59	'60	'61	'62
ARGENTINA								
Gen. San Martin	68° 08' S,	67° 08' W	X	X	X	—	—	—
Melchior	64° 20' S,	62° 59' W	X	X	X	X	X	—
Teniente Camara	62° 36' S,	59° 54' W	X	X	X	★	★	★
Almirante Brown	64° 53' S,	62° 53' W	X	X	X	★	★	★
Gen. Belgrano	77° 58' S,	38° 48' W	X	X	X	X	X	X
Ellsworth[1]	77° 43' S,	41° 07' W	—	—	X	X	X	X
Esperanza	63° 24' S,	56° 59' W	X	X	X	X	X	X
Decepcion Is.	62° 59' S,	60° 42' W	X	X	X	X	X	X
Orcadas (S. Orkneys)	60° 45' S,	44° 43' W	X	X	X	X	X	X
Teniente Matienzo	64° 58' S,	60° 03' W	—	—	—	—	X	X
AUSTRALIA								
Mawson	67° 36' S,	62° 53' E	X	X	X	X	X	X
Davis	68° 35' S,	77° 58' E	X	X	X	X	X	X
Macquarie Is.	54° 30' S,	158° 57' E	X	X	X	X	X	X
Wilkes[2]	66° 15' S,	110° 32° E	—	—	X	X	X	X
BELGIUM								
Roi Baudouin	70° 26' S,	23° 19' E	—	X	X	X	★	—
CHILE								
Yankee Harbor	62° 32' S,	59° 46' W	★	★	—	—	—	—
Coppermine Cove	62° 23' S,	59° 41' W	★	★	—	—	—	—
Capitan Arturo Prat	62° 29' S,	59° 39' W	X	X	X	X	X	X
Gen. Bernardo O'Higgins	63° 19' S,	57° 54' W	X	X	X	X	X	X
Pres. Gonzalez Videla	64° 49' S,	62° 52' W	X	X	X	X	X	X
Pres. Pedro Aguirre Cerda	62° 56' S,	60° 36' W	X	X	X	X	X	X
FRANCE								
Kerguelen	49° 20' S,	70° 14' E	X	X	X	X	X	X
New Amsterdam	37° 50' S,	77° 34' E	X	X	X	X	X	X
Dumont d'Urville	66° 40' S,	140° 01' E	X	X	X	X	X	X
Charcot	69° 22' S,	139° 02' E	X	X	—	—	—	—

[1] Formerly a US IGY Station; occupied by Argentina Jan. 1959 by agreement with US.
[2] Formerly a US IGY Station; occupied by Australia Jan. 1959 by agreement with US.
★ Summer seasons only.

Stations and Countries	Geog. Coordinates	1957	'58	'59	'60	'61	'62
				Years Maintained			
JAPAN							
Syowa	69° 22′ S, 39° 35′ E	X	—	X	X	X	⋆
NEW ZEALAND							
Scott	77° 50′ S, 166° 48′ E	X	X	X	X	X	X
Hallett[1]	72° 18′ S, 170° 18′ E	X	X	X	X	X	X
Campbell Is.	52° 32′ S, 168° 59′ E	X	X	X	X	X	X
NORWAY							
Norway Station[2]	70° 30′ S, 2° 52′ W	X	X	X	—	—	—
SOUTH AFRICA							
Gough Is.	40° 53′ S, 9° 51′ W	X	X	X	X	X	X
Marion Is.	46° 53′ S, 37° 52′ E	X	X	X	X	X	X
Tristan da Cunha	37° 03′ S, 12° 19′ W	X	X	X	X	X	—
Sanae[3]	70° 30′ S, 2° 52′ W	—	—	—	X	X	X
UNITED KINGDOM							
Port Lockroy (Base A)	64° 50′ S, 63° 31′ W	X	X	X	X	X	⋆
Deception Is. (Base B)	62° 59′ S, 60° 34′ W	X	X	X	X	X	X
Hope Bay (Base D)	63° 24′ S, 56° 49′ W	X	X	X	X	X	X
Stonington Is. (Base E)	68° 11′ S, 67° 00′ W	X	—	—	—	X	X
Argentine Is. (Base F)	65° 15′ S, 64° 16′ W	X	X	X	X	X	X
Admiralty Bay (Base G)	62° 03′ S, 58° 24′ W	X	X	X	X	—	—
Signy Is. (Base H)	60° 43′ S, 45° 36′ W	X	X	X	X	X	X
Prospect Point (Base J)	66° 00′ S, 65° 20′ W	—	—	—	X	—	—
Anvers Is. (Base N)	64° 46′ S, 64° 05′ W	X	?	—	—	—	—
Adelaide Is. (Base T)	67° 46′ S, 68° 54′ W	—	—	—	—	X	X
View Point (Base V)	63° 32′ S, 57° 23′ W	—	—	—	—	X	—
Detaille Is. (Base W)	66° 52′ S, 66° 48′ W	X	—	—	—	—	—
Horseshoe Is. (Base Y)	67° 48′ S, 67° 18′ W	X	X	X	X	—	—
Halley Bay (Base Z)	75° 31′ S, 26° 36′ W	X	X	X	X	X	X
Shackleton (TAE)	77° 59′ S, 37° 09′ W	X	—	—	—	—	—
Fossil Bluff	71° 20′ S, 68° 17′ W	—	—	—	—	X	X
Grytviken, S. Georgia	54° 16′ S, 36° 30′ W	X	X	X	X	X	X
Bird Is.	54° S, 38° 05′ W	—	—	—	—	—	⋆
USSR							
Mirnyy	66° 33′ S, 93° 01′ E	X	X	X	X	X	X
Vostok I	72° 08′ S, 96° 34′ E	⋆	—	—	—	—	—
Vostok	78° 27′ S, 106° 52′ E	—	X	X	X	X	⋆
Lazarev	69° 58′ S, 12° 55′ E	—	—	X	X	—	—

[1] Jointly with the US.

[2] Occupied by South Africa in January 1960 following an agreement with Norway. Renamed 'Sanae'.

[3] Occupied by South Africa in January 1960 following an agreement with Norway. Formerly Norway Station.

⋆ Summer seasons only.

Stations and Countries	Geog. Coordinates	1957	'58	'59	'60	'61	'62
				Years Maintained			
Pionerskaya	69° 44′ S, 95° 30′ E	X	X	—	—	—	—
Komsomolskaya	74° 05′ S, 97° 29′ E	—	X	—	—	—	—
Sovetskaya	78° 24′ S, 87° 35′ E	—	X	—	—	—	—
Novalazarevskaya	70° 45′ S, 11° 58′ E	—	—	—	—	X	X
Molodyozhnaya	67° 48′ S, 46° E	—	—	—	—	—	★
Oazis[1]	66° 16′ S, 100° 44 E	X	X	—	—	—	—
Polyus Nedostupnosti	82° 06′ S, 54° 58′ E	—	★	—	—	—	—
UNITED STATES							
McMurdo Sound[2]	77° 51′ S, 166° 37′ E	X	X	X	X	X	X
Little America	78° 11′ S, 162° 10′ W	X	X	—	—	—	—
Byrd	80° 01′ S, 119° 31′ W	X	X	X	X	X	X
Amundsen-Scott	90° S	X	X	X	X	X	X
Hallett[3]	72° 18′ S, 170° 18′ E	X	X	X	X	X	X
Wilkes[4]	66° 15′ S, 110° 31′ E	X	X	—	—	—	—
Ellsworth[5]	77° 43′ S, 41° 07′ W	X	X	—	—	—	—
Little Rockford	79° 16′ S, 147° 30′ W	—	★	★	★	★	★
Beardmore	83° 17′ S, 175° 45′ E	—	★	★	★	★	★

[1] In Jan. 1959 Oazis was turned over to Poland, which occupied it briefly during the summer season.

[2] Primarily used as a Naval Air Facility and logistics centre.

[3] Jointly with New Zealand.

[4] Occupied by Australia since January 1959.

[5] Occupied by Argentina since January 1959.

★ Summer seasons only.

Index